THE LIVING PLANT

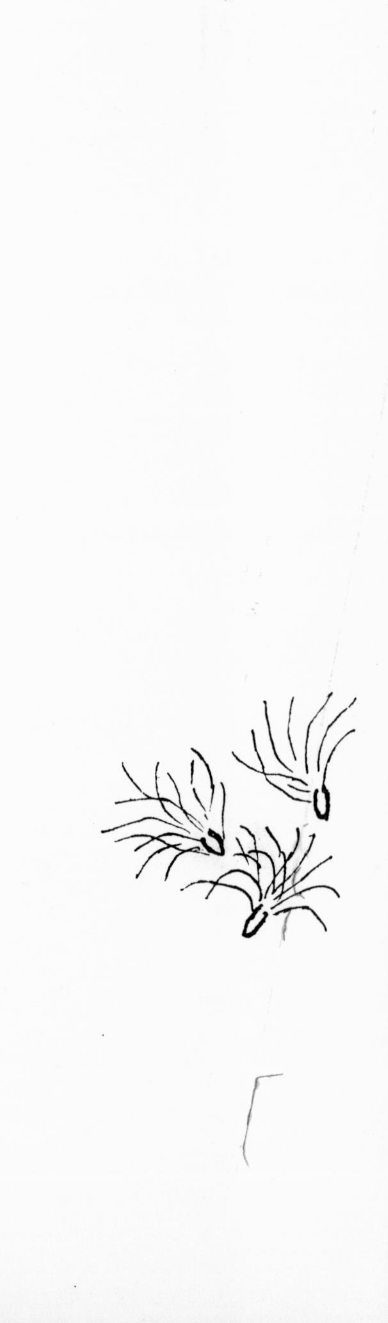

The Living Plant

an introduction to botany, with illustrations by the author

ALAN J. BROOK
University of Edinburgh

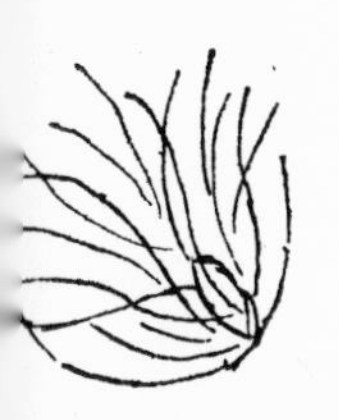

ALDINE PUBLISHING COMPANY
Chicago

First published 1964
Aldine Publishing Company
64 East Van Buren Street
Chicago 5, Illinois
Edinburgh University Press, Edinburgh
Library of Congress Catalog Card Number 64-14298

for Rosemarie

Printed in Scotland

FOREWORD

I was invited by the Edinburgh University Press to write an introductory text-book of botany which would be more comprehensive in detail and more radical in conception than the generality of such books. My chief aim has been to present botany as a scientific discipline no less fascinating and vital than is zoology: hence my title, *The Living Plant*.

Botany, to many people, implies little more than the collecting and naming of flowers. For this reason it has become the Cinderella of school curricula; and even in some universities it is often regarded as a 'soft option'. I hope that this book will help to dispel these misconceptions; not that it attempts to make botany difficult or abstruse, but rather because it tries to communicate something of the intellectual appeal of the subject, which indeed demands – along with other biological disciplines – specialized thinking and reasoning, of a high order. Only by capturing the imagination in this way can we attract more and better students to this most important life science. And there is a great need for botanists of calibre. A diversity of botanical problems awaits investigation. Plants of many types are being increasingly used in other fields of scientific research. But, most important of all, the malnutrition of two-thirds of the present population of the world, and the problem of how to feed the vastly increasing world population, demands that every resource of botanical science be employed to increase the supply of food, both on land and in the oceans. For in both elements plants are the basic source of our food.

This book is not based on any set lecture course. It is my expression of what is required for an introduction to botany at first-year university level and of the best way to fill that need. To make the student feel from the outset that he is dealing with living organisms, I have dealt first with some aspects of plant growth and development. The student thereby comes in contact, at the beginning, with some of the recent exciting developments in the study of cells, electron microscopy, and plant hormones. With basic concepts about growth in his mind, he is then brought to consider the growth forms of plants and their life histories. Here the basic architecture of flowering plants, and the more important modifications, are outlined. Again, in order to present plants as growing, living entities, Plant Anatomy is approached developmentally, with attention focused on cell differentiation and on the formation of tissues and tissue systems in roots, stems, and leaves.

Classical flowering-plant morphology and taxonomy, which was often given such prominence in older text-books, has been reduced to a minimum, and such over-emphasized topics as seed dispersal, and insectivorous plants, are more or less ignored. On the other hand, subjects where great and exciting advances are at present being made and which are of fundamental biological importance, have been given special prominence. Thus there are quite detailed treatments of the water relations of plants; enzymes; photosynthesis; respiration; heredity; evolution; nucleic acids; and also viruses. The final section of the book presents a survey of the plant kingdom from the bacteria to the angiosperms. Here I thought it appropriate to include descriptions and life histories of the alga *Chlorella*, now used so extensively in physiological investigations, and of the fungus *Neurospora*, of significance in genetical studies.

A very high proportion of the illustrations are original and many are of plants kindly supplied by the Royal Botanic Garden Edinburgh, whose staff took a great deal of trouble to secure the most suitable material. I would like to extend special thanks in this connexion to Messrs S. J. Armstrong, L. J. Buchan, and A. Snoddy. Grateful thanks are also due to Mr Ross Eudall who took the colour photographs at figures 153 & 290.

Much of the text has been read and commented on by my colleagues in the University Botany Department. Those whom I wish to thank in particular are Dr M. M. Yeoman (plants in relation to water and respiration), Mr A. J. Tullet (for allowing me to use freely the content of a pamphlet prepared for students on osmosis), Dr J. K. Heyes (photosynthesis and nucleic acids), and Dr A. F. Dyer (meiosis and heredity and for many excellent cytological photomicrographs). Mr Roy Wattling of the Royal Botanic Garden is also to be thanked for valuable comments, and for providing fungal material for illustrations, for the chapter *Eumycophyta*.

To my wife, I am indebted for many suggestions which have improved the intelligibility of the written word, and especially for the great care taken in the preparation of the index.

Alan J. Brook
Edinburgh, February, 1964

CONTENTS

Part I

THE GROWTH AND DEVELOPMENT OF FLOWERING PLANTS

1 Seeds and Germination. *The Embryo; Dormancy; Conditions necessary for germination; Germination in different seed types.* 2

2 Growth and Development. 19

3 The Mechanics of Growth. *The Cell; Cell division; Meristematic regions; Measurement of growth; Factors affecting growth; Circumnutation.* 25

4 Growth Responses to Stimuli. *Auxins; Irritability – tropisms; Tactic movements.* 44

5 Life Histories and the Growth Forms of Plants. *Annuals; Biennials; Suckers, rhizomes, corms and bulbs; Woody perennials.* 55

6 Buds and Leaves. *Leaf base; Leaf stalk; Lamina* 76

Part II

CELL DIFFERENTIATION AND THE INTERNAL STRUCTURE OF PLANTS

7 The Primary Body: The Anatomy of Roots. *Epidermis; Cortex; Vascular cylinder; Lateral root formation.* 92

8 The Primary Body: The Anatomy of Stems. *Epidermis; Cortex; Vascular Cylinder; Transition from root to stem; Leaf and branch traces.* 106

9 The Primary Body: The Anatomy of Leaves. *Epidermis; Mesophyll; Vascular supply; Axillary buds; Flower buds.* 115

10 The Secondary Body: Secondary Thickening. *Vascular cambium; Soft-woods; Hardwoods; Medullary rays; Annual rings; Sapwood and heartwood; Secondary phloem; Cork formation; Lenticels; Abscission; Wound tissues and grafting.* 124

Part III

PLANT NUTRITION

11 The Plant in Relation to Water. *Some properties of water.* 148

12 The Entry of Water into Plants. *Osmosis; Plasmolysis; Root pressure; Imbibition.* 154

13 Water and Soils. 164
14 Transpiration. *Xerophytic plants* 170
15 Mineral Nutrition. *Antagonism; Symptoms of mineral deficiences; The Soil as a source of mineral elements; The Nitrogen Cycle.* 179

Part IV

PLANT NUTRITION : METABOLISM

16 The Products of Plant Metabolism: Carbohydrates, Fats, and Proteins. *Carbohydrates; Fats and oils; Proteins.* 190
17 Enzymes. 200
18 Photosynthesis. *The Carbon Dioxide Cycle; The Problem of photosynthesis; Chloroplasts and their structure.* 205
19 Catabolism and Respiration. *Respiratory quotients; Factors influencing respiration; Respiration and the mitochondria; Biochemical phases of respiration.* 220
20 Translocation. 227
21 The Plant and its Environment. *Climatic factors; Edaphic factors; Biotic factors; Plant communities; Plant succession.* 229

Part V

REPRODUCTION, HEREDITY, EVOLUTION

22 Reproduction. *Meiosis.* 242
23 Flowers. *Physiology of reproduction; The Flower; Pollination; Fertilization; Endosperm development; Embryo development.* 254
24 Seeds and Fruits. *Seeds and their development; Fruits and their development.* 295
25 Heredity. *Mendelian inheritance; Heredity and environment; The Cytological basis of Mendelian inheritance; Mutations; Polyploidy.* 304
26 The Nucleic Acids and Heredity. 314
27 Viruses. 319
28 Evolution. *Species; Isolation; Large Scale Evolution; Palaeontology and evolution; Natural selection; Evolution and genetics; Neo-Darwinism.* 324

Part VI

THE PLANT KINGDOM – A SURVEY

29 The Origins and Diversity of Plant Life. 336
30 Classification and Nomenclature. 339

31 Bacteria. *Structure of the bacterial cell; Reproduction and growth; Bacterial plant diseases.* 343

32 Divisions Cyanophyta, Rhodophyta, Chlorophyta, *Class Chlorophyceae;* Chrysophyta, *Class Bacillariophyceae;* Phaeophyta, *Classes Isogeneratae, Heterogeneratae, Cyclosporae;* (Algae). 351

33 Division Eumycophyta. *Class Phycomycetes; Class Ascomycetes; Class Basidiomycetes* (Fungi)*; Mycorrhizae; Lichens.* 385

34 Division Bryophyta. *Class Hepaticae* (liverworts); *Class Musci* (mosses). 420

35 Division Pteridophyta. *Sub-division Filicopsida* (Ferns); *Sub-division Sphenopsida* (Horsetails); *Sub-division Lycopsida* (Club mosses). 437

36 Division Spermatophyta (Seed Plants). *Class Gymnospermae; Class Angiospermae.* 458

GLOSSARY 471

SUGGESTIONS FOR FURTHER READING 500

INDEX 503

PART I

THE GROWTH AND DEVELOPMENT OF FLOWERING PLANTS

CHAPTER 1

SEEDS AND GERMINATION

The word *seed*, in addition to its precise, scientific meaning as the mature fertilized *ovule* of a flowering plant, also connotes a beginning, source, or germ from which something springs. It is therefore appropriate to begin the study of botany by examining the form and function of these packets of dormant life, which are produced by most flowering plants as the culmination of a season's growth; for each contains the germ or beginning of a new individual. In the case of the Flowering Plants (the more advanced members of the Plant Kingdom), as with the more advanced animals, the offspring in the early stage of their lives are dependent for their nutritional needs, and for security and protection, on the mother plant. In the evolution both of plants and animals, a most significant trend has been the increasing care taken by the parent of the offspring, a condition which would seem to be an essential accompaniment to increasing complexity of the organism. This evolutionary trend will be briefly outlined in later chapters. In the case of the more primitive members of the Plant Kingdom, such as the seaweeds and fungi, the products of reproduction are liberated very soon after being formed, to face alone the many hazards of life without the provision of a food supply to help them on their way. The offspring of flowering plants, in contrast, spend their initial formative period in the security of the *ovary* (the womb of the female flower), and only after completing a period of development are they set free as seeds (fig. 1). As such they are provided with sufficient food to enable them to grow into *seedlings*, by which time they can manufacture their own food. From then on they lead an independent existence.

Most seeds are the culmination of a plant's activity for a particular year. Some plants, referred to as *annuals* or *ephemerals*, wither and die soon after they have produced their seed, which thus acts not only as a means of reproducing and dispersing the plant's progeny, but, more important, as the vehicle within which the plant can survive from one year, or one favourable growing period, to the next.

THE EMBRYO

The vital, living part of any seed is the *embryo* (see figs. 2-9). It is from this, which comprises rudimentary root, stem and leaves, that the mature plant will eventually develop. At the same time as the embryo takes form within the parent ovary, its future nutrition is provided for by the development of a special tissue, *endosperm*. This will enable the seed, after being shed from the parent plant, and when conditions are suitable, to complete its development to the seedling stage independently of any external food supply. The principal nutritive substances contained in the

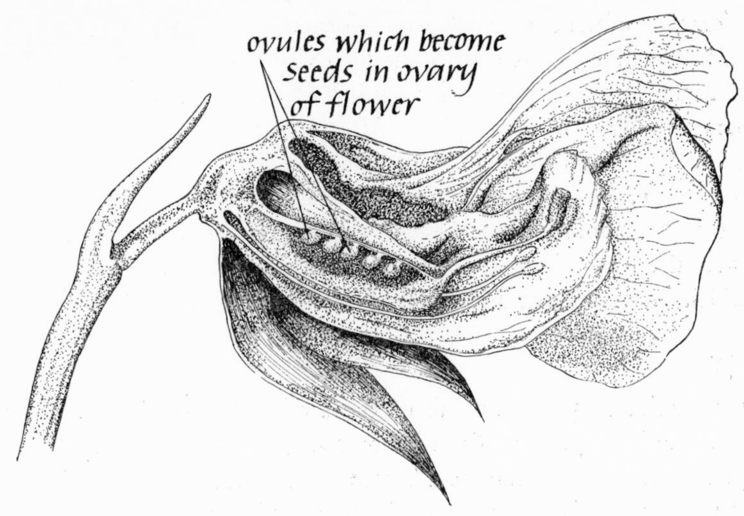

Figure 1 *Longitudinal section of the flower of the garden pea* (Pisum sativum), *showing ovules protected in their ovary.*

endosperm may be carbohydrates (such as starch or sugar), protein, or in some cases oil or fat. These substances may occur alone or in various combinations. The endosperm, which means 'within the seed', is comparable in many ways with the 'white' surrounding the yolk of a hen's egg; it is the yolk, from which the embryo chick develops, that is the egg proper. As the chick gestates, it draws on the protein-rich food contained in the 'white'. In a similar way, as the embryo of the seed develops, it draws on its associated endosperm, though the way in which the endosperm is utilized varies considerably with different types of seeds. In some seeds the entire endosperm is taken up by what might be described as the precocious development of the first leaves of the embryo, the *cotyledons*, which then occupy a major part of the seed. Typical of this type are the seeds of the broad bean (fig. 2), which, since they contain no *free* endosperm, are referred to as *albuminous* or *non-endospermic* seeds. In other seeds, the embryo has not drawn on the endosperm to nearly the same extent by the time the seed is shed, and they thus contain proportionately much more free endosperm. This is taken up by the embryo only when further development proceeds, with the process of germination. *Endospermic* or *exalbuminous* seeds, as this latter category are called, are typical of, though not exclusive to, cereals, such as wheat, oats, barley, and maize (figs. 6-9).

The embryo and its food supply, whether stored as free endosperm, or in its cotyledons, are soft delicate structures, in themselves unprotected against such hazards as frost or drought, the possible depredations of fungal attack, bacterial or virus infection, or even against the digestive juices of birds and other animals which might ingest them. Their all-important protection, however, is afforded by a hardening and thickening of the ovule walls which form the seed coat or *testa*. The development of this protective coat is usually the final visible stage in the production of the seed. During the process, the seed loses much of its surplus water. It is then ready to be separated from the parent plant. After separation occurs, a scar, called the *hilum*, can usually be seen on the testa, marking the place where the seed was attached by the stalk or *funicle* of the ovule. Another feature frequently recognizable on the mature seed coat is a minute pore, the *micropyle* (fig. 2). This is not to be confused in function with the pore of the same name in the membrane of certain animal eggs, through which sperm reaches and fertilizes the ovum.

DORMANCY

The next active stage in the life of the seed is its *germination*. This can be thought of as the birth process of the infant plant, when the seedling develops from the embryo sheltered within the seed. There may, however, be a considerable delay between the dispersal of the seed from the parent plant and the occurrence of germination. Some seeds can, and in certain cases must, germinate almost as soon as they fall from the parent plant. Willow seeds, for example, die if they do not germinate within about ten days of being shed. Beech and oak seeds must germinate in the autumn or spring following their production. Many seeds, however, can lie *dormant* for years and still retain the power of germination. In exceptional cases this period may exceed a hundred years, though accounts of the successful germination of various types of seeds which had lain among the treasures of Tutankhamen's tomb for more than four thousand years are quite without foundation. There is, however, a fully authenticated account of the viability of seeds of the Indian lotus *Nelumbium speciosum*, dug up from mud deposits in a Manchurian lake, where geological evidence showed that they had been buried for at least four hundred years.

In contrast to accidentally enforced dormancy such as this, there are many seeds which actually require a certain period of dormancy before germination can take place. Investigations of this obligatory dormancy indicate several reasons why certain types of seeds require such a period of rest. These include the degree of impermeability of the seed coat to water, a condition which gradually changes, for the testa usually becomes increasingly permeable with age. In dry conditions, increases in permeability take place very slowly, but seem to proceed much more rapidly when the seeds are subjected to the moisture variations of a temperate environment. In other seeds the testa may be impermeable to oxygen, the presence of which, as will be shown later, is essential for germination. Or again, the embryo within the seed may be immature when shed and thus not capable of germinating; in other cases the embryo requires no further development as such, but some measure of 'after ripening' is still essential. In these cases, even when the seed coat has been removed and all the normal conditions requisite for germination are supplied, there is no germination of the seed. Here it seems that certain changes in the physical and chemical, as distinct from the morphological, condition of the embryo must take place before germination can proceed.

In all dormant seeds, *respiration* (see Chapter 19), the vital energy-liberating activity associated with all life, is greatly reduced, as it is in animals which hibernate during unfavourable climatic conditions. By this process, however, enough stored energy is drawn upon to maintain the spark of life within the seed. But though a seed's ability to remain dormant may persist for a hundred years or more, sooner or later its ability to germinate is lost and the seed dies. Death is not caused by the exhaustion of the stored food supply from which the seed obtains the minute amounts of energy necessary to survive. It is in most cases due to irreversible changes (*denaturation*) in the fundamental chemical structure of the living matter of which the embryo is formed. Only if the condition of the seed remained completely unchanged would the power to germinate be retained indefinitely – and a condition of static equilibrium is never possible with living matter.

THE CONDITIONS NECESSARY FOR GERMINATION

When the period of dormancy is ended, and provided that no internal condition such as 'after ripening' still limits its germination, the embryo can proceed to the next stage of development. For this a supply of water, oxygen, a suitable temperature, and with some seeds certain conditions of light, are prerequisites.

Water Supply

When peas or beans are taken fresh from their pods they have fleshy, succulent bodies and contain a considerable amount of water. If such seeds were left to ripen in their pods instead of being picked, they would quite soon dry out and lose much of this water, possibly to the extent of nine-tenths of their total weight. The testa at the same time would become tough and resistant. Although so much water has been lost, the embryo within, remarkably, does not die, as would parts of a mature plant if dried to the same extent. The important prerequisite for germination is that the seed makes good this water-loss, for only in the presence of water can the food reserves on which the developing seedling is to depend during the first phase of its existence be transformed from their stored state into usable, nutritive substances. Thus the renewal of life is usually marked by swelling of the seed, and by the consequent smoothing out of any wrinkles which may have appeared in the testa as the seed dried out. With this uptake of water the internal pressure in the seed may become so great that the testa eventually ruptures. The magnitude of this force can be simply demonstrated by filling a narrow glass bottle with germinating bean seeds and, as a safety precaution, placing it in water. The swelling beans will soon shatter the bottle.

A point of interest in the initial stages of germination is the manner in which the water re-enters the seed. The main question is whether it does so through the testa as a whole or principally through the pore in the testa, the micropyle. Water can certainly be readily ejected from the latter, as for example by squeezing a bean seed which has been previously soaked. Some indication of the relative importance of the testa and micropyle in this process of water uptake can be gained by taking two samples, each of twelve bean seeds, blocking the micropyles of one set with wax, and then comparing the average gain in weight over a standard time with the other untreated sample, which thus acts as a control. Such an experiment should show that although water enters more readily through the micropyle there is nevertheless a significant uptake by way of the testa.

With different kinds of seeds the proportion of water absorbed, in relation to their dry weight, varies greatly. Observations of the amounts absorbed by various types of air-dry seeds under comparable controlled experimental conditions have revealed that in general those of the pea and bean family (Leguminosae) are conspicuous for the large amounts of water taken up. Gains of as much as 150-200% of their original dry weights are not uncommon for seeds of this type; while cereals and seeds containing considerable reserves of oil or fat, for example those of sunflower and castor oil, seem to absorb only relatively small amounts, of the order of 40-60% of their dry weight.

The power of a seed to absorb water does not necessarily mean that the seed is alive and capable of germination. The initial absorption of water is to a very large extent dependent on certain physical properties of the testa. Nor does it follow that because a seed fails to absorb water it is dead, for the coats of many seeds are so hard that they remain impermeable for a long time; in many cases the rate of absorption is so slow as to be imperceptible. Such conditions are well illustrated by an experiment once carried out with the hard seeds of *Robinia*, one of the Acacias. In addition, this experiment demonstrated quite forcibly the great variations in behaviour which may be encountered from seed to seed in a given sample. Some four hundred seeds were placed under conditions normally requisite for germination. By the end of a year only ten had germinated, while in the following two years only three more produced seedlings. Observations continued for thirty-two years and throughout this period an occasional seed would from time to time germinate.

Although the example of *Robinia* is somewhat exceptional there are nevertheless many groups of plants with highly impermeable seed coats and in consequence their germination may be a discouragingly slow process. It can often be hastened artificially by slightly damaging the testa by filing or chipping and thereby facilitating the entry of water. Alternatively, provided that care is taken not to overdo the treatment to the point of causing damage to the embryo, germination of impermeable seeds can usually be hastened by immersing them in concentrated hydrochloric acid; or, as is often done with spinach seeds (*Spinacea oleracea*), by soaking for a few hours in warm water before sowing. The effectiveness of such pre-treatment can be easily demonstrated with two comparable samples of broom seeds (*Cytisus scoparius*), one of which has had the testa scraped with a file while the other is untreated. If the treated and untreated seeds are provided with conditions suitable for germination, very significant differences will be found in the time taken by the samples to germinate.

Temperature

This environmental factor is important in governing the time taken for seeds to attain their maximum degree of swelling, for increases in temperature bring about certain changes in the physical properties of the seed and seed coat, allowing a more rapid intake of water. In addition to this relationship between temperature and water absorption, increases in temperatures, within limits, also speed up vital chemical changes and especially those involved in the mobilization of food, which take place in the seed at this crucial time. Although some seeds can germinate at temperatures only a few degrees above freezing point, the optimum for many common seeds of economic importance, such as wheat, oats, barley, peas, etc., is in the region of 25-31°C. These seeds will often germinate more rapidly at even higher temperatures, but the percentage of successful germination will probably be much less. At higher temperatures there is a danger that the protein of the living matter of the embryo may become denatured and irrevocably damaged, like the irreversible coagulation of a hen's egg when it is boiled. The seeds of plants from tropical climates require higher temperatures than those from more temperate regions. Melon (*Cucumis melo*) and cucumber (*C. sativus*) seeds, for example, will not germinate below about 16°C and germination is most successful in the region of 40°C.

Oxygen Supply

That an adequate supply of oxygen (as well as water and a suitable temperature) is essential for germination can easily be demonstrated with most seeds. If seeds are submerged in water, especially water previously boiled to drive off the dissolved oxygen and other gases, germination will not take place. Indeed, if left for any length of time in these conditions the seeds will almost certainly show signs of decay. The failure of seeds to germinate in water-logged soils is usually due to lack of oxygen; once a soil in this condition dries out and air can circulate within it, germination may often proceed normally. Similarly if seeds are sown too deeply or are accidentally carried down to considerable depths by digging or ploughing they will almost certainly fail to germinate because of the very slow rate of diffusion of oxygen from the upper soil and from the atmosphere down to the lower layers.

The reason why oxygen is needed for germination is as follows. After the entry of water into the seed, the complex food reserves stored in the endosperm or cotyledons must be broken down with the aid of catalyst-like substances called *enzymes* (see Chapter 17). The reserves are then prepared in the form of much simpler, water soluble substances. This is achieved by a very common and important type of reaction which, since it involves the addition of water, is known as *hydrolysis*. When germination begins, the resulting soluble foods, which in their insoluble form had been held in reserve in the dormant seed, are rapidly transferred to the growing regions of the embryo. In these localities of great activity a beginning is made in forming the new tissues of the future seedling. A continuous supply of energy is required for these dynamic processes of transformation, translocation and construction. The necessary energy is lodged within the stored carbohydrates, proteins and fats of the seed and is released in the process of respiration, mentioned earlier, which is common to all living organisms. In respiration oxygen is used up; and carbon dioxide, water and the all important supply of energy are released (see Chapter 19).

Thus throughout germination until the seedling has green parts and can provide its own food as a result of *photosynthesis*, growth and the production of new tissues takes place entirely at the expense of those food reserves within the seed which were originally provided by the parent plant. This is amply demonstrated by the fact that cotyledons or endosperm become progressively more shrivelled as germination proceeds (see fig. 3.4). Further proof can be provided when the dry weights of samples of seeds are determined at periods throughout germination. They will show a steady decline until the seedling starts to manufacture its own food by photosynthesis (see Chapter 18).

Light

A further external condition which may be necessary before certain seeds can germinate is *light*. The influence of this factor, however, is varied and complex and by no means fully understood. Most seeds, and especially those of agricultural importance, are indifferent to the influence of light. There are, however, quite a number of seeds which are known to be 'light sensitive' and whose germination is favoured by exposure for a period to light. A complementary category has been described as 'light hard'. In these, germination is positively retarded in the presence of light.

GERMINATION IN DIFFERENT SEED TYPES

Having considered in some detail the parts played by the various factors necessary to set the process of germination in motion, it is now appropriate to follow out the basic changes which take place as germination progresses in seeds of various types.

Broad Bean (*Vicia faba* L., figs. 2 and 3)

The seed of the broad bean is kidney-shaped and protected by a tough, brown seed coat, on the straighter edge of which there is the elongated scar of the hilum. Between this and a prominent ridge is the micropyle, which can be seen with a lens. The seed coat is extremely difficult to remove when the seed is dry but by soaking it for several hours it will become much softer, swelling considerably in the process. In this state the testa can be easily dissected away to reveal the embryo, which in the bean fills the entire space of the seed. Its most conspicuous features are the two large flattened cotyledons, or seed leaves, lying side by side. If these are carefully separated it will be found that they are joined at the base to a small, curved body which is compressed between them. This, the *plumule*, will eventually develop into the shoot of

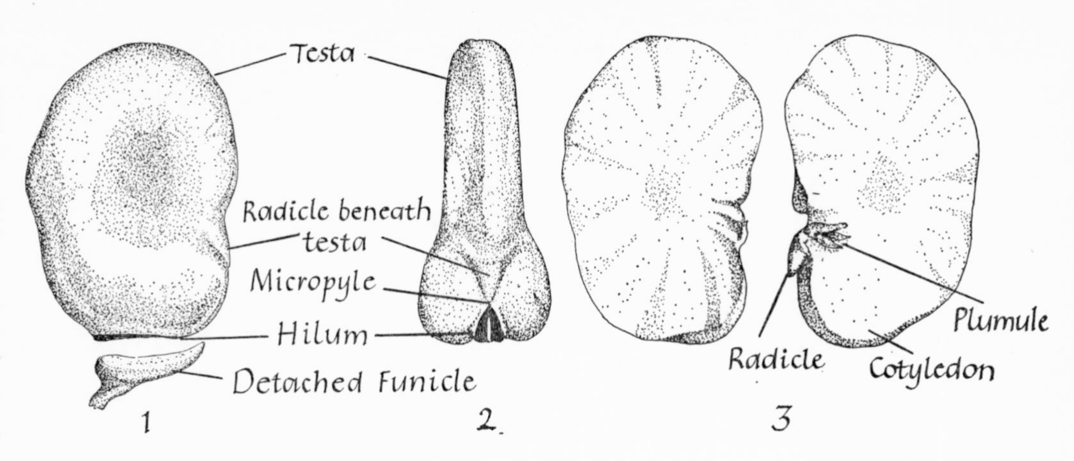

Figure 2 *Broad bean seed*
1 and 2 *Views showing external features.*
3 *Testa removed and cotyledons separated.*

the seedling. Continuous with the plumule and pointing in the opposite direction outwards from the cotyledons, is a small, peg-like body, the *radicle* or primary root of the new plant. In the bean seed all the food reserves are stored in the cotyledons; there is no endosperm. If the cotyledons of this non-endospermic seed are tested with iodine they turn blue-black, indicating the presence of abundant starch, while with Millon's reagent which turns red in the presence of protein, they react strongly.

Further examination of the soaked bean will reveal that the tip of the radicle fits into a small pocket. During germination this pocket acts like the wick of a lamp and draws up moisture from the soil, mainly through the micropyle. The radicle soon begins to increase considerably in size and in so doing ruptures the seed coat. Its further growth tends to split the testa wider and wider apart. Side roots soon appear from the primary root, so that at an early stage in germination the developing seedling becomes firmly anchored in the soil. Simultaneous with the continued growth of the radicle and its side roots, important changes begin to take place in the plumule, and parts of it, such as the portion between the cotyledons and the two embryonic leaves, begin to lengthen. However, since the cotyledons remain tightly fixed below ground within the seed, and the root is firmly fixed in the soil, the growth of this region, the *epicotyl*, causes it also to break through the now considerably weakened seed coat. As the epicotyl emerges it is hook-shaped, and it is the curve of this hook which breaks through the seed coat. Rapidly increasing in length, it pushes its way upwards through the soil, dragging after it the first small tender pair of leaves, to which it affords a measure of protection. When these leaves are free of the seed coat and the soil the curved epicotyl quickly straightens. The leaves then open, take up a position with their greatest area exposed to the light, and rapidly turn green. Through-

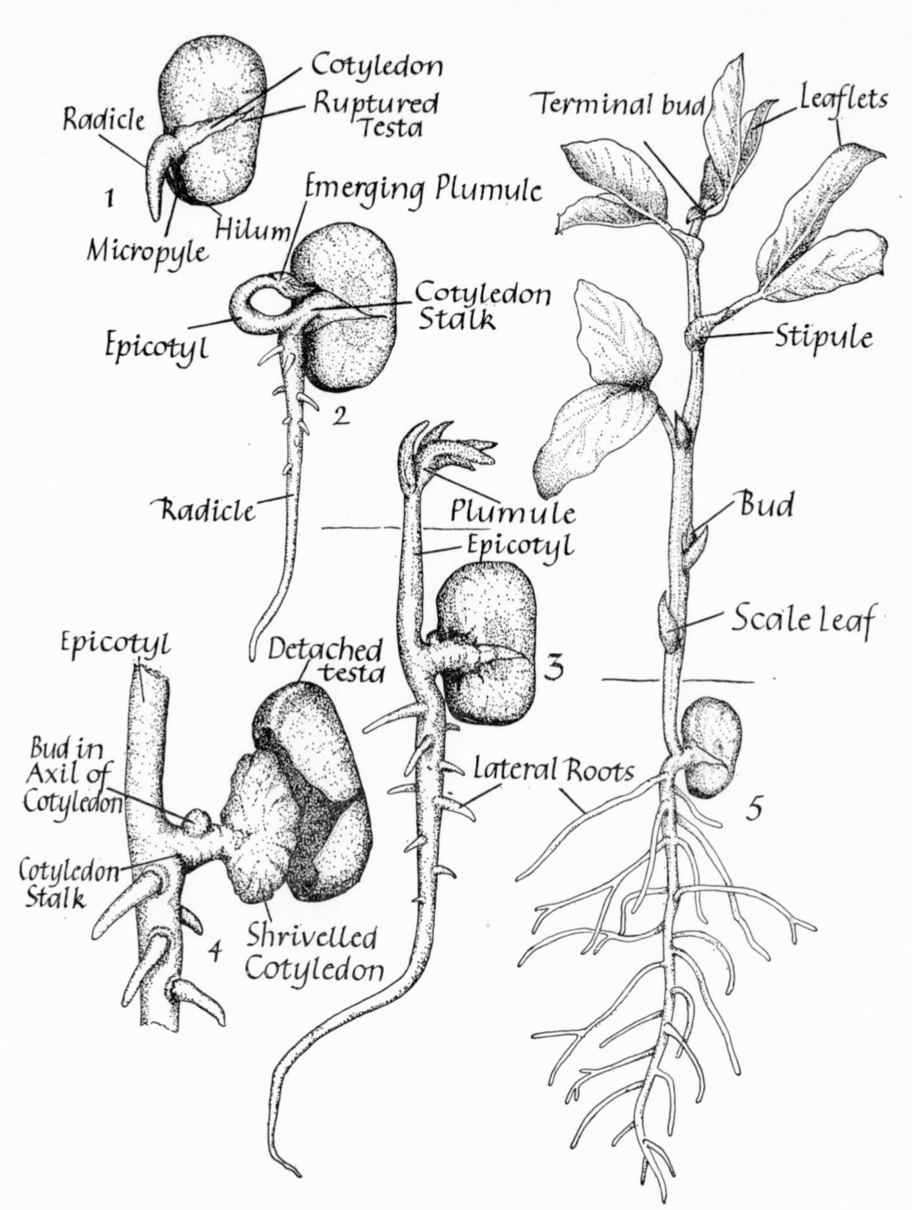

Figure 3 *Broad bean; stages in germination*

1 *Emergence of radicle.*

2 and 3 *Emergence of plumule and the appearance of lateral roots.*

4 *Testa removed to show shrivelled cotyledons and the endogenous origin of lateral roots.*

5 *Young bean plant.*

out these changes, whereby the embryo has been transformed into a seedling, the cotyledons remain below ground within the ruptured remains of the testa. If examined when the first two leaves are fully expanded, it will be found that the cotyledons have shrunk considerably owing to the utilization, during the seedling's development, of the food reserves stored within them. Because the cotyledons remain permanently under ground, throughout germination, they are described as *hypogeal.*

Castor Oil (*Ricinus communis* L., figs. 4 and 5)

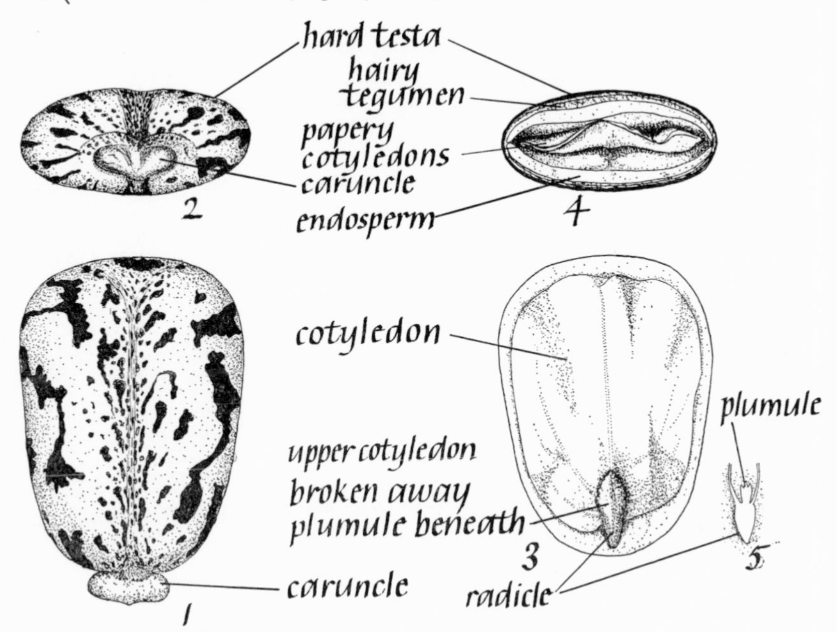

Figure 4 *Castor oil seed*

1 and 2 *Views showing external features.*

3 *Testa removed and one cotyledon broken away.*

4 *Seed cut across to show internal features.*

5 *Part of embryo showing relation of cotyledons to plumule and radicle.*

The castor oil provides a good example of germination in seed of a different type. It is an endospermic seed in which the embryo occupies only a small part. Most of the space within the testa is taken up by white, fleshy endosperm in which the food reserves are stored, thus differing markedly from the bean. Another point of contrast is that this food reserve in the endosperm consists of oil, the source of castor oil. An external feature to be noted is that neither hilum nor micropyle is visible, because they are covered by a warty outgrowth of the testa, called the *caruncle*. The testa of the castor oil seed is so hard that even after soaking in water it must be chipped off in order to be removed. Once it has been removed, a more delicate inner coat, the *tegumen*, will be found. Within this is the fleshy endosperm which, like the cotyledons

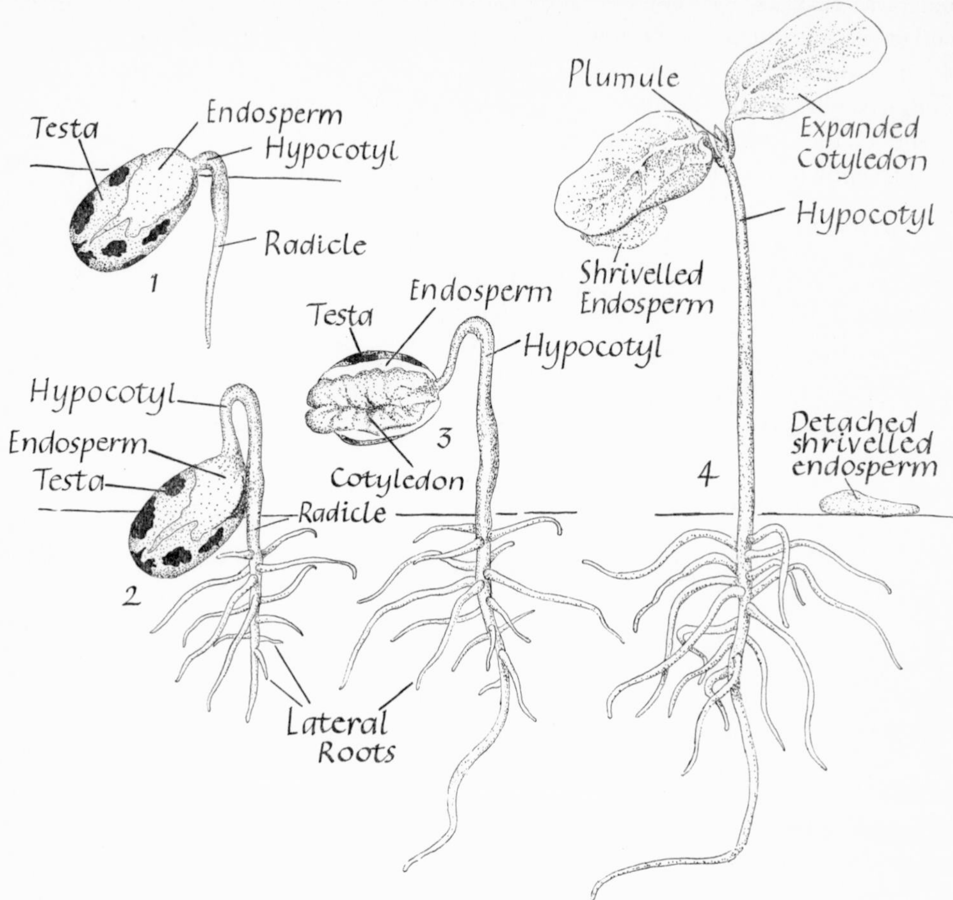

Figure 5 *Castor oil; stages in germination*
1 *Emergence of radicle.*
2 *Emergence of hypocotyl.*
3 *Emergence of cotyledons.*
4 *Opening of cotyledons and detachment of the endosperm.*

of the bean, splits quite easily into two. On each of the inner faces of the resulting two halves a delicate leaf-like structure with distinct veins will be found. These are the cotyledons, which clearly occupy only a very small proportion of the total volume of the seed. At the base of one of the cotyledons, and attached to it, is the radicle, the pointed end of which is directed outwards, while the blunt end is the plumule. The stalks of the cotyledons are barely discernible.

In the germination of the castor oil seed, as in that of the bean, it is in the region of the testa covering the radicle that water is first absorbed, causing the warty caruncle to increase in size and become much softer. The water is passed on to the radicle beneath, which again is the first part of the embryo to increase significantly in size, so much so that it causes the eventual rupture of the testa above it. The radicle, on bursting through the testa, grows downwards and soon anchors the seed in the soil by the production of lateral roots. While this is proceeding, there takes place an elongation of that portion of the embryo which lies between the region where the lateral roots originate and the point of attachment of the cotyledon stalks which were so difficult to see in the resting seed. This part of the embryo, since it is below the cotyledons, is named the *hypocotyl*; it can be distinguished from the radicle by its reddish colour. The bean, too, has a hypocotyl, but as it undergoes little development it is very difficult to distinguish from the radicle.

As the hypocotyl lengthens it forms a hook, like the epicotyl of the bean, and it is this strong rounded portion of the embryonic stem which first appears above the soil. The hypocotyl begins to straighten out as growth proceeds and the cotyledons, with the delicate plumule protected between them, are dragged out of the soil. At this stage the endosperm has almost disappeared, for the cotyledons while in the soil, have been absorbing from it food reserves with which to nourish the developing seedling. Indeed the cotyledons have grown considerably and have at this stage well marked stalks or *petioles*. By the time the hypocotyl has straightened completely, these cotyledons, now well above ground, have expanded their green blades to serve as the first functional leaves of the seedling. This they continue to do until several true leaves are formed by the further growth and development of the plumule. Because they are raised above the soil on germination, these cotyledons of the castor oil are termed *epigeal*.

The number of cotyledons which seeds possess is the character used to separate the flowering plants of the Plant Kingdom into its two groups, the *Monocotyledons* and *Dicotyledons* (see Chapter 30). The seeds of the bean and castor oil both bear two cotyledons and are thus dicotyledonous plants. The seeds of grasses, cereals and the Lily family have only one, and are therefore monocotyledonous plants. The structure and germination of some monocotyledons will now be examined.

As with dicotyledonous seeds, the single cotyledon of the monocotyledons may be hypogeal or epigeal in its germination, and both endospermic and non-endospermic seeds occur in this division, though the former are the more common by far.

Maize (*Zea mais* L., figs. 6-8)

The seed of maize is a good example of an endospermic monocotyledonous seed with a hypogeal cotyledon. Seeds of such cereals as wheat or barley germinate in a similar way and have a somewhat similar structure. Because of the smaller size of these seeds, however, the details are less easy to observe than in maize. Examination of the external features of the maize seed reveals two scars: one, the former point of attachment to the corn-cob, at the narrower end; the other, which consists of a minute projection, at the opposite, broader end. This projection is what remains of the *stigma* of the flower from which the seed developed. The presence of this scar indicates that the seed is still enclosed within the ovary wall. The maize grain, therefore, is really a *fruit*, containing a single seed. Its seed coat is so closely united to the surrounding ovary wall that the two layers cannot be easily distinguished; and the micropyle cannot be seen. The two sides of the seed are distinctly flattened and on one of these a light coloured depression indicates the position of the embryo.

The internal structure of the seed can best be seen by cutting the seed in half lengthways along a line joining the attachment and stigma scars. Internally, it appears to be divided into two triangular portions separated by a diagonal line joining these scars. The embryo occupies the triangle whose base is at the attachment scar end, while the endosperm occupies the complementary triangle. The main visible features of the embryo are a short radicle, enclosed in a cap-like root sheath, or *coleorhiza*, and a plumule encased in a similar sheath, the *coleoptile*. On the inner side of the radicle and plumule, and where these two organs meet, there is a large shield-like cotyledon on a very short, thick stalk. This single cotyledon does not merely look like a shield, for which reason it is called the *scutellum*, but it also acts as such, its entire margin being extended to surround and thereby protect the radicle and plumule, leaving only a small aperture opposite the latter. With regard to the triangle occupied by endosperm, two regions can be distinguished, a white and relatively soft portion next to the embryo and a yellow flinty substance furthermost from it.

As with the germination of the dicotyledonous seeds already examined, the radicle is the first part of the embryo to receive water, the absorption of which is probably facilitated by the chaff-like material which persists in the region of the former point

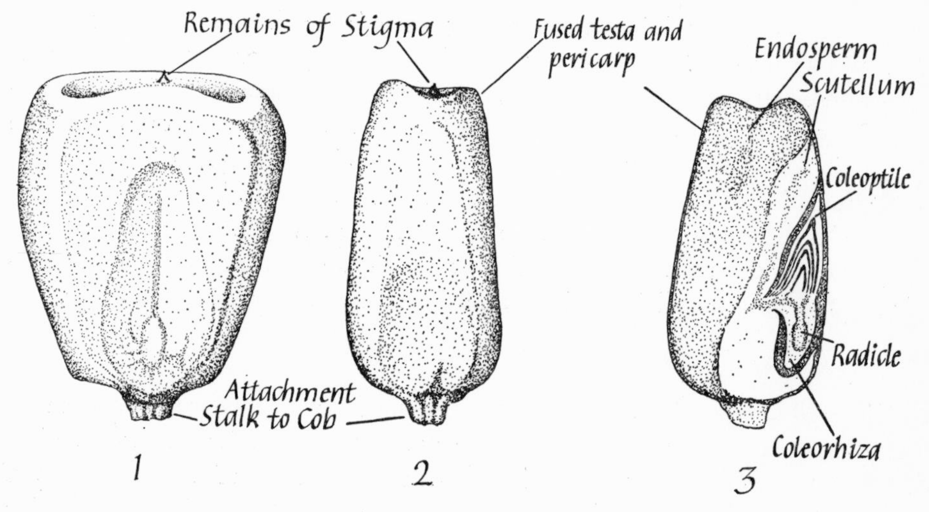

Figure 6 *Maize seed*

1 and 2 *Views showing external features.*

3 *Longitudinal section to show internal features.*

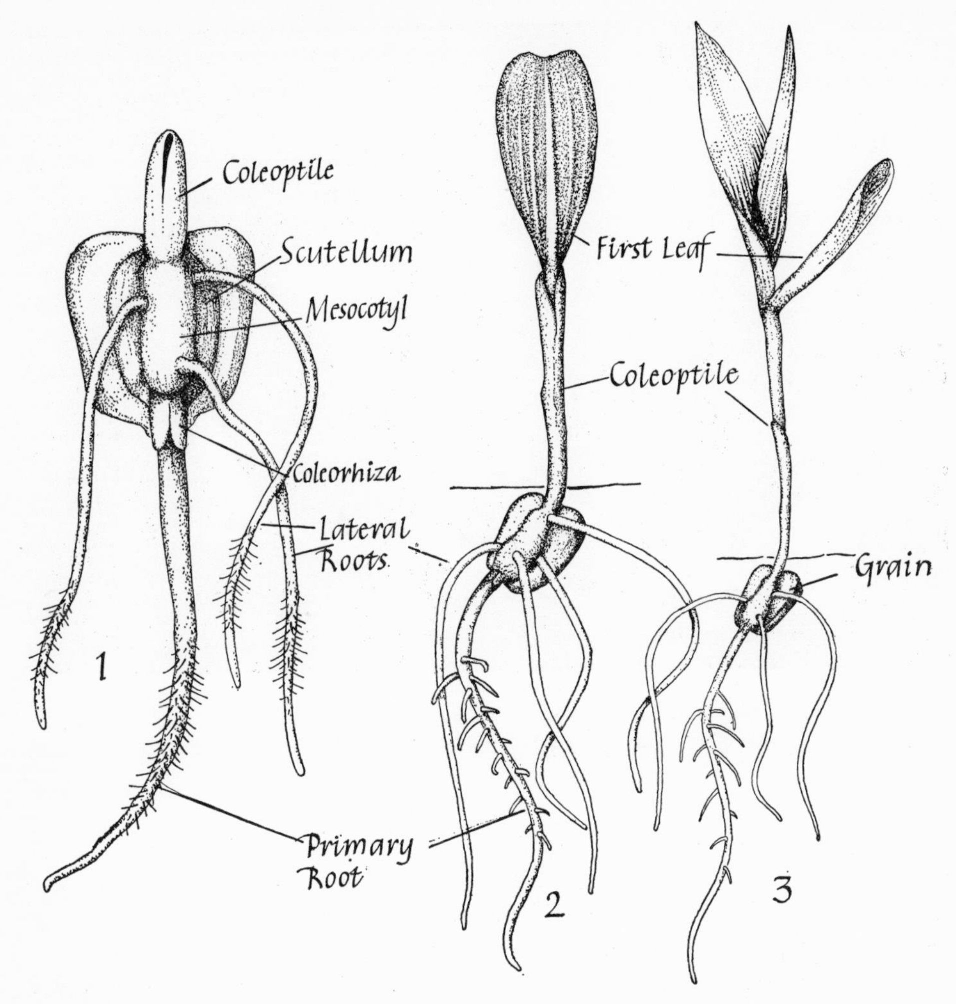

Figure 7 *Maize seed; stages in germination*

1 *Emergence of primary and lateral, adventitous roots and coleoptile.*

2 *Emergence of first leaf from the coleoptile.*

3 *Young maize plant.*

Figure 8 *Germinating maize seeds showing primary roots with root hairs and in some, the emergence of the coleoptile and first leaf.*

of attachment of the grain. Again it is the radicle which first bursts through the combined seed coat and fruit wall. This extension of the radicle also splits the root sheath, the remains of which can be clearly seen in the germinating grain. The plumule makes its appearance soon after the radicle but unlike that of the castor oil seedling its emergence is the result of its own growth and not that of the hypocotyl. Moreover, it remains unbent during its passage upwards through the soil. Its delicate growing point and young leaves are completely protected by an outer sheath, the coleoptile, which is tough and pointed. When the coleoptile reaches the light it quickly stops growing and the leaf within bursts through the tip and expands to form a green, lanceolate leaf, soon to be followed by others. One further difference in the germination process of this and most other monocotyledonous seeds as compared with dicotyledonous plants, is that the radicle, which in dicotyledons usually grows into a sturdy main root, is soon followed by the development from the hypocotyl of a number of similar *adventitious roots*.

It is therefore clear that during the process of germination, the single cotyledon remains below the soil within the seed. As the seedling develops, the cotyledon is absorbing food materials, which have become mobilized in the adjoining endosperm, to pass on to the growing embryo.

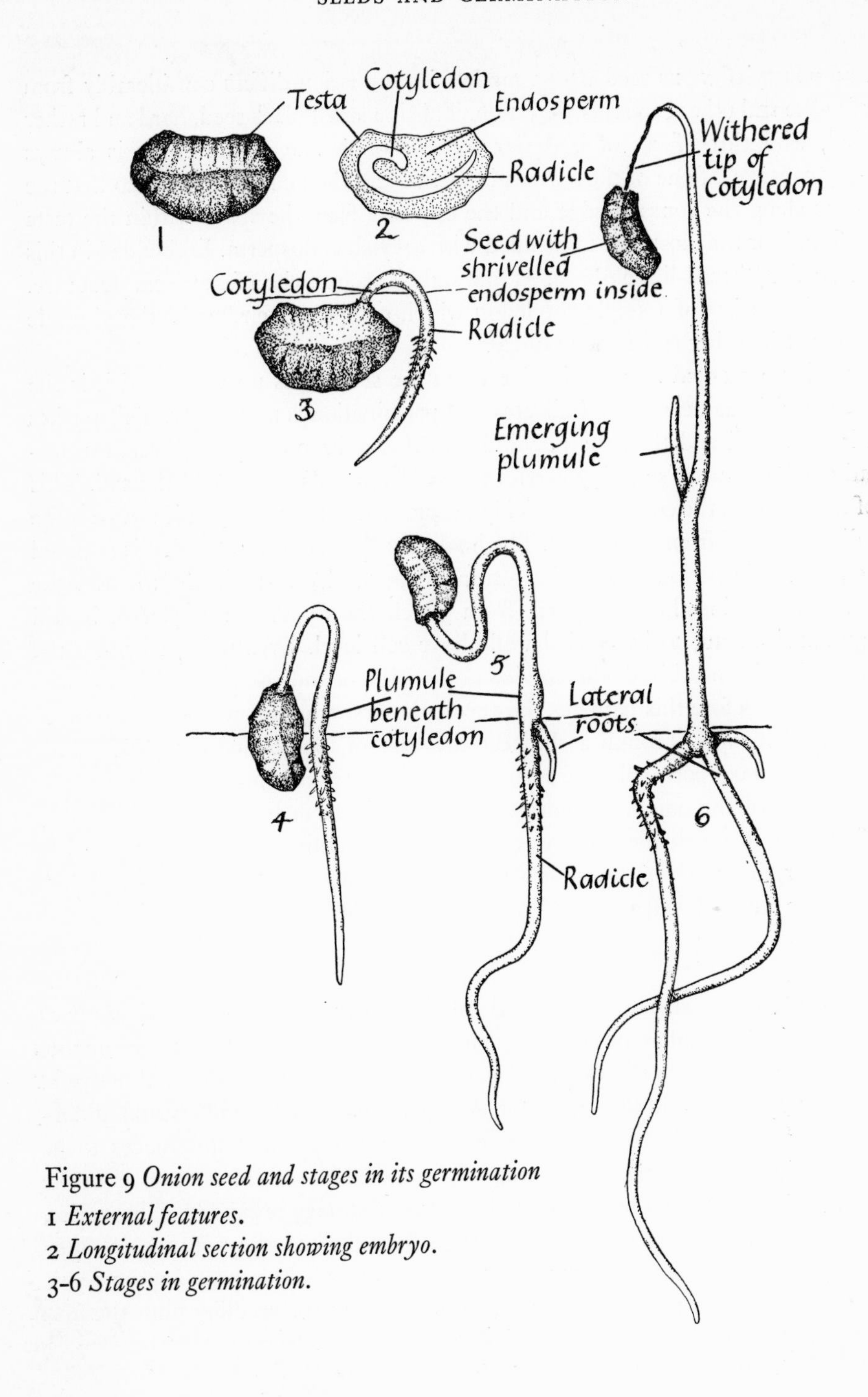

Figure 9 *Onion seed and stages in its germination*
1 *External features.*
2 *Longitudinal section showing embryo.*
3-6 *Stages in germination.*

Onion (*Allium cepa* L., fig. 9)

A monocotyledonous seed whose mode of germination differs considerably from that of maize and other cereals is the onion. This is a small black seed, hard and rather wrinkled, with three faces of irregular form, though one of the edges is always markedly concave. If one of these seeds is soaked and then cut lengthwise so that the cut passes along the concave edge and the opposite face, the space within the testa will be found for the most part to be filled with greyish endosperm. Embedded in this is a pale, coiled, thread-like embryo. At first sight it seems to be a featureless structure. However, it consists of a single cotyledon which completely ensheaths the plumule and tapers at its other end to the radicle.

There is no marked increase in size when the seed takes up water and it is the appearance of the radicle which indicates that germination is under way. This pushes down into the soil and then the remainder of the embryo elongates, becomes prominently arched and in so doing carries the seed upwards and out of the soil. This part of the embryo, the cotyledon, quickly becomes green so that soon it can be quite easily distinguished from the radicle. The hook-like shape of the cotyledon is retained for a considerable period and by its continued upward growth it often causes the testa, which contains the endosperm from which the tip of the cotyledon is still drawing nourishment, to be carried well above soil level. Eventually, when all the endosperm has been utilized, the cotyledon tip withers and the more or less empty testa drops off. Before this happens, however, the first true leaf will have appeared, having forced its way through a slit near the base of the cotyledon. At this stage several adventitious roots will have sprung from the cotyledon just above the radicle. The cotyledon of the onion, though very different in form from that of the maize seed, functions in much the same way. In maize the entire structure is merely an organ of absorption while in the onion all but the absorbing tip emerges from the seed, soon turns green and helps further in nourishing the developing seedling by its photosynthesis.

This survey of the structure and mode of germination of seeds of various types shows that seeds from different kinds of plants, when mature and ready to germinate, have marked differences in their internal structure, in the nature of the food reserves, and in the way in which they are stored. Apart from such fundamental differences as the number of cotyledons present, the most important differences to be observed are in the form and functioning of these seed leaves. They may, as in the bean, remain below ground and serve as large fleshy storage organs or, as in maize, act only as a means of transferring food materials from the endosperm to the developing embryo. In other cases, as in castor oil and onion seeds, they may appear above ground and function as the first photosynthetic organs of the seedling until the first true leaves appear.

CHAPTER 2

GROWTH AND DEVELOPMENT

The last chapter surveyed the growth of different parts of the embryo, such as the radicle and plumule. Their growth leads to the development of the embryo, first into a seedling and then into a plant capable of an independent existence. No clear-cut distinction can be made between these two fundamental biological processes, *development* being the qualitative aspect of *growth*, which is essentially a quantitative matter. Growth is a process which can be expressed in terms of measurement or weight; development is a phenomenon to be observed and described.

Growth can be defined as an irreversible increase in the size of an organ, or organism, usually accompanied by an increase in dry weight. The operative word is 'irreversible', for (see p. 6) a dead seed may increase considerably in size by the purely physical process of imbibing water. Such a seed can, however, be made to give up this water quite readily and in so doing it will shrink back to its original size; clearly a reversible process. In contrast, the protruded radicle of a seed which has germinated can never be made to shrink back into its testa, for since germination there has been a continuous addition of living material to it. It has increased in size irreversibly, and therefore exhibited growth. Like the plumule which will later grow out of the testa and push its way upwards through the soil to expand its first leaves to the light and thus develop as a shoot, so the radicle, as it grows, changes its shape and form, though in a less striking way. Apart from growing longer, it becomes much stouter, and quite soon produces lateral roots. Increases in the complexity of an organism as shown by these growing parts of the embryo provide an excellent example of the essentials of development.

Provided growing conditions are suitable, development continues far beyond the seedling stage. After germination and the successful establishment of the seedling, the root and shoot systems of the plant are theoretically capable of indefinite extension. In the bean, for instance (fig. 3), the radicle continues to penetrate deeper into the soil, to develop as the primary root or *tap root*, from which numerous lateral roots are produced; these in turn produce their own laterals, each potentially capable of unlimited growth. The bean's shoot system is continuous with the root system, and consists of a quadrangular main stem terminated by a bud. This bud, like all buds, is a telescoped portion of the shoot, consisting of an embryonic stem protected by densely crowded, overlapping, immature leaves. Below the terminal bud, successively older and increasingly well-developed leaves are borne laterally on the stem, though the two or three lowest may be merely pale-coloured scales. Each point on the stem at which a leaf occurs is termed a *node*, and the portion of stem between adjoining

Figure 10 *Broad bean plant showing flowers in the axils of its leaves. This plant has thus entered the phase of reproductive development.*

nodes, an *internode*. As the stem grows and the shoot system develops, a lateral shoot in embryo forms as a bud in the angle between each leaf and the primary stem, that is in each leaf *axil*. Each of these *axillary buds* is a potential lateral shoot, and if or when they develop, they become replicas of the primary shoot, bearing a further series of leaves and axillary buds. In this way the shoot system develops outwards in all directions and, like the root system below ground, is potentially capable of indefinite extension.

Not all buds are leaf buds. At a certain stage of the plant's development a different type of bud, the flower bud, is produced (fig. 10). Whereas each leaf bud is theoretically capable of indefinite extension, once a flower bud has fully developed and performed its reproductive function there can be no further growth of the shoot in that direction. In many plants, the development of these buds into flowers, followed by the formation of fruits and seeds, marks the completion of the life cycle. It is convenient to consider this life cycle as comprising three stages. First, germination, when the embryo develops into a seedling; secondly, vegetative development, during which period the major production of roots, stems and leaves takes place and the plant attains its full stature; and thirdly, reproductive development, when flowers, fruits and finally seeds are produced. These successive steps merge into one continuous process and in many plants the entire cycle is completed within a single growing season. Such plants are termed *annuals*, in contrast to *perennials* which survive from year to year. Even in the latter there is, however, a definite yearly cycle of development comparable to the complete cycle of annual plants. In place of germination there is renewal in the activity of resting buds; during vegetative development, although new roots, branches and leaves are produced, new buds, also, are formed in the axils of the leaves, to develop in subsequent years: and, as in annuals, there is a third phase, reproductive development.

By taking periodic measurements, much can be learned about growth during these phases of development. Measurements of the length of the main shoot of some suitable plant (the bean will do) throughout its life cycle, from the time when it first appears above ground as a seedling until it eventually produces its own seed, reveal a gradual acceleration in the rate of elongation of the shoot until a maximum rate is attained. With the reproductive phase of the plant's development, and the appearance of flowers, the rate of elongation declines until no further increases in length are observable. Growth has in fact ceased. Alternatively, if an agricultural crop such as wheat or oats was sampled, dry weight determinations might be made at regular intervals of samples comprising a constant number of plants, taken throughout the growing season until the harvest. Such weighings would doubtless show a slight initial decrease in dry weight as the seed's food reserves were used up in germination. However, from the time the leaves appeared and the developing plants were able to support themselves by their own photosynthesis, there would be a rapid acceleration in the rate of growth until a peak rate was reached. This would then be maintained until the crop attained maturity with the production of its grain. During this latter period, the rate of increase in dry weight would gradually decline and eventually stop. A slight decrease in weight might even be recorded in the final stages of the crop's life history.

If these observed increases in dry weight, or in length, are plotted against time on a graph, the resulting curve is *sigmoid*, or S-shaped (fig. 11). Such a curve represents the typical pattern of growth not merely of whole plants but also of their individual parts, and indeed of living organisms in general. From such a graph it is possible to distinguish again three phases of growth; an initial period of slow growth, a middle period of rapid growth and a final phase, again of slow growth. These three phases together constitute what is generally called 'the grand period of growth', which can be expressed graphically in another way by plotting the *daily* increments of growth observed against time (fig. 11).

Although this 'grand period of growth' is common to plants and animals, there are several important differences in its occurence in these two kingdoms of the living world. Probably the most striking characteristic of growth in plants is its restriction to certain very localized regions; in the growth of the animal body, on the other hand, all parts tend to increase in size together, until the organism has attained its full stature. The presence in a plant of these growing regions can be demonstrated by

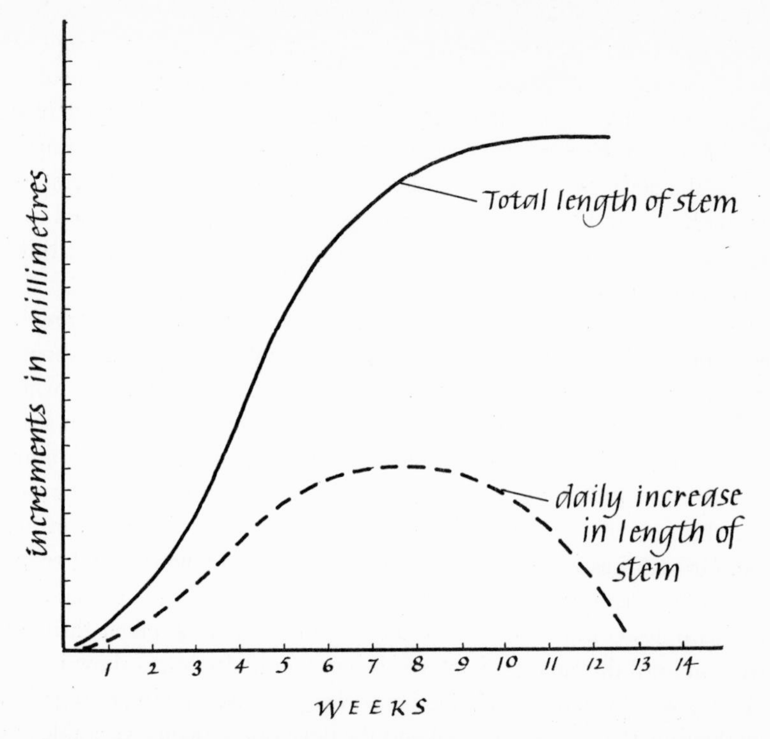

Figure 11 *Graph showing* (*solid line*) *the* grand period of growth *by plotting the total length of a stem against time, and* (*dotted line*) *its daily increments of growth over the same time.*

considering once again the germinating bean seed and repeating an experiment which the distinguished German botanist, Julius Sachs, first performed in the mid-nineteenth century.

The actively growing radicle of a germinating bean is marked with Indian ink into segments of equal length. As the radicle grows longer it will be found that these marks are no longer equidistant one from another. Segments where the markings have become most widely separated are clearly those where maximum growth has taken place. In the elongating radicle this occurs in a region some little way behind the root tip. The results of such an experiment, presented graphically by plotting the increments of growth which have taken place during a given time for each of the segments marked on the radicle, are shown in fig. 12. The localization of growth to the region behind the root tip applies to all subsequently formed roots of the plant.

Similar experiments can be performed on the young growing shoot of a bean seedling. Here too it will be found that the region of maximum growth is located some distance behind the shoot apex. But in older shoots, possessing a series of well marked nodes and internodes (see p. 19), although growth is considerable in the region

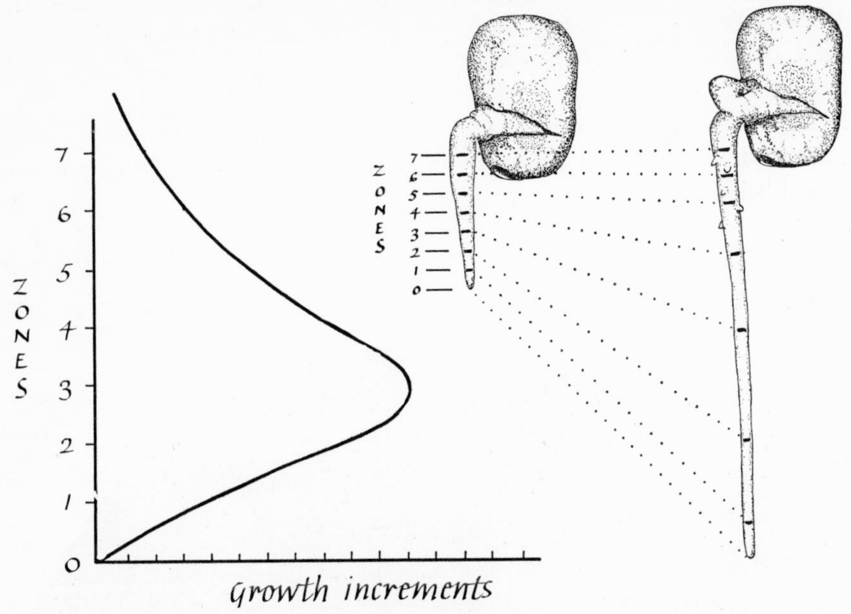

Figure 12 *Marking experiment to show zones of maximum growth of a root.*

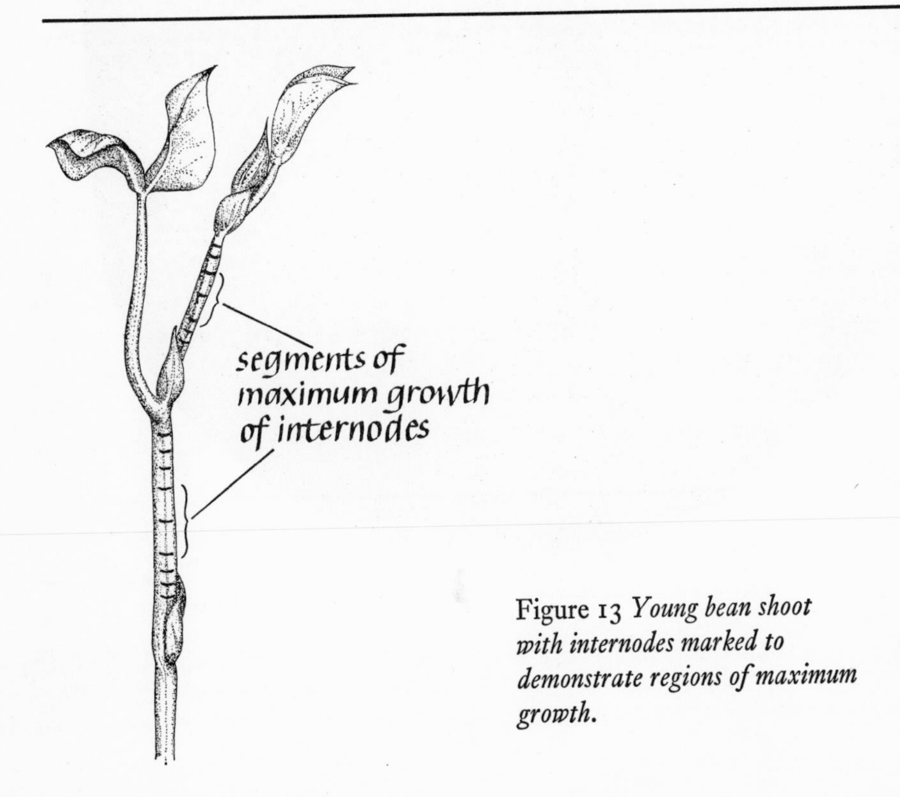

Figure 13 *Young bean shoot with internodes marked to demonstrate regions of maximum growth.*

between the shoot apex and the uppermost node, it is nevertheless usual to find growth persisting and even being greatest in a number of internodes beneath, so that the stem as a whole consists of a series of separate growing regions. Each of these regions of so-called *intercalary growth* can also be shown, by appropriate marking experiments, to have a segment of maximum growth more or less in the centre of each internode, with growth gradually diminishing to zero towards the nodes both above and below (see fig. 13).

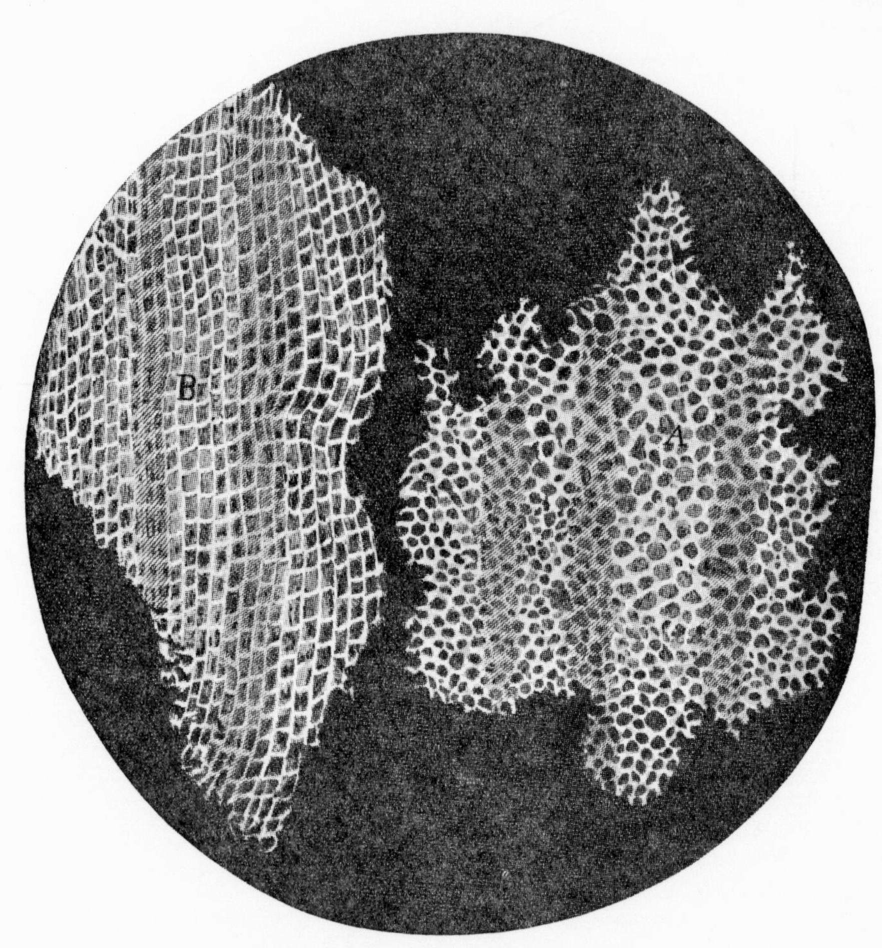

Figure 14 *Hooke's plate of cork cells in horizontal* (A) *and vertical section* (B).

CHAPTER 3

THE MECHANICS OF GROWTH

Marking experiments, as described in the last chapter, indicate that there is a localization of growth in roots and shoots, but provide no information about the mechanism of growth. Insight into the actual internal processes which produce increases in length can be gained only by looking *inside* one of these regions. The further aspect of the problem – how the energy for growth is first stored, then transferred to growing regions, and finally transformed into vital energy – will be considered later in the chapters on plant metabolism.

Because of its comparatively simple form, a young primary root offers the best material for an investigation of the mechanics of growth. However, merely by cutting a growing root, or by splitting it lengthwise with a knife, and then examining the cut surface with even the best of hand lenses, one will obtain no indication of any internal structure. To achieve this, very thin slices, or *sections*, of the root must first be cut. With some of the more robust roots, these can be produced by sectioning the root transversely with a very sharp, flat-ground razor. In many cases, however, the root must first be held rigid by embedding it in paraffin wax; the sections can then be cut with a *microtome*, a miniature bacon slicer, which can cut slices of only a few thousandths of a millimetre (*microns*) in thickness. These very thin sections are then carefully spread onto a glass microscope slide and the wax dissolved away. After appropriate staining, and subsequent protective covering with a very thin square or circle of glass (a coverslip), the internal structure of the root can then be revealed by examination under the much higher magnification of a microscope.

The invention of the microscope is probably the most important event so far in the history of biology. The first treatise in microscopy was by Robert Hooke (1636–1703), 'curator of experiments' for the Royal Society. Through his book *The Micrographia, or some Physiological Descriptions of Minute Bodies Made by Magnifying Glasses and Enquiries Thereupon*, Hooke launched the study of microscopic anatomy which, though a purely descriptive account of a hitherto unexplored field of human enquiry, was one nevertheless destined in later years to lead to the central discovery of biological science, the *cell*. One of the many objects which Hooke investigated was a piece of cork. He described it as being 'all perforated and porous, much like a honeycomb, but that the pores of it were not regular, yet it was not unlike a Honeycomb in these particulars; first in that it had a very solid substance in comparison with the empty cavity that was contained between; next in that these pores or cells were not very deep, but consisted of a great many little boxes, separated out of one continued long pore by certain Diaphrams'. The word 'cell' in Hooke's day had the

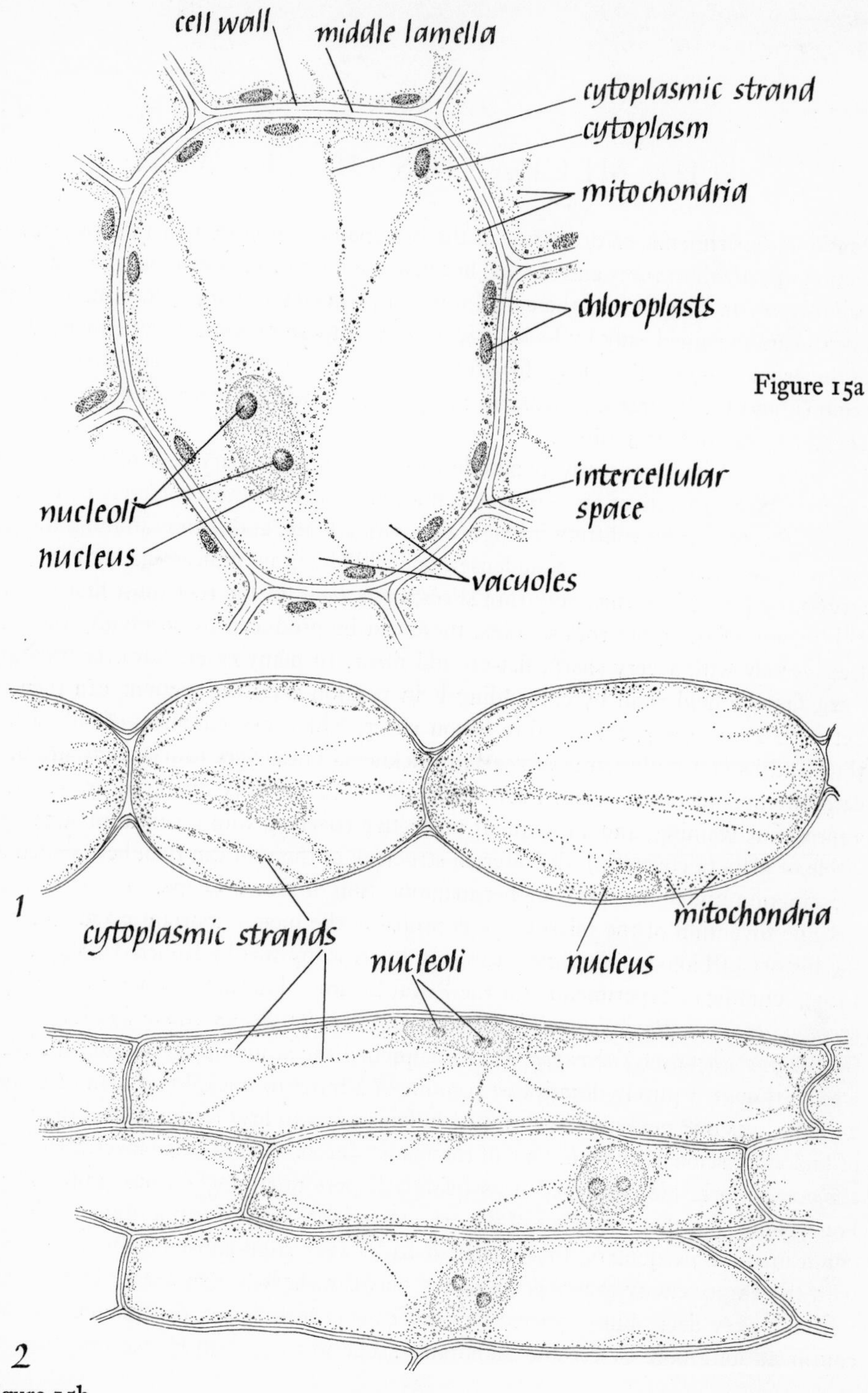

Figure 15a

Figure 15b

discrete meaning of a 'a little room' and that is in fact what he considered these spaces, which he observed in cork, to be (fig. 14).

THE CELL

The thin sections of a root, when examined, will be found to be composed entirely of such 'little rooms'. In fact all plants and their organs, and animals as well, are made up of cells. This fundamental biological fact, established only in the mid-nineteenth century, leads to the important generalization that, just as the unit of chemical structure is the molecule, so the unit of biological structure is the cell. Those cells in the piece of cork, which Hooke was the first to describe, were, however, dead, and he was looking, in fact, only at the so-called cell walls. It was more than a hundred and fifty years after Hooke's discovery before biologists began to investigate and describe the internal details of living cells: a task in which they were greatly helped by considerable improvements in the optical systems of the microscope.

Cells, the units of which every organism is composed, change in appearance with age, increasing in size and often undergoing radical alterations in shape as they grow and develop. Again, the cells of plants are in many ways very different from those of animals, and amongst plants themselves there is much diversity of cell form. This applies not only to different kinds of plants, but to different parts of the same plant. Because of this great variety, it is hardly possible to describe a typical, mature plant cell. However, in order to give a generalized picture of this fundamental biological unit, it is possible to construct what might be termed an hypothetical, undifferentiated, mature, living cell. The main features of such a cell are shown in fig. 15a.

Each cell has two parts, the living *protoplast*, and the inert *cell wall*, which is a product of and which encloses the former. The wall supports and protects the protoplast, but though it is relatively thick it is composed of fairly elastic material. The shape of any cell consequently depends on the mutual pressures exerted on the wall by adjoining cells whose walls fit closely together for most of their length, except at the corners, where *intercellular spaces* occur. Immediately within the wall and completely lining its inner surface is the *cytoplasm*. This part of the protoplast is a tenuous layer consisting of a hyaline fluid material bounded without and within by very delicate *membranes*, the *plasmalemma* externally and the *tonoplast* internally.

By examination of certain cells, as for example the staminal hairs of *Tradescantia* spp., or cells stripped from the inner epidermis of an onion (fig. 15b) it can be shown that the cytoplasm is a far from passive and immobile part of the cell, but exhibits constant streaming movements. In the majority of mature cells the entire central portion is occupied by a cavity, the *vacuole*, filled with a watery fluid, *cell sap*, in which many

---

Figure 15a *A generalized plant cell showing typical principal components.*

Figure 15b 1 *Cells which form the staminal hairs of* Tradescantia virginiana.
2 *Cells from the inner epidermis of an onion scale.*

substances vitally important to the functioning of the cell, and to the life of the plant as a whole, are dissolved. The cytoplasm may, however, traverse the vacuole in the form of delicate, web-like strands. Because of the relation between certain physical properties of cell wall, cytoplasm, and bounding membranes on the one hand, and the materials which accumulate in the vacuolar sap, on the other, the living cell is prevented from collapsing, by the maintenance of *turgor* (see p. 157). Indeed each living cell may be compared to an inflated football, the wall corresponding to the external leather case, the cytoplasm to the inner rubber bladder and the vacuole and its sap to the air-filled space inside. It must be recognized, however, that cells within a plant are not isolated entities but extremely fine cytoplasmic strands (*plasmodesmata*), which traverse the walls of adjoining cells, connecting neighbouring protoplasts (fig. 18).

Moreover, the cytoplasm, is not just a homogeneous layer of living matter lining the inside of the cell wall. A number of characteristic and usually easily observable bodies can be seen within this living material, the most prominent of which is the *nucleus*. This dense, opaque body, spherical in shape, may be suspended in strands of cytoplasm across the centre of the cell, or often it may lie in the cytoplasm adjoining the cell wall. Within the nucleus, which is surrounded by a *nuclear membrane*, it is frequently possible to distinguish one or more small highly refractive spherical bodies, the *nucleoli*. The nucleus has claimed a great deal of attention from those biologists – cytologists – who make a special study of cells. This is because, apart from being the most conspicuous organ in the cell, it has a very important part to play and undergoes remarkable changes each time a cell divides (figs. 16 and 19). During this process, characteristic thread-shaped bodies emerge from the nucleus. These structures, the *chromosomes*, play a dominant role in the transmission of the characters and attributes which are passed on from cell to cell and eventually from organism to organism by the process of heredity, thus ensuring that organisms will be like their parents – and different from other organisms. That the nucleus is also essential for the proper functioning of the cell has been demonstrated by delicate experiments in which the nucleus has been removed. Although such enucleate cells can survive for considerable periods, they are often unable to construct or synthesize new cellular material.

Other inclusions of the cytoplasm, in some cases much less conspicuous, are concerned with the various chemical processes occurring within the cell, to which the general term *metabolism* is given. These are *catabolic* activities which involve the breaking down of complex compounds into simple ones with an accompanying release of energy. This energy becomes available for constructive or *anabolic* activities by which other complex substances essential for the survival and growth of the cell, and of the organism of which it is part, are built up. Most prominent of the inclusions intimately involved in metabolic activity are the *chloroplasts* which contain the green photosynthetic pigment, *chlorophyll*. These, however, only occur in certain specialized cells, principally in leaves. Although in some simple plants (algae) there may be only one or a few chloroplasts of quite elaborate form in each cell (cf. *Spirogyra*,

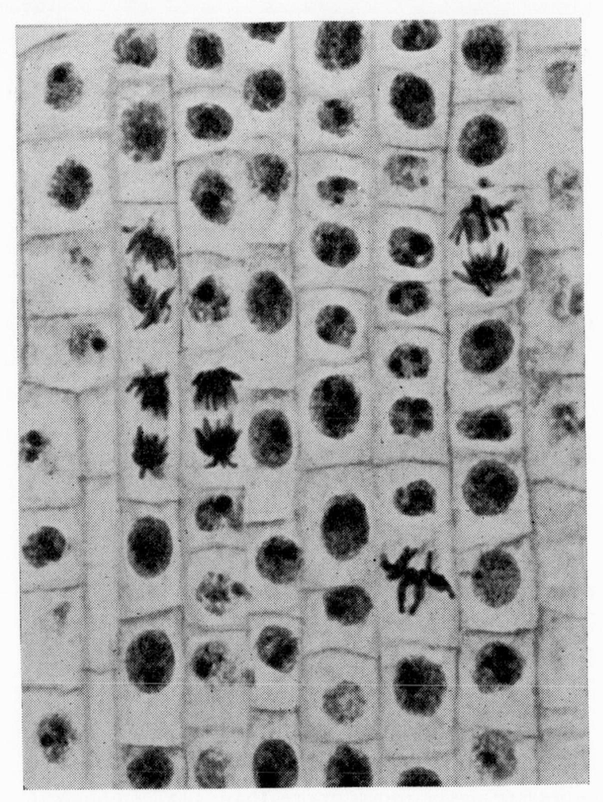

Figure 16 *Cells from part of a longitudinal section of a broad bean root undergoing cell division. The dark, finger-like bodies are chromosomes.*

p. 368), in the green parts of Flowering Plants many of the cells contain a considerable number of these bodies, usually disc-shaped, about 5-10μ in diameter and 3-4μ thick. By grinding and pulverizing the leaves of spinach or nettle (*Urtica dioica*) in a mortar so that the cells are broken up, a suspension of chloroplasts can be obtained (for details see p. 213). If a drop of this is examined under the high power of a microscope, each chloroplast can be seen to have an internal structure of small granules, *grana*, which contain green chlorophyll. This chlorophyll is the substance which, more than any other, characterizes the Plant Kingdom and separates it from the Animal Kingdom; it is chlorophyll that makes plants what they are – the primary producers of the world's organic matter. Through the agency of this green pigment, which absorbs energy from sunlight, carbon-containing organic compounds (carbohydrates) are built up from CO_2 and water in the most remarkable and very complex life-process, *photosynthesis* (see Chapter 17).

Much smaller than the chloroplasts are the *mitochondria*. They are nevertheless of great importance for the successful functioning of every living cell, in that they

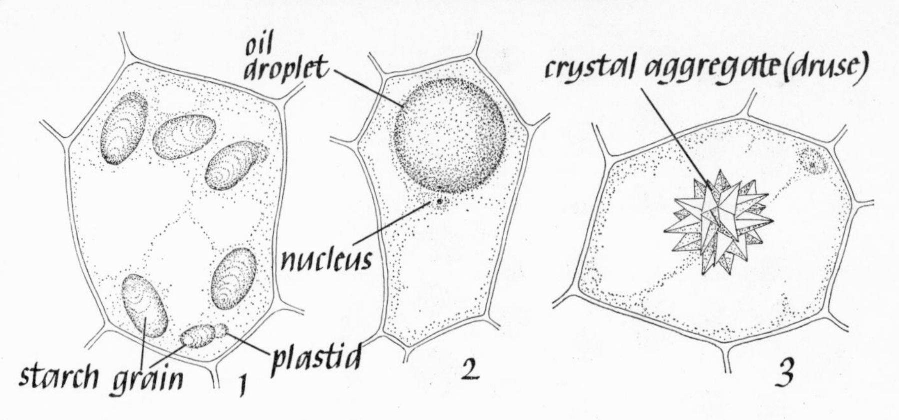

Figure 17 *Ergastic substances in cells*
1 *Starch grains.*
2 *An oil droplet.*
3 *A crystal aggregate or druse.*

play a crucial role in its energy relations. One of the probable functions of these minute organs is to act rather like electricity transformers, stepping down the considerable amounts of energy released from various catabolic processes to a lower, usable level, and then releasing it for many metabolic activities in a form with which the cell can cope (see Chapter 19, p. 224). In many plants the mitochondria are almost too small to be seen under the microscope, for even at their largest dimension these rod-shaped or spherical bodies are never much more than 1–2μ. They can, however, be seen quite well with even a student microscope, in healthy, living staminal hairs of *Tradescantia* spp. When these hairs are examined under a $\frac{1}{12}$in. oil immersion objective, the jerky, jostling movements of considerable numbers of mitochondria can be observed as they are carried along in the actively streaming cytoplasm (see fig. 15 (B) 1).

Some cytoplasmic inclusions which can be seen much more clearly than mitochondria are not, however, directly concerned with the functioning of the cell. These are referred to by the general term *ergastic substances*, so called because they are the products of the working or metabolic activities of the cell. They are mainly food reserve materials of which the most conspicuous are fat droplets and, to a lesser extent, starch grains. In some cells, characteristically shaped crystals of various substances may also be found (see fig. 17). Crystal aggregates are termed *druses*.

Submicroscopic Structure

A most significant and exciting advance in the exploration of the structure of cells and their components has been the development of the electron microscope. The magnification of the optical microscope is largely determined by the objective which has a maximum of about 100 or at best 120 diameters. The eyepiece can increase this by about 15 times so that a total magnification of × 1500 diameters or slightly more, can be obtained. With the electron microscope total magnification from × 20,000 up to 100,000 diameters can be achieved.

This makes possible the exploration of the 'submicroscopic' organization of cells, and shows that the cell wall, the cytoplasm, and its various inclusions each have a complex internal structure of their own. The cytoplasm, for example, far from being a rather formless, structureless mass, is shown to consist of a fine network of membranous canals, the *endoplasmic reticulum*, lined with small, dense particles called *microsomes* or *ribosomes*. These have a very important part to play in protein synthesis. The grana of chloroplasts and even the minute mitochondria possess complex internal structures of their own, related to their important functions. Only in the

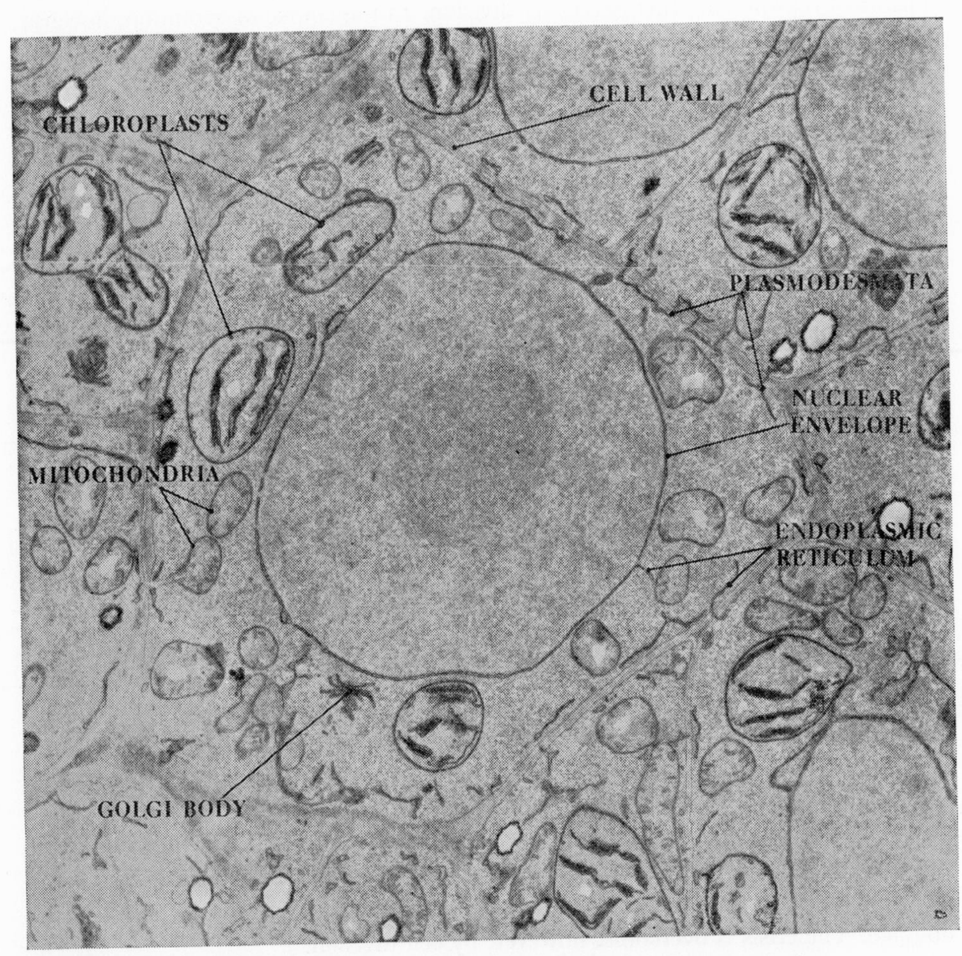

Figure 18 *Electron micrograph of a cell from the stem apex of* Lupinus albus (*Permanganate fixation*). (*Preparation and photograph by A. J. Tullett.*)

case of investigations on the nucleus has the electron microscope so far failed to reveal very much more about the structure of this important cell organ than has been discovered with the light microscope (fig. 18).

Meristems

In the realm of biology it is rarely possible to formulate laws comparable with those of the exact sciences, such as physics and chemistry. One such law, however, is that all cells are derived from pre-existing cells, and that the manner in which they are produced – by cell division – is basically the same throughout the living world. In primitive plants, such as those with single cells, or some filamentous algae, *all* the cells perform *all* the essential life-processes (see *Chlamydomonas* p. 355, *Chlorella* p. 359, etc). They all look alike, all take part in all metabolic activities, and all are capable of reproducing themselves by division. In the course of evolution, however, as plants have become more complex and specialized, the process of new cell formation has become progressively separated from other functions. In the more advanced members of the plant kingdom new cells are in the main produced only in certain regions of the plant by groups of cells which, being endowed with perpetual youth, are capable of dividing more or less indefinitely. There are two general types of these so-called *meristematic* regions ('meristem' is from a Greek word meaning divisible). The first occurs at the tips of roots and shoots, the *apical* meristems. They initiate growth in length, and adjoin the regions of these organs in which visible increases in length can be demonstrated (see p. 22.) Secondly, there are *lateral* meristems, arranged parallel to the sides of the organs in which they occur, causing them to increase in thickness. Consideration of these however must be left to the chapter on secondary thickening (see p. 124).

CELL DIVISION

The outstanding activity within a meristematic region is cell division. It is clearly essential to have some understanding of the nature of this important process. The growth of an individual cell is accompanied by the creation of new protoplasm through the activity of that already present. Consequently, the bulk of living matter increases. The interchange of materials, both from outside the cell and also between the cytoplasm and nucleus – across the all important membranes surrounding these cellular regions – is essential for the continuation of this synthesis. As cytoplasm and nucleus increase in volume, the area of the membranes across which interchanges occur does not increase at the same rate. At some stage the rate of these important interactions, because of the change in surface to volume ratio, becomes inadequate to support any further production of new protoplasm. This critical limiting point is almost certainly reached when the amount of nuclear and cytoplasmic material has doubled. The crisis is overcome, however, by cell division.

Cell division, although one continuous process, is usually recognized as having two phases. The first and most striking, called *mitosis*, is the division of the nucleus.

This is followed by *cytokinesis*, the division of the cytoplasm, and the laying down of a new cell wall between the two newly formed nuclei. Mitosis and cell division are often apparently regarded as synonymous terms. Mitosis, however, strictly refers only to the division of the nucleus. In fact mitosis can take place as a matter of course in certain plants or plant organs without cytokinesis: very much less frequently cytokinesis may take place without mitosis.

The outstanding feature of cell division is the exact reduplication of the cell and its contents brought about by a series of remarkable changes, various aspects of which have been the subject of intensive study by biologists for a considerable time. Undoubtedly the most conspicuous and exciting part of the process is mitosis, the division of the nucleus, which will now be considered in some detail.

Mitosis and Cytokinesis (figs. 19 and 20).

Prior to the onset of mitosis the cell nucleus is usually described as being at *interphase*, or in a metabolic condition. In this state, under the high power of a good microscope it can be seen to consist of an intricate network of very fine, twisted threads probably closely appressed to the nuclear membrane. Because these threads stain very deeply with certain dyes commonly used in microscopy, they are named *chromatin* threads, or *chromonema* (from the Greek for a coloured thread). It is not possible at this stage to distinguish the threads individually, but as mitosis advances they become increasingly shorter and thicker, until they can be recognized as coiled individuals. Careful inspection of the contracting threads, which as they come to assume an individual form are referred to as *chromosomes*, reveals that they are longitudinally double. Each chromosome in fact consists of two chromonemata (the plural of chromonema) lying closely parallel to one another. The longitudinal halves of each chromosome, which become increasingly apparent as mitosis proceeds, are called *chromatids*. These double threads contract still further and some investigators suggest that a *matrix* accumulates around them. This initial stage of mitosis, the *prophase*, ends when the chromosomes begin to group themselves across the equator of the nucleus and the nuclear membrane and the nucleoli disappear.

Mitosis has now entered the middle stage or *metaphase*. Accompanying the disappearance of the nuclear membrane, it can be seen that a *spindle* of delicate fibres begins to form in the cytoplasm. This structure arises from two points on opposite sides of the nucleus. From these points, or *poles*, the spindle radiates inwards towards the equator of the nucleus. By the time the nuclear membrane has disappeared completely, the chromosomes, now thick, obviously double and fully contracted, become grouped across the middle of the spindle. The chromosomes in certain plants, although fully contracted, may still be of considerable length and only one point on each lies equidistant from the poles. This so-called mechanical centre, or *centromere*, is a non-staining portion of the chromosome and the only part in actual contact with the spindle at its equator. The remaining portions of the chromosomes, the arms, are variously disposed in relation to the point of attachment. It is from this point of

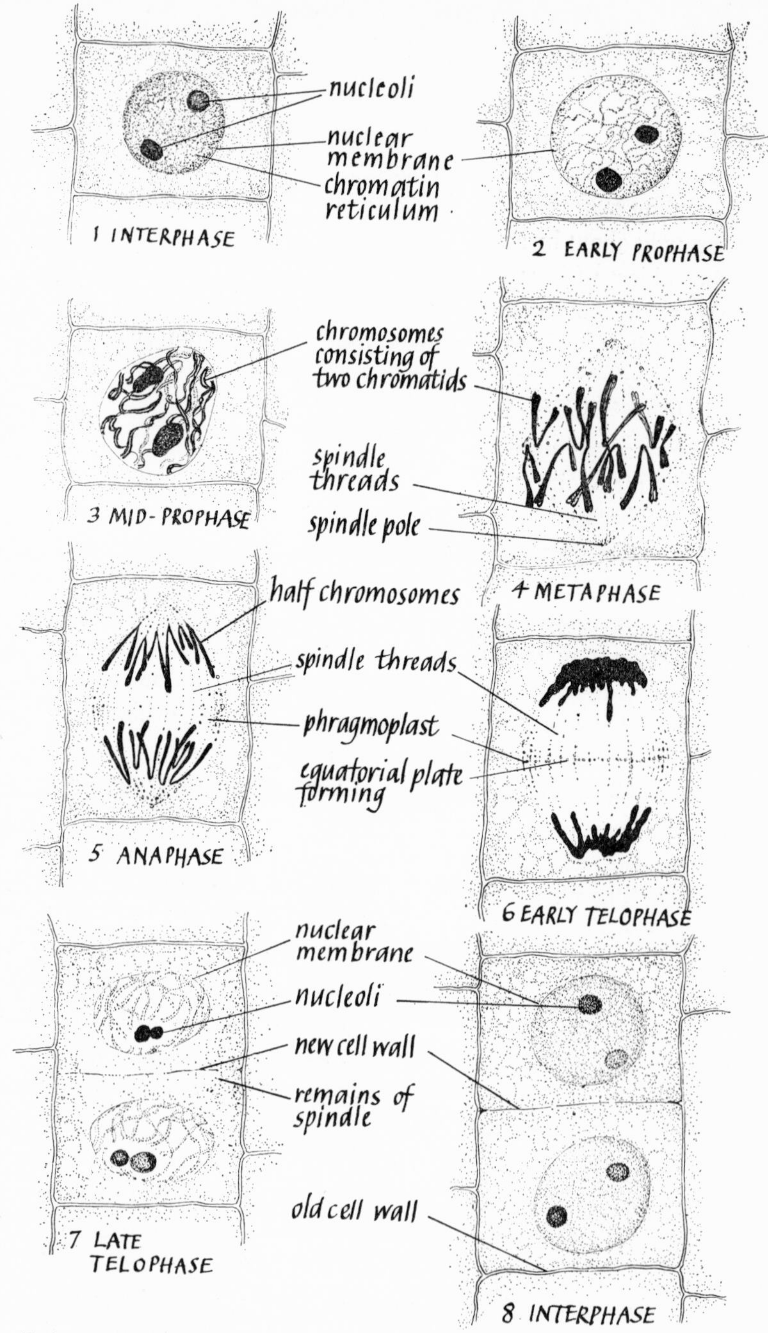

Figure 19 *Principal stages in mitosis in the cells of broad bean root*

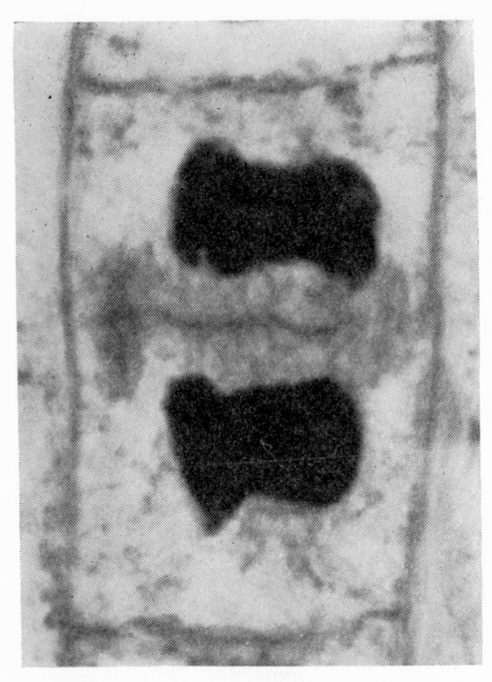

Figure 20 *Cytokinesis in a cell from a l.s. of broad bean root, showing the phragmoplast (the dark grey areas to right and left of the cell between the nuclei) and the cell plate (the dark line, central, between the nuclei).*

attachment that the next stage of mitosis, the separation of the longitudinal halves of each chromosome, the chromatids, is initiated.

During this separating stage, called *anaphase*, the essential purpose of mitosis is achieved. The longitudinally double chromosomes split lengthwise into two daughter chromosomes and each then moves to one of the opposing poles, with the centromeres leading the way. This process produces an exactly equal division of the chromatic material of the nucleus. Anaphase is completed when the *daughter chromosomes* reach the pole. The final stage, or *telophase*, of mitosis then takes place. In this, the changes observed in the chromosomes during prophase are reversed, the coiling of each chromosome relaxes and the resulting chromonemata re-form into the more or less uniform network of threads, which ramify throughout both the newly formed nuclei. At the same time the nucleoli begin to re-form in association with specific regions of specific chromosomes (*nucleolar chromosomes*), and nuclear membranes re-envelope the two new *metabolic* nuclei.

As the nucleus is passing through the later stages of division the second important part of cell division, cytokinesis, is initiated. At telophase, or even during late anaphase, the spindle becomes less conspicuous, and round its equator a barrel-shaped system of fibrils, the *phragmoplast*, begins to form (fig. 20). Small droplets then appear across the equator of this structure and these gradually unite to form a continuous, film-like *cell plate* along which new cell wall material, which eventually divides the original cell in two, is laid down. Thus the division of the cell into two identical daughter cells is achieved.

The composition of the material forming the cell plate has not yet been fully investigated but it is believed to contain cementing *pectic* substances which later constitute the *middle lamella* of the cell wall. It is this adhesive layer which holds adjacent cells together, and after its formation each of the protoplasts of new daughter cells lays down, over the middle lamella, the cell wall itself. The wall is composed of *cellulose*, *hemicellulose* and pectic substances (see p. 194 *et seq.*).

Clearly the outstanding feature of mitosis is the behaviour of the chromosomes. In every mitosis, from the first stages in the formation of an embryo within a seed and at every division of every meristematic cell, each chromosome in each nucleus splits longitudinally. This results in a perfectly equal division of the nuclear contents so that the amount of nuclear material and the number of chromosomes is constant in every cell of the plant body.

Mitosis can best be studied either in appropriately-stained longitudinal sections of actively growing root tips, or by *squashes* of such tips. Although the latter technique, upsets the natural distribution of cells within the root, and frequently of the chromosomes within the cell, it is nevertheless easy and rapid and most valuable especially for studying chromosome morphology (fig. 21).

At metaphase the chromosomes, then fully contracted, can in squash preparations often be seen to be clearly differentiated along their length. Indeed in many plants every chromosome of the total complement is readily distinguishable from its neighbours by such visible characters as relative length, or the length of the arms as determined by the position along the chromosome of the constriction at the centromere. In nucleolar chromosomes there can often be distinguished a prominent unstained region, the *secondary constriction* or *nucleolar organising region*, and also a small terminal knob known as a *satellite*. If these various characters of the chromosome complement of the nuclei of certain plants (e.g. *Vicia*, *Tulbaghia*, *Crepis* spp.) are carefully examined it will be found that the chromosomes can be separated into morphologically identical pairs, so that each vegetative nucleus has a double set of chromosomes (fig. 21). The origin and significance of this duplication of chromosomes in each nucleus, one set being derived from the male, the other from the female parent, and the vital role played by the nucleus and its chromosomes in reproduction and in heredity will, however, be considered later (see Chapter 25.)

MERISTEMATIC REGIONS

In a developing seed, cell division at first occurs, or can occur, in more or less every cell of the embryo as it is forming. During germination, however, as development of the embryo proceeds towards the seedling stage, the production of new cells becomes confined to definite groups of cells which constitute the meristematic regions, and are directed towards the growth of the plant. Many of the other cells become considerably modified and soon become involved in other vital activities. The adult plant is thus composed both of mature, differentiated cells of considerable diversity, grouped together to form tissues, which carry out specialized functions

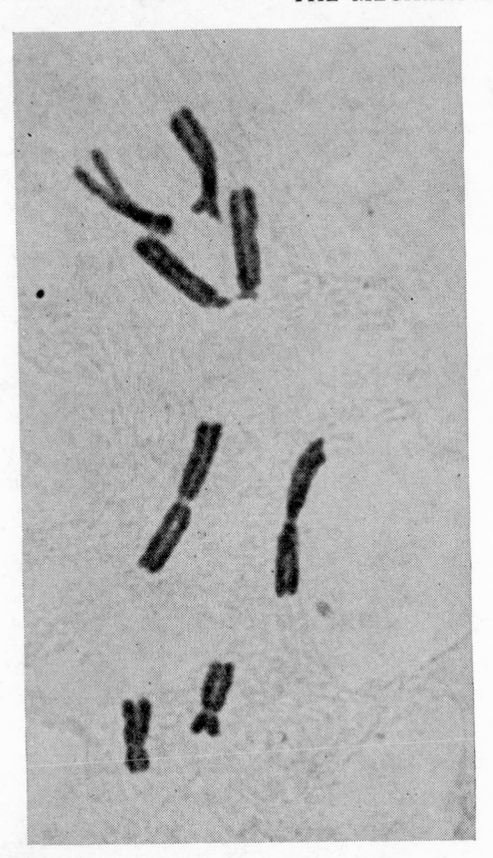

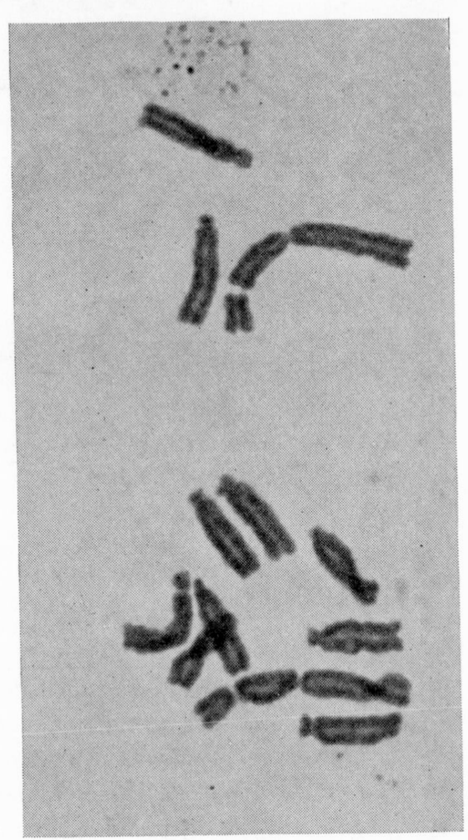

Figure 21 *Acetic orcein squashes of roots tips showing diploid chromosome complements*
(*Left picture*) Crepis pulchra – *in this preparation the homologous chromosomes are perfectly paired.*
(*Right picture*) Vicia faba – *note the two very long chromosomes with prominent secondary constructions.* (*Preparations and photomicrographs by Dr A. H. Dyer.*)

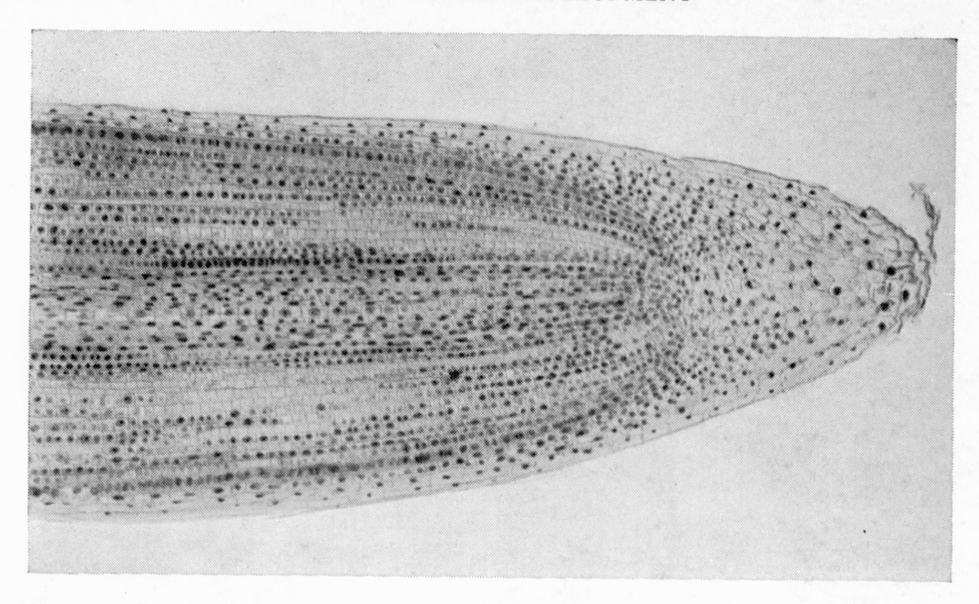

Figure 22 *Longitudinal section of root tip of broad bean.*

(see p. 92); and of permanently juvenile meristematic tissues, whose dividing cells are the initiators of all growth.

The growing tip of the root of a germinating bean seed is an excellent example of a meristematic region, the internal cellular structure of which can be seen by examining a longitudinal section under the microscope (see fig. 22). At the extreme tip of the root is the *root cap* or *calyptra*, a protective sheathing of cells which is being continually renewed by the division of the living cells just beneath it. This renewal is necessary because the cap suffers considerable wear as the root penetrates the soil. Behind the cap is the root meristem itself, a comparatively small mass of cells occupying not more than 2-3 mm of the root's length. It is composed of small, rectangular, thin-walled cells without vacuoles, each having dense cytoplasmic contents and containing a prominent nucleus. The division of these cells is the initial process in the chain of events which together constitute growth. The most important feature of these meristematic cells, however, is that not merely do they continually add new cells to the plant body by their division, but that half the products of these divisions never mature into adult cells but retain their meristematic powers. In consequence the root (and shoot) always has a potential for further growth, provided these meristematic cells remain alive.

The cells produced by the root meristem can be seen as a zone behind the meristematic region. In this zone marked changes in the size and proportions of the cells and in the appearance of their contents can be observed. The most significant alteration in the cells of this zone is that they increase in length, a change which leads to the visible, measurable elongation of the root. Moreover, it is the force exerted by these enlarging cells which causes the root tip to penetrate deeper into the soil. A similar zone of elongating cells occurs behind the apical meristem in shoots, causing the growing shoot to force its way out of the soil and upwards into the air (see p. 9 *et seq.*).

Cell elongation is thus the most obvious and indeed the measurable phase of plant growth. The process is effected primarily by the uptake of water by the cells of the elongating zone, with the result that each cell expands in a manner somewhat similar to the football mentioned in the analogy drawn earlier (see p. 28). The cell walls, however, unlike the leather case of the football which restricts and limits the expansion of the bladder within, are sufficiently elastic to allow quite considerable stretching. If this stretching is irreversible then there will be true cell elongation and growth will have taken place. It may be thought that – as happens when any material is stretched – the elongation of these cells must lead to a gradual reduction in the thickness of their walls. This, however, is not so, for any decrease is compensated for by the deposition of additional wall material through the activity of the living cytoplasm. The cell wall remains more or less constant in thickness during this phase of growth.

The prelude to elongation is the *vacuolation* of the cytoplasm in the cells produced by meristematic activity. Elongation is caused by the inflation of each cell's vacuole by the uptake of water. The vacuole then becomes a very prominent feature of all the cells in the zone of enlargement. Accompanying this change, the cytoplasm comes to occupy only a narrow layer (like the bladder of the football) bounding the inside of the cell wall, though (as in the case of the wall) new material is also added to it. Cell enlargement, therefore, is not merely an increase in the volume of the cell brought about by its inflation as a result of water uptake and vacuolation, but is a vital process in which newly synthesized material is added by cellular activity both to the wall and to the cytoplasm.

It should now be clear that plant growth is the product of two vital processes which can take place only in active, living cells. The initial process is the production of new cells by cell division in meristems, followed by a second phase of increasing vacuolation resulting in cell elongation. It has already been stressed that seed germination is essentially a phenomenon involving growth (see p. 22) and some consideration has been given to the factors controlling this process. In the stages following this initial period of a plant's growth the same set of factors, temperature, oxygen supply, water supply and light, all continue to play an important part. However, before considering the way in which these affect the growth of the later stages in the life of the plant, it is necessary to know how to measure accurately increments in the growth of various plant organs, such as shoots or roots; organs which afford suitable material for growth studies.

MEASUREMENT OF GROWTH

Increases in the length of even the most rapidly elongating parts of the majority of plants are usually so small that they are difficult to measure directly. It is therefore necessary to use some magnifying apparatus. The shoots of young bean plants during the period of rapid vegetative growth provide excellent material for study. Increases in their length, under different experimental conditions, can be measured by a device called a growth lever or *lever auxanometer*. This lever is pivoted asymetrically so that one arm is much longer than the other. The short arm is attached to a growing shoot, the growth increments of which will then be magnified by the movement of the longer, free end of the lever. This end terminates in a pointer which moves down a graduated scale on which growth can be measured while the end of the lever attached to the shoot rises with the elongation of the shoot. The *drum auxanometer* is an elaboration of the growth lever: it automatically records, at regular intervals, increments in growth by means of a needle on the free arm of the lever which scratches a clockwork-driven, smoked drum rotating about its vertical axis (see fig. 23).

Another method of measuring growth which is used especially for the *coleoptiles* of cereals such as wheat or maize seedlings (which are excellent experimental material) is by means of a horizontal vernier microscope. This can also be employed for studies of the conditions affecting the growth of roots.

FACTORS AFFECTING GROWTH

We have seen that the mechanism of growth is initiated by active, meristematic cells. As was the case with the embryo in the germinating seed, during the later stages of a plant's growth the meristematic region of the growing organs must be provided with materials both for the synthesis of new cells and for the energy required to support this constructive activity. Because of this latter requirement, growth is very dependent on respiration, and all growing regions must therefore have an adequate supply of oxygen. Moreover, there must be a plentiful supply of water to these regions, not only for the metabolic activities associated with synthesis and respiration, but also in order to maintain *cell turgidity*, a condition especially important for the second phase of growth, cell enlargement.

Plant growth can be shown by suitable experiments to be considerably influenced by temperature. Minimum, maximum and optimum growing temperatures can be determined. As was the case with the germination of seeds, tropical plants will tolerate a higher range of temperatures, and their growth optima will generally be higher than those for the plants of temperate zones, while the range over which arctic plants grow is correspondingly lower. Irrevocable damage to the living contents of a plant's cells may occur through the harmful effect of the freezing of the cell sap, if temperatures are too low, or through denaturation of the all-important cell proteins, if too high. Under such extreme conditions growth ceases altogether and the death of the plant would probably follow.

It will be remembered that although in the initial stages of seed germination, light may be a prerequisite of growth, in the majority of cases seeds would seem to be indifferent to this factor. In the later stages of plant development, however, when shoots

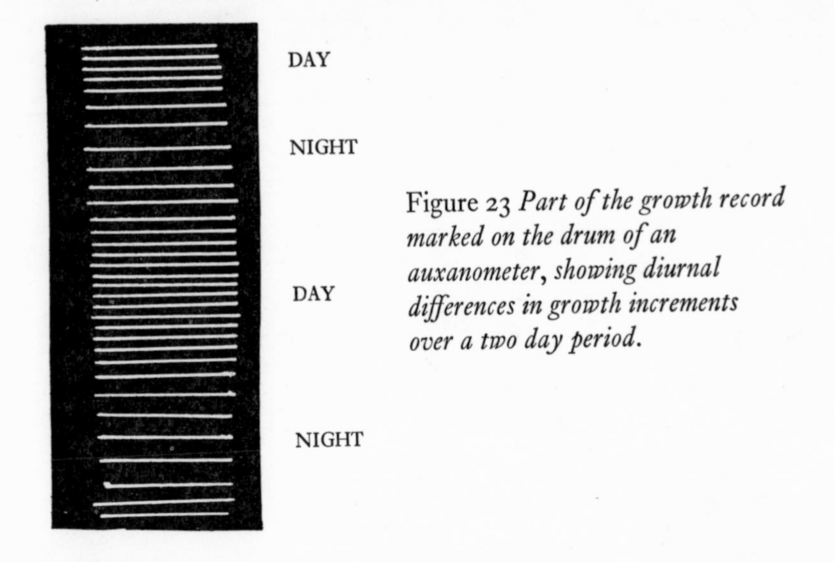

Figure 23 *Part of the growth record marked on the drum of an auxanometer, showing diurnal differences in growth increments over a two day period.*

and leaves have been produced, light has both direct and indirect effects which are of the greatest importance on growth.

With regard to the indirect effect on growth, light is the ultimate source of energy in the most important of all processes carried out by green plants, photosynthesis. In this process the plant produces all the food materials from which it eventually obtains the energy necessary for growth. Indeed, even in plants such as the fungi, without chlorophyll and thus unable to photosynthesize, growth is still dependent on their ability to utilize organic matter produced by the photosynthesis of green plants, so that their growth too is indirectly dependent on light.

The direct effect of light on growth becomes very apparent after a plant placed in the dark has been deprived of light for several days. There is a loss of green colour and an exceptional growth of the internodes, so that the plant assumes a yellowish, straggling appearance. In such *etiolated* plants, as this condition is termed, there is in addition little development of new leaves (fig. 24.2). Experiments using a drum-type auxanometer under the natural alternation of light and darkness, that is of day and night, also show this effect though in a less dramatic way. Provided there is no significant drop in temperature at night, as so often happens in nature, to mask the accelerating effect of darkness on growth, the markings on the auxanometer drum will show that the elongation of a growing shoot is greater by night than by day (see fig. 23). Thus the marks will be farthest apart after mid-night and closest together just after mid-day. In natural conditions, the acceleration of growth in darkness would seem to be of considerable advantage to plants. Moreover even reduced light has an effect which can be seen by comparing the form of plants growing in the shade of a wood or a hedge, with the same species in open situations exposed to full sunlight (see also Phototropism, Photonasty and Phototaxis).

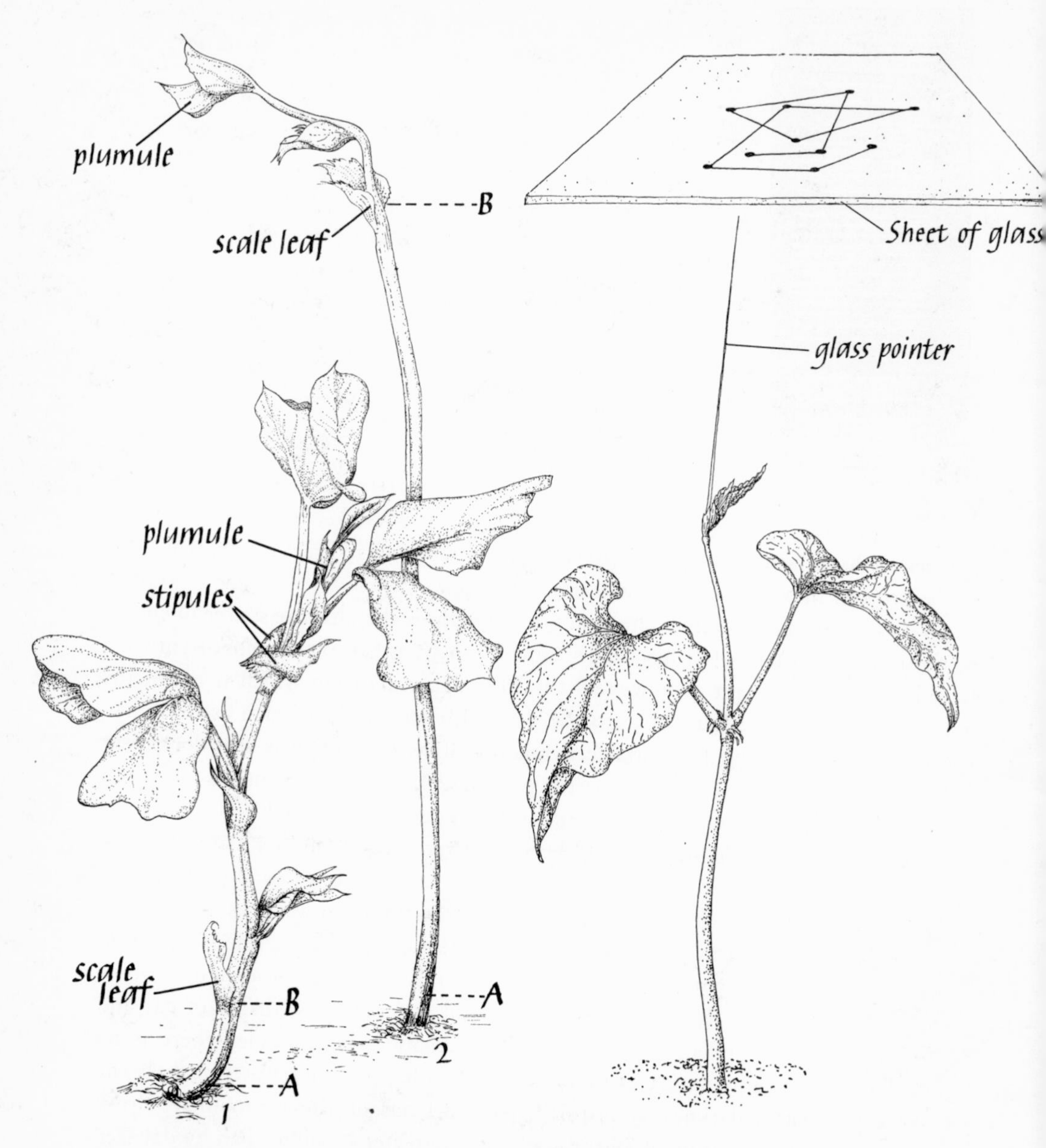

Figure 24 (*left*) *Normal* (1) *and etiolated* (2) *plants of broad bean of the same age. Note the inhibition of leaf production and the very much longer internodes in* (2).

Figure 25 (*right*) *Experiment to demonstrate circumnutation in a growing stem of runner bean.*

CIRCUMNUTATION

Observations on the apex of an elongating shoot show that it does not grow upwards in a straight line but follows an approximately spiral course. Like all growth phenomena the amplitude of this *circumnutation*, which is exhibited by roots as well as shoots, is usually small and must therefore be magnified to demonstrate its occurrence. This, however, can be done quite simply by placing a square sheet of window glass horizontally above some suitable growing plant to which a pointer of finely drawn glass tubing has been affixed with soft wax, so that it stands in line with the tip of the stem (fig. 25). The movements of the apex will then be magnified by the pointer, the position of which as it rotates can be marked with a wax pencil on the glass at regular intervals of time. In making these marks, however, the point of the needle must on each occasion be aligned through a predetermined fixed point positioned between the needle and the glass. To eliminate the possible effect on the experiment of another type of growth curvature, to be considered later (see p. 48), the plant should be surrounded by a black paper cylinder at least as tall as the plant itself. Since climbing plants usually exhibit the most pronounced circumnutation, this experiment is best performed with a young plant, either of kidney bean (*Phaseolus vulgaris*) or scarlet runner (*P. multiflorus*). With these, one complete rotation of the stem apex should be observed in about two hours.

Although circumnutation is a phenomenon still not fully understood, it would seem to be due to the occurrence of a zone of more rapid growth, the position of which moves continuously round the stem (or root) in a fixed direction, either clockwise, or anticlockwise, so that as the apex grows upwards it describes this characteristic spiral course.

CHAPTER 4

GROWTH RESPONSES TO STIMULI

Many plant organs respond to external factors, such as light, or gravity, by growing either towards or away from the source of stimulus. Study of these responses has led to a fuller understanding of plant growth; and indeed to the most far-reaching discoveries in this important aspect of botany.

The subject of plant growth curvatures has for long interested scientists, Charles Darwin among them. It was not till 1928, however, that a Dutch botanist, Fritz Went, by a series of ingenious experiments gained the first insight into the causes of such curvatures. This led to the remarkable discovery that all plant growth is regulated by hormone-like chemical compounds. *Hormones* are organic substances which do not supply nourishment but perform regulatory functions such as controlling the heartbeat in animals. Moreover, hormones are made in one part of the organism but exert their function in another part; they have therefore to be moved from the place where they are formed to the place where they are to function.

Went, in his experiments, excised the tips of oat seedling coleoptiles grown in the dark, and placed the cut surface of each on blocks of agar jelly (fig. 26). After two or three hours the tips were removed and the agar blocks were then placed to one side of the cut surface of other coleoptile stumps whose tips had just previously been removed. The seedlings curved away from the blocks, indicating that the side of each coleoptile adjacent to the block was growing more rapidly than the other. To confirm that something which had passed from the coleoptile tip into the agar block was indeed responsible for this effect, a block which had not had a decapitated tip sitting on it was also placed to one side of a coleoptile stump. This caused no growth curvature. The experiment therefore suggested that the coleoptile tips were producing a substance which could stimulate the growth of the part of the plant beneath it, and that this substance could diffuse into an agar block and then, later, be released to produce its regulatory effect. Substances of this sort have since been shown to occur in a wide range of plants, and because they play a part in adding to or augmenting growth, have been termed *auxins*.

Auxins

The most widely distributed of the auxins, *indoleacetic acid* (frequently abbreviated to *IAA*), has been isolated in pure form from maize seeds, as well as from yeast and another fungus. Various synthetic substances have also been found to possess similar growth-promoting properties. The study of auxins has now progressed to the stage when the curvature of test plants may be compared with curvature produced

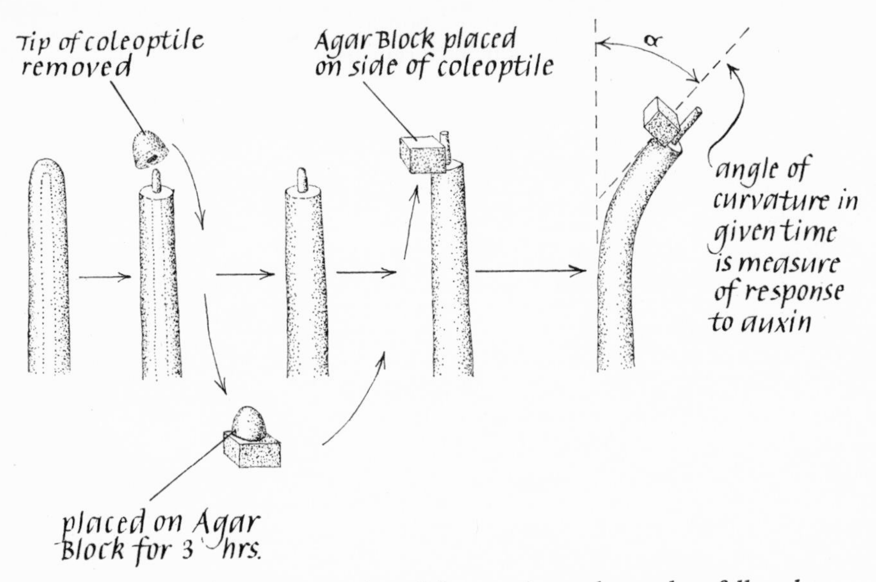

Figure 26 *Diagrammatic representation of the experimental procedure followed to demonstrate the bending of an oat coleoptile as a result of the one-sided distribution of auxin.*

by agar blocks containing a known concentration of chemically-pure auxin. The degree of curvature can in consequence be used for the quantitative determination of the effects of plant-growth substances, since curvature is proportional, within wide limits, to the concentration of growth-promoting substance in the applied block (fig. 26). More recently techniques have been developed whereby straight growth rather than curvature tests are used to determine auxin concentrations.

Experiments such as those performed by Went show that in oat coleoptiles auxin is formed in the extreme tip and is in some way translocated to the region of elongation, which does not seem able itself to produce this substance. Similarly in the root, auxin can be shown to be produced in the tip, and translocated to the adjoining zone of elongation. Thus in the plant as a whole this remarkable substance would seem to be synthesized in only a few isolated localities and transported from them to regions of elongation, there to exert its effect. This movement of auxins is unique in that it exhibits a definite polarity. In coleoptiles, for example, it has been demonstrated that auxins always move from apex to base even against a concentration gradient. This implies that auxin transport is not simply a process involving diffusion where there is a movement from a region of high to one of low concentration, but like so many of the processes in living things is dependent on a supply of energy.

Although experiments with oat coleoptiles proved that the response to auxin took place in the region of cell elongation, it is still uncertain just how the auxin exerts its all-important effect. For a time it was thought that auxin increased the elasticity of the cell wall, giving it further powers of extensibility. Recent indications are, however, that rather than there being a redistribution of material already existing in the wall, as would be the case if there was merely an increase in elasticity, new material is incorporated into it. It has been suggested, though not confirmed, that *IAA* causes changes in the permeability of the protoplasmic cell membranes (see p. 27), allowing more water to enter the cell and thereby bringing about its enlargement. Only one point is fully confirmed and that is that auxins act only on cells with active living contents.

Kinetins and Gibberellins

The impact of the discovery of auxin in the botanical world was such that for a considerable time many botanists came to think of it as the only plant hormone. At an early stage in his work, however, Went had stressed that other hormone-like substances might be produced by plants. In recent years this prediction has been borne out by the recognition of two other types of substances which regulate growth. The first of these, now called *kinetin*, was discovered by a group of American workers. Among its properties is its ability, in conjunction with auxin, to promote cell division in plant tissues and cause the formation of buds and roots; in addition it may accelerate the germination of seeds. In a series of exciting experiments with kinetin American botanists have grown entirely new plants from small pieces of tissue taken from the central part of the stem of the tobacco plant (*Nicotiana*) in the presence of kinetin and auxin.

The other very important group of growth-substances are the *gibberellins*, the first of which, though discovered some time before auxin, was neglected for many years. This was largely because its occurrence was originally reported in a Japanese botanical journal, and Japanese is a language which few European or American scientists can read. This report related to a disease of rice, caused by a fungus *Gibberella fujikuroi* (the generic name *Gibberella* refers to the shape of the reproductive structure of the fungus and means 'little hunch-back'), which made the diseased plants grow much taller than healthy plants, though with reduced vigour and fertility. The critical experiment which indicated that a growth substance was involved showed that the complete symptoms of the disease could be produced merely by treating rice seedlings with cell-free liquid in which some of the fungus had been growing. This experiment clearly suggested that some substance released *by* the fungus, which acted like a growth substance, and not the fungus itself, caused the disease.

Early in the 1950s scientists in Britain and the U.S.A. became interested in the gibberellins. As a result of their investigations and those of Japanese workers at least four different types of gibberellins are at present known. Much interest now centres on these substances and a great variety of tests and experiments is being conducted with them. For example, the majority of flowering plants tested (at least several hundred species) respond, often quite dramatically, to its application. Doses of one millionth part of a gram can result in two-threefold increases in height but without producing

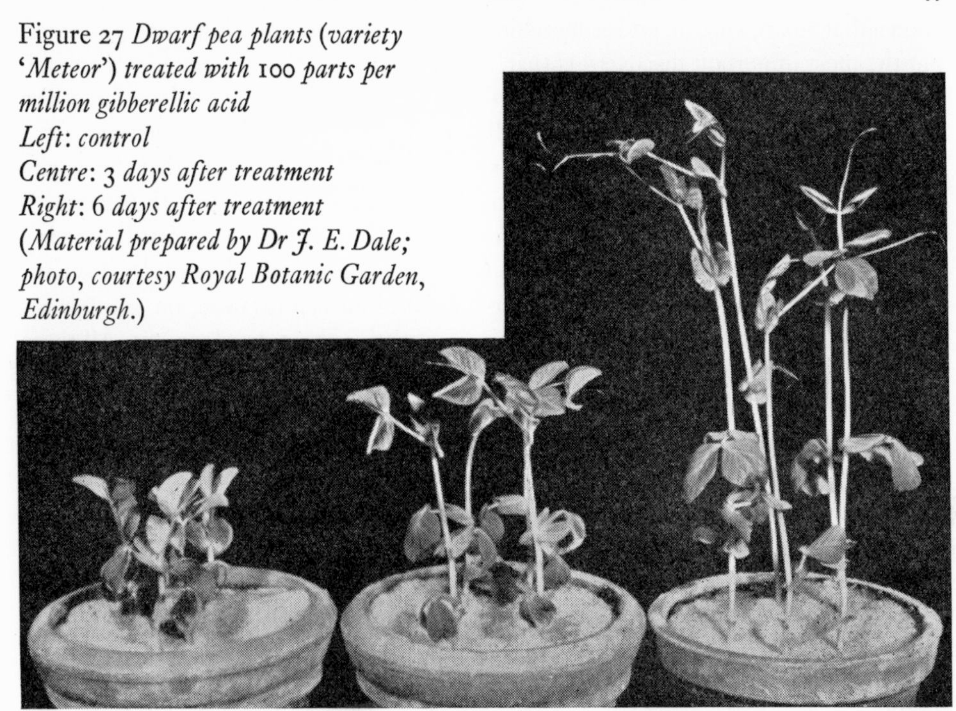

Figure 27 *Dwarf pea plants (variety 'Meteor') treated with* 100 *parts per million gibberellic acid*
Left: *control*
Centre: 3 *days after treatment*
Right: 6 *days after treatment*
(*Material prepared by Dr J. E. Dale; photo, courtesy Royal Botanic Garden, Edinburgh.*)

abnormalities of form (fig. 27). It has recently been found that seeds, leaves, stems, roots and flower buds of a variety of plants contain substances which produce the same growth responses as the known gibberellins.

It was at first thought that gibberellin, like auxin, produced its response through the second phase of the mechanism of growth – cell elongation – and had no effect on the first phase – cell division. It is now clear, however, that under certain conditions it may in fact affect both of these phases of growth. This can be seen in plants called rosette plants which normally do not produce stems and whose leaves appear to arise directly from the root. By treatment of these plants with gibberellin, stem production can be readily induced and this striking morphological change involves not only cell elongation but results primarily from a very marked increase in cell division.

Other effects of giberellins include the regulation of the flowering of plants, for by appropriate treatment this process can be induced in conditions under which it would not normally occur. The subject will be considered in some detail later (see Chapter 23). Gibberellins are also able to overcome the necessary period of dormancy of certain seeds (see Chapter 1) and to promote germination. In addition, they are able to break the dormancy of winter buds of trees.

The discovery of these growth-regulating substances and the recognition of the part they play in the growth and development of plants make the study of these phenomena even more exciting and remarkable than was at first imagined. It is now known that auxin, kinetin, and gibberellin control a large number of growth processes; but the most important discovery is that, while they may affect the same processes, it seems that they do so in different ways, for one substance cannot replace the other; they are fundamentally different, chemically and physiologically. It has been suggested that for the growth of any plant all three substances are required, but that the way in which they develop (here we return to this qualitative aspect of growth (see p. 19)) depends on the ratio of the amounts present. To sum up: within each plant there is a remarkable chemically-controlled system for regulating growth. The plant, it seems, does not depend on one chemical for the regulation of cell division, on another for the control of cell elongation, and on a third for root or shoot development. All these processes are regulated by a delicately balanced system which depends for its action on the levels, or ratios, of supply of *three* relatively non-specific substances. It has recently been established that in addition to hormones, *hormone inhibitors* occur. These would also appear to play a vital role in controlling growth and may be particularly important in relation to dormancy. Although no such inhibitors have yet been isolated and identified, there is no doubt that when they are, many interesting problems of growth physiology will be nearer their solution. In addition there may be unexpected uses for them in both agriculture and horticulture (pp. 143 and 297).

IRRITABILITY

The way in which plants respond to certain external stimuli is closely linked to the regulation of growth. Plants, like animals, respond to changes in their environment by certain complex internal activities, and thus demonstrate what is termed *irritability*. In a plant, this expresses itself as a growth curvature or *tropism*; in animals as some form of nervous activity.

Phototropism

One of the most readily observed examples of this sort of response is known as *phototropism*, which can be demonstrated even in seedlings by subjecting one side of the plumules or coleoptiles, as the case may be, to light. These organs then show positive phototropism, by growing towards the light, the mechanism for such a response being a retardation or inhibition in the rate of growth of the side towards the light while the side away from the light increases its growth rate.

Charles Darwin, whose theory of evolution by natural selection had such a profound effect on biological thought in the mid-nineteenth century, made the first contribution to the study of phototropism. By shielding various portions of grass coleoptiles with little opaque caps, he demonstrated that the extreme tip is the region which receives the light stimulus (fig. 28). Some time later a Danish botanist pursued the matter further and showed that the light stimulus is transported from the tip of the coleoptile to the basal growing region, by some diffusible chemical substance which could cross a thin layer of gelatine.

These observations were made some time before the discovery of auxin, but as

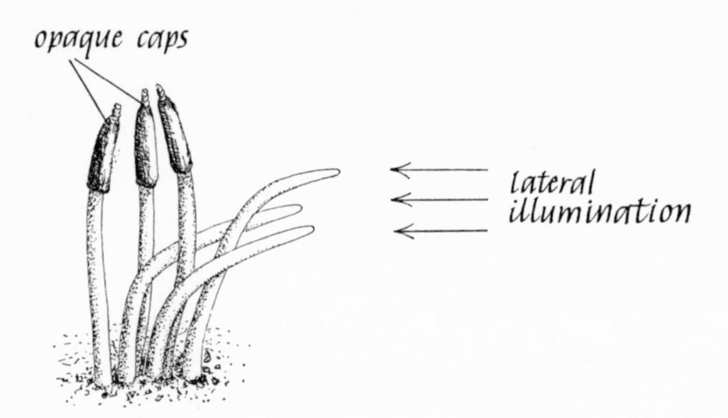

Figure 28 *Experiment to show that the phototropic stimulus is in the coleoptile tip.*

investigations with auxins progressed it was soon demonstrated that in fact the exposure of a coleoptile tip to unilateral light produces an unequal distribution of auxin in the two sides of the coleoptile tip, resulting eventually in a growth response. In contrast to shoots, many roots exhibit negative phototropism.

Geotropism

Another important plant-growth response is *geotropism*, which, as the name implies, involves a positive or negative growth curvature in relation to the earth's gravitational field. Such a response can be readily demonstrated by placing the radicle of a bean seedling in a horizontal position. After quite a short time, the plumule tends to grow upwards and assume a normal upright position, while the root curves downwards away from the horizontal. Since roots grow towards the stimulus of gravity they are said to be *positively* geotropic, in contrast to shoots which are *negatively* geotropic (fig. 29).

As with phototropism, the geotropic response is also due to an unequal distribution of auxin. In coleoptiles placed horizontally, for example, it can be demonstrated that there is a much greater production of auxin in the lower side of the coleoptile tip, which results in unequal growth of the two sides. The geotropic response of roots differs from that in the above-ground organs of the plant (fig. 30). There is an essential difference in the response of roots and stems to auxin: root growth is inhibited and not stimulated by the application of auxin, so that when roots are placed in a horizontal position, although there is a similar accumulation of auxin in the lower side as is found in shoots, because of this inhibitory effect the upper side of the root grows most rapidly to give a positive geotropic curvature. Root growth inhibition is now used as an assay technique in quantitative plant hormone studies (see p. 45).

Growth substances exert an effect not only on the elongation of stems, but are known to control the fall of leaves and fruits. They also play an important part in the

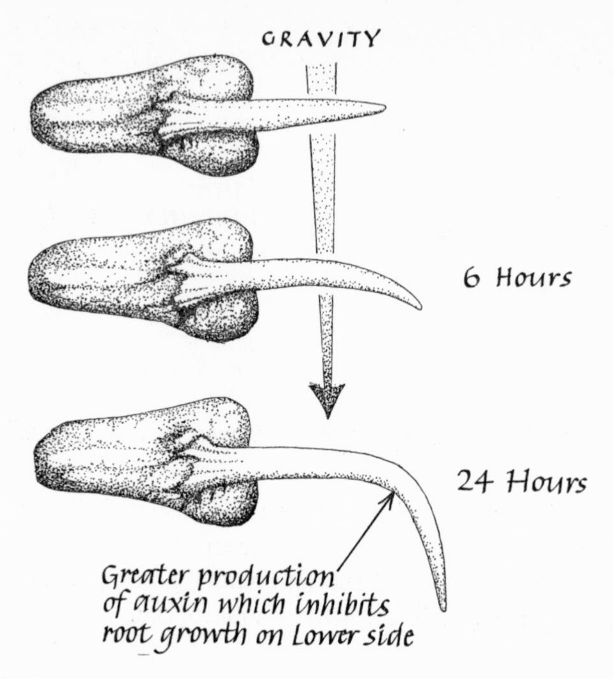

Figure 29 *Stages in the geotropic response of a root of broad bean*, Vicia faba.

initiation of root formation on stems. In horticultural practice this latter property is of considerable significance, for very many plant species can be propagated by planting pieces of cut stems in a light soil or sand. After a time new (adventitious) roots form round the base of the stem where it has been cut (see fig. 31). However, more certain and extensive production follows after such cuttings have been treated with auxin. Various pastes, powders and solutions containing synthetic compounds chemically related to *IAA* and not necessarily plant auxins are now widely used in horticultural practice to induce this root growth. In fact the success of this treatment is so great, that many species previously difficult or impossible to root naturally can now be readily propagated following hormone treatment.

Auxins also have important agricultural applications. Many substances chemically related to natural auxins possess auxin-like activity at low concentrations, but are extremely toxic to many plants at higher concentrations. This toxicity is fortunately selective and affects broad-leaved dicotyledonous plants whilst monocotyledonous species such as grasses and cereals are much less sensitive. The most widely used of these substances is a selective weedkiller, *2.4.dichlorophenoxyacetic acid* (generally referred to as *2.4-D*) which is particularly useful in the control of weeds growing in lawns and amongst cereal crops such as wheat, barley and oats. Because of widespread agricultural applications a great deal of research is now being undertaken to determine the value of other chemicals in this connection. Studies on the more

Figure 30 *Tomato plant placed on its side showing a strong negative geotropic response after 12 hours.*

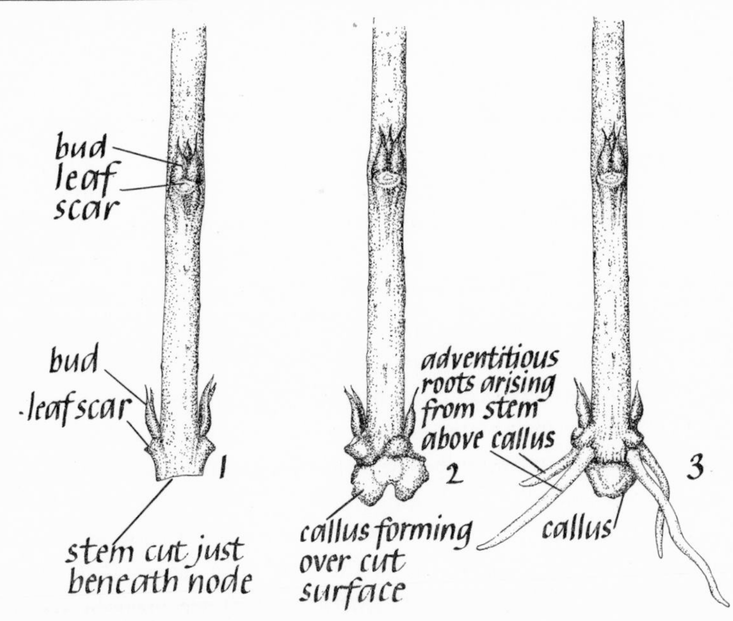

Figure 31 1-3 *Callus formation and adventitious root production in cut stems of privet* (Ligustrum japonicum).

fundamental aspects of this problem of weed control, and especially on how these chemicals exert their remarkable and economically valuable effects, are being actively explored.

NASTIC MOVEMENTS

Figure 32 *Sleep movements* (*nyctinasty*) *in leaves of wood sorrel* (Oxalis acetosella).

In addition to tropic movements, in which plant organs respond to external stimuli by growing either towards or away from a source of stimulus, some plant organs also exhibit movements which are independent of the direction of application of the stimulus. Such *nastic movements*, as they are termed, are usually not growth movements but commonly caused by changes in the turgor (see p. 157) of specialized groups of cells. *Nasties* are most common in bilaterally symmetrical organs such as leaves and the petals of flowers, and the direction of a particular nastic movement is to a large extent dependent on the structure of the leaf or petal stimulated. The most readily observable and widely occurring nastic movements are 'sleep movements' or *nyctinasties* in which the leaves and flowers, especially of tropical plants, fold up at night. A common European example is to be found with the leaves of the wood sorrel (*Oxalis acetosella*) whose leaflets fold along the mid-rib and then droop down at night (see fig. 32). Some of these movements (*photonasties*) are occasioned by changes in light intensity as in the case of closing of the flowers of daisy (*Bellis perennis*) and dandelion (*Taraxacum officinale*). Others (*thermonasties*) are brought about by temperature changes and of these a striking example can be observed when tulip flowers are brought into a hot room. The nastic movements of the tulip is however a *growth*

Figure 33 *Haptonastic movements in a sensitive plant, the aquatic* Neptunia oleracea.

movement brought about by an increase in the growth rate of the upper side of the petals.

Some sleep movements can be induced in certain leaves (*e.g. Oxalis*) if they are touched repeatedly, say by flicking with a finger. Such *hapto*-or *thygmonastic* movements are most striking in the sensitive plant, *Mimosa pudica* and the related *Neptunia oleracea* (fig. 33). When touched, even quite lightly, its leaflets fold inwards very rapidly, while if the stimulus is more vigorous, the whole leaf will droop downwards. Moreover, a very strong stimulus applied to one leaf may be transmitted to neighbouring leaves. In this transmission of the stimulus through the plant, it seems very probably that hormones are implicated.

TACTIC MOVEMENTS

There is yet one other important category of plant movements which, although not growth movements, must be briefly mentioned. These are the *tactic movements* made from place to place by small, motile primitive plants which commonly consist of only a single cell, or by the motile reproductive cells of others (e.g. liverworts and ferns). The movements of such cells can frequently be shown to be a response to external stimuli. Hence *phototaxis* is exhibited when the unicellular green alga

Chlamydomonas (see p. 355) in culture, swims towards light and so congregates on the more brightly illuminated side of the vessel in which it is being grown; *chemotaxis* is shown by certain bacteria (Chapter 31) when they move in response to the chemical stimulus of a high oxygen concentration which occurs in the immediate vicinity of a leaf of the aquatic plant *Elodea canadensis* actively photosynthesising (see Chapter 18).

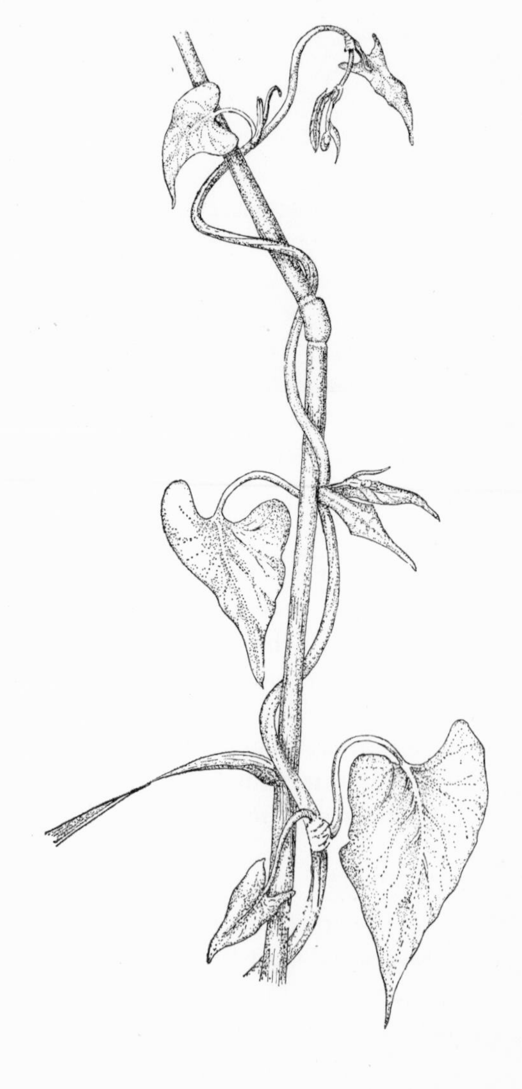

Figure 34 *A climbing plant, black bindweed* (Polygonum convolvulus) *supported on a grass stem.*

CHAPTER 5

LIFE HISTORIES AND THE GROWTH FORMS OF PLANTS

Only the briefest consideration has so far been given to the form of plants once they have passed the seedling stage. This stage can be considered to have been passed when the plant begins to form normal leaves and to produce branches. The form and arrangement of these leaves and branches, which constitute the shoot system, show the utmost diversity in different species of plants. Some plants, for example, may attain heights of only a few inches; others may be procumbent, growing close to the ground; others, again, may attain heights of several hundreds of feet. The form which a plant comes to assume during the course of its vegetative development is referred to as its *growth form* or habit. The *erect habit*, in which the stem is constructed so that it is able to support itself, is by far the most common growth form. Some plants, however, called *climbers* (fig. 34), can maintain an upright habit for a limited time only, unless they find some means of supporting themselves by twisting round and anchoring themselves to other stronger, erect vegetation. Plants with a particular habit are very often found in certain environments. Thus climbers are frequently found in hedgerows or thick forests; short lived annuals as weeds in gardens and agricultural land; ephemerals in deserts. It should, however, be noted that the habit may vary under different environmental conditions.

Notwithstanding this great diversity in form, all plants show a remarkable similarity in their basic architecture; that is, in the arrangement of their root systems and in the way in which leaves, buds and branches are borne in relation to the stem.

ANNUALS

Shepherd's purse, *Capsella bursa-pastoris*, an *annual* plant commonly found in gardens and farmland, illustrates this fundamental arrangement clearly (fig. 35). Like most flowering plants, shepherd's purse has a body consisting of two readily distinguishable parts living under very different conditions. There is an above-ground shoot system bearing leaves and branches, and an underground root system. The former is, in the main, green in colour, the latter, when washed free from soil, white. At ground level there is a rosette of leaves; below this – continuous with the stem though demarcated by an uneven, wrinkled line – there is a prominent main root called the *tap root*, which tapers to a fine point. This main root bears smaller, lateral or secondary roots which grow outwards and slightly downwards at an acute angle. These in turn bear further branches so that the root system appears as a rather irregular tangle of threads. There is, however, a degree of order in such systems, for if the root of a

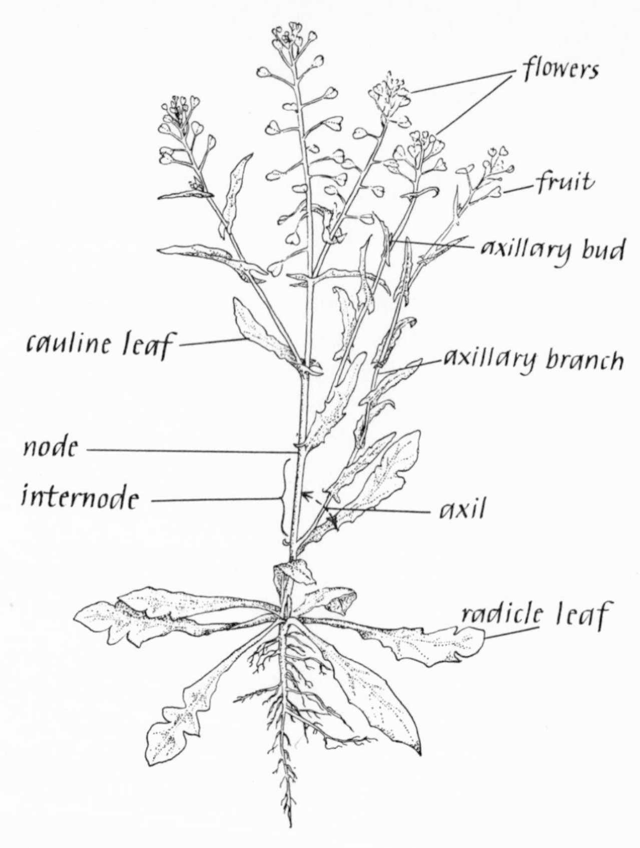

Figure 35 *A flowering and fruiting plant of shepherd's purse*, Capsella bursa-pastoris.

bean seedling is examined carefully it will be found that the secondary roots are arranged in four fairly regular lines running down the length of the main root with the oldest and longest at the top where it joins the shoot, the youngest and shortest at the tapering tip (fig. 36).

As the root grows, branch roots particularly (but the main root also) may be forced to change direction as they meet obstacles in the soil. Other effects on root growth may be due to environmental conditions in the soil such as local differences in soil moisture, which cause the roots on one side of the plant to grow well while those on the opposite side are stunted. This means that while the plant has the potential for a regular, symmetrical root system, the final form is usually highly irregular.

Special interest attaches to the way in which lateral roots are formed. Although these occur in shepherd's purse, their origins can be seen much more clearly in two-week-old bean seedlings. If the tips of the radicles of such seedlings are examined, small excrescences can be seen at certain places. Further up the root, minute laterals,

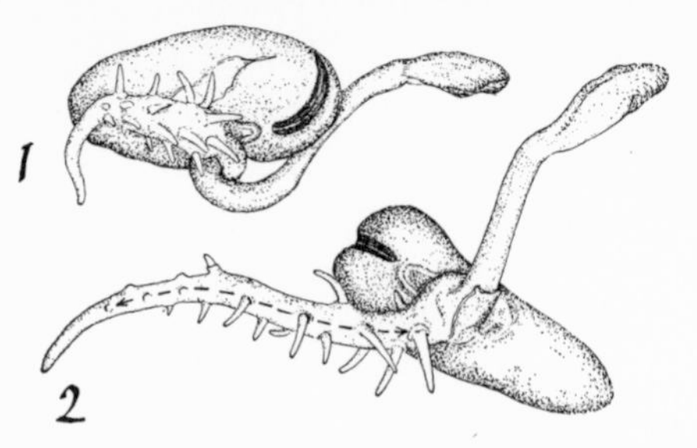

Figure 36 1 and 2 *Lateral root formation in the broad bean* (Vicia faba). *Note specially in 2 orderly arrangement of successively produced laterals one below the other.*

one or two millimetres long, will be found breaking through the main root surface. From the thickest, oldest regions of the root the laterals will be a centimetre or more in length and round the base of each there will be found a small, though distinctive, collar. This is formed by the torn tissues of the primary root where the lateral broke through. These *lateral roots* are in fact formed inside the root and hence are *endogenous* in origin. As they grow, they force their way through the parent tissues and out to the surface (fig. 36 and fig. 3.3).

In monocotyledonous plants the radicle of the seedling is replaced at an early stage in development by a number of adventitious roots which arise from the base of the stem. These form the *fibrous root* systems which occur especially in grasses and cereals. Although adventitious roots arise most commonly from stems, certain leaves (e.g. *Bryophyllum*) produce them readily when placed on soil.

The shoot system of shepherd's purse, like the root system, has a main vertical axis. This too bears lateral branches. These branches are not, however, arranged in four rows but in a spiral (cf. phyllotaxis, p. 83); like roots, they may branch repeatedly. All the lateral branches arise within the angle formed between a leaf and the stem. This angle is termed the *leaf axil* and branches arising therefrom are described as *axillary*. Branches always arise in this relation to a leaf, so that one cannot find a branch without a leaf, or else the scar marking the position of a leaf now shed, at its base. The leaves themselves consist of two fairly well defined regions, the leaf stalk or *petiole* and the expanded, flat blade or *lamina*. Two types of leaves, however, occur in shepherd's purse; a rosette of *radical* leaves at ground level and the *cauline* leaves which occur higher up the main axis and on its branches. The point on the stem or branch at which a leaf or leaves arise is called a node: internodes are the portions of the stem between two nodes.

In shepherd's purse, the leaves borne on the main axis and its branches are without petioles: in this respect they differ from those of the basal rosette. The lamina in these *sessile* leaves arises directly from the stem. From the base of the lamina two projections clasp the stem on either side. All the leaves, including those of the basal rosette, are arranged on the stem in a spiral, a fact which may be verified by picking them off in careful sequence. Since there is a spiral arrangement of leaves there tends to be a spiral arrangement of branches (see also p. 84).

Not every leaf axil on the plant produces a branch, but careful examination will show that in every leaf axil there is a minute bud. A bud may be defined as a rudimentary or embryonic shoot with an extremely short axis (the internodes of which have not yet elongated) protected by closely crowded, overlapping, immature leaves. The minute tip of this well-protected shoot is the meristematic growing point which, when it becomes active, initiates the growth and extention of the embryonic stem.

In a large number of plants the main axis and each branch ends in a *terminal bud* potentially capable of indefinite extension. In shepherd's purse, however, the terminal buds of the main axis and its branches are not leaf buds but flower buds. When they develop, each flower is produced at the end of a short stalk. The flowers, which together form an *inflorescence*, are in fact branches spirally arranged on the stem bearing them; but they do not arise in the axils of leaves. In this respect shepherd's purse is unusual, for as a rule flowers, like other branches, are axillary, and their stalks may bear leaves as do other stems. It must be emphasized that while a terminal leaf bud is capable of indefinite extension, once a flower bud has opened and flowered the axis bearing it cannot increase in length in that direction. No such limitation on the direction of growth is ever imposed on any part of the root system.

The complete life history of shepherd's purse is usually completed within a few weeks. Although it is not unusual for such plants to have such a short life cycle, most annuals germinate, grow to their full stature, flower and produce seed over a somewhat longer period of from six to seven months.

BIENNIALS

Many plants, however, take two seasons to complete their life cycle and for this reason are termed *biennials*. Common examples are mullein (*Verbascum thapsus*), foxglove (*Digitatis purpurea*) and docken (*Rumex obtusifolius*). During the first year of life these plants produce only a basal rosette of leaves. In that first year many biennials also lay up a store of food in their tap roots, which in consequence become greatly swollen. Their leaves persist throughout the winter, but in spring, as soon as light and temperature become favourable, vigorous growth of the shoot system begins, at the expense of the food stored in the root. Quite soon a tall spike is produced bearing many flowers which in turn form numerous seeds. Because the roots of many biennials contain a considerable store of food they are used as food by man, so that these plants, such as turnip (*Brassica campestris*), carrots (*Daucus carota*) and beet (*Beta vulgaris*), except when specifically grown for seed, are never allowed to flower. They are dug up when the root is sufficiently large and in an edible condition. If these vegetables are allowed to flower and their tap roots are then examined, their shrivelled condition will be apparent. This is because the food accumulated in them during the previous year has been utilized in the production of flowers and seed.

Biennials do not store food exclusively in the root. In the radish (*Raphanus sativus*) for instance, the swollen part bears no lateral roots and in fact corresponds to the hypocotyl of the seedling. The root below, with its many fibrous laterals, is

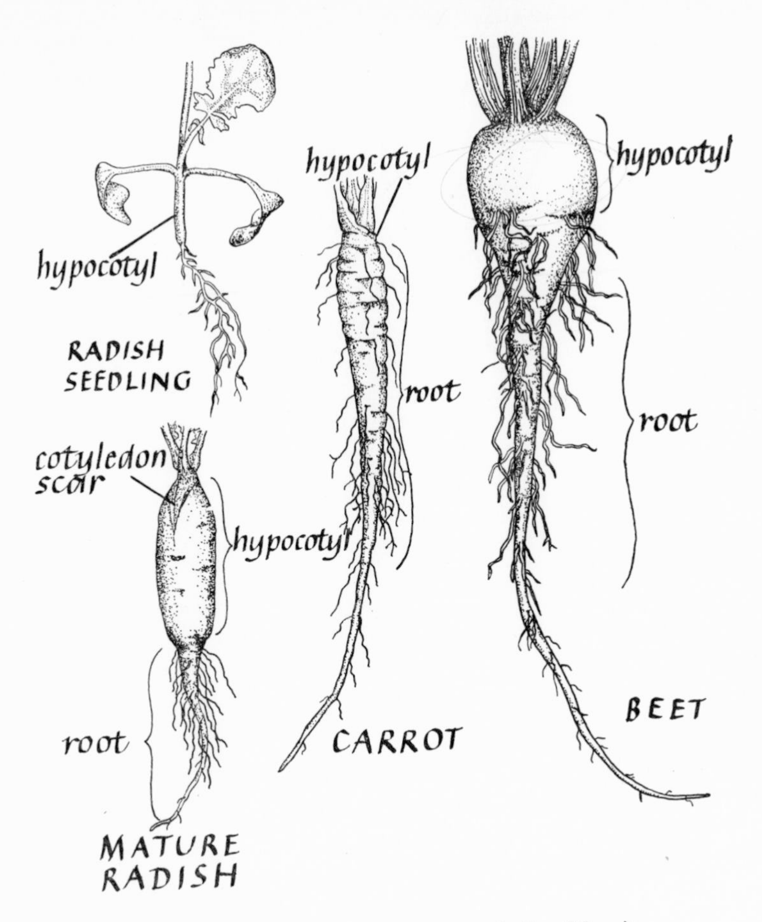

Figure 37 *The modification of roots as storage organs* (*after Skene*).

but little swollen. In the carrot, lateral roots can be seen over the whole length of the swollen portion, the hypocotyl being represented by only a small region at its top. The beet is intermediate in condition (fig. 37).

PERENNIALS

The third type of life history is in *perennial* plants, which differ first and foremost from biennials in that their vitality is not exhausted after reproduction. Perennials do not usually flower in their first year. Indeed in some cases flowering may not take place until they are several years old. However, once it starts it usually takes place each year; despite this, sufficient food material is stored away to support renewed growth each spring. Perennials show great diversity of growth forms, many of which can be related to their ability to survive unfavourable periods, such as winter in temperate or arctic climates, or drought in arid parts of the world. The most obvious,

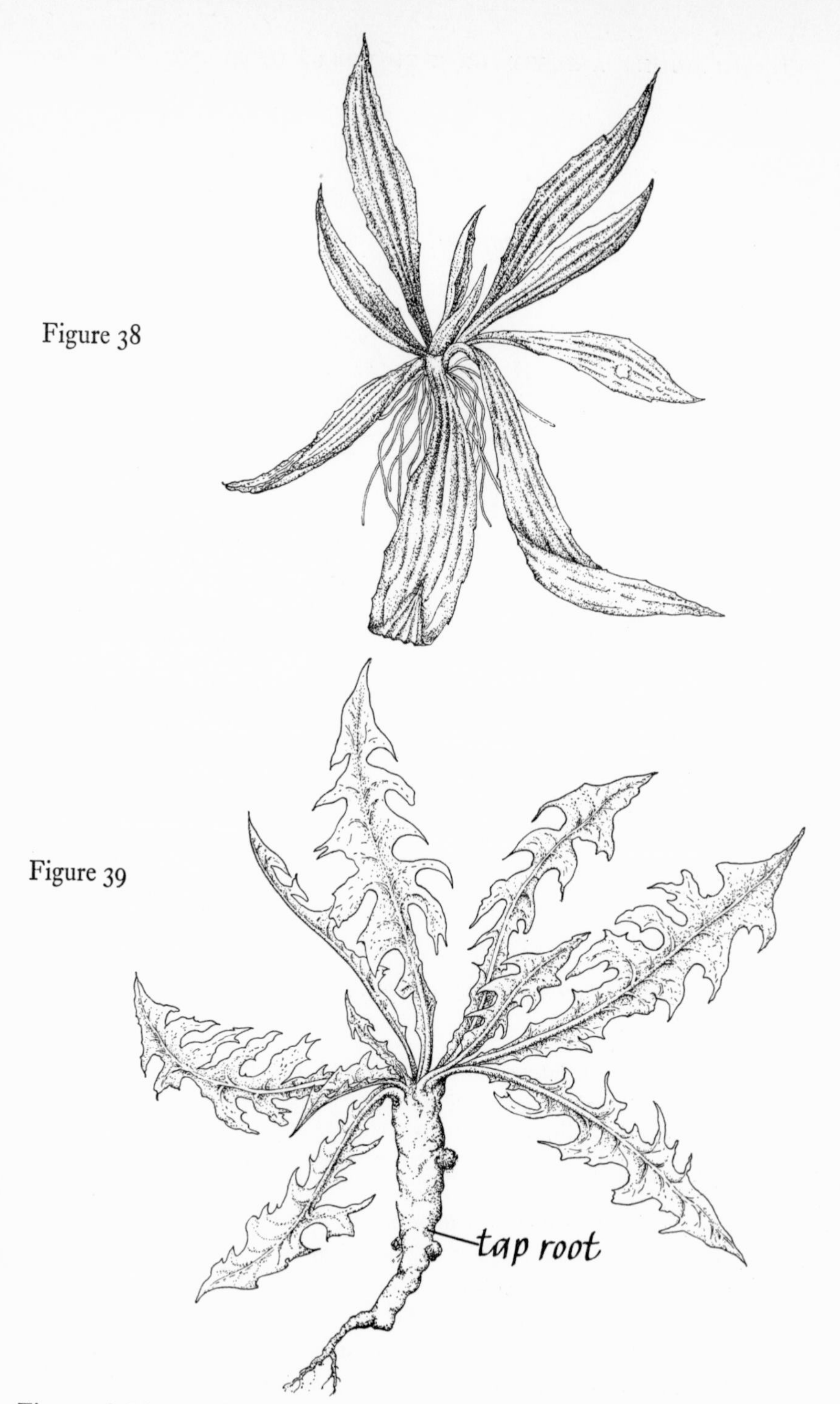

Figure 38 *Plantain* (Plantago lanceolata), *a perennial plant of rosette habit.*
Figure 39 *Dandelion* (Taraxacum officinale), *a perennial plant with stout tap root.*

common example of perennial plants are trees, which survive for hundreds, and in some cases thousands, of years.

Many herbaceous plants without persistent, woody stems are, nevertheless, perennial in habit. Several such *herbaceous perennials* are common weeds in gardens. Daisy and plantain (*Plantago* spp.) survive each winter in lawns as a rosette of leaves, able to withstand frost, while the dandelion, in addition, stores up food in a deep, stout tap root (figs. 38 and 39).

The creeping buttercup (*Ranunculus repens*) also survives the winter in the form of small rosettes, after the flowering stems and larger outer leaves have died down in the autumn. In early summer the rosette grows and flowers, but it also forms special side branches which bend down and grow out over the ground. These creeping branches, from which the plant gets its name, produce leaves, and from some or all of the leaf nodes, roots may be formed. As in the axils of all leaves, buds are produced, from which new rosettes may develop. The internodes die back after some months so that each rosette achieves an individuality and becomes a new plant. By this method of vegetative reproduction, as distinct from reproduction by means of flowers and seed, a single creeping buttercup plant may produce a very considerable number of new plants each year (fig. 40).

The strawberry (*Fragaria vesca*) is another herbaceous perennial plant which reproduces vegetatively by means of prostrate, rooting stems, or *runners*. Unlike the buttercup, however, these bear only very reduced leaves (scale leaves, whose only function is the protection of buds) except at the tip, where rooting takes place. Here a new rosette, and hence a potential new plant, is formed. Strawberry plants are in fact propagated by separating and replanting these rosettes (fig. 41).

A further example is provided by the silverweed (*Potentilla anserina*), at the end of whose runners a small pair of leaves is produced. The bud in the axil of one of these leaves eventually develops to form the next section of the runner, whilst that in the axil of the other, if the runner roots at this point, forms a new rosette. The apical bud of the runner will probably not develop further, or it may give rise to the yellow, miniature, rose-like flower; so that the silverweed runner is composed of a series of sections, each arising from an axillary bud from the previously formed section. This type of branching is termed *sympodial* and should be compared with the *monopodial* development of the creeping buttercup, in which each internode is derived from the apical bud of the internode just formed. If, however, as sometimes happens, the apical bud produces a flower, then further growth is no longer possible in this direction and any further growth of the runner must be sympodial (fig. 42).

SUCKERS, RHIZOMES, CORMS AND BULBS

The aerial parts of many herbaceous garden plants such as hollyhock (*Althaea rosea*) larkspur (*Delphinium ajacis*), lupin (*Lupinus nootkatensis*) and columbine (*Aquilegia vulgaris*), and the undesirable weeds, nettle and coltsfoot (*Tussilago farfara*), die back to below ground level in winter so that only the underground parts persist.

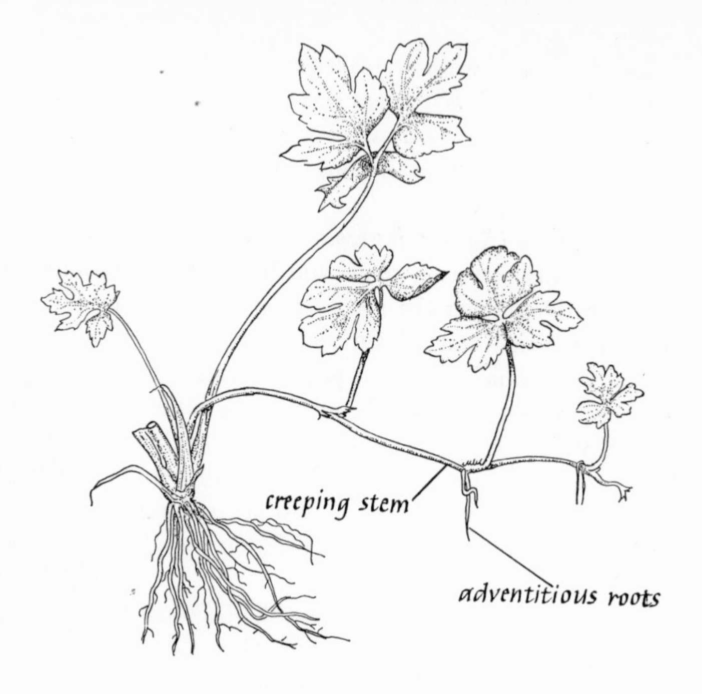

Figure 40 *The stem of the creeping buttercup* (Ranunculus repens).

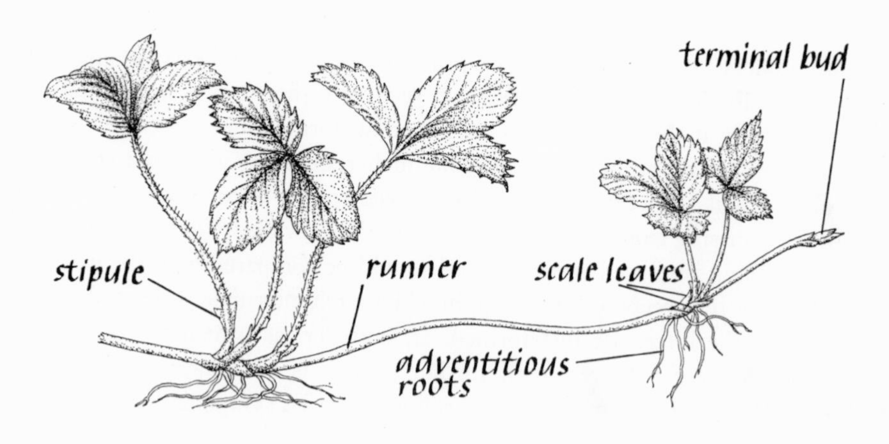

Figure 41 *Runners of strawberry* (Fragaria vesca).

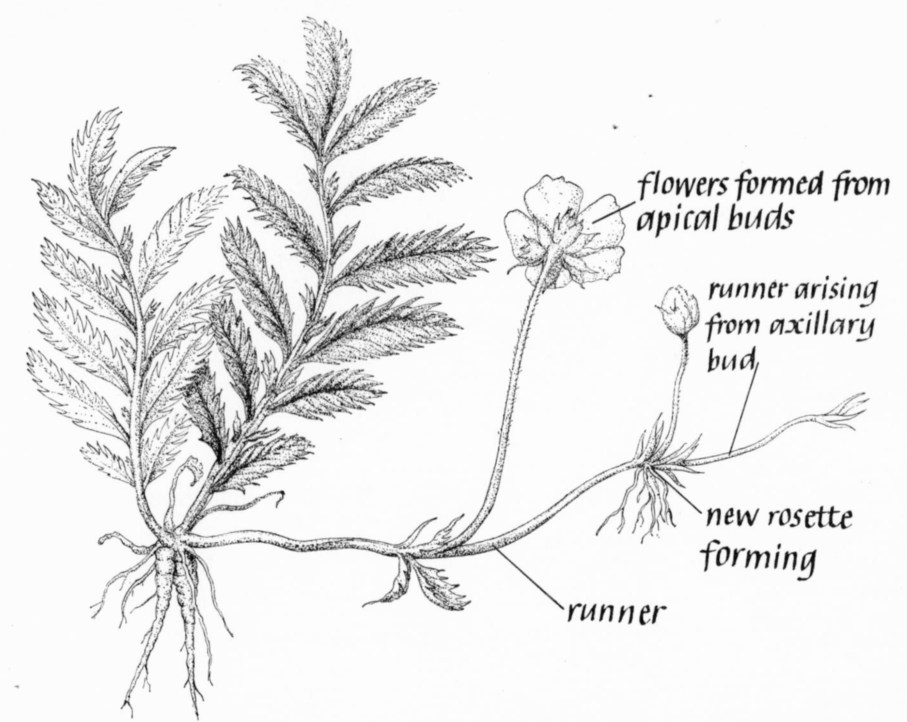

Figure 42 *The silverweed* (Potentilla anserina) *showing runners and rosette formation.*

This buried portion of the plant, protected against frost beneath the soil, frequently contains a store of food which permits rapid production of a large plant in the following spring, though in addition it may also play a part in the vegetative reproduction of the plant.

Some of these plants which survive the winter underground are in many ways similar to those which produce above-ground runners. Such plants, of which garden mint (*Mentha viridis*) is an example, if examined when they appear above ground in spring, will be found to have arisen by the upward growth of a horizontal underground stem. That this is a stem and not a root is indicated by the presence of distinct nodes. Each node can be recognized by the presence of two small, white, scale-leaves, in the axils of which are buds. Some of these buds grow to produce underground runners or *suckers* which are set free from the parent plant on its death and decay in autumn. In spring adventitious roots arise from these suckers, whose growing points turn upwards out of the soil to form new plants (fig. 43).

As in all perennating organs, underground stems contain at least some stored food. However, in many underground stems the storage is very considerable, so that they become greatly swollen, as for example in the Jerusalem artichoke (*Helianthus tuberosus*), the suckers (or *tubers*) of which are used as a vegetable. The potato

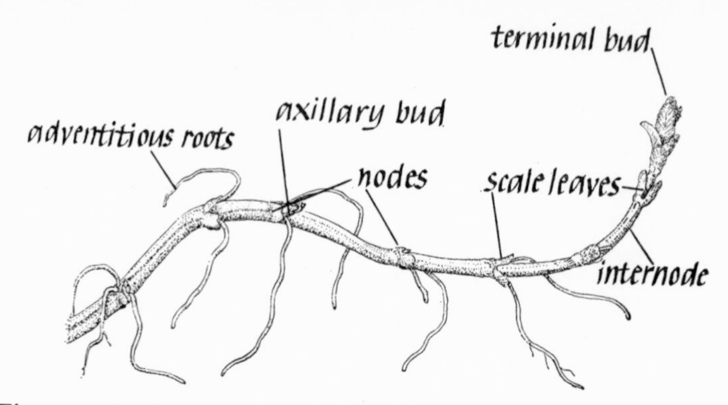

Figure 43 *Underground stems* (*suckers*) *of garden mint* (Mentha viridis).

(*Solanum tuberosum*) is yet another, but more specialized, underground stem containing a large store of food. From each potato tuber planted in spring, a stem develops, which grows out of the soil into a leafy shoot. As is normal, branches arise in the axils of the leaves and some branches (stolons) grow from the axils of scale-leaves in the part of the shoot below ground. These underground branches eventually thicken at their ends to form the tuberous swellings, potatoes. Evidence that the tuber is indeed a stem, is provided by scale leaves arranged in a spiral on its surface. In the axil of each there can usually be found three buds, the so-called 'eye' of the potato. Mature potatoes become covered with a protective layer of cork and the withered remains of the underground stem of which it was once a part may still be seen. The scale-leaves will also have withered away, though the buds which form the eyes can be easily distinguished. The earthing up of potatoes is done to stimulate the production of as many underground branches as possible and hence a bigger crop of tubers. In addition, it keeps the light away from any tubers which may develop near the surface. In this respect one also finds confirmation of the fact that tubers are parts of stems and not roots, for in the light they turn green. An even more striking demonstration of this fact can be seen when under exceptional conditions, usually injury or disease, some of the axillary buds of the aerial portion of the plant produce tubers, for then the character of the scale-leaves and axillary buds are unmistakable (fig. 44).

Many common perennial plants, excellent examples of which are to be found in woodland floras, will be found to grow from horizontal underground stems called *rhizomes*. The wood anemone (*Anemone nemorosa*), for example, springs from a thick, rhizome, from the tip of which arises the flower stalk and a few leaves (fig. 45). In the axil of one of the latter is a bud which becomes active in early summer, thereby increasing the length of this underground stem. Further extension ceases during the winter when the above-ground parts have died down, but in the following spring the apical bud grows upwards to produce the new flowering shoot. Growth in length by this particular portion of the shoot can then no longer occur, and subsequent increase

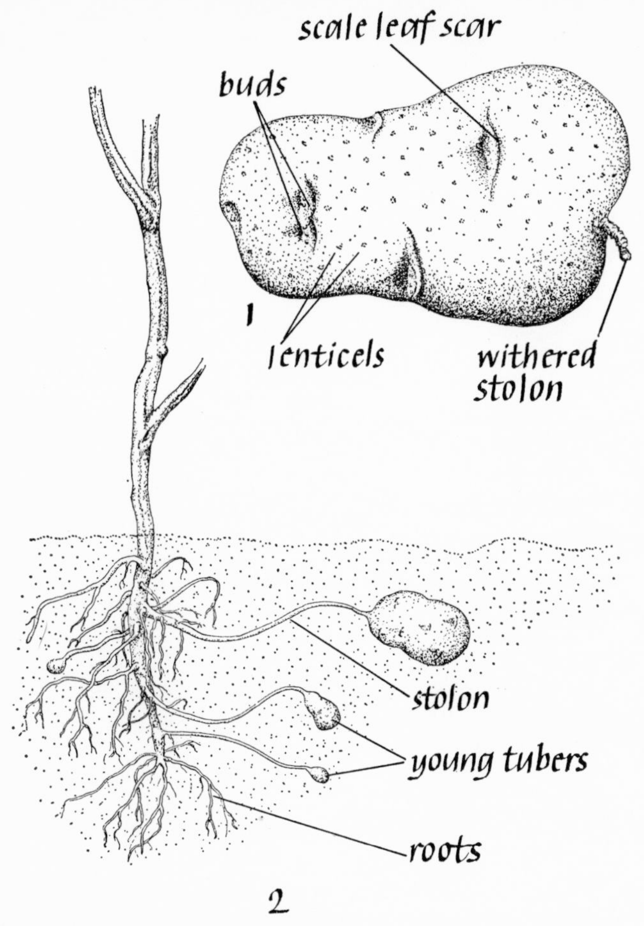

Figure 44 1 and 2 *Tubers of the potato* (Solanum tuberosum).

in length of the rhizome is from an axillary bud, so that growth is sympodial. Many grasses, reeds and sedges have slender rhizomes, which also show sympodial growth. Not all rhizomes, however, are sympodial; the main shoot of the moschatel (*Adoxa moschatella*), for example, persists and extends year after year so that growth is monopodial, while that of the flowering shoots is axillary. Rhizomes frequently throw off lateral branches, which in the case of plants of horticultural value (e.g. *Iris*) may be separated artificially for vegetative propagation, or by the decay under natural conditions of the older parts (fig. 46).

Some underground stems grow more or less erect and differ from rhizomes primarily in this respect. These *root-stocks* occur in primrose (*Primula vulgaris*), meadow buttercup (*Ranunculus bulbosus*), and rhubarb (*Rheum officinale*). It is clear that they are stems, for they are covered with the basal remains of the foliage leaves

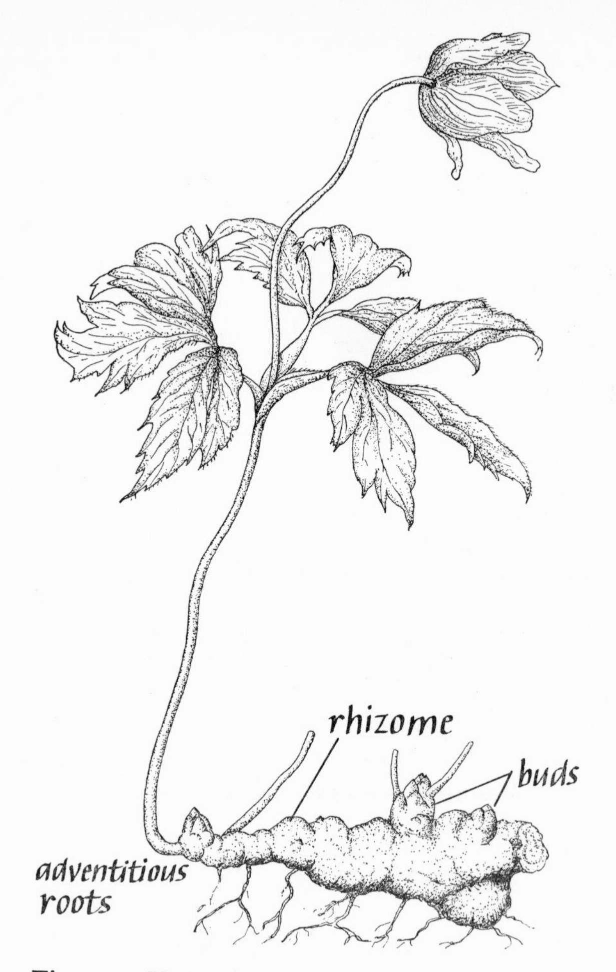

Figure 45 *Underground rhizome of wood anemone* (Anemone nemorosa).

of previous years, between which arise adventitious roots. In the primrose (fig. 47) the root-stock, being erect, grows upwards, yet the plants always remain close to the ground. This is because some of the roots contract and pull the stock into the ground, while the deeper-seated, oldest portion at the base decays.

Corms are yet another specialized type of erect-growing root-stock. They are in fact round, much swollen underground stems covered with a number of loose-fitting, withered, brown, old scale-leaves. The top of the corm bears one or more buds, beside which is a scar marking the remains of the flower and leaves of the previous year. Corms of crocus (*Colchicum* spp.), for example, which are planted in autumn, send out a mass of fibrous roots during the winter, and early in the spring the buds grow out into shoots. Each shoot produces a flower surrounded by several lanceolate foliage leaves circled by a sheath of pale, thin scale-leaves. If the corm is sectioned

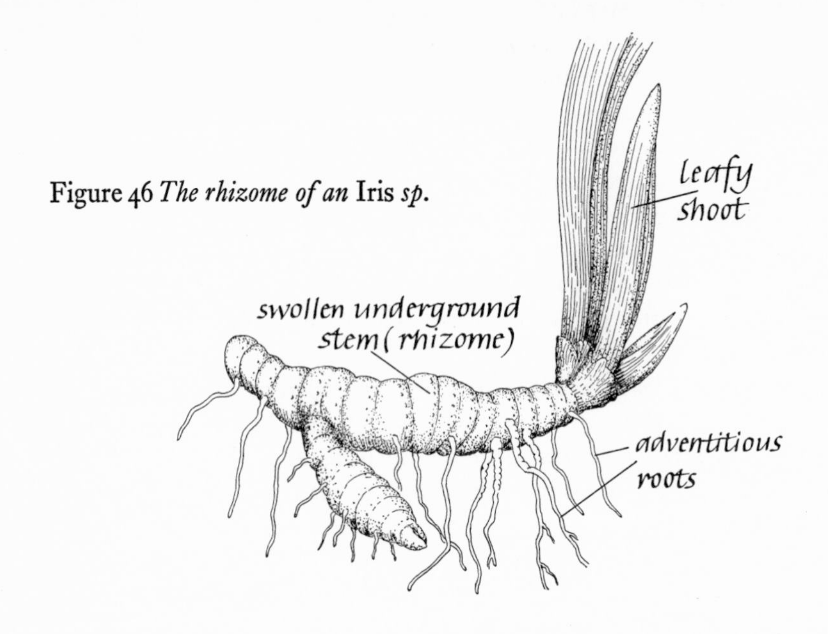

Figure 46 *The rhizome of an* Iris *sp.*

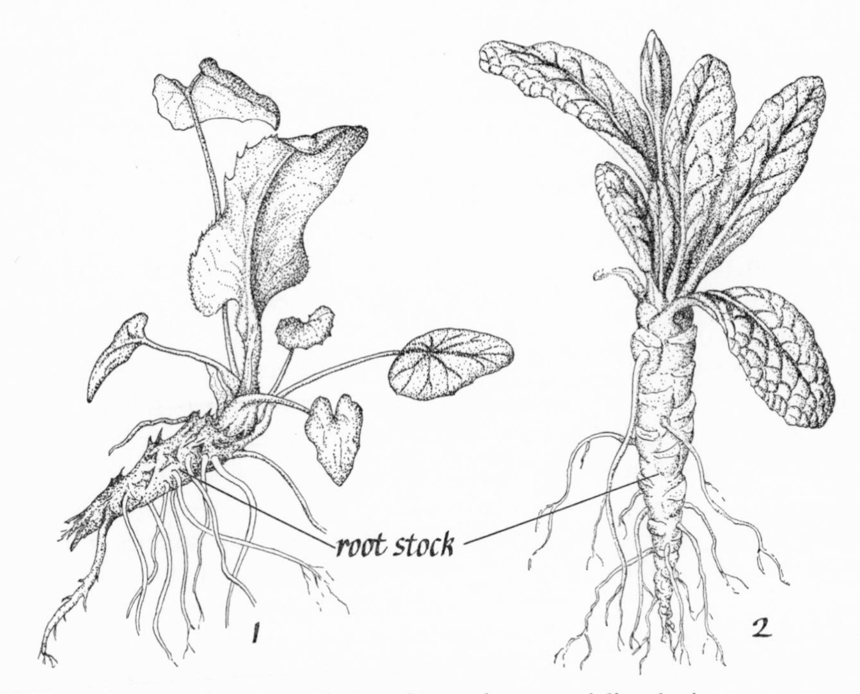

Figure 47 1 *Root stock of leopard's bane* (Doronicum pardalianches).
2 *Root stock of primrose* (Primula vulgaris).

longitudinally just before flowering, it will be seen that the flower and leaves arise from a short stem connected with the corm. This short stem becomes a new corm, which (if examined when the plant has flowered) will be found to have swollen considerably, while the lower one from which it developed will be found to have become shrivelled. By autumn it has become merely a dark mass beneath the new corm. In the axils of one or more of the foliage leaves, buds develop which will give rise to flowering shoots and eventually to the corms of the following year. Growth is therefore sympodial, for the bud which develops first into a flowering shoot and then into a new corm is axillary. A mature corm is in fact the basal part of a shoot, the apical portion of which, after producing flower and leaves, withers away, while its buds are all lateral (fig. 48).

A final category of herbaceous plants that winter underground are those which do so by means of *bulbs*. Bulbs are resting buds surrounded by large leaves swollen with stored food, while the underground stem is a flat, basal disc from which adventitious roots arise. When conditions in spring favour growth, these adventitious roots elongate rapidly and, when well established, the centrally situated bud develops and carries upwards through the soil the new foliage leaves, and the flower protected within them. This development is at the expense of food stored in the swollen, outer, older leaves of the bulb which therefore begin to contract. The new foliage leaves above ground, however, manufacture food which is subsequently passed downwards into buds which have been formed between the flowering axis and the storage leaves, and are therefore axillary in position. Since these buds also receive any surplus food from the storage leaves, they increase in size rapidly, so that, as the aerial shoot dies down, the original bulb is replaced by several daughter bulbs enclosed in the shrivelled remains of their parent. This sympodial growth is typical of tulip. In *Narcissus* and *Galanthus*, on the other hand, where the fleshy scales are the swollen bases of foliage leaves of preceding seasons, growth is monopodial. New foliage leaves arise from the flat basal stem, in the axil of one of the leaves there appears the flowering shoot; while the terminal bud of the main axis, which persists from season to season, can be found at its side (fig. 48).

The bulb is a kind of bud, specialized for food storage. Although bulbous plants are common in gardens, many of them have been introduced into Europe from arid regions of the world such as Asia Minor and South Africa. In these countries, heat and drought, rather than frost and cold, are the unfavourable conditions from which the plants must escape by resting underground. In their natural environment it is the onset of the rains, usually in the cooler season of the year, that stimulates them into activity. Drawing on their large stores of food, they flower in late winter or early spring.

Most of the perennials examined so far have an annual cycle consisting of vegetative growth, flowering, and a rest period underground after the aerial parts of the plant have died back. The essential feature of these plants is that although the old parts may die away, they have produced new parts which may give rise to several new plants by vegetative propagation without having to make an entirely fresh start from seed, as do annuals. Seed production can take place as well, so that these perennials may have two modes of reproduction.

WOODY PERENNIALS

A most important group of perennial plants are the woody perennials, trees and shrubs, which are distinguished by the possession of a permanent, above-ground shoot system. This, in addition to forming the starting point for each year's growth, is added to each year and thus may attain very considerable dimensions.

The distinction between trees and shrubs is not a clear one. In general, however, shrubs are smaller than trees and become divided up close to the ground into a number of branches of more or less equal size, thus contrasting with trees, which have a distinct main stem or trunk. Although some shrubs have a prostrate habit, most woody perennials grow erect and are thus completely exposed to winter conditions. In some, the leaves are retained throughout the winter, but in such *evergreens* the leaves are either reduced in size like the narrow needles of pine (*Pinus*

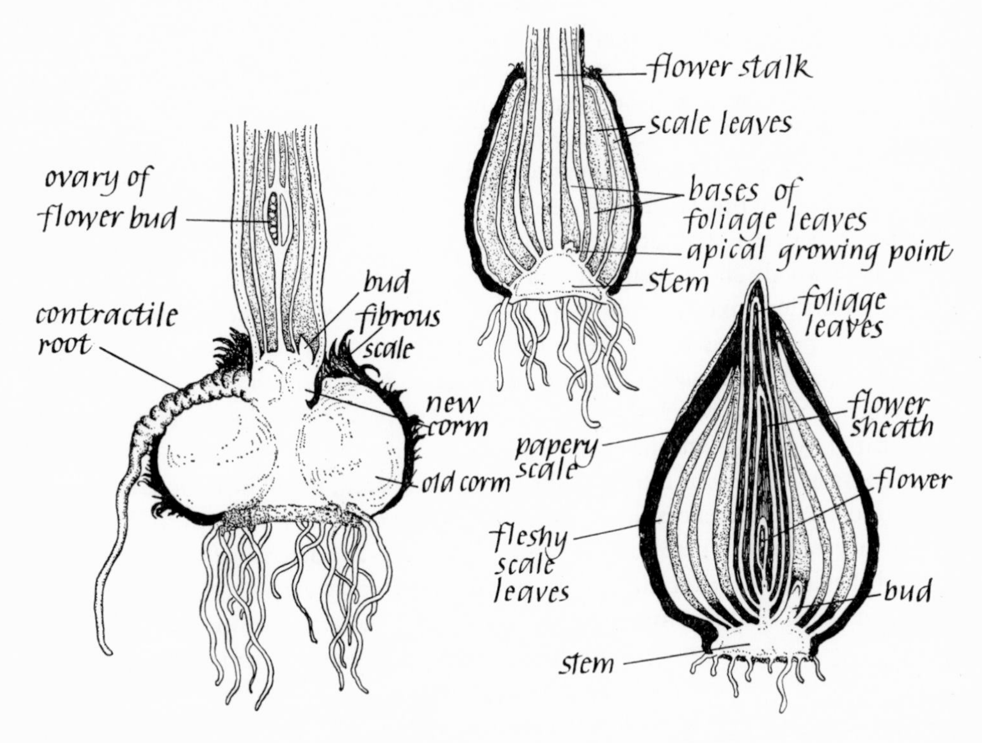

Figure 48 (*Left*) *Crocus corm in March.*
(*Centre*) *Snowdrop bulb in February.*
(*Right*) *Tulip bulb in December* (*after Skene*).

spp.) and spruce (*Picea* spp.), or are tough, shiny and leathery as in laurel (*Laurus*) or holly (*Ilex*). The significance of these leaf modifications will be discussed under Transpiration (Chapter 14). Most trees and shrubs, however, lose their leaves in autumn so that, in the case of these deciduous perennials at least, a part of the shoot system dies back.

Even in the largest trees the general architecture of the shoot and root system is basically the same as in the small annual shepherd's purse previously described. With regard to the root system a tap root is at first produced. Then as the plant becomes older and larger and requires considerable support, the laterals growing near the soil surface develop strongly to form what may best be described as a horizontal platform, spreading over a wide area round the tree. The shoot consists of a main axis bearing branches which have arisen from buds produced in the axils of leaves. The main axis and branches are protected by a corky bark (see p. 138).

Deciduous trees form buds of a rather special kind, the immature leaves and embryo shoot within being enclosed in hard, tough scales fitting closely together. These resting, or winter, buds are formed at different times in different trees (see also Chapter 6). For example, in beech and oak the shoots tend to stop growing in early summer and the winter buds are formed by the end of June, while in poplars (*Populus* spp.), sycamore and maples (*Acer* spp.) shoot growth continues much longer and the resting buds may not be formed until autumn. In all cases, however, these resting buds become very prominent in autumn, when they can be seen just above each scar left by the leaves after they have fallen. The scars which mark the position of former leaves are usually crescent shaped. These are crossed by a series of dots. These dots are the broken ends of *vascular strands* (see fig. 51), the main channels of conduction between stem and leaf, and vice versa. In some trees, as for example beech, each woody shoot may end in a terminal bud, but these have no subtending *leaf scar*. Further important features of the twigs of trees and shrubs are the small, variously shaped excrescences with which all mature woody shoots are pitted. These are *lenticels*, and are concerned in the exchange of gases from the air to the inside of the branch, a process which is prevented except at these points by the impermeable, corky bark (see p. 141 and fig. 49).

If the twigs of various trees and shrubs are compared, it will be noticed that there are considerable differences in their appearance, especially with regard to the way in which they branch. These differences in branching are determined fundamentally by the behaviour of the terminal bud, and this in turn may very largely determine the form and shape of the mature tree or shrub. In some trees the original plumule of the seedling continues to grow year after year. The meristem of the main axis thus persists from year to year, and is indeed potentially immortal, lengthening in spring and producing a new bud in autumn (fig. 50). This *monopodial* growth gives rise to a tall, straight axis, typical of many conifers and poplars. Lateral buds in these trees do of course develop into side branches, which may branch again and again but these branches are always subsidiary to the main axis. The oldest and largest lat-

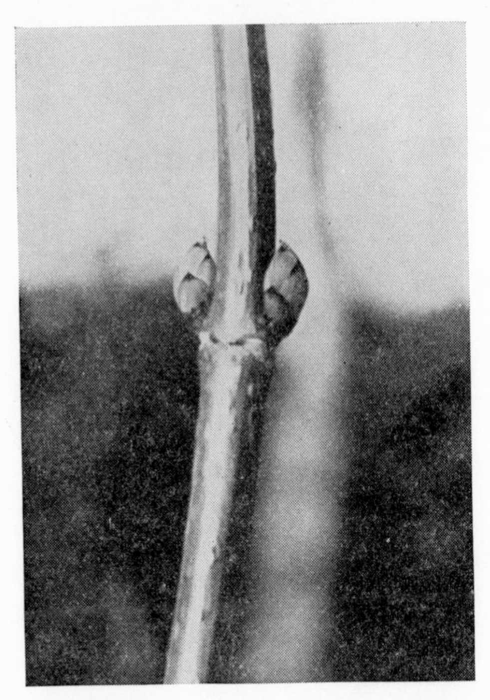

Figure 49 *Lenticels of the surface of a winter twig of elder* (Sambucus niger).

erals develop furthest from the growing point with successively smaller branches closer to it. It is because of this essentially regular manner of branching that such trees often have a perfectly symmetrical, conical shape, as exemplified by a typical 'Christmas tree'. In many deciduous trees, after a certain height has been reached, some of the side branches attain a size similar to that of the main stem so that a crown is formed, consisting of several great branches of almost equal size. The shape of the crown depends very much on how the limbs leave the trunk. Thus if they point up at an angle, the crown tends to be high and narrow, as in beech, while a low, broad crown is produced, as in oak, if they spread horizontally.

The other main type of branching, which is found in lime and elm, is *sympodial*. Although in summer a twig of one of these trees will be found to have a well-marked terminal bud, it may be noticed that this withers and eventually dies as autumn approaches. Its place, however, is ultimately taken by an axillary bud situated just beneath it. As the terminal bud withers, the adjacent axillary bud increases in size and comes to occupy a position at the extreme end of the branch, while the shrivelled terminal bud, or its scar, can be seen to one side. These *lateral buds*, whose true origins are revealed by the presence of a leaf scar but whose position is now terminal, give rise to the increase in length of the branches in the following season, so that the axis comes to be built up of a series of lateral branches, which, however, form an apparently continuous whole (fig. 50).

In some trees both monopodial and sympodial branching may occur, the latter,

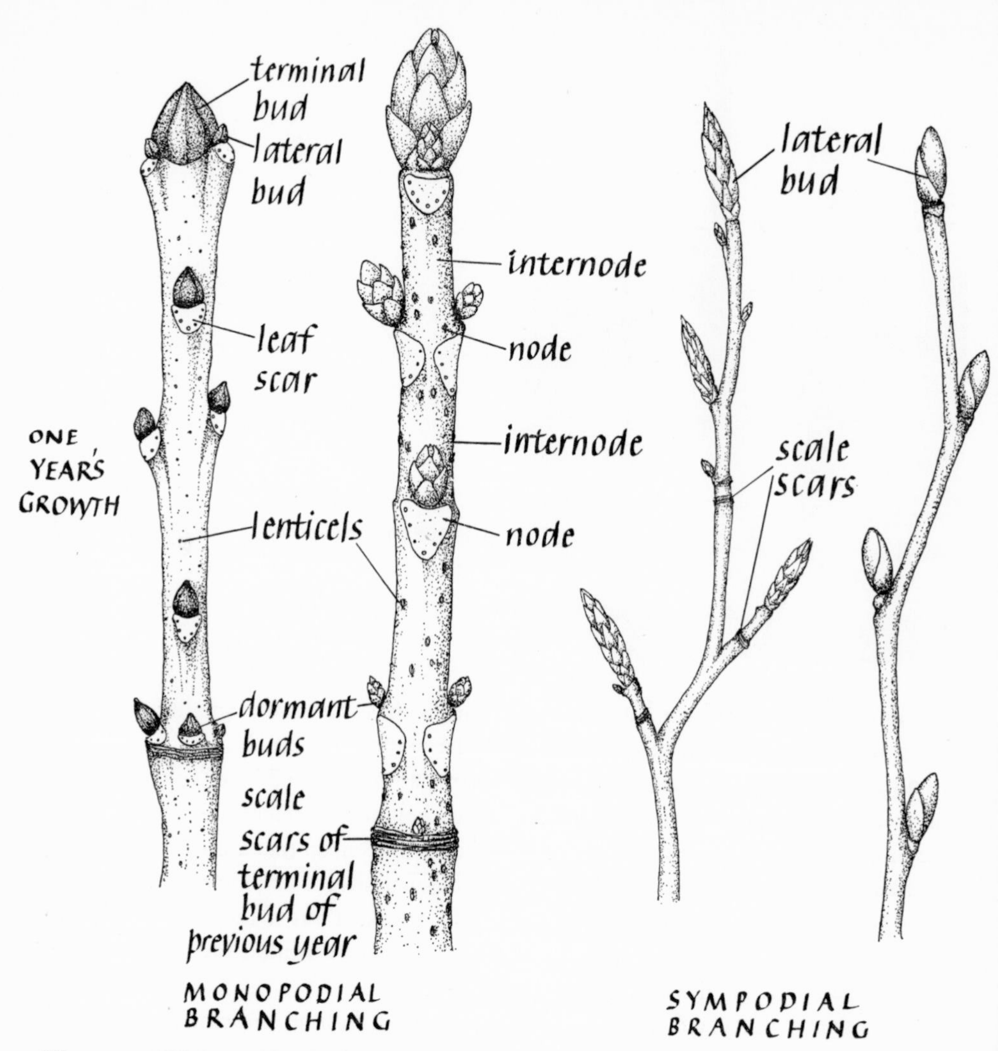

Figure 50 *Winter twigs of ash and horse chestnut showing monopodial branching, and of beech and elm showing sympodial branching.*

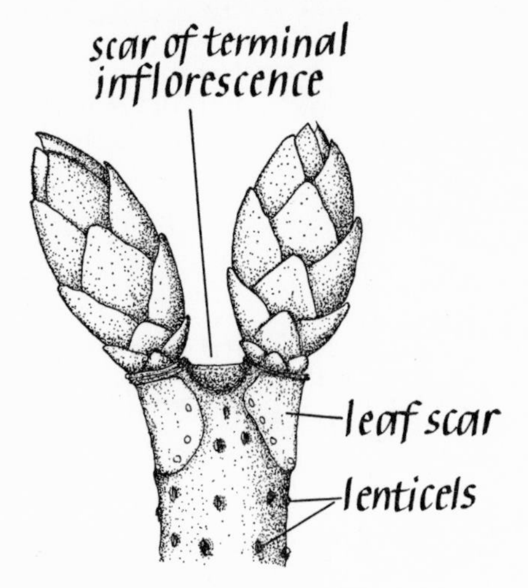

Figure 51 *Tip of winter twig of horse chestnut* (Aesculus hippocastranum) *showing buds, leaf scars and inflorescence scar.*

however, as for example in horse-chestnut, being associated with flowering. It will be remembered that with monopodial growth, when a flower is produced, growth in that direction comes to an end. Thus in horse-chestnut the inflorescence is produced from a terminal bud, but when reproduction is completed the stalk of the flower is shed leaving a large, round, terminal scar. The nearest lateral bud, however, takes over the function of this terminal bud, and in the following season the branch it produces replaces that which produced flowers (fig. 51).

Some trees and shrubs show a somewhat different type of sympodial branching, in which, on the death or transformation of the terminal bud into an inflorescence, two (rather than one) lateral buds take its place, giving the branch which subsequently develops, a forked appearance. Lilac, and on occasion horse-chestnut, shows this *dichasial branching* (fig. 52).

It must be emphasized that not all the buds formed on a tree develop. If they did the whole plant would become an inextricable mass of branches. In fact only a small proportion of the buds produced develop: the vast majority remain inactive. The inactivity of these resting or *dormant buds* may last almost throughout the life of the tree, though when circumstances demand – and these circumstances are very often the injury of other active parts of the plant – they are ready to unfold and grow out as branches.

This fact can be demonstrated with quite young plants, for even in these the bud in the axil of each leaf usually remains inactive provided that the terminal bud of the shoot is present and growing vigorously. If, however, the terminal bud is removed, one or more of the axillary buds will begin to develop and indeed the uppermost one will in all probability take over the functions of the decapitated apical bud, and like

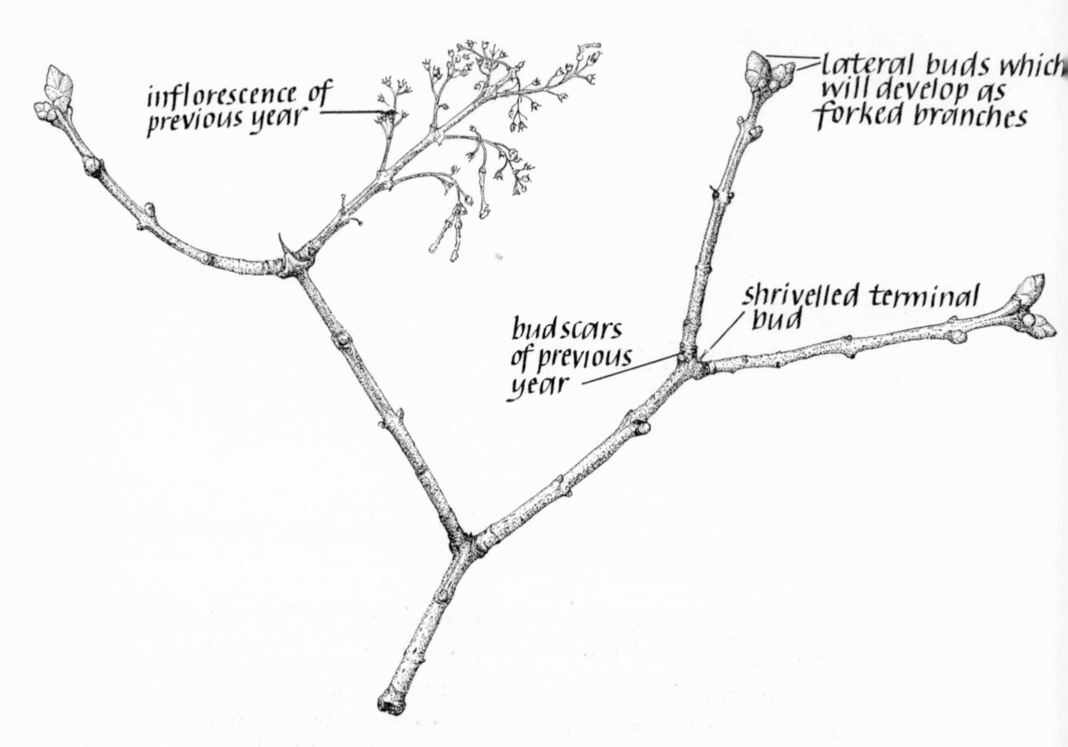

Figure 52 *Winter twig of lilac* (Syringa vulgaris) *showing dichasial branching.*

it suppress the growth of axillary buds below (fig. 53). The completeness of apical dominance varies in different types of plants and is reflected in their shape and habit. In tall, unbranched species this dominance is complete, whilst in much branched forms, such as shrubs, it is much less so. The shrubby habit can be induced as in hedge making, which depends on the plants' response to cutting off the tops of the upper branches, which stimulates the production of numerous laterals.

It is now known that auxins are involved in *apical dominance*, and like the effect of auxin on other aspects of growth, it is a polar phenomenon (see p. 45). Auxin seems to be synthesized by the terminal bud but can only move downwards to exert its inhibitory influence on the buds below it. Experiments have in fact been carried out to determine whether or not this important, controlling influence of the apical bud is in fact identical with auxin. Young broad bean plants which had their terminal buds removed were found, when left to grow for a few days, to show axillary bud development. If, however, the terminal buds were replaced by small agar blocks containing auxin, all the axillary buds remained dormant. Though much has still to be discovered about the mechanism of bud inhibition, experiments of this sort nevertheless further demonstrate the vitally important part played by plant hormones in controlling development and the growth of plant organs.

Many branches which develop on a tree are lost later in life, for those on the lower part of the trunk may die and sooner or later fall. This process is much more apparent in trees growing in woods than in open situations; the former have tall, clean trunks (*boles*) while the latter bear large, well developed branches quite low down.

Figure 53 *Apex of young Norway spruce* (Picea excelsa) *the apical bud of which (left of centre) has been killed. The lateral bud on the right is taking over the function of the apical bud.*

CHAPTER 6

BUDS AND LEAVES

For much of a plant's life, leaves are the most conspicuous feature of its shoot system, and the main site of the synthesis of the food from which it grows. There is therefore a good deal to be said for the popular notion that herbaceous plants, at least, are little more than collections of leaves. These important appendages begin life as outgrowths of the stem apex, so that when a terminal bud is dissected under a hand lens (the water plant, *Hippuris*, provides excellent material), a succession of overlapping leaves can be removed. These are progressively smaller towards the apex, where they occur as barely perceptible protuberances. A somewhat different view on the early development of a leafy shoot may be gained by halving lengthwise the large bud of the winter vegetable, Brussels-sprout (*Brassica oleracea*) (fig. 54). In this, as in all buds, the young leaves are crowded together and thrown into numerous folds, which makes the bud firm and compact. Its centre is occupied by the axis, which tapers to the apical meristem. Below, and on either side, the developing leaves occur, the youngest and smallest being nearest the meristem. In the axils even of quite young leaves, minute buds (which in turn contain the telescoped form of a shoot in miniature) can be distinguished.

The Brussels-sprout is a summer bud in which the young inner leaves are protected by the larger leaves on the outside. In the winter buds of deciduous trees, each is entirely covered by tough, close fitting brown scales shielding the delicate young leaves within. In the buds of poplar and horse-chestnut, further protection is given by a layer of sticky varnish.

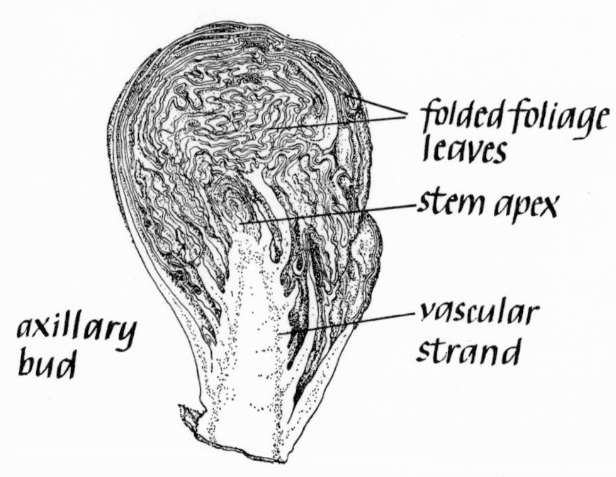

Figure 54 *Longitudinal section of a bud of Brussels-sprout* (Brassica oleracea).

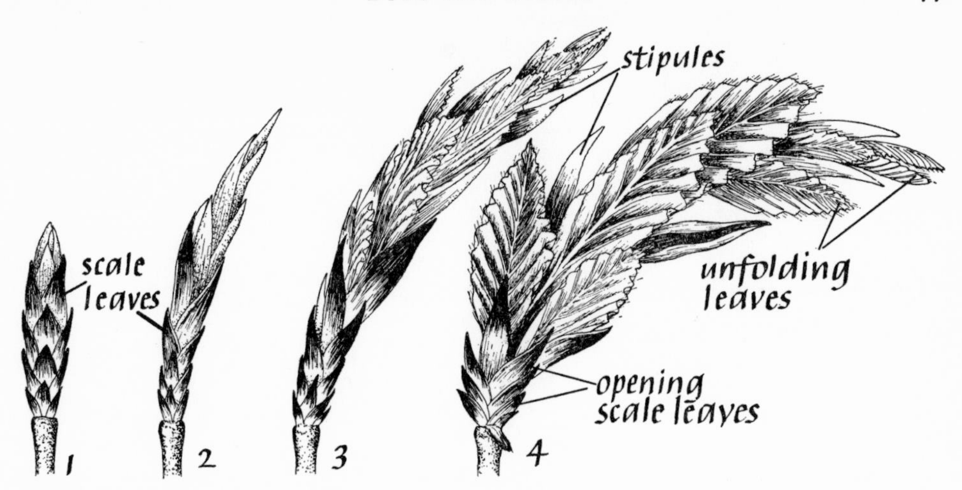

Figure 55 *Stages in the opening of a bud and unfolding of the leaves of beech* (Fagus sylvatica) (*after H. M. Ward*).

Such bud scales, though at first sight very different from foliage leaves, are merely special modifications of the basal portion of the leaf, the upper part being absent. Some, however, are entire leaves, though very small and leathery, and in cases such as lilac and privet it is difficult to draw any clear distinction between bud scales and true foliage leaves. Scale leaves in bulbs, it will be remembered, in addition to being protective in function, may also act as storage organs. Thin membranous scales also protect the buds of many underground stems (see p. 63 and p. 66).

When a bud expands in spring, the shoot within begins to elongate, by means of the growth and extension of its telescoped internodes, while the leaves at each node develop rapidly and unfold. Consequent on this expansion the bud scales are forced apart, but, since there is little or no lengthening of their internodes, they remain as a collar at the base of the growing shoot (figs. 55 and 56). Eventually they are cast off, to leave only closely set rings of scars to mark the position where they occurred. It should be clear, since these bud scale scars are produced only by the events marking the start of each growing season, that the intervals between each series of scars on a shoot define the extent of each year's growth. The growth movements of bud scales and young leaves are nasties (see p. 52) and in their early development these organs grow more rapidly on their lower sides (*hyponasty*). This causes them to bend upwards and inwards enclosing the tip of the axis. At a later stage growth is most rapid on the upper side (*epinasty*), so that the scales and leaves spread outwards away from the central axis.

As in the case of the Brussels-sprout, the dissection of winter buds will show that the shoot contained within is remarkably well developed. Moreover, observations of these buds as they burst will reveal that the changes which accompany and follow their opening are principally concerned with rapid increase in size; indeed, in many

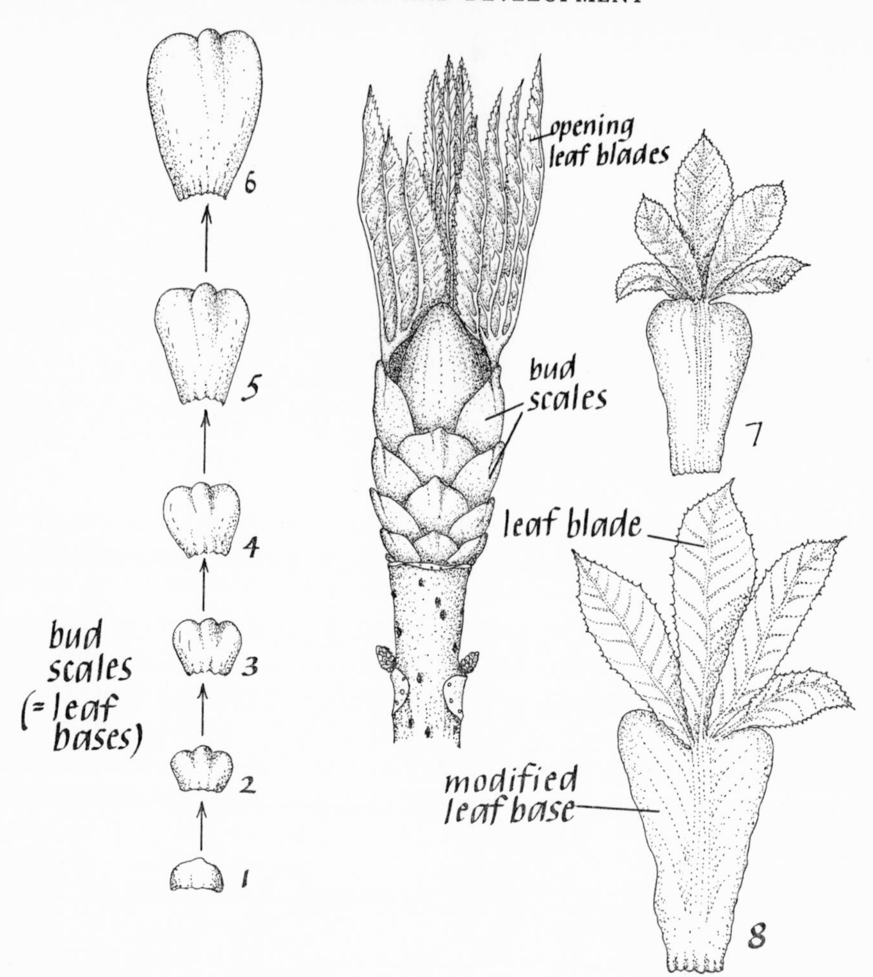

Figure 56 *The opening of a bud of horse-chestnut* (Aesculus hippocastranum) 1–8 *are successively removed bud scales.*

trees and shrubs the entire expansion of their leaves to full size may take only a few weeks.

During the course of this unfolding and expansion, it soon becomes possible in many leaves to distinguish three fairly well defined regions. These are the *leaf base*, where the leaf joins the stem, the petiole or *leaf stalk*, which bears at the end the most important and conspicuous part, the *leaf blade* or lamina (fig. 57.1). Since leaves show the greatest variety of shape and form, it is not always possible to distinguish these three regions in the leaves of any given plant: many are without clearly defined leaf bases, others (e.g. Groundsel (*Senecio vulgaris*) fig. 57.3) referred to as sessile leaves, may be without petioles, and in some specially modified leaves the lamina may be absent, with the result that the leaf has the form of a *needle* or a *spine*.

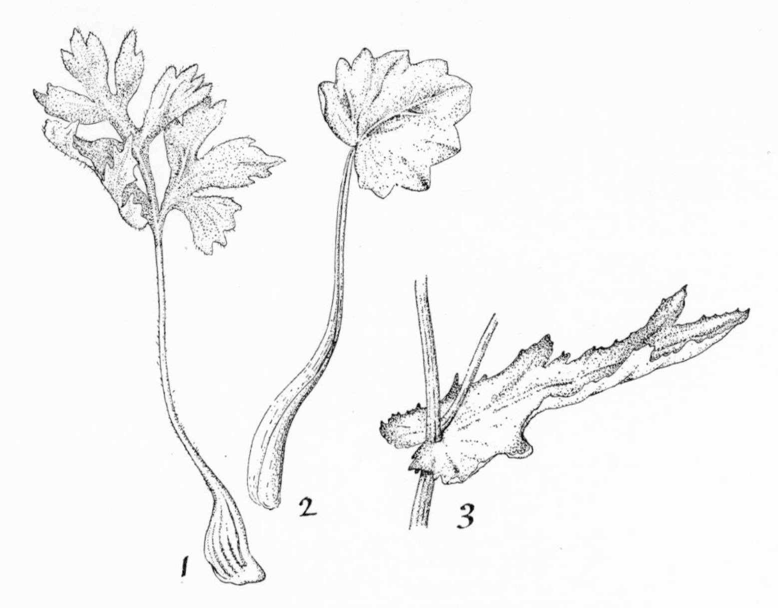

Figure 57 1 *Leaf of bulbous buttercup* (Ranunculus bulbouss).
2 *Leaf of celandine* (R. ficaria).
3 *Leaf of groundsel* (Senecio vulgaris).

LEAF BASE

In many plants the region where the leaf adjoins the stem becomes thick and fleshy, especially when the lamina is large. In these plants the *leaf base*, then termed a *pulvinus*, often retains the ability to bend throughout the life of the leaf. This plasticity confers the important advantage of enabling the leaf to adjust its position in relation to light. Extreme examples of this phenomenon are the sleep-movements shown by some plants, whereby the leaf takes up markedly different positions in light and darkness (see p. 52).

Modifications of the leaf base occur in grasses, in which it is expanded to such a degree as to extend round the stem, forming a *leaf sheath*. In some plants, such as the mullein (*Verbaseum thapsus*) and celandine (*Ranunculus ficaria*) (fig. 57.2), this intimate connection with the stem from which the leaf arises is even more pronounced, the leaf base in such cases extending for some distance down the axis. The probable function of these enlarged bases is to give protection to the adjoining axillary buds. This, however, may also be afforded in some plants by the production of leafy outgrowths of the leaf base, called *stipules*.

Stipules also show much variety in shape and form, and in certain cases are of such a size that they may easily be mistaken for entire leaves, whose functions they in fact fulfil. In the garden pea, for example, the leaves are reduced to whip-like *tendrils*, while large leaf-like stipules at the leaf bases are these plants' principal photo-

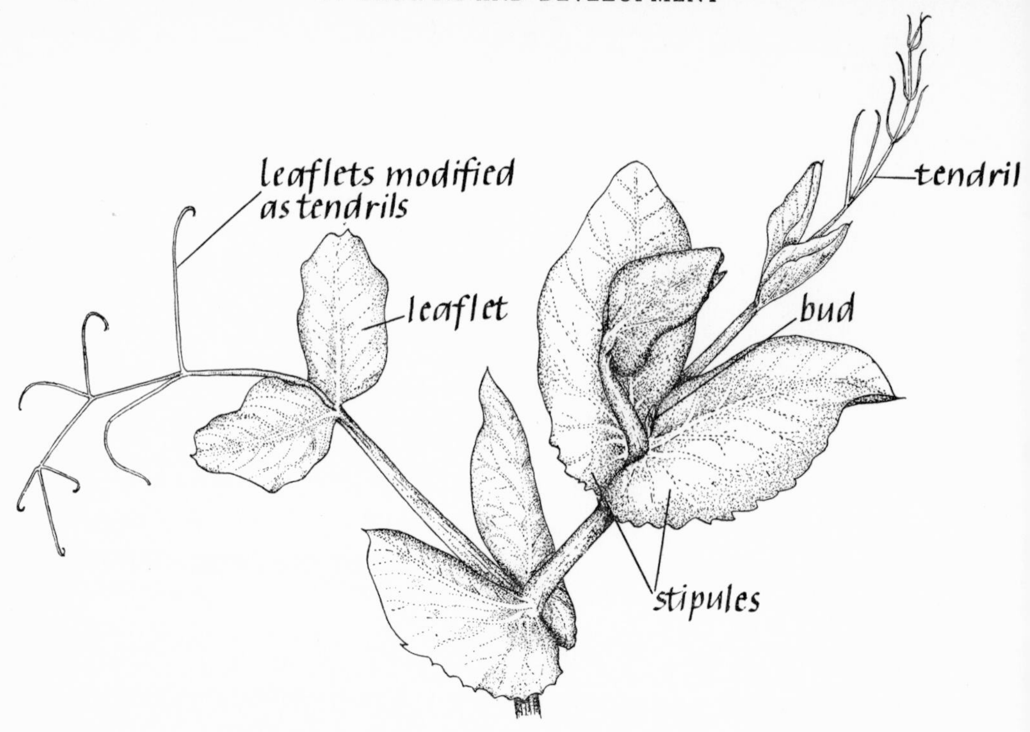

Figure 58 *Shoot of garden pea* (Pisum sativum) *showing leaves modified as tendrils and large stipules.*

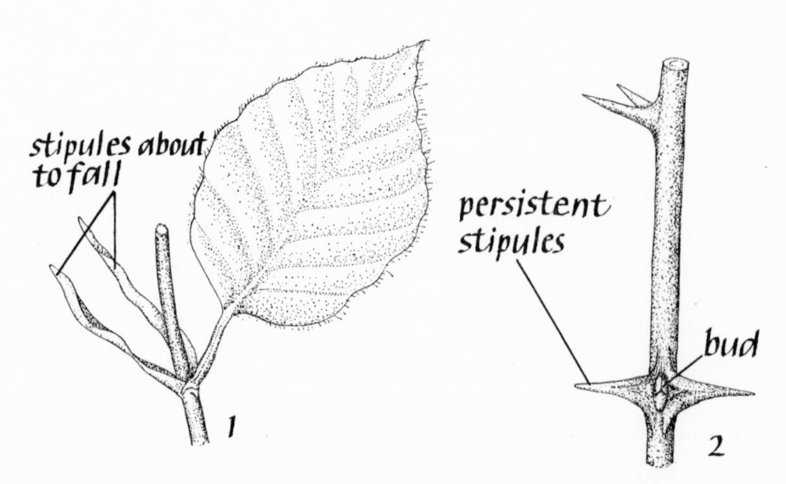

Figure 59 1 *Temporary stipules of* Fagus sylvaticus. 2 *Persistent stipules of* Robinia pseudacacia (*after H. M. Ward*).

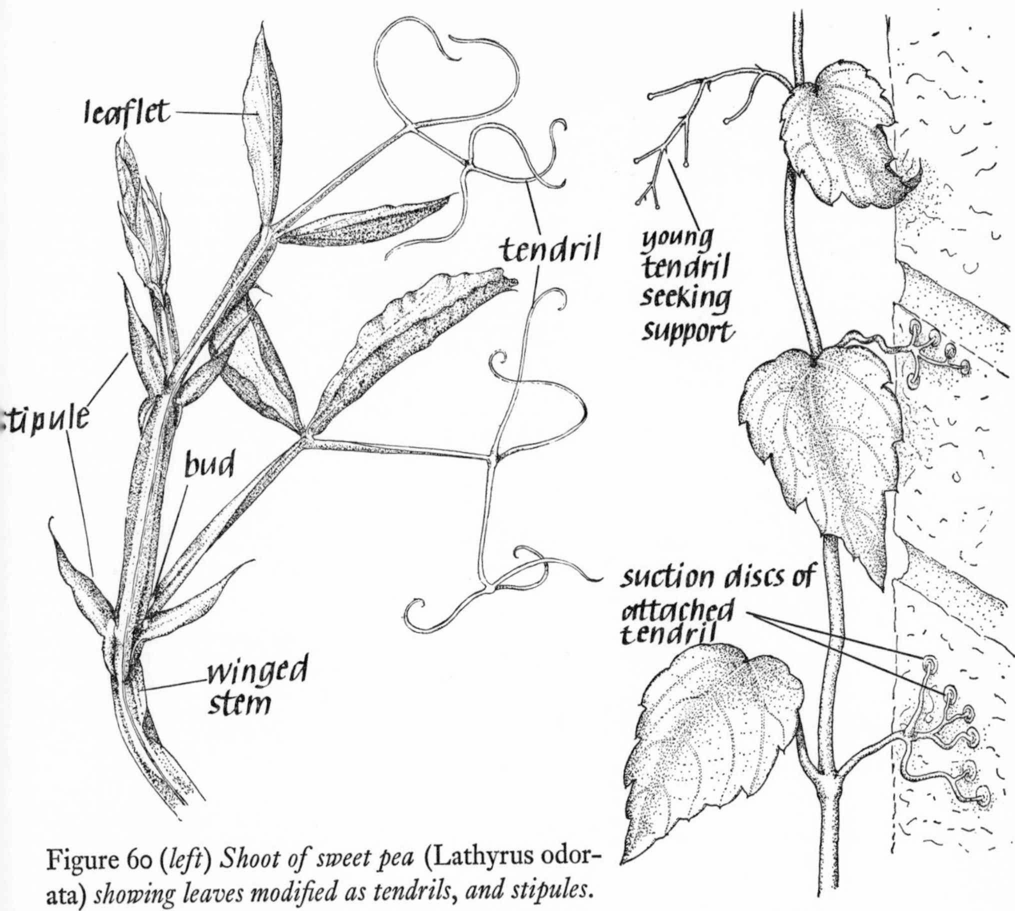

Figure 60 (*left*) *Shoot of sweet pea* (Lathyrus odorata) *showing leaves modified as tendrils, and stipules.*
Figure 61 (*right*) *Tendrils with ends modified as suckers in Virginia creeper* (Parthenocissus tricuspidata).

synthetic regions (fig. 58). At the other extreme, stipules may be very small and scale-like and, as in the beech, drop off after the leaf has unfolded; or occur as spines, as in the false acacia, *Robinia pseudacacia*, which persist for many years (fig. 59).

Although tendrils are commonly modified leaves or leaf parts (fig. 60), in some plants these climbing organs are modified stems, as for example in the Virginia creeper (*Parthenocissus tricuspidata*, fig. 61) and probably in the white bryony (*Bryonia dioica*, fig. 62). In Virginia creeper the tips of the branches, which are negatively phototropic, become slightly swollen at their ends. On meeting some suitable surface, an adhesive substance is secreted from them and they flatten out to form very tenacious suckers which adhere firmly to the surface. All tendrils when young are nearly straight and their tips show marked circumnutation (see p. 43), an autonomic movement which clearly increases their chances of coming into contact with some support.

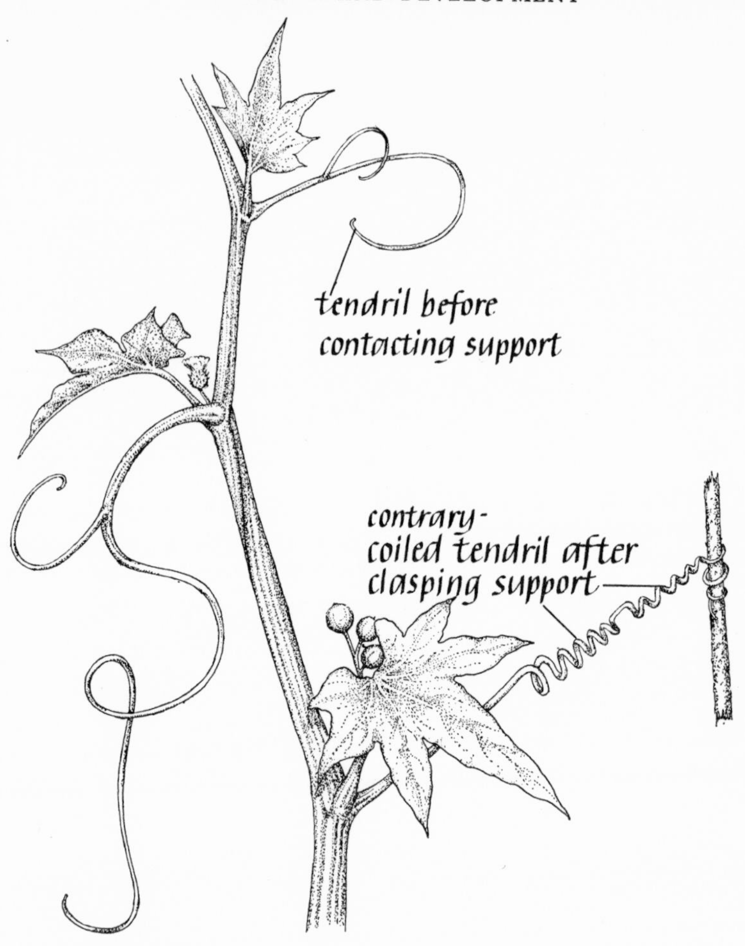

Figure 62 *Tendrils of the white bryony* (Bryonia dioica).

When contact is made, the side of the tendril opposite to that touching the support grows more rapidly so that a growth curvature results. This touch or *haptotropic* (sometimes termed *thygmotropic*) movement brings parts of the tendril into contact with the support. Thus it continues to encircle it and so becomes more and more firmly attached.

LEAF STALK

The leaf stalk or *petiole*, when present, bears at its end the flattened lamina. Although continuous with the stem, the petiole usually differs markedly from it in shape. Commonly it is curved on its lower surface, and usually flattened or concave in section on the upper, so that it appears semi-lunar in cross-section. This shape is mechanically suited to give maximum support to the lamina and hold it in a horizontal position with some rigidity, though not inflexibly. The petiole, like some leaf bases,

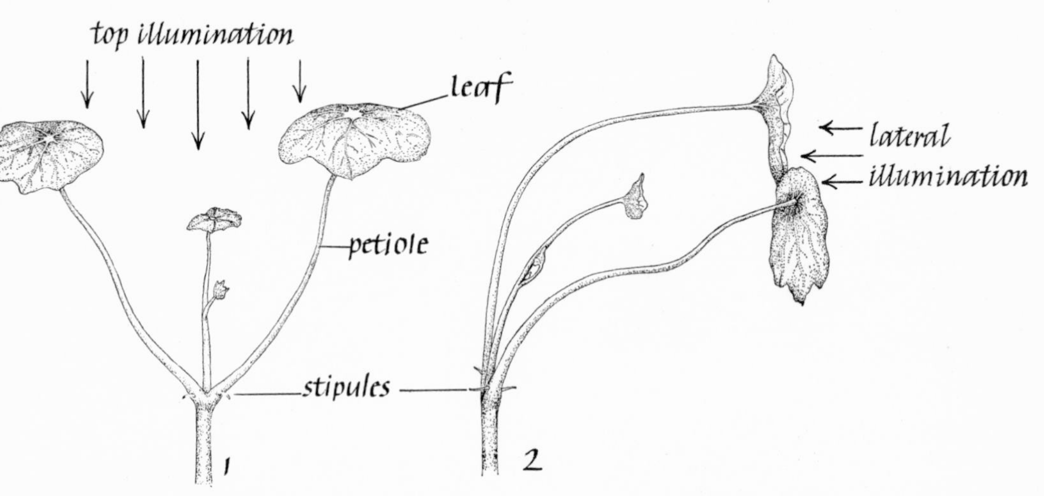

Figure 63 *Curvature of petioles of garden nasturtium* (Tropaeoleum majus) *in response to light*

1 *Leaves in 'normal' position with light from above.*

2 *Leaves directed towards light source, thus showing phototropic response.*

also plays an important part in adjusting the position of the leaf in relation to light. That changes in position are made can be judged from the fact that when mature, the leaf blade has very often radically altered its position in relation to the stem which bears it, and so becomes as fully exposed as possible to the light (fig. 67).

The movement involved in this adjustment, being a directional growth response to an external stimulus, is a tropic movement (see p. 48). A simple experiment to demonstrate this phototropism can be carried out with young potted nasturtium plants (*Tropaeloeum majus*). One such plant should be placed in a box which is open at the top, so that the plant is illuminated from above, and another should be in a similar box placed on its side, so that the nasturtium receives only lateral illumination. Within twenty-four hours quite marked differences can be seen in the two plants. The first, lit from above, will have a straight stem with petioles extending laterally from the axis so that each lamina is horizontal with a maximum of the leaf surface exposed to the light which comes from above. In the plant lit from the side, the stem apex will be found to have curved towards the light, but the most striking change will be in the petioles. These will show growth curvatures such that the leaf blades are in a nearly vertical position; again with their maximum surface presented to the source of illumination (fig. 63).

Phyllotaxis

Although the phototropic movements of the petiole mentioned already provide

Figure 64 *Shoot of* Rhodedendron sanguineum *viewed from above showing phyllotaxis.*

a mechanism which brings about an adjustment of leaf position in relation to light, leaves are, in addition, borne on the stem in such a way that there is a minimum of overshadowing by those immediately above. Indeed, they occur on the stem in a fashion so orderly that it can be expressed with mathematical precision. Two basic types of arrangement or *phyllotaxis*, as it is termed, can be recognized: *spiral* and *cyclic*. It has already been noted that there is a spiral arrangement of leaves in shepherd's purse; however, the phyllotaxy in this plant can best be appreciated by tracing out the leaf positions with a thread. This should be tied to a petiole near the foot of the stem and then carefully wound round and up the stem so that it touches successive leaf bases until that leaf is reached which stands directly above the one to which the end of the cotton is tied. The thread will now have formed a spiral consisting of two complete turns round the stem. Moreover, it will be found to have touched five leaf bases in all, including the last though not the first to which it is attached. This same arrangement usually occurs on any particular portion of the stem examined and on all the stems of a given species.

Phyllotaxis is represented by a quotient, the numerator of which is the number of turns of the spiral, and the denominator the number of leaves within it. Thus in shepherd's purse the *divergence*, as this representation of phyllotaxis is termed, is $\frac{2}{5}$, and the *angle of divergence* between successive leaves on the spiral is 144° ($=\frac{2}{5} \times 360°$).

There is considerable diversity of spiral arrangements and, though a large number of dicotyledonous plants have a divergence of $\frac{2}{5}$, the simplest arrangement is in plants like beech whose leaves are alternate and whose divergence is $\frac{1}{2}$ (angle of divergence 180°). In such cases, one leaf occurs at each node and each is exactly opposite those

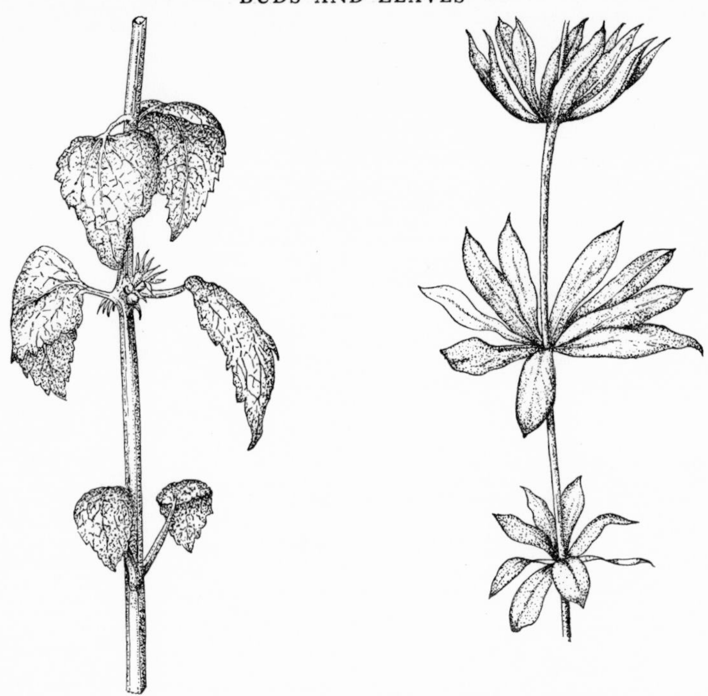

Figure 65 (*left*) *Oppositely arranged leaves of red dead nettle* (Lamium purpureum). Figure 66 (*right*) *Verticillate arrangement of leaves of sweet woodruff* (Asperula odorata).

on the nodes above and below, and directly above and below the leaves two nodes away. This arrangement occurs in the grasses (see fig. 71), whose leaves occupy two longitudinal rows, whilst in the sedges and many monocotyledonous plants there are three longitudinal rows in each spiral, the divergence being $\frac{1}{3}$ (120°). *Rhododendron* and holly with divergences of $\frac{3}{8}$ and the dragon tree (*Dracena*), with a divergence of $\frac{5}{13}$ are amongst the most complex of leaf arrangements. These higher divergences are, however, usually accompanied by shorter internodes and a more compact grouping of the leaves (fig. 64).

In the second category of phyllotaxis, cyclic or *whorled*, two or more leaves develop at each node. Its simplest expression is seen in various members of the nettle family, the Labiatae, where every node bears two leaves opposite one another, while those of the next node either above or below lie exactly at right angles to these. (fig. 65) The divergence of such oppositely placed leaves is $\frac{1}{4}$ and the angle of divergence between each leaf 90°. In many plants, however, the leaves arise in a circle of four, five or sometimes more at each node, an arrangement described as verticillate, as in the sweet woodruff (*Asperula odorata*) (fig. 66).

The very obvious significance of leaf arrangement is that it results in a minimum of overshadowing by successive leaves on any particular stem. This is impressively demonstrated in the sycamore by examining a young erect shoot from above, when

Figure 67 *Leaf mosaics*

1 *Erect shoot of Norway Maple* (Acer platanoides) *showing opposite, decussate arrangement and horizontal display of leaves.*

2 *Lateral horizontal shoot showing arrangement of leaves to give minimum of overlapping. Note marked differences in length and orientation of pairs of petioles* (*after H. M. Ward*).

Figure 68 *Under surface of leaf of the giant water lily* (Victoria regia) *showing very strong ribs which support the lamina.*

it will be seen that successive pairs of leaves lie in the middle of the gaps between the preceding pair. Any overlap is further minimized by the fact that the upper leaves are smaller, while the larger lower leaves have longer petioles which carry them further out from the stem. Such an ordered arrangement of leaves may be referred to as a *leaf mosaic* (fig. 67). It should be noted that in leaf mosaics the minimum shading of the leaf blades from adjoining leaves is also brought about, at least in part, by phototropic movements.

LAMINA

The lamina or blade, a typically thin flattened expanse, is the most obvious and distinctive part of normal leaves. The delicate tissues of these, the plant's most important appendages, are supported by a skeleton or framework of thickened and mechanically firm ribs (fig. 68). Removal of the softer tissues between these ribs or veins, such as occurs through natural decay in autumn produces a *leaf skeleton.* The most prominent feature of this skeleton is the midrib, which is continuous from the petiole to the tip of the lamina. Branch veins, successively smaller in size towards the leaf margins, diverge from it, forming a fine network. There is a considerable diversity in the arrangement, the *venation*, of the veins of leaves. The *reticulate venation* just described is characteristic of most dicotyledonous plants, but within this category there may be only a single midrib, with laterals branching off

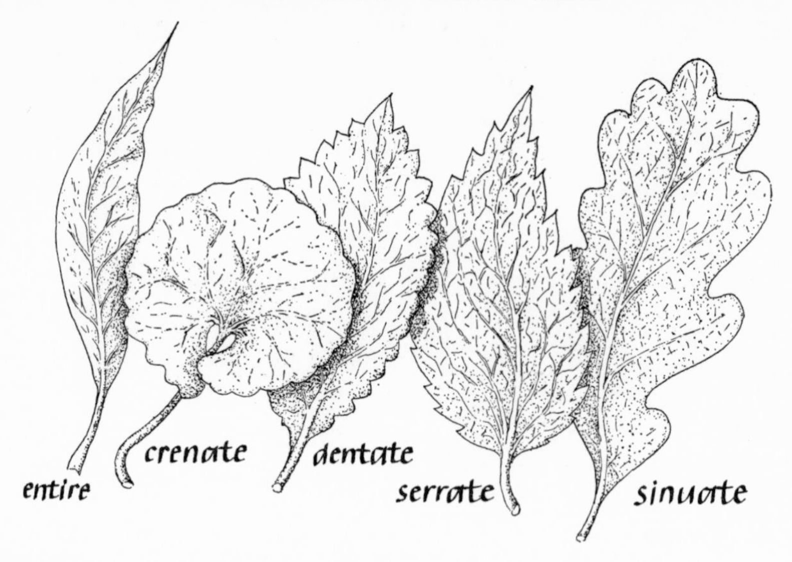

Figure 69 *Some different types of leaf margins.*

on either side, as in privet (*Ligustrum vulgare*); such venation is termed *pinnate* since it resembles a feather. In ivy (*Hedera helix*), several equally prominent veins arise from the petiolar end of the leaf and diverge outwards towards the leaf margin, like the fingers of an open hand. For this reason the venation is described as *palmate*. The leaves of the majority of monocotyledonous plants show *parallel venation*, for although they too possess several equally prominent veins, these generally run parallel to one another and are cross-connected by smaller, transverse veins.

Dicotyledonous plants, especially, show an enormous diversity of leaf shapes (fig. 69); though many leaves, such as those of yellow water lily (*Nuphar luteum*), have a smooth regular outline, a large number have numerous incisions along their margins. These may be slight and form a regular series of teeth round the edge of the leaf, as in poplar or elm, or the indentations may be so considerable that, as in ivy, the leaf is divided into separate lobes which are frequently constant in number for a given plant. In many leaves, however, the incisions are so deep that the leaf is divided into a number of distinct leaflets, each of which may have its own petiole. Because they are made up of several leaflets such leaves are described as *compound* in contrast to undivided, *simple* leaves (fig. 70).

Compound leaves are of two types, *compound pinnate* in which the leaflets are arranged in two rows on each side of the leaf stalk, as in ash (*Fraxinus excelsior*) and laburnum (*Laburnum anagyroides*); and *compound palmate* in which leaflets like the fingers from the palm of the hand radiate from the apex of the petiole, as in horse-chestnut (*Aesculus hippocastranum*) (fig. 70). The petioles of such compound leaves could, at first sight, be mistaken for branches bearing small leaves. Careful examination, however, should reveal that none of the leaflets have buds in their axils, and

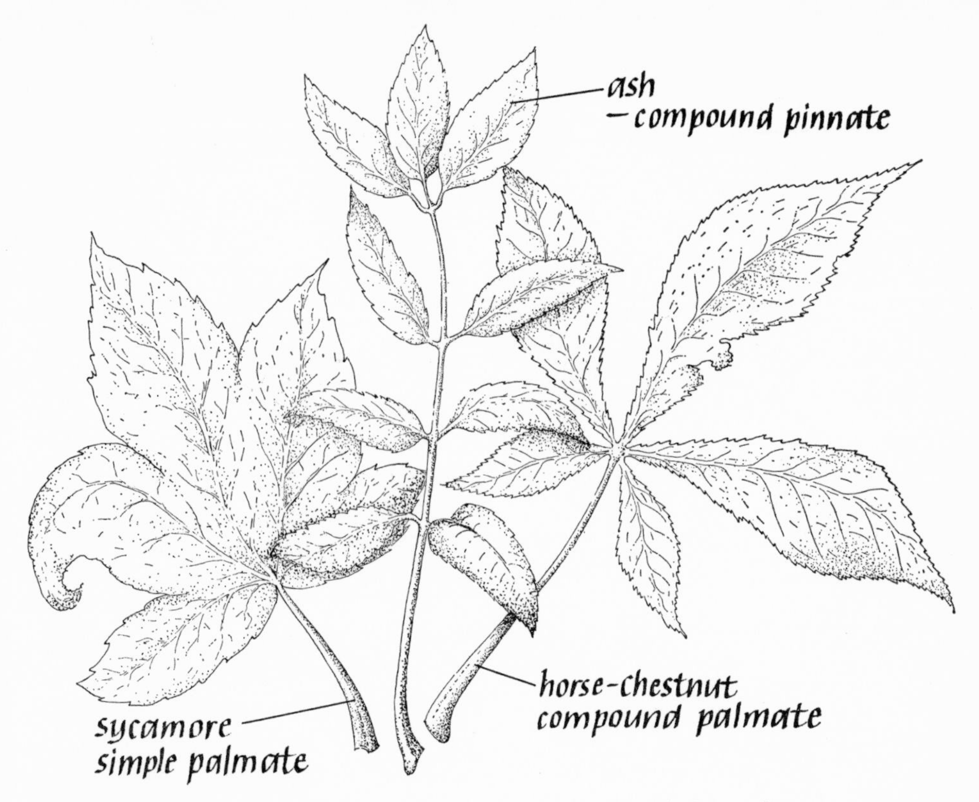

Figure 70 *Simple palmate, compound palmate and compound pinnate leaves.*

moreover there is no apical bud at the end of the petiole. The compound leaf terminates either in a leaflet or blind point and thus has no potential for further development.

The majority of monocotyledonous plants have leaves which are sessile and narrowly *linear* or strap-shaped, as in the grasses and such bulbous plants as *Narcissus* spp. In the latter, for example, the strap-shaped lamina expands towards its base within the bulb into a wider, almost colourless, sheath (fig. 48). Grass leaves, too, have sheathing bases which, however, encircle the main axis, and each is fairly sharply demarcated from its adjoining blade which arises at an angle from it. At this point of demarcation of the two regions of the leaf there occurs on the inner side of the sheath a thin membranous *ligule* (fig. 71). The outermost sheath, which encircles those of younger leaves, and the main axis, can be opened and pulled back to reveal an axillary bud.

The leaf margins of monocotyledonous plants are usually smooth in outline, and an additional distinctive feature is that the leaves are most frequently borne in a more or less upright position. In this way both upper and lower leaf surfaces are equally exposed to light and other environmental influences. In consequence of this, it seems there is little difference in the nature of the two leaf surfaces, which are usually smooth and glossy. In contrast, the leaves of dicotyledonous plants, which typically are borne horizontally, have markedly different upper and lower surfaces. Thus the upper surface may be smooth or wrinkled, while the lower, on which the ridges formed by the main veins often stand out prominently, may be covered with a *bloom*, or with *hairs* which may be soft or bristly.

Clearly leaves show enormous variety of shape and form. Because of this they often serve as valuable aids for the identification of plants and for this reason it is important to have precise terms to describe their many characters. Only a few have been mentioned in the above account, but in attempting to identify plants in the field with a flora many more will undoubtedly be encountered. Most good floras contain a glossary explaining their meaning. The following are the main points to be noted when describing leaves. Firstly, whether the venation is parallel or reticulate, and if the latter whether it is pinnate or palmate. Secondly, whether the leaf is simple or compound and the shape of the leaf or leaflets, paying particular note to the form of the leaf margins. In this connection, careful note should also be made of the shape of the leaf apex. Thirdly, it must be noted whether the leaf is sessile or petiolate, stipulate or *exstipulate* (that is, without stipules); the general form and texture of both upper and lower leaf surfaces must be carefully described. Finally, the arrangement of the leaves in relation to the axis (phyllotaxis) should be determined.

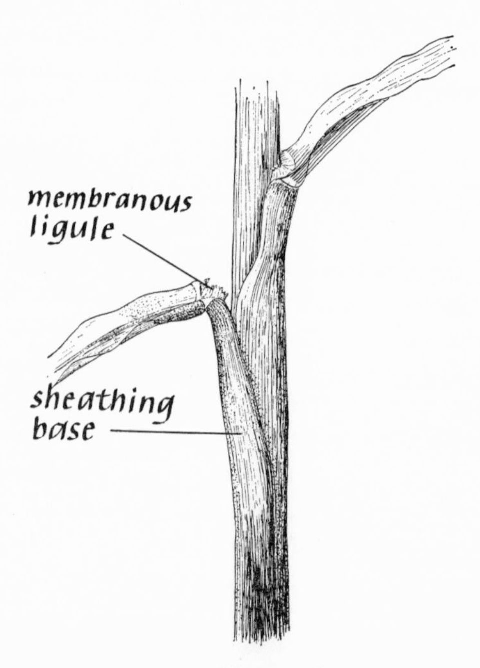

Figure 71 *Alternate arrangement of leaves of maize* (Zea mais). *Note ligules which form a point of demarkation between lamina and leaf base.*

PART II

CELL DIFFERENTIATION AND THE INTERNAL STRUCTURE OF PLANTS

CHAPTER 7

THE PRIMARY BODY : THE ANATOMY OF ROOTS

In examining the internal structure of the radicle of the germinating seedling (see p. 27), and the cellular changes underlying the growth of this part of the young plant, only two phases of growth were considered. These were cell division and cell enlargement. In many simple plants such as certain algae and fungi these are the only stages involved in growth, but in more advanced members of the plant kingdom, including some of the more elaborate algae, as for example certain red and brown seaweeds, a third and very vital change – *cell differentiation* – may take place. Differentiation transforms apparently identical cells, either during or after cell enlargement, into highly specialized cells or groups of cells, collectively termed *tissues*, which fulfil a particular physiological function. During this process cells become altered both in size and shape, but in particular become specialized with respect to their wall structure and living contents. Thus, following germination, as a seedling grows and develops into a mature plant, a profound change takes place in the shape and form of the majority of its cells.

The various organs of the plant which have their origins in the apical meristems of the root and shoot undergo, as they develop, a period of expansion, particularly in length. The entire growth of the plant during this phase of expansion is termed its primary growth, and the plant body so formed, the *primary body*. Most monocotyledons and a few dicotyledons during the whole course of their life form only a primary body, consisting of *primary tissues*. In gymnosperms (see Chapter 36), the majority of dicotyledons, and a few monocotyledons, however, after the primary body has been laid down, an often considerable thickening of roots and stems takes place as a result of *secondary growth*. The secondary tissues added in this way form the secondary body and supplement and reinforce some of the primary ones. In certain cases a new secondary tissue may be formed to replace a primary one which is unable to continue its proper function.

It is now germane to study the form and character of the cells, and their arrangement in the tissue systems which make up the internal structure or anatomy of roots, stems and leaves of the primary body of typical dicotyledonous and monocotyledonous plants. Consideration will then be given to the formation of *secondary tissues* and their arrangement in the thickening *secondary body*. The functioning of these systems will be dealt with in the section devoted to the physiology of plants. (Chapters 11 to 20.)

The cells of the apical meristem of the root divide repeatedly, adding new cells to the body of the plant, while themselves remaining meristematic. This, however, is not the most active region of cell division, there being a much more frequent division of cells in a zone extending for some distance above the apex. Beyond this region cell division becomes much less frequent, the cells become vacuolated and in consequence elongate, while further from the apex many begin to differentiate, assuming particular shapes and characteristics relative to their positions in the root, and appropriate to their various functions.

These various regional aspects of growth can be seen fairly well in a longitudinal section cut through the middle of a root apex (fig. 72). In addition to the constantly renewed, protective *root cap*, the *calyptra*, which is several layers of cells thick and covers the root apex, there are three distinct tissue regions quite close to the apex. Eventually they will form on the outside the *epidermis*, on the inside the central *vascular cylinder*, and between them the *cortex*. The initial differentiation of these regions is produced by differences in the distribution and orientation of cell divisions and in the subsequent degree of enlargement of the cells resulting from them. Since,

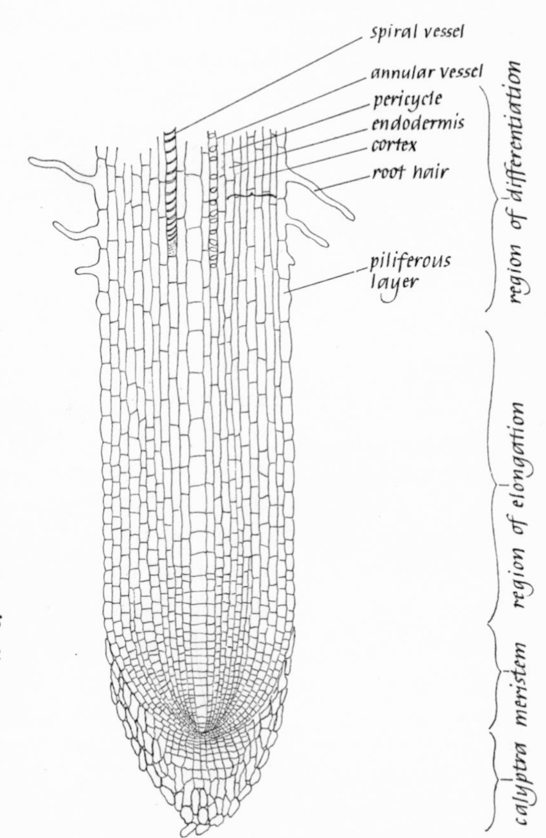

Figure 72 *Diagram of a longitudinal section through a typical root from its tip to the region of cell differentiation (afterHolman and Robbins).*

throughout this period of growth, new cells are being continually formed at the root apex, so the various tissues which subsequently develop from them in varying ways, are also continually forming. Thus a careful examination of the root apex, backwards from the cap, will reveal the whole sequence of development through which a given group of cells passes. Each stage in differentiation through which a given part of the root passes from inception to maturity may be found at any time in sections cut progressively further and further behind the apex. Gradual differentiation in time can thus be seen in spacial extent, down the length of the growing root. Thus, in a transverse section of a root just above the region of elongation, differentiation into three tissue systems is quite clear. There is a central core of *vascular tissues*, surrounded by a broad cylinder of *cortical cells*, the whole being bounded on the outside by the *epidermis* (fig. 74).

Epidermis

The epidermis in this region of early differentiation is specialized as an absorbing region, the functioning of which may be facilitated by the fact that many of its cells become extended outwards as *root hairs*, which form the *piliferous layer*. Epidermal cells below this region, which are not so developed, can also absorb water and mineral salts, but the root hairs greatly increase the absorbing surface of the root. The hairs arise as small *papillae* in the zone of elongation and reach their full development in the region where at least some vascular tissues are partly mature. They usually die off in older parts of the root and hence tend to be less and less frequent in sections cut progressively further above the zone of root extension (fig. 72).

Cortex

Immediately within the epidermis is the cortex, a broad cylinder of living cells which are thin walled, polyhedral in shape, and almost as long as wide. Cells of this type, which occur in many parts of the plant, are described as *parenchymatous*. Tissues composed of these rather unspecialized, undifferentiated cells, are often referred to as *fundamental* or *ground* tissue, since other tissues appear to be embedded in it. The term *parenchyma* is in fact an embodiment of this concept and means 'poured beside', being derived from the Greek 'para', beside, and 'en-cheim', to pour. Indeed early notions of parenchyma conceived it as a semi-liquid substance, poured round the firmer, more rigid tissues, which were considered to be formed before it.

A common feature of the parenchyma in the cortex of many roots is that the cells do not fit closely together, there being conspicuous *intercellular spaces* between them. Frequently there are considerable accumulations of starch grains within the cells, for this region is often one of storage (fig. 73).

Some differentiation of the cortical cells may take place immediately beneath the epidermis, to provide an additional protective tissue. This differentiation occurs in the region of the root beyond the zone of root-hair formation and where water absorp-

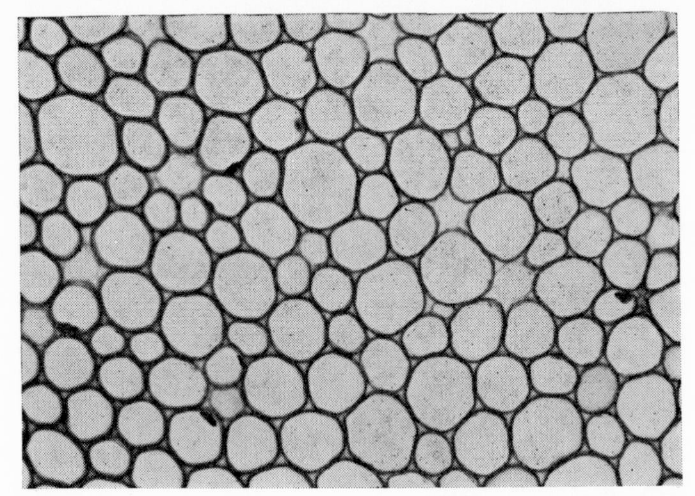

Figure 73 *Parenchyma in t.s. of a root of* Zea mais. *Note conspicuous intercellular spaces.*

tion no longer takes place. Transverse sections of the region, taken from different plants, show this *exodermis*, as it is termed, as one or several layers of cells whose walls are typically thickened by a fatty substance, *suberin* (see p. 140). This is laid down inside the primary walls of the cells. It may later be covered with cellulose thickening (fig. 74).

The innermost layer of cells of the cortex also frequently becomes differentiated as an 'inner skin' or *endodermis*. The special characteristic which develops in these cells is a band of thickening, also containing suberin, which completely encircles the cell within the radial and transverse walls (fig. 75). An outstanding feature associated with this *Casparian strip* is that the cytoplasm of the endodermal cell is firmly attached to it, a feature of some significance in considerations of the function of this localized thickening. In most monocotyledons the Casparian strips of the endodermal cells develop thick secondary walls in the older parts of the root. The extent of the thickening, however, is very uneven, being thin or non-existent on the outer walls of each cell, but very considerable on the inner tangential walls. Thus it appears in transverse sections as crescent or U-shaped (fig. 76). Not all the endodermal cells in the root become thickened. Those remaining unthickened are termed *passage cells*. They occur singly, though often at definite intervals, round the endodermis and are assumed to be passageways for the radial transfer of food materials between the cortex and centrally situated *vascular cylinder*.

Vascular Cylinder

Immediately within this specialized, innermost layer of cortical cells occur the outermost layer, or layers, of the vascular cylinder. In transverse sections taken from the root in the piliferous zone, this outermost region, called the *pericycle*, consists of

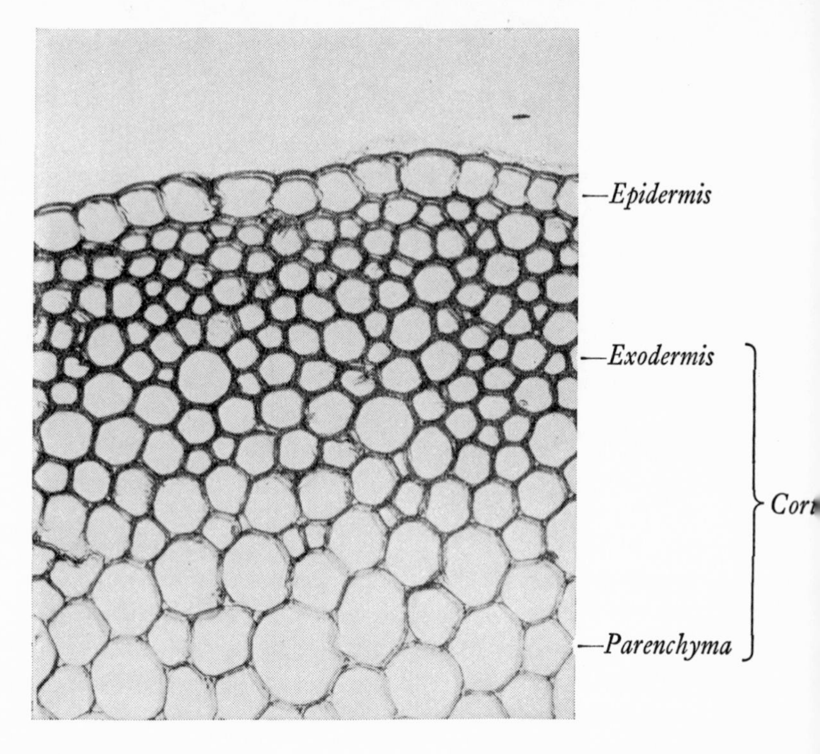

Figure 74 *Thickened cells of the exodermis in outer regions of cortex of root of* Zea mais.

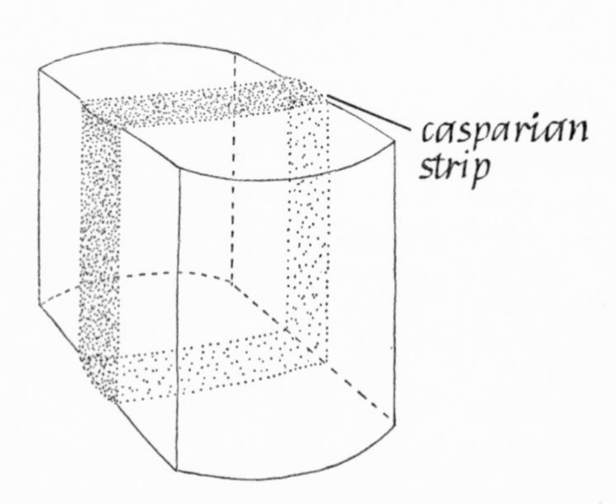

Figure 75 *Diagrammatic representation of an endodermal cell in perspective, showing its Casparian strip.*

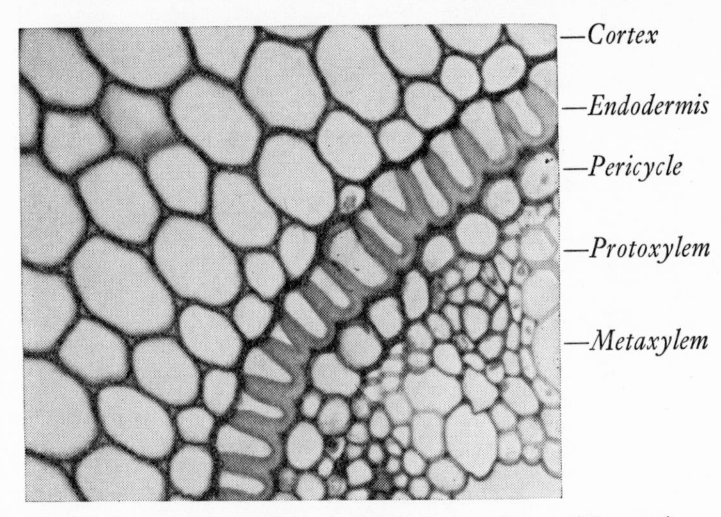

Figure 76 *U-shaped endodermal cells in t.s. of root of* Zea mais.

one or more layers of thin-walled parenchyma cells. In sections from older parts of the root, and especially in those of monocotyledons, these cells will usually be found to have undergone a marked change, in that they become *sclerified*. The *sclerenchyma* which results is *mechanical tissue* consisting of thick walled cells without living contents. Sclerenchyma means a 'hard infusion' and such cells may be long tapering fibres or short squat *sclereids* whose walls are thickened with one of the most important of cell substances, *lignin*, which gives wood many of its special properties. As well as occurring in roots, sclerenchyma is also present in many stems and leaves. It may occur as separate strands or sheaths protecting the vascular tissues, or it may be scattered through them (see figs. 88 and 91).

The most conspicuous feature of the vascular cylinder as seen in transverse sections of many dicotyledonous roots, especially when stained with *safranin*, or even *iodine*, is a three- or more armed star of thick-walled cells which are usually noticeably larger than any other in the cylinder (figs. 77 and 78). Moreover, the cells towards the centre of the star are larger than those occupying the arms, though in sections from younger parts of the root, the walls in the central region will probably still be thin walled and hence remain unstained. In many roots the 'star' may have only two arms and exist as a ridge or band of cells running across the vascular cylinder. In a few roots, on the other hand, it may have from five to eight, or even more arms. Depending on the number of arms present, roots are referred to as *diarch*, *triarch*, *tetrarch*, etc. Monocotyledons always have *polyarch* roots with twelve to twenty arms (fig. 79).

Xylem The star constitutes the principal water-conducting tissue in the root, called the *xylem*. In its fully developed condition this is a complex tissue containing many different types of cells, both living and non-living. Its most distinctive and

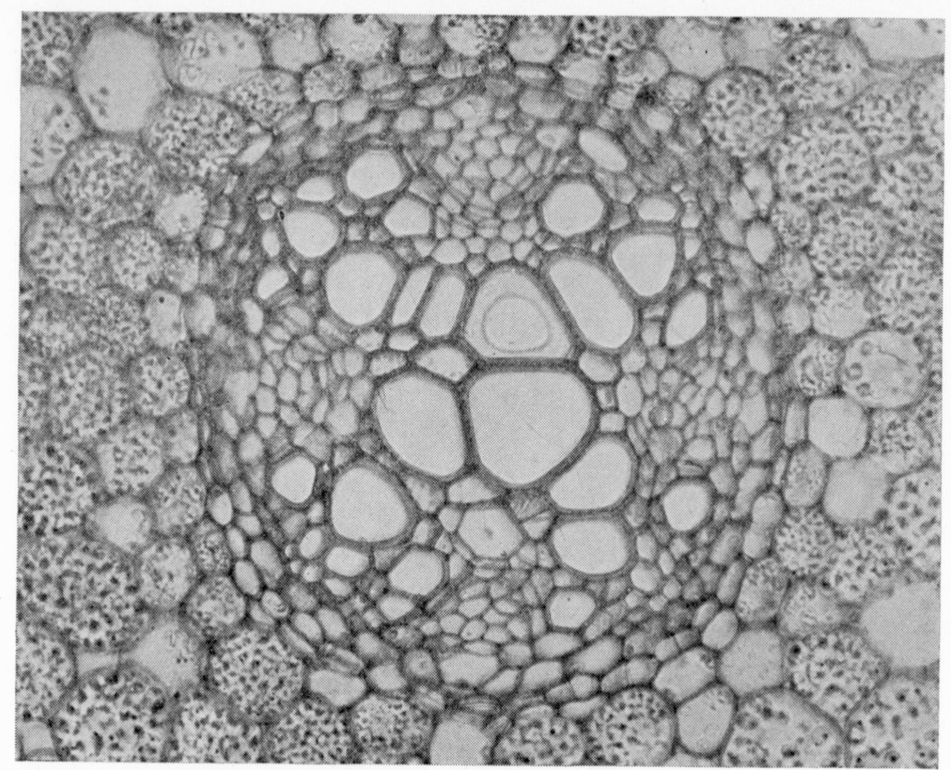

Figure 77 *T.s. root of* Ranunculus *showing vascular cylinder. Note 4-armed tetrarch xylem star surrounded by endodermis and pericycle, and the crescents of phloem between the xylem arms. The granules in the parenchyma of the cortex are starch grains.*

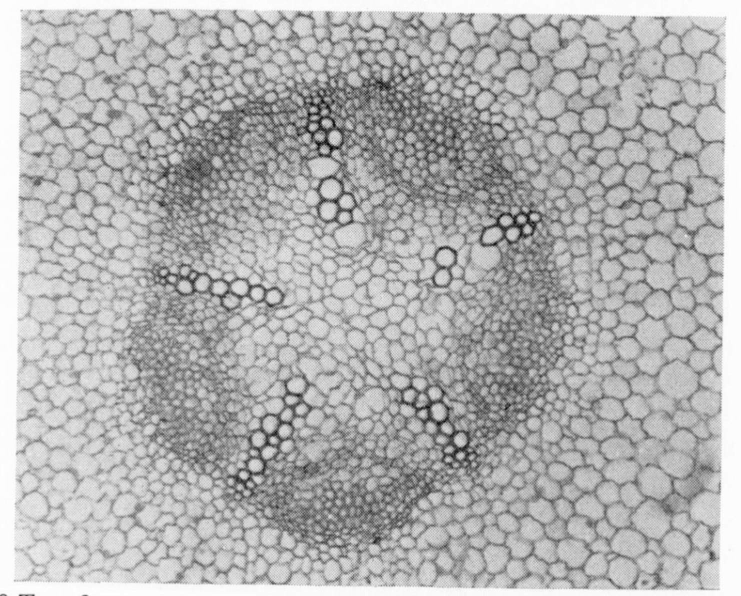

Figure 78 *T.s. of a young pentarch root of* Ranunculus *sp. showing maturation of metaxylem vessels towards the centre of the star the arms of which are tipped by small protoxylem vessels.*

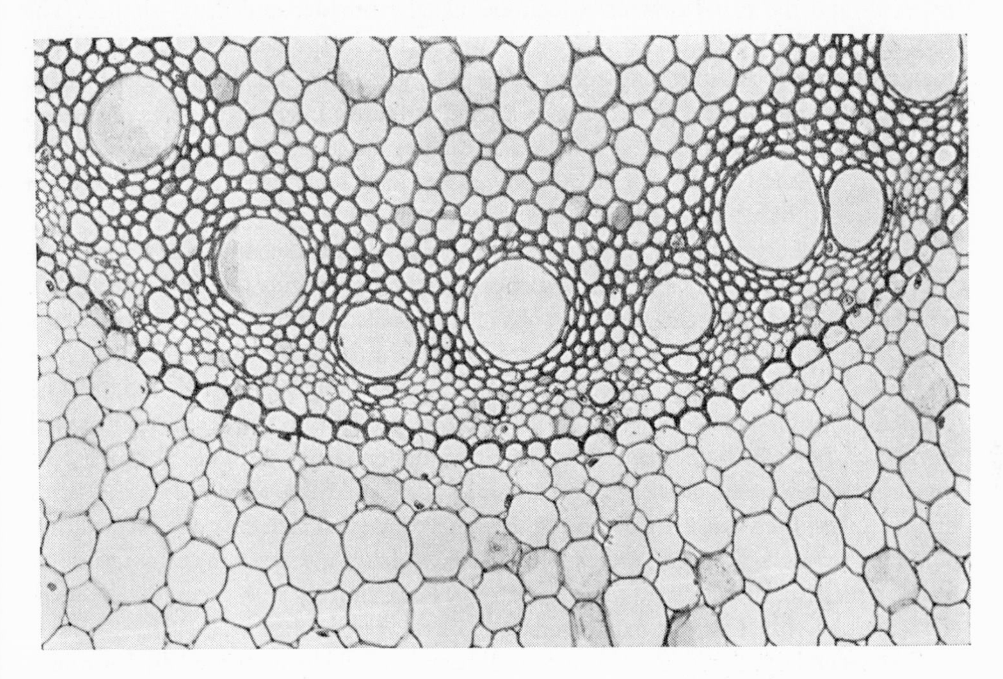

Figure 79 *T.s. of root of* Zea mais *showing part of the vascular cylinder bounded by the endodermis with its typically U-shaped thickenings. The large cells in the vascular cylinder are metaxylem vessels: above each are one, or at most two, protoxylem vessels.*

characteristic components, however, are the *tracheary elements* (so-called because they superficially resemble the trachea of animals), which are concerned with the conduction of water. Associated with these elements there may also occur living parenchyma cells, whose primary function is the storage and *translocation* (see Chapter 20) of food substances, and *sclerenchyma fibres* whose function is mainly supporting.

In its development in the root, the xylem makes its first appearance in the region of root-hair formation; the cells in the tips of the xylem star are the first to differentiate (fig. 78). For this reason these cells are called the *protoxylem*, meaning the first-formed xylem. The xylem formed later, towards the centre of the star, is of larger cells and is termed the *metaxylem*. In the region of the root where it is formed, elongation will normally be completed and the Casparian strips should be apparent in the endodermis.

The highly specialized tracheary elements of the xylem are mostly elongated cells which, as they mature, lose their living contents. In this process of maturation their walls become thickened in various ways by the deposition of lignin. Two distinctive types of tracheary elements occur in the xylem: the narrow, frequently *fusiform tracheids* and the *vessel elements* which are usually broader and drum-shaped. The fundamental difference between them, however, lies in the fact that the vessel elements become fused into long tubes and at the same time their end walls become perforated so that their watery contents are able to move freely through as in a series of pipes or tubes. It is for this reason that each series of such elements is termed a vessel. In tracheids on the other hand, the passage of water from cell to cell is through fine pores or pits which occur between adjacent elements.

Each vessel originates from a longitudinal series of meristematic cells which elongate and expand laterally and during the process become vacuolated (pp. 27 and 39). The first obvious change in the end walls of these cells leading to their perforation is that the middle lamella (see p. 36) seems to swell in the areas which are to become perforated, while other portions of the wall become thickened with lignin. The swollen parts of the primary wall then break down, probably as the result of some vital activity of the cell's living protoplast, leaving an open lattice of lignified wall across the ends of each vessel element. The protoplast dies and disappears and so the series of open tubes, the vessels, made up of these interconnected elements, are formed (fig. 80). These vessels, however, are usually of limited length, though in certain trees, as for example, ash, they are said to be up to 10 ft. long. In trees with exceptionally wide elements, individual vessels may extend almost their entire height.

The secondary, lignified walls of tracheids and vessel elements are laid down in a variety of ways, the particular manner depending not only on the species of plant in question but also on the stage in its development when the elements are forming. Generally a much more limited area of the primary wall becomes thickened in the first formed xylem elements than in those formed later. Thus in the protoxylem of the root, thickenings are deposited along the length of the earliest formed elements as a series of rings (*annular vessels*), in the next as spirals (*spiral vessels*) and later as

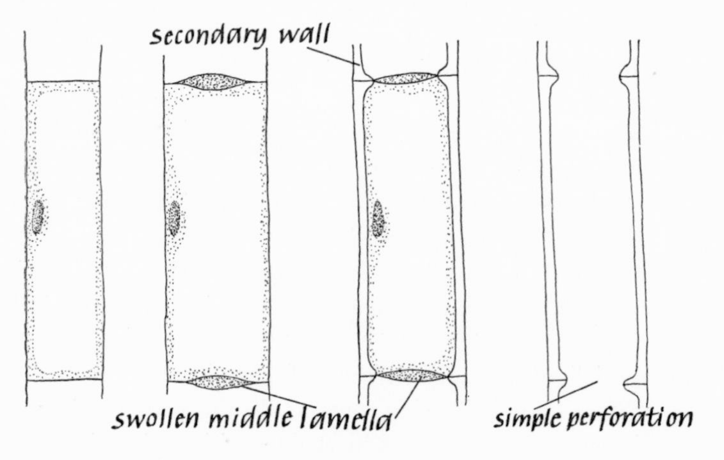

Figure 80 *Stages in the formation of a vessel* (*after Esau*).

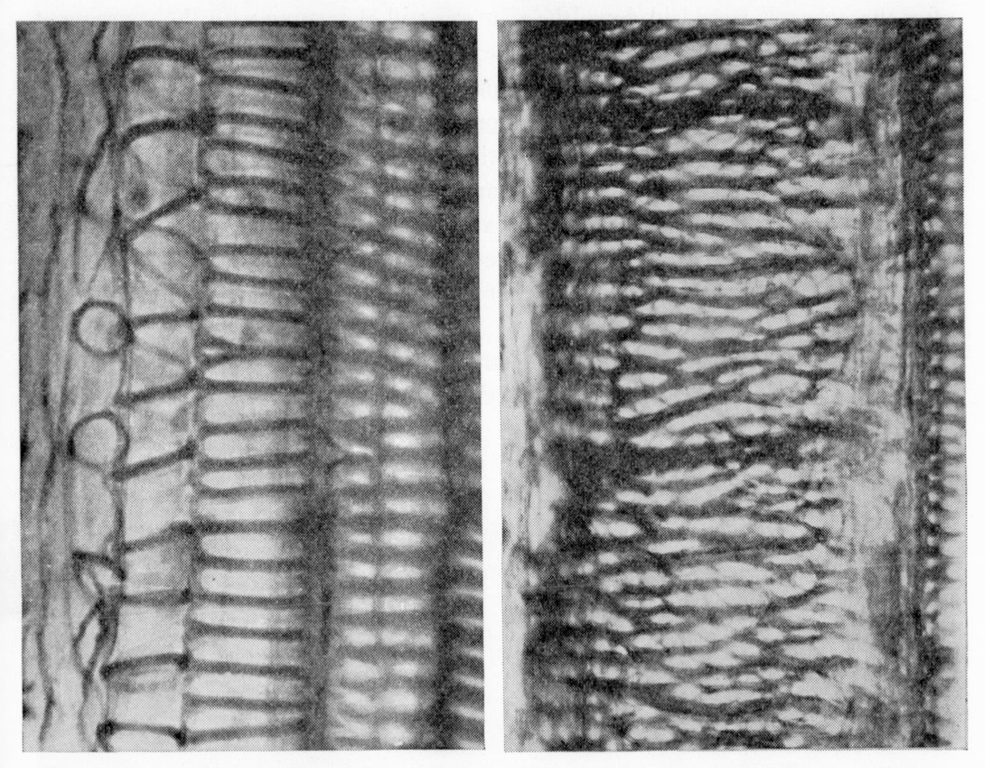

Figure 81 *L.s. of stem of* Helianthus *showing from right to left annular and spiral vessels of protoxylem and spiral and scalariform vessels of the metazylem. Note greater diameter of the later formed vessels.*

Figure 82 *Part of l.s. of stem of* Helianthus *showing a reticulately thickened vessel. The broader lines running across the vessel mark the limits of the individual elements of which it is composed.*

spirals in which the coils are interconnected, so that the thickening has a ladder-like, or *scalariform* appearance. Elements formed still later have their secondary walls even more extensively thickened as a net and are hence termed *reticulate* vessels (figs. 81 and 82). The most extensive type of thickening occurs in tracheary elements whose walls are perforated only by fine pores or *pits*. These pits are common in sclerenchyma fibres in tracheids and in the last of the xylem vessels to be formed in the primary body. This extensive type of thickening is also characteristic of all vessels in xylem laid down in the secondary body of the plant (see p. 124 *et seq.*).

In a radial longitudinal section of a dicotyledonous root, cut through the middle of one of the xylem arms, some of the different types of thickened vessels described above may be seen. Thus the protoxylem vessels adjacent to the pericycle have annular thickening, the rings of which are often widely separated. This indicates that after these vessels were laid down the root was still elongating with the consequent stretching of the unthickened walls of these cells. Some of the spiral vessels occurring next to it, towards the centre of the root, may be similarly stretched, though successively formed vessels of this type show a correspondingly closer arrangement of their spirals. The increasingly wider vessels of the metaxylem with their scalariform reticulate thickening or pits, differentiate towards the centre of the root. In monocotyledonous roots with their twelve to twenty xylem rays, usually only one large reticulately thickened metaxylem element is developed within each ray. Beyond these, towards the centre of the root is a core of thin-walled parenchymatous cells which constitute a *pith* (fig. 79).

Phloem Between each of the arms of the xylem star in the root a quite different type of conducting tissue, the *phloem*, develops, some of the elements of which may mature even before the protoxylem. The phloem is concerned with the downward

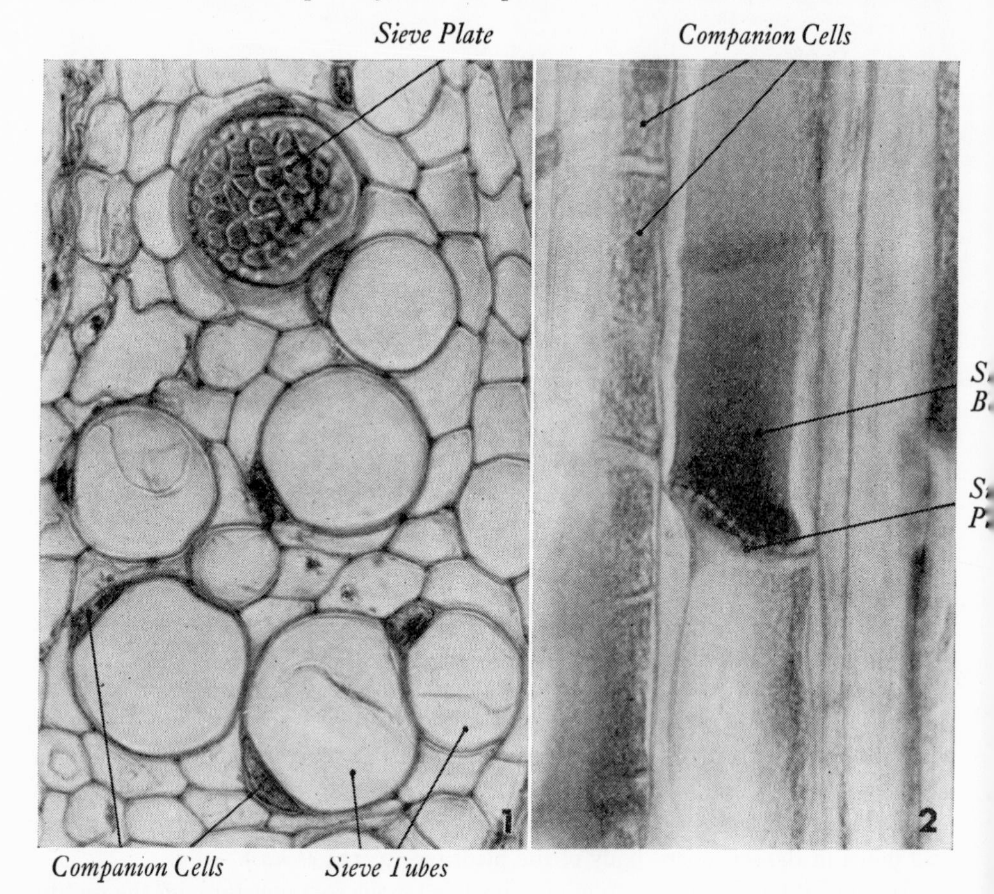

Figure 83 1 *T.s. of phloem, and,*
2 *L.s. of phloem of* Momordica cochinchinensis, *showing sieve tubes (one with sieve plates), sieve plate in surface view, and companion cells.*

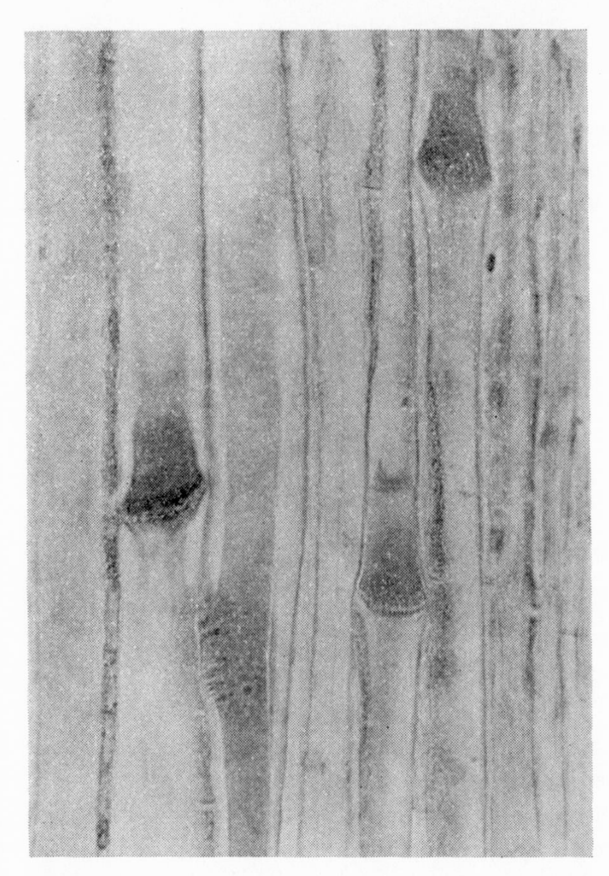

Figure 84 *Sieve tubes and companion cells in l.s. of the phloem of* Momordica cochinchinensis.

conduction of food materials and like the xylem consists of several types of elements. The most conspicuous and highly specialized of these are the *sieve tubes* which, like the xylem vessels, consist of longitudinal series of elongated cells placed end to end. Unlike xylem vessels the lateral walls are generally rather thin and unlignified. Their end walls, however, are specially thickened to form *sieve plates*, the most characteristic elements of the phloem. As their name implies, these are pitted structures (fig. 83). It is probable that the thin membranes closing these pits are ultimately absorbed so that each end wall becomes completely perforated and adjacent cells in the series are in more or less open communication with each other. Sometimes the whole end of the element forms the sieve plate, though often, in obliquely inclined end walls, there may be a number of perforate sieve areas, thus forming a *compound sieve plate*. Sieve areas may also form on the lateral walls of some sieve elements in certain plants.

The protoplast of the sieve element is unusual in that it loses its nucleus during the course of its maturation. Moreover, the sieve areas between adjoining cells are penetrated by connecting strands of cytoplasm, which in some plants may be extremely thin, though in others they may be several microns in diameter. Each protoplast, though *enucleate* (without a nucleus), exhibits certain vital characteristics, the most striking of which is the deposition of a substance, called *callose*, round each connecting strand of cytoplasm, so that it forms a pad across the sieve area (fig. 84). Under certain conditions, the callose, a carbohydrate staining with *aniline blue*, may disappear and then reappear. In old inactive sieve elements there is no callose and no connecting strands, so that the sieve areas are quite open, perforate discs. The sieve elements of dicotyledons also contain a rather viscous, proteinaceous substance termed the *slime* which seems to be derived in part from the contents of the vacuole (fig. 84).

Always intimately associated with each sieve tube, and in fact derived from them, are special parenchymatous cells, *companion cells*. One or more of these are formed early in the differentiation of each sieve element by longitudinal divisions of the latter. They are narrower and often shorter than the sieve members, with which they are interconnected by pores; unlike them, their protoplasts retain their nuclei (fig. 83). These cells, however, die when the sieve tubes cease to function. Other parenchymatous cells may also occur in the pholem; and in the primary vascular tissues of roots these occur as elongated cells running parallel with the sieve tubes.

Sclerenchyma fibres – mostly long cells with tapering ends – and lignified walls may also occur in the outermost parts of the phloem. These *phloem fibres* as they are termed, are comparatively rare in the phloem of primary roots.

Lateral Root Formation

The outward extension of the root system of the primary body is effected by the production of lateral roots. These, because of their internal or *endogenous* origins, break their way through the outer tissues of the primary root to its outside. They arise most commonly from cells in the pericycle, though in certain roots endodermal cells may initiate their development. However, whether originating in the pericycle or endodermis, they always arise in some fairly definite relation to the vascular tissues of the parent root. In fact their place of origin in most cases depends on the pattern of the xylem star. In diarch roots, laterals arise between the phloem and xylem; in those with triarch, tetrarch or pentarch roots they arise adjacent to the protoxylem ridges; in polyarch roots they develop opposite the phloem (fig. 85).

The first sign of lateral root formation is the division of several adjoining pericyclic (or in certain cases endodermal) cells *periclinally*, that is parallel to the outer surface of the parent root. Further divisions of these cells occur both in the same direction and at right angles to it, that is *anticlinally*. The resulting accumulation of cells forms a protrusion which, as it grows, penetrates the cortex and, as the cells divide and expand still further, eventually emerges at the root surface. The endodermis may in some cases keep pace with the developing lateral root by anticlinal divisions. Other cortical cells, however, are pushed aside and crushed as the new root tip advances towards the surface. During its advance the meristem of the lateral itself is laid down and this in turn gives rise to the root cap towards the outside, while internally the differentiation of the three main tissue systems of the new root – epidermal, cortical and vascular – becomes apparent. Later, the xylem and phloem differentiate within the vascular cylinder and soon become connected with the corresponding tissues of the parent root. The connection itself is effected by the differentiation of some of the pericyclic cells into xylem and phloem.

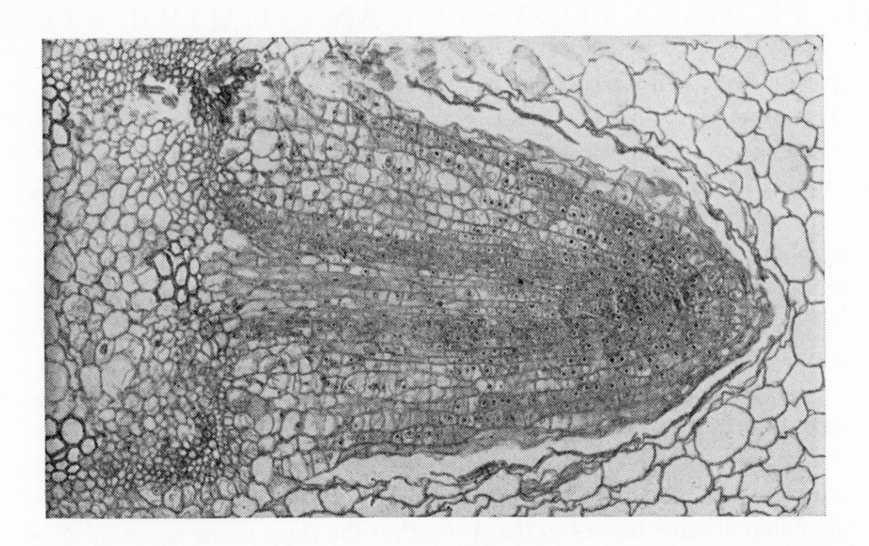

Figure 85 *Endogenous lateral root formation in* Pisum sativum. *Note that the lateral has arisen adjacent to a protoxylem ridge and that it is pushing its way through and crushing the cortical cells. The calyptra and main tissue regions of the lateral root can already be distinguished.*

CHAPTER 8

THE PRIMARY BODY : THE ANATOMY OF STEMS

The apical meristem of the shoot, as of the root, consists of certain cells which, since they are the source of all body cells, are termed *initials*. The first products resulting from the division of these cells are still capable of actively dividing. Their later vacuolation and consequent increase in size, however, and more especially changes in the rate and orientation of their divisions, soon foreshadow the highly organized primary body, with its tissues composed of variously differentiated cells. The apical meristem is therefore a complex of embryonic cells, with recognizable areas of differentiation, each of which will play its part in the organization of the mature shoot. This meristem is more elaborate than in the root since, in addition to initiating new stem tissue, it also has a part to play in the production of *leaf primordia*. These primordia are groups of cells from which all leaves have their beginnings. Moreover, the origins of *lateral branches*, which appear first as buds in the axils of the leaves, can be traced to the apical meristem. As in the root, however, the apical meristem merges gradually with the differentiating tissues so that beneath it the three tissue regions, *epidermal*, *cortical* and *vascular*, can be discerned (fig. 86).

In the simpler vascular plants, such as ferns and horse-tails (see Chapter 35), there is only one initial cell at the stem apex. In flowering plants, however, groups of apical initials occur, and two or more layers of these are usually present. The upper or surface layers divide at right angles to the meristem surface. Beneath these surface layers there are several more layers of initials whose cells divide in various planes. By such divisions this internal body, or *corpus* of cells, adds bulk to the apex; while the surface, covering layer, or *tunica* (the same word as 'tunic') keeps pace with this increasing bulk which it continues to cover. As the tunica and corpus go on forming new cells, those formed earlier begin to differentiate and eventually become part of the various tissue regions below the apical meristem.

Epidermis

The outermost layer of the tunica gives rise to the epidermis of the stem. As in the root, this consists of a single layer of cells like a skin, which cover the whole of the primary body. Early in its differentiation, the outer wall of the epidermis usually thickens, and becomes covered with a wax-like material called *cutin*, which restricts water-loss from the surface of the plant. As well as limiting water-loss, however, cutin also hinders the exchange of gases between the inner regions of the plant, and the air. This exchange is essential for respiration and photosynthesis. On the other hand, respiration is assisted by the fact that the epidermis of all parts of the shoot, and of

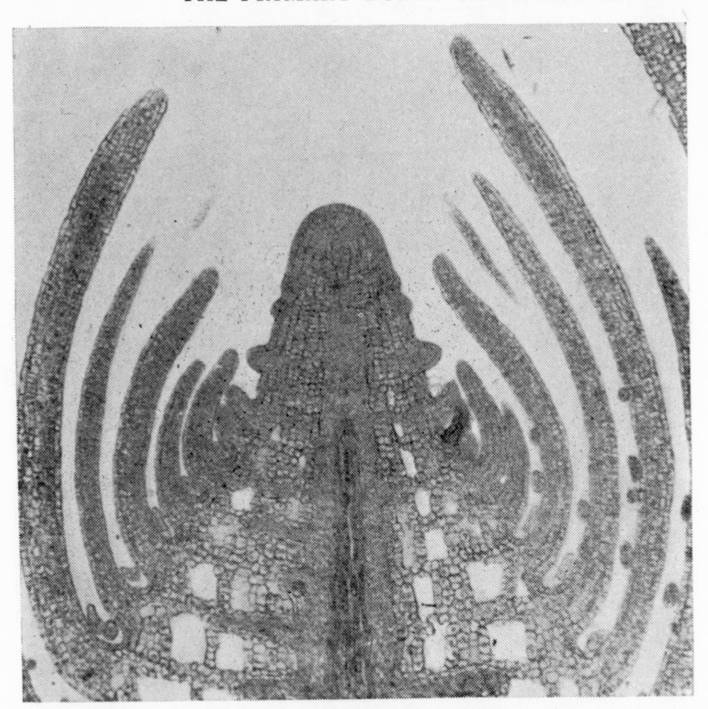

Figure 86 *L.s. of stem apex of* Hippurus *showing leaf and bud primordia. Epidermal, cortical and vascular tissue regions can be distinguished.*

the leaves in particular, is perforated at intervals over its surfaces by a system of pores which communicate with the internal tissues. The aperture size of these pores, which are called *stomata*, is regulated by pairs of specialized epidermal cells, the *guard cells*. Their detailed structure will be considered in a later section dealing with the anatomy of leaves (Chapter 9). The unspecialized cells of the epidermis in the stem are most often tubular in shape. As the stem lengthens these cells become elongated, with their longitudinal axes parallel to the long axis of the stem (see fig. 15b.2).

Cortex

The cortex of the primary stem is usually composed of parenchyma and its cells very often contain chloroplasts. In older parts of the stem, however, several of the outer layers of the cortex may have cell walls thickened with cellulose, especially in the angles. Cells of this type are named *collenchyma*. These cells, which can be thought of as a type of parenchyma structurally specialized for support, are elongated living cells. They are usually longer and narrower than the adjacent parenchyma, though they intergrade with it. Collenchyma is the typical supporting tissue of growing organs, and its peculiarities of growth and structure permit the changes which accompany increases in length to be made, without loss of strength. These cells

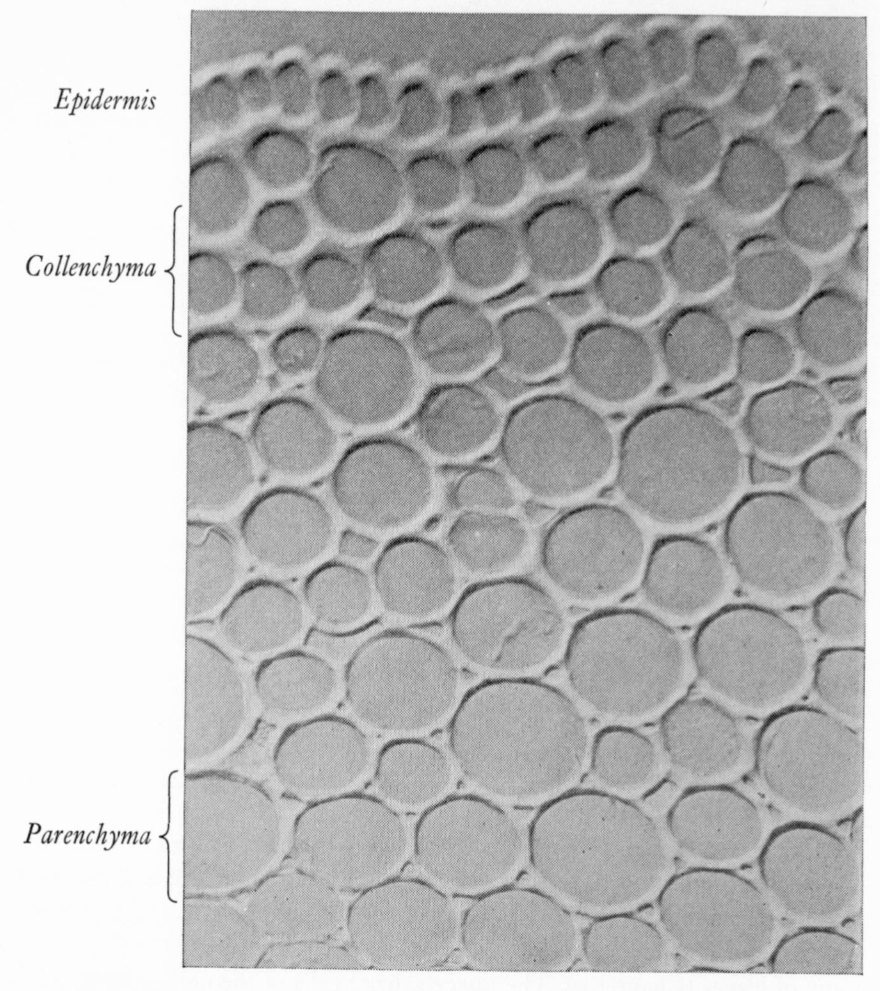

Figure 87 *Collenchyma grading into parenchyma in a t.s. of stem of* Mercurialis perennis (*unstained material*).

combine tensile strength with flexibility and plasticity (fig. 87). Typically, the boundary of the cortex and vascular cylinder is not so pronounced in the stem as in the root. Instead of an endodermis with well defined wall characters, the innermost layer of cortical cells often contain abundant starch grains so that the boundary is often a *starch sheath*. Only in a comparatively small number of plants is there a development of Casparian strips in the innermost layer of cortical cells of the stem.

Vascular Cylinder

The vascular tissues which in dicotyledonous stems form the inner boundary with the cortex, are arranged, not as an unbroken cylinder, but as separate groups or *vascular bundles* of closely associated xylem and phloem. The ground tissues between these bundles are of parenchyma. These *interfascicular regions*, as they are termed, may in some stems be only a few cells wide, so that the vascular tissues in fact appear to form a perfect cylinder. In many other cases they are broad, quite conspicuous bands, many cells in width. However, whether broad or narrow, these strips of parenchyma are called *pith rays* or *medullary rays*, since they connect the ground tissue of the cortex with the pith or *medulla*, a group of parenchymatous cells which occurs in the middle of the ring of bundles (fig. 88).

The pith, is in fact the innermost part of the ground tissue, and it contains smaller parenchymatous cells on the outside and larger ones, with prominent intercellular spaces, towards the centre. In some stems the pith forms a very conspicuous region, in others the central portion is destroyed during growth, with the result that there remains a central hollow cylindrical cavity.

Most commonly, the vascular bundles in dicotyledonous stems have their xylem and phloem arranged side by side (*collaterally*), with the phloem outside xylem (fig. 89). In certain dicotyledonous plants (members of the Cucurbitaceae for example) phloem occurs both to the outside and inside of the xylem. Bundles with internal and external phloem are termed *bicollateral* (fig. 90). More rarely there may be a concentric

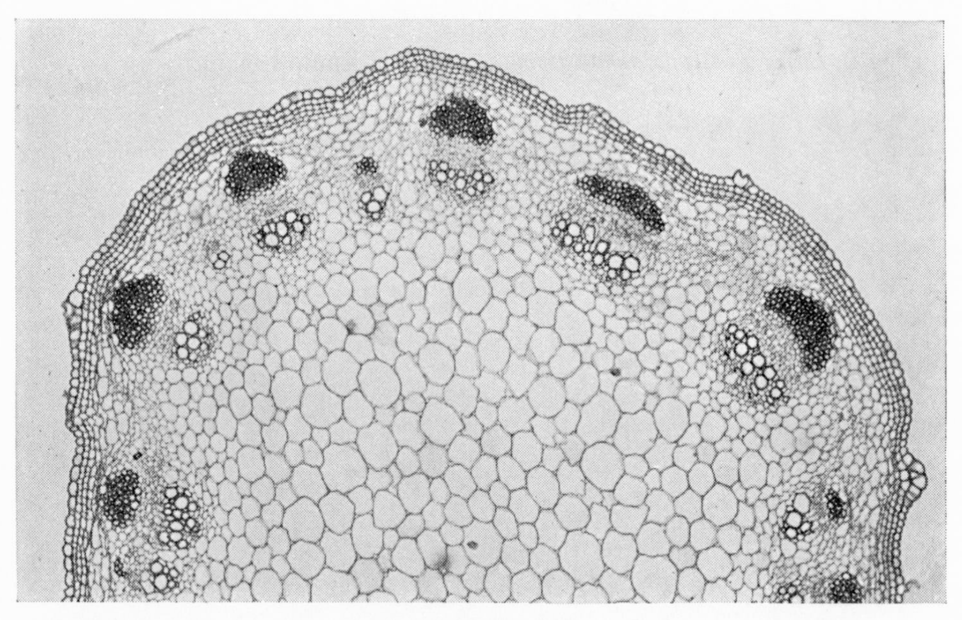

Figure 88 *Part of a t.s. of stem of* Helianthus annuus *showing ring of separate vascular bundles each capped by a group of sclerenchyma fibres (small dark cells). Between these and the xylem, with its conspicuous vessels, is situated the phloem. The centre of the stem is occupied by a large pith of parenchyma.*

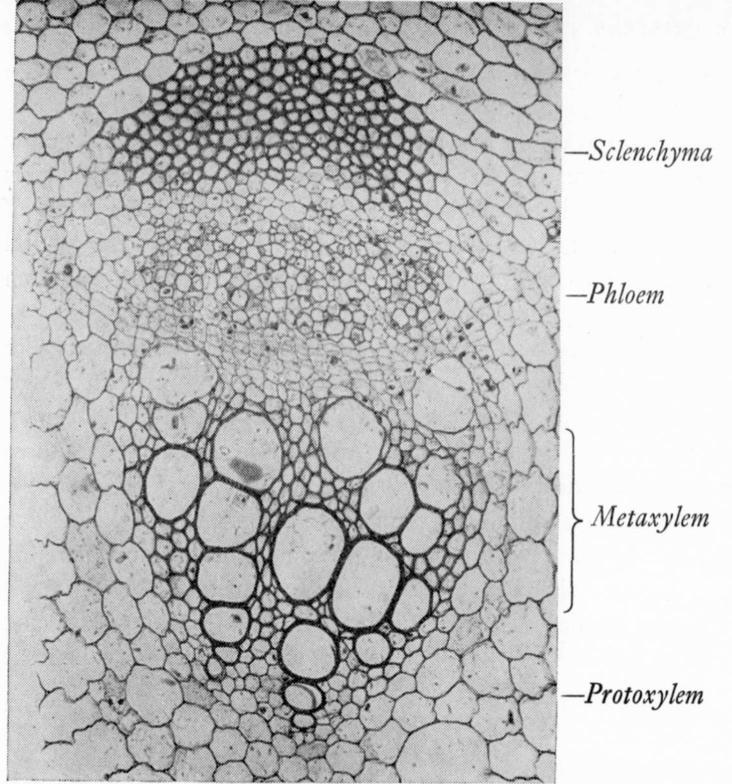

Figure 89 *T.s. of a vascular bundle from the stem of* Helianthus annuus.

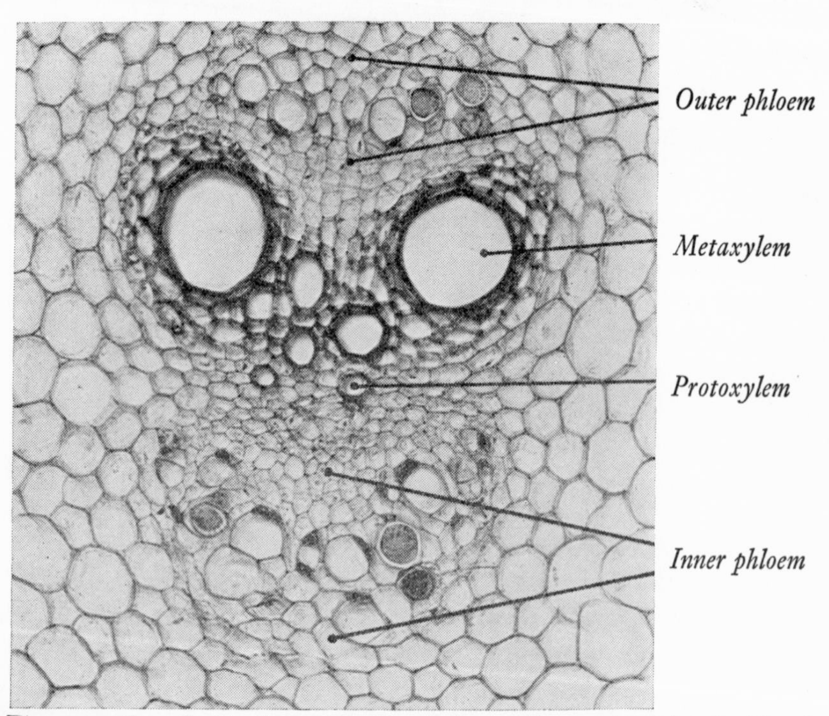

Figure 90 *T.s. of a bicollateral bundle of* Momordica cochinchinesis. *Note inner and outer phloem.*

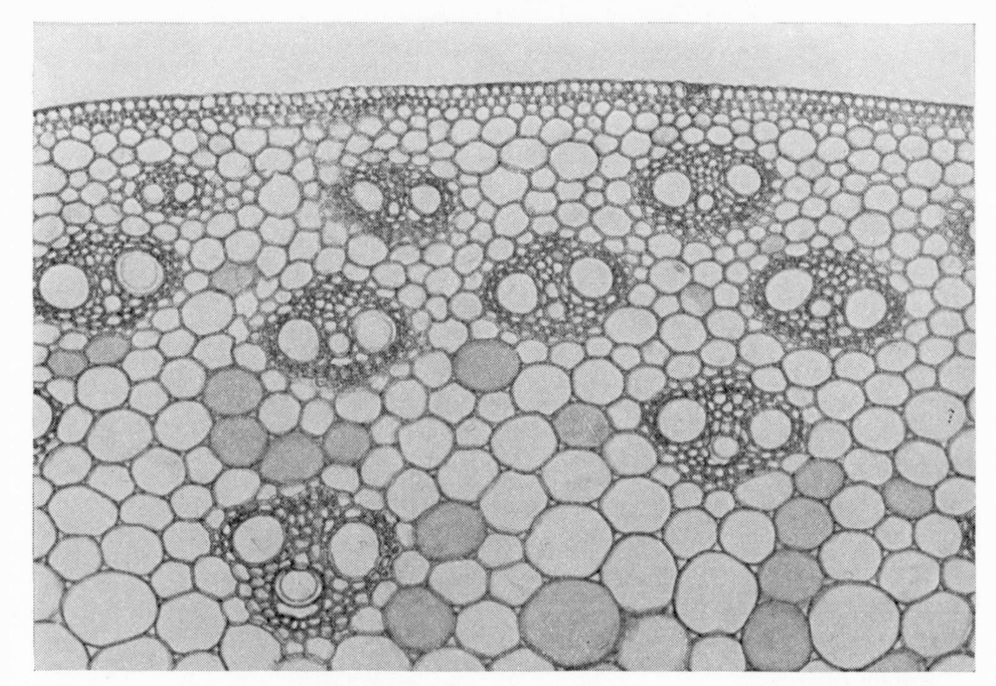

Figure 91 *Part of a t.s. of the stem of* Zea mais *showing the scattered vascular bundles.*

arrangement of the vascular tissues with the phloem completely surrounding the xylem, or the xylem the phloem. In monocotyledonous stems the division of the ground tissue into cortex and pith is less obvious, and often non-existent. Transverse sections of such stems show the bundles not in a single ring or intersected cylinder, but scattered throughout the section. Hence there are no medullary rays (fig. 91).

In different plants the constituent elements of the xylem in the vascular bundles vary in arrangement and differ in proportion. The first-formed xylem, the protoxylem – in contrast to the situation in the root – is found on the inside of each bundle which in a longitudinal section of a typical dicotyledonous stem will be seen to consist, as in a root, of vessels with *annular* and *spiral thickenings*. These may show clear signs of having been drawn out while the young stem has still been increasing in length. Wider metaxylem vessels with *reticulate*, or *scalariform thickening*, and then pitted vessels, are produced towards the outside of each bundle (figs. 81 and 82).

The phloem which is adjacent to and lying outside the last formed of these elements, consists, as in the root, of sieve tubes and their associated companion cells, and with these elements there is also phloem parenchyma. The phloem fibres often form a cap at the outer limits of this tissue. Indeed the presence of these groups of strengthening cells helps to mark the limits of the phloem, for, unlike the root, there is usually no layer of pericyclic or endodermal cells bounding the vascular cylinder in the stem and thereby separating it from the cortex (fig. 88). In the stems of

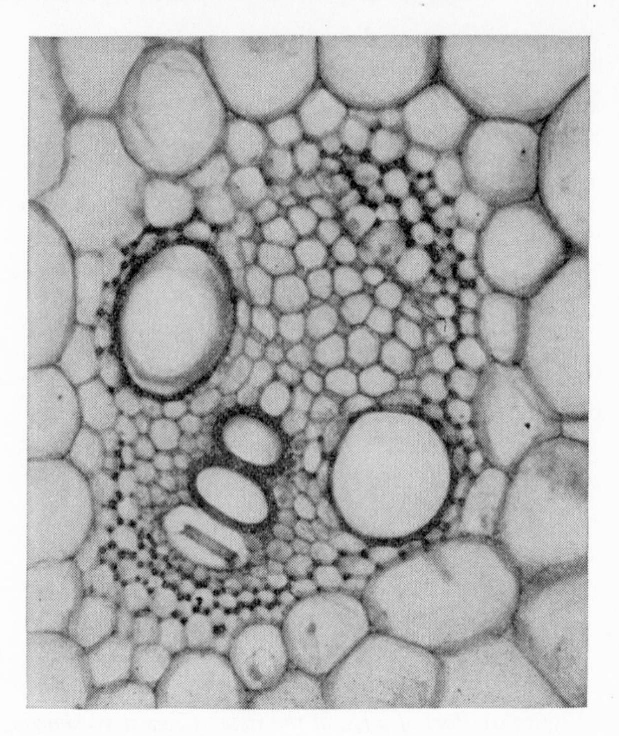

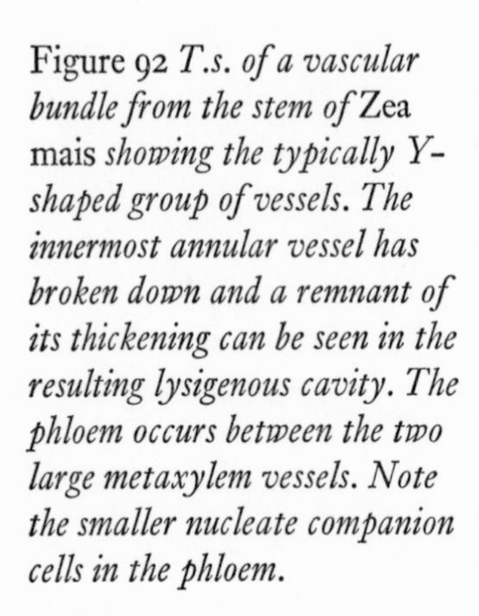

Figure 92 *T.s. of a vascular bundle from the stem of* Zea mais *showing the typically Y-shaped group of vessels. The innermost annular vessel has broken down and a remnant of its thickening can be seen in the resulting lysigenous cavity. The phloem occurs between the two large metaxylem vessels. Note the smaller nucleate companion cells in the phloem.*

some dicotyledons these fibres may form a continuous or almost continuous ring round the vascular cylinder.

In monocotyledonous stems the scattered bundles are collateral, but of a rather special type. In transverse sections the xylem appears as a short V- or Y-shaped group of vessels, with the protoxylem at the base and directed towards the centre of the stem. One or two extremely large metaxylem vessels constitute each of the arms flanking the phloem which occurs between them. In the maize stem for example there are only two pitted metaxylem vessels, on each side of the phloem. Below these are one or two spiral or annular protoxylem vessels associated with xylem parenchyma. The innermost (first formed) annular vessel commonly shows signs of having broken down as a result of very rapid elongation of the stem during early development. This breakdown leaves a so-called *lysigenous cavity*. Each of these scattered bundles in the older, mature regions of the monocotyledonous stem becomes surrounded by a protective sheath of sclerenchyma (fig. 92).

Transition from Root to Stem

The foregoing examination of the structure of the primary root and stem in dicotyledons and monocotyledons has shown that these regions of the axis have marked anatomical differences, especially in regard to the arrangement of their vascular tissues. In a typical dicotyledonous stem, the xylem and phloem, for example, occur collaterally in bundles arranged in a ring round a central parenchymatous pith; whereas in the root, these tissues are radially alternate in their arrangement, with a group of phloem occuring between ridges or xylem which exists either as a central wedge or as a star.

The change from the one arrangement to the other takes place in a portion of the axis termed the *transition zone*, which is usually at soil level. This region, commonly quite short, may in some cases be only a few millimetres long. Externally, this part of the axis may show a change in thickness; internally, there is usually a lateral and outward displacement of the tissues, which correspondingly increases the diameter of the vascular cylinder. Accompanying this, between root and stem, there may be a twisting and inversion coupled with a multiplication or a joining of strands, so that the number of protoxylem groups in a given root and stem do not necessarily correspond. Such splitting, twisting and fusion of the vascular strands can be followed in a series of transverse sections taken at successive levels within the transition zone.

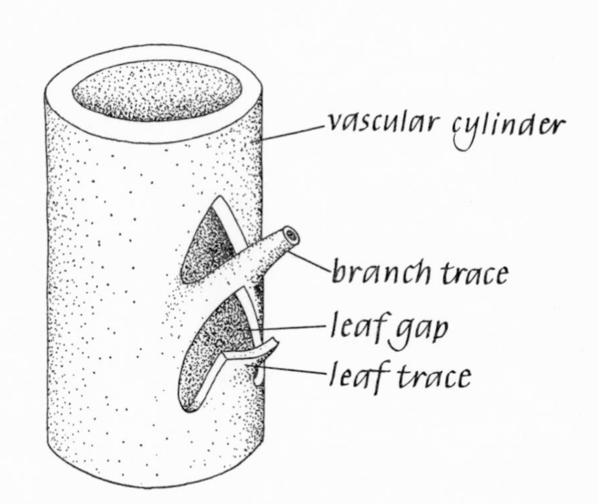

Figure 93 *Diagrammatic representation of a vascular cylinder with a branch and leaf trace.*

Leaf and Branch Traces and their Associated Gaps

Because of the structural continuity between leaves and the stems on which they are borne, there is an intimate connection between their respective vascular systems, which can be observed in transverse sections of the stem at each node. In these regions one or more strands of vascular tissue pass outwards through the cortex into the leaf. The presence of these strands makes the nodal anatomy more complex than that described above for the internodal regions of the stem (fig. 93).

Each of these strands, traced downwards through successive levels in the stem beneath the point where a leaf is attached, may be found to occur as an independent strand or bundle, joined to the vascular tissues of the stem and passing through one or more nodes and internodes below. Such a bundle, extending from the base of the leaf to its junction with the vascular system of the stem, consists of xylem and phloem, and is termed a *leaf trace*. A leaf trace may therefore be defined as a vascular bundle located in the stem, but directly related to a leaf and representing the lower part of the vascular supply to that leaf. The number of traces supplying the leaves of different species range from one to many, though it tends to be constant for any given species of plant. Within the petiole, or the leaf base – though in these regions the bundles can no longer be termed *traces* – they may, depending on the species, either fuse or divide.

In monocotyledons, many vascular strands supply each parallel-veined, alternately-arranged leaf, whose base encircles the stem. Thus numerous traces enter the leaf from every side; those supplying a given leaf are in many cases of two distinct sizes. Large traces occur towards the outside of the axis in their lower course but higher up approach the centre whence they diverge outwards rather acutely as they pass into the leaves. Smaller traces tend to remain round the periphery of the stem. In consequence, the bundles or traces from successive leaves, when examined in transverse sections, appear irregularly scattered through the stem but tend to be most frequent and smaller towards the outside.

Like leaves, in whose axils they develop, branches, also, have intimate connections with the vascular system of the main axis. In dicotyledons two strands or *branch traces* usually arise (but sometimes there is only one) just above the leaf with which they are associated, and connect its vascular system to that of the main stem. The two traces which supply a branch, unite within a short distance to form a complete cylinder. Branch traces may form a conspicuous part of the primary vascular cylinder of the main axis.

The point in the stem from which a leaf or a branch-trace begins its outward passage is marked by an interruption in the vascular system. These nodal regions are termed *leaf* and *branch gaps* and are formed of parenchyma. In transverse section each gap looks much like an interfascicular area between which cortex and pith become continuous. The gaps, however, do not constitute permanent breaks in the continuity of the axial vascular supply, for lateral connection of these tissues occur round the gaps both above and below them.

CHAPTER 9

THE PRIMARY BODY : THE ANATOMY OF LEAVES

Leaves are organs of limited growth, and in this respect are unlike both root and stem. As a leaf begins to grow and unfold within its bud, all its cells, like those in the embryo of a germinating seed, are meristematic and capable of division. During the process of unfolding, the cells divide actively, and enlarge. The third phase of growth follows when they differentiate, to form the various tissues which will fulfil the leaf's main function: photosynthesis. By the time the leaf is fully expanded every cell has thus passed through the three phases of growth – division, enlargement and differentiation – so that all form part of the leaf's permanent tissue.

Leaf formation begins, at various points down the sides of the apical meristem, with the division of small groups of cells which lie parallel to the surface. Each group forms a lateral prominence on the side of the apex (and constitutes the *leaf base*). Since leaves are borne on the axis in a well-defined order and with great regularity, the prominences which herald their appearance are positioned with a definite relationship one to another. From these simple prominences the leaf eventually develops, in all its complexity, as a photosynthetic organ. No matter what its final shape or form may be, every leaf contains the three basic tissue systems present in the primary root or stem, though of course these are considerably modified. Thus the epidermal system protects the highly specialized and very prominent ground tissue or *mesophyll* which constitutes the bulk of the leaf, and this in turn is permeated by the vascular system, with its profusely ramifying veins.

Epidermis

The leaf epidermis is most commonly one cell thick, and its most characteristic features are the *stomata*. These regulatory pores are generally restricted to, or at least most frequent on, the lower surface. They are disposed with some regularity amongst the adjoining, compactly arranged, epidermal cells, which in surface view appear polyhedral, fitting together like the pieces of a jigsaw puzzle (figs. 94 and 95). As in the stem, the epidermis protects from water-loss the tissues internal to it, as well as providing some mechanical support. The outer epidermal cell walls are frequently cutinized, though the thickness of this protective layer seems to depend on environmental conditions. The epidermal cells of plants grown in fairly moist habitats, for example, have thinner cutinous layers than those of the same species from very dry habitats, which may even have thick, lignified walls.

The stomatal apertures, which provide the very necessary paths of gaseous exchange between the internal tissues of the leaf blade and the atmosphere, are each

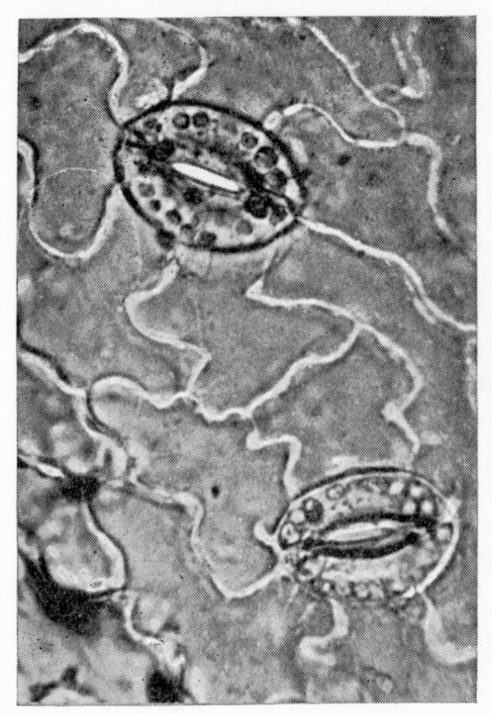

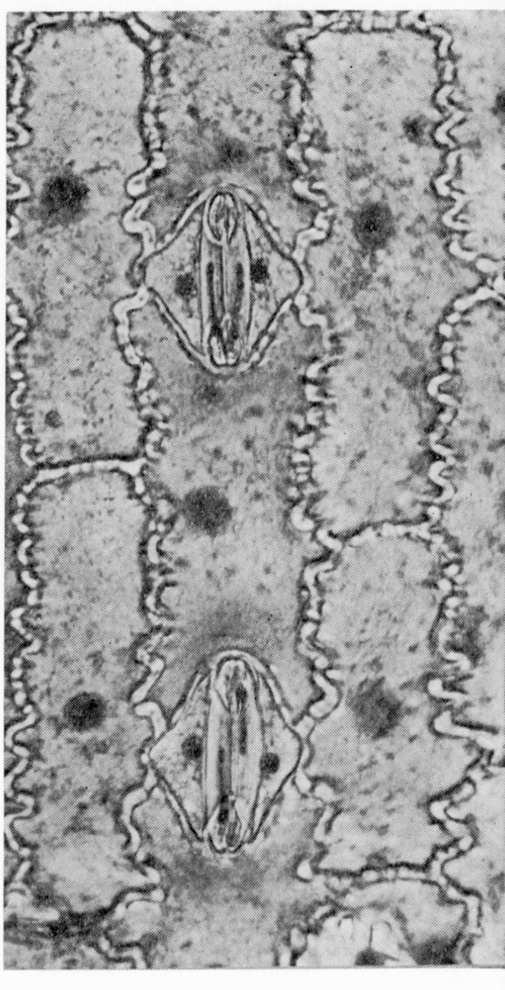

Figure 94 *Polygonal epidermal cells and stomata from lower surface of leaf of* Saxifraga stolonifera. *Note that the chloroplasts are restricted to the guard cells of the stomata.*

Figure 95 *Epidermal cells and stomato of leaf of* Zea mais.

bounded by two specialized epidermal cells. Changes in the shape of these *guard cells* bring about the opening and closing of the apertures. Each stomatal unit, or *stoma*, comprises the pore and its two guard cells, and may be surrounded by cells differing little from other epidermal cells (fig. 96). In many plants, however, each stoma is bounded by somewhat smaller but distinctive *subsidiary epidermal cells* (fig. 97). In dicotyledonous plants there are four different types of subsidiary cells. These are: the irregular-celled type in which several unmodified cells surround each stoma; the unequal-celled type, with three subsidiary cells, one distinctly smaller than the other two; the parallel-celled type with one or more cells flanking each side of the stoma and parallel to its long 'axis'; finally the cross-celled type with a pair of subsidiary cells whose common walls are at right angles to the long axis of the guard cells.

When viewed from above, guard cells are most commonly crescent-shaped, but

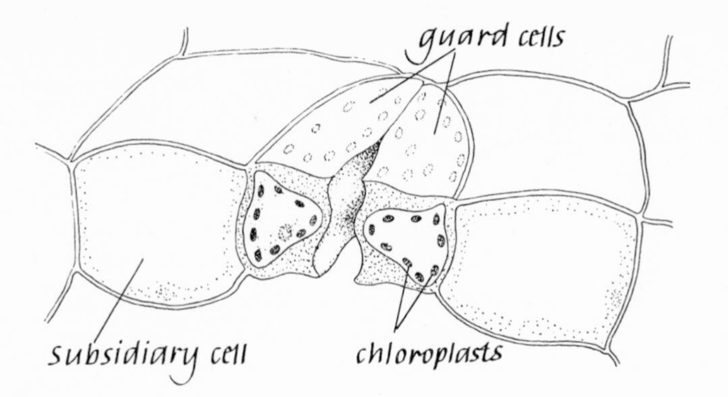

Figure 96 *Diagram of a stoma*

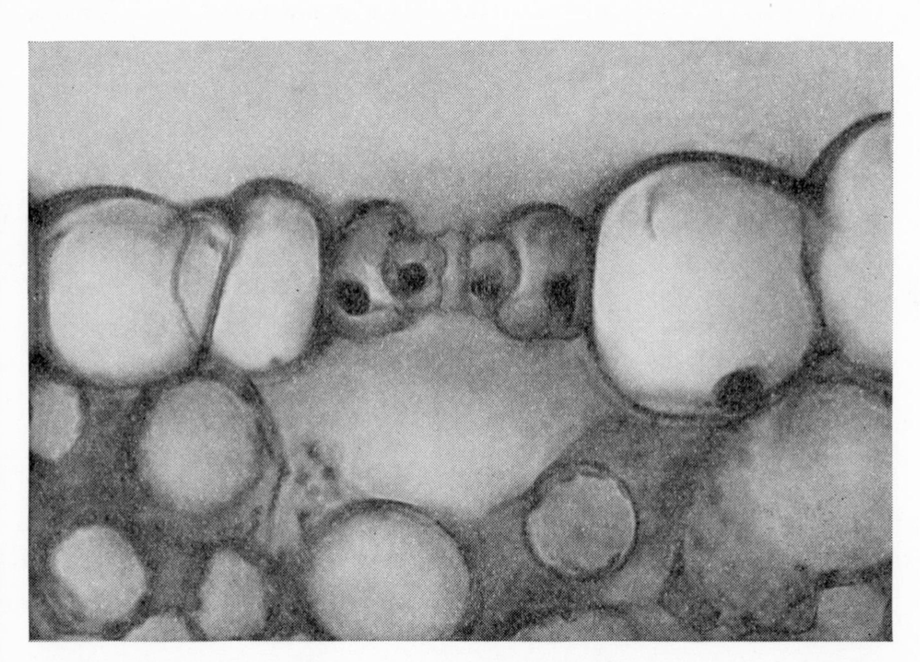

Figure 97 *Stoma in t.s. of leaf of* Tradescantia virginiana. *Note guard cells with closing flaps and subsidiary cells; also sub-stomatal chamber.* (*Photomicrograph from slide prepared by Dr R. F. Lyndon.*)

when sectioned midway across the narrow axis of the stoma, they can be seen to have unevenly thickened walls, a feature which plays an important part in their opening and closing (see p. 217). In addition many stomata may be found with wedges of wall material protruding, externally over the *stomatal pore*, and in some cases, internally, over the *sub-stomatal chamber* beneath (fig. 97).

In many plants, certain of the epidermal cells of leaves (as in the young parts of the root, and commonly, of the stem also) grow outwards to a considerable length. Such cellular outgrowths are *hairs* whose main function would seem to be to provide protection. This protection may be against water-loss (see p. 176), against excessively high light intensities – as in the case of many alpine plants whose leaves appear to have a silvery covering – or against animals. Examples of the last are the tough pointed hairs of thistles (*Cirsium* spp.) or the stinging hairs of the nettle (fig. 98). Not all hairs, however, are simple extensions of epidermal cells, for many are multicellular and may be variously branched or star-shaped. Some leaves have glandular hairs whose specialized cells in certain cases secrete pleasant smelling essential oils; as for example mint, lavender (*Lavandula vera*) and the garden geranium *Pelargonium* (fig. 99).

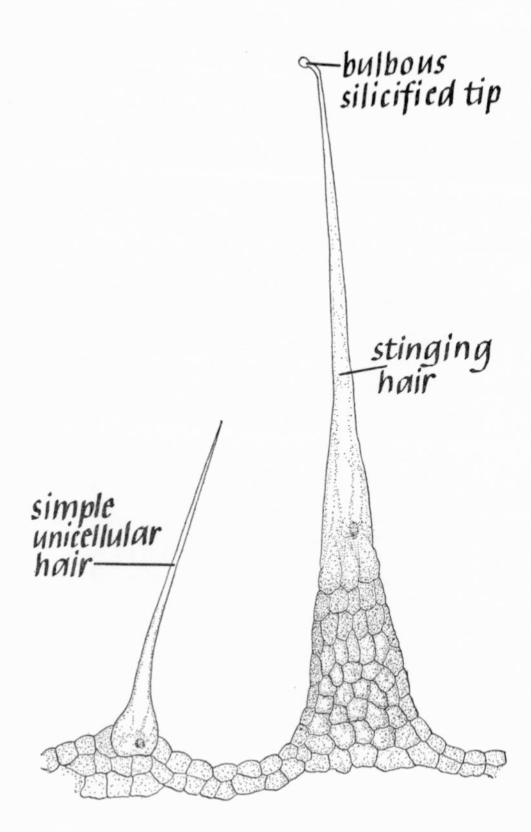

Figure 98 *Stinging hairs from the leaf of nettle* (Urtica dioica)

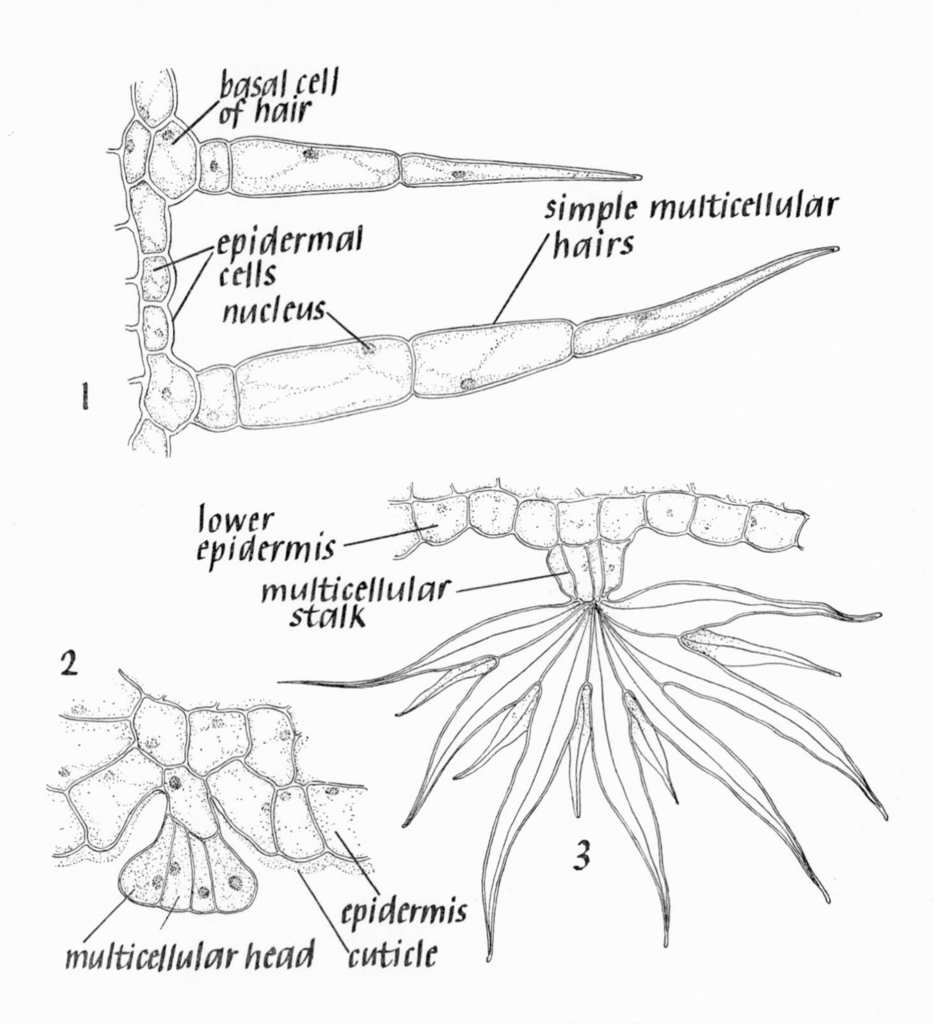

Figure 99 *Modification of epidermal cells as hairs and glands*

1 *Simple multicellular hairs from* Cucurbita *sp.*

2 *Gland cells from lower epidermis of leaf of* Ligustrum japonicum.

3 *Multicellular hair from leaf of* Hippophae rhamnoides.

Mesophyll

The ground tissue, or *mesophyll*, of the lamina is bounded on each side by the epidermis, and is specialized as photosynthetic tissue. Basically it is parenchymatous with many large intercellular spaces between some of its cells, and the cells contain many chloroplasts. In dicotyledons, the mesophyll is typically differentiated into two types of parenchyma, the *palisade tissue*, so-called because its elongated cells are arranged in one or two regular rows like a fence, and the *spongy parenchyma*, so-called on account of its conspicuously open texture which provides a system of intercellular spaces. The palisade layer is usually found immediately beneath the upper epidermis, and in the transverse section of a typical dicotyledonous leaf the long axes of these cells can be seen orientated at right angles to the leaf surface. In some leaves there is more than one layer of palisade cells, while in others such cells occur beneath both upper and lower epidermis. The leaves of many monocotyledons stand erect, and have no palisade layer; in its place the mesophyll is made up of small rounded cells (figs. 100 and 101).

The spongy parenchyma of the mesophyll of the majority of dicotyledonous leaves shows a much greater variety of cell shapes than the palisade layer, in contrast to which it has a predominantly horizontal continuity, the connections between adjoining cells being mostly parallel to the leaf surface. Stomata open into the inter-

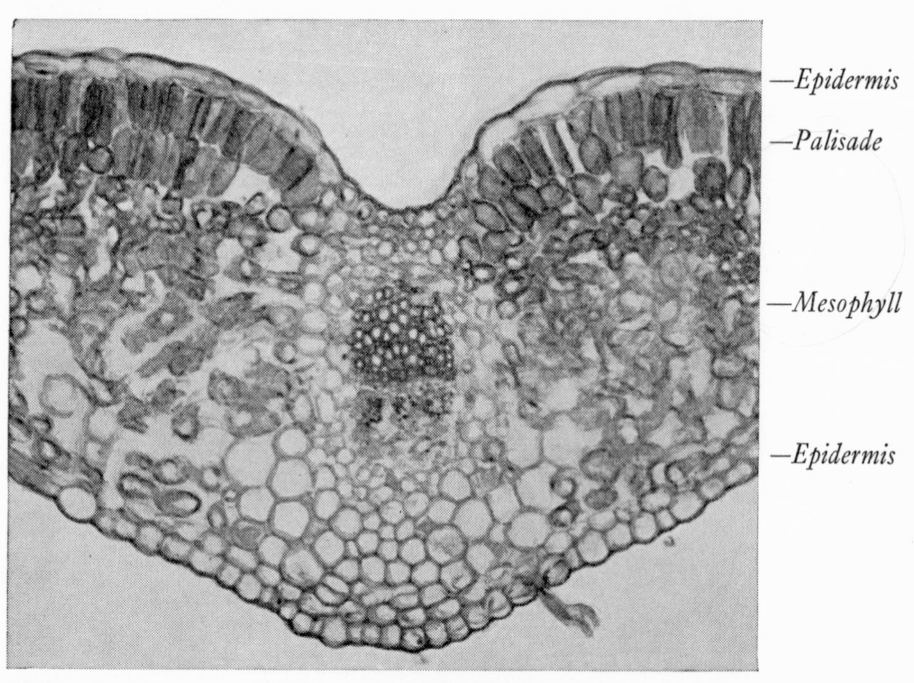

Figure 100 *T.s. leaf of* Helleborus *sp. in region of mid-rib showing, from top to bottom, the upper epidermis, palisade layer, spongy mesophyll, and lower epidermis.*

cellular spaces permeating this tissue, and each such space, adjoining a stoma, is consequently termed a sub-stomatal chamber. The extremely open arrangement of the spongy mesophyll, with its large surface area, is associated with the interchange of gases between the leaf cells and the internal air in the leaf tissue. The mesophyll, moreover, has a close relationship with the vascular tissues of the leaf, which form a ramifying but interconnected conducting system between the palisade and spongy parenchyma.

Vascular Supply – Petiole

In *petiolar leaves*, the conducting tissues of the vascular supply traverse the leaf stalk to the lamina as bundles whose constitution, and that of the tissues adjoining them, is comparable with the primary tissues of the stem. Thus there is an epidermis with comparatively few stomata, and a parenchymatous cortex containing chloroplasts which in part may become differentiated as collenchymatous or sclerenchymatous supporting tissue. As in the stem, the *petiolar bundles* may be collateral or bicollateral, and when seen in transverse section may form a broken ring, similar to those of the stem, though in some leaves there may be additional bundles both within and outside this ring. Frequently, however, the vascular tissues of the petiole are represented by a single bundle which in transverse section appears as a crescent; its concave surface, in which the xylem is contained, is uppermost, and the phloem below.

Vascular Supply – Veins

The largest bundles in the lamina occur in the midrib, and contain amounts of vascular tissue comparable with the petioles which bear them and with which they are continuous. All the bundles of the lamina are surrounded by parenchyma containing only a few chloroplasts, so that the tissue associated with these larger veins rises above the general surface of the leaf, usually on the lower side. This gives the leaf its typically ribbed appearance. Some rigidity is frequently given to these ribs by collenchyma which occurs beneath the epidermis on one, or sometimes both, sides of the vein. Even the small bundles embedded in the mesophyll are enclosed within sheaths of compactly arranged parenchyma. These *bundle sheaths* extend to the very ends of the bundles, so that no part of the vascular tissue is exposed to the air of the intercellular spaces of the mesophyll (fig. 101).

The lateral veins which diverge from the main veins usually consist of small strands of xylem and phloem, and these tissues gradually diminish in amount towards the extreme ramifications of the veins. Frequently the very ends of the veins comprise xylem only. Moreover, although vessels occur in the xylem of the larger veins, and sieve tubes occur in the phloem, towards their ends, the xylem elements are represented merely by tracheids and the phloem only by parenchyma. At the bundle extremities where the veins end, these may be reduced to a single tracheid with close annular or spiral thickenings (fig. 102).

The principal veins in monocotyledonous leaves contain bundles in the form of a

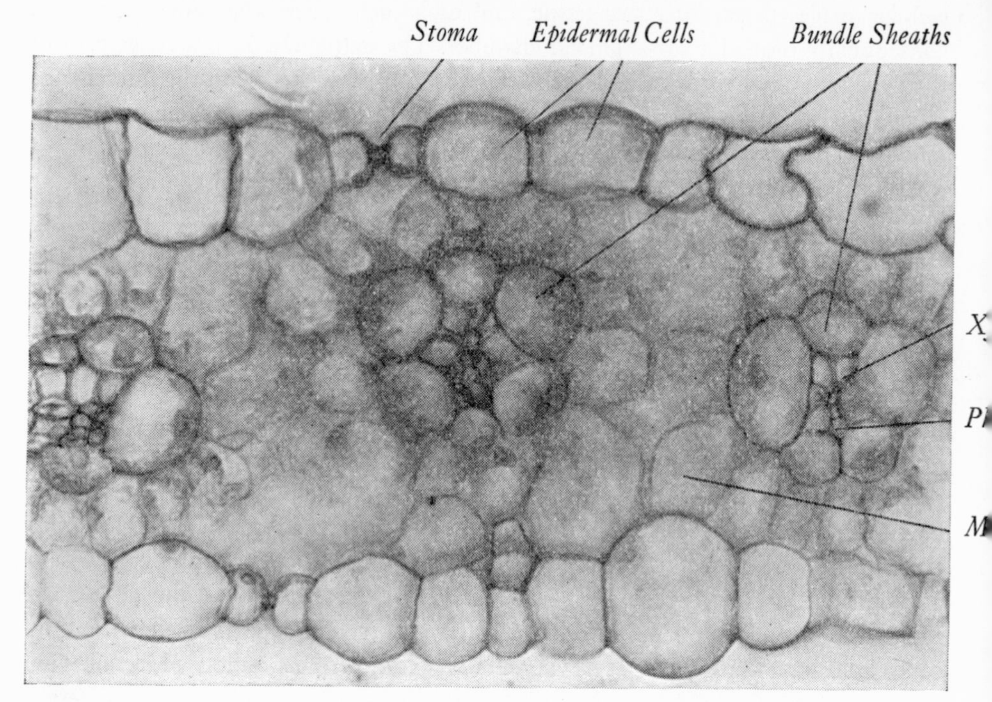

Figure 101 *Transverse section of leaf of* Zea mais *showing vascular bundles encircled by parenchymatous bundle sheaths.*

V or Y similar to their stem bundles. The smaller veins which commonly extend from one large parallel vein to another contain, like those of dicotyledons, very few conducting elements, though single *sieve-elements* may occur in them along with the *tracheary-elements*. A further distinctive feature of monocotyledon leaves, many of which stand almost vertically so that both surfaces receive almost equal amounts of light, is that there is little or no difference in the anatomy of each side of the leaf. The leaf of onion is almost cylindrical and its tissues have a radial organization with the palisade layer, for example, encircling the leaf beneath the epidermis.

Axillary Buds

Axillary buds are usually initiated later than the leaves with which they are associated. In many cases they are first visible in the axils of the second leaf down from the stem apex. As a result of anticlinal divisions in the superficial layers and mainly periclinal divisions in those beneath, the bud grows outwards and so becomes increasingly prominent. At quite an early stage in their development the cells of axillary buds can be seen to be arranged in much the same way as in the parental shoot, with tunica and corpus. Moreover, leaf primordia can be distinguished as increasingly large prominences down the side of the bud (see fig. 86).

Flower Buds

At a certain stage in its development an apical meristem, either terminal or axillary, may cease to produce foliage leaves and in its place initiate the development of a flower. The sequence of development of these apical meristems is characteristic for different plants and depends on the type of inflorescence which they normally bear. The most striking change apparent during this transformation is the rapid and usually quite sudden elongation of the axis, especially in plants with a rosette habit (see p. 55). Accompanying the extension of the axis there is also a marked increase in the width of the apex so that it becomes broad and flattened. The various floral organs (sepals, petals, stamens, etc., see Chapter 23) are initiated in much the same way as leaves – that is, by periclinal divisions of cells lying beneath the outer layer of the apex. The primordia so formed soon appear as protuberances and from them the floral organs develop. As their development progresses, the area occupied by the apical meristem decreases. Since in many cases the ovules arise from this small, remaining terminal region, further growth in this direction, which up to the time of the change from leaf to flower production was potentially unlimited, is no longer possible (see p. 73).

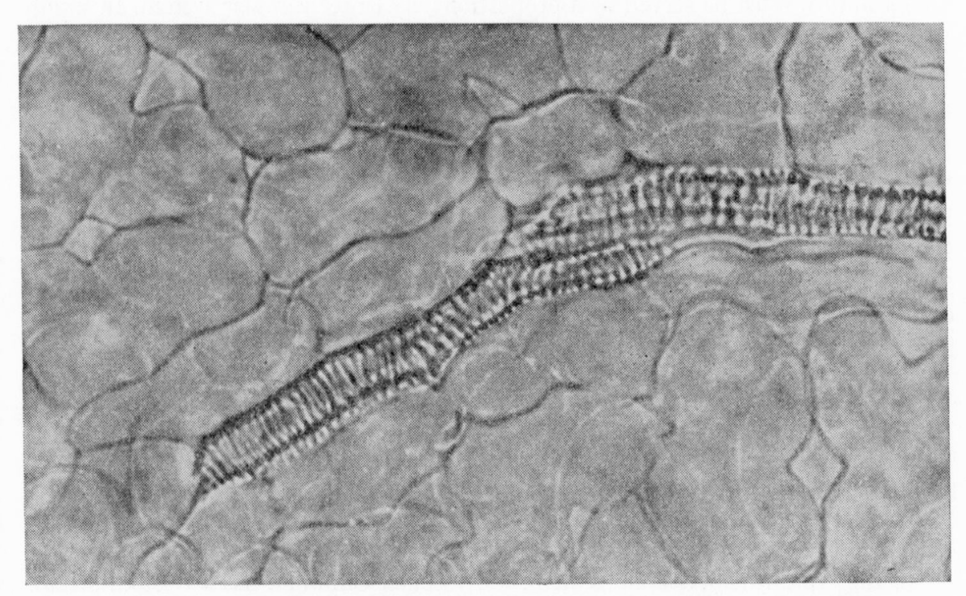

Figure 102 *Vein ending in leaf of* Sibthropia europaea *treated with chloral hydrate. The veins here are reduced to single tracheids with spiral thickenings. These are isolated from the intercellular spaces by a continuous layer of parenchyma, the bundle sheath.*

CHAPTER 10

THE SECONDARY BODY : SECONDARY THICKENING

As a result of cell division and enlargement, the primary body of the plant increases not only in extent, but in girth also. This thickening, often diffuse, is not restricted to any particular tissues, though it may be limited to the cortex, to the pith, or to both. In monocotyledons it is usually most marked immediately beneath the apical meristem; indeed, throughout the whole life of certain palms, increase in girth is almost wholly a matter of cell enlargement.

After the primary body has been formed, further development of the shoot system, even in an annual plant, results in a very considerable increase in leaf area, which in turn must be served by a proportionately larger vascular system. In woody perennials, whose shoot systems not only survive, but increase in extent from year to year, the vascular tissue must be capable of corresponding increases. Both in annuals and perennials these needs are met by the development of a meristem which arises between the primary xylem and phloem, and when active produces additional or *secondary xylem* and *secondary phloem*. When fully formed, this meristem, the *vascular cambium* – which because of its position is termed a *lateral meristem* – forms a continuous cylinder or sheath of living cells between the xylem and phloem both in stems and roots (figs. 103 to 107). The annual renewal of activity of the vascular cambium makes it possible for woody perennials to attain very considerable girth, indeed, to become trees.

Amongst the flowering plants, this lateral secondary growth, or *secondary thickening*, occurs principally in dicotyledons; in monocotyledons it is rare. But it occurs in some ferns (see p. 438) and in all the cone-bearing plants or gymnosperms, to which group such trees as pine, spruce and larch (*Larix europea*) belong (see p. 462).

Vascular Cambium

In the typical dicotyledonous stem, the vascular cambium has a twofold origin. In part it is formed by the division of cells, which have remained meristematic, between the primary xylem and phloem of the vascular bundles – the *fascicular cambium*; in part by the initiation of divisions in the rays of parenchyma between the bundles – the *interfascicular cambium* (fig. 104). Fascicular and interfascicular cambia together form the ring of meristematic cells which give rise to the *secondary vascular tissues*. In many herbaceous dicotyledons, as for example, sunflower, the bundles are markedly separate, and the interfascicular cambium can be readily distinguished. In woody perennials, on the other hand, the interfascicular regions are only a few cells

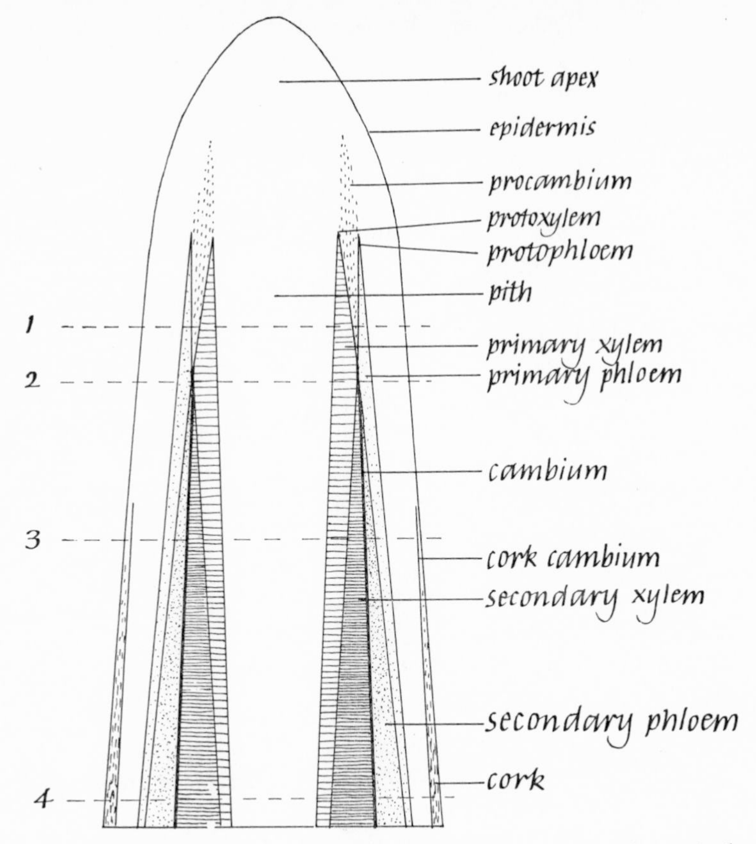

Figure 103 *Diagrammatic representation of a longitudinal section of a typical dicotyledonous stem showing the inception of the vascular and cork cambiums and the progressive development of the secondary tissues derived from them. The numbers* 1-4 *indicate the levels from which the sections shown diagrammatically in* Figure 106 *have been taken.*

wide, so that the parenchyma or medullary rays appear merely as radial streaks. In such plants, the rays which extend from cortex to pith are called *primary rays*, for they correspond in position to the original rays between the primary vascular bundles. The later-formed, secondary rays do not extend so far.

The cells of the cambium are highly vacuolated; in this respect they differ quite markedly from the meristematic cells in the apex of both root and stem. The cells of the fascicular cambium, called the *fusiform initials*, are spindle-shaped, with wedge-shaped ends, being many times longer than wide, and usually rectangular in transverse section. In the interfascicular region the cells are called the *ray initials*, and are about as long as wide: that is, *isodiametric*. When the cambial cells become active, they divide periclinally, producing new cells towards the xylem on the inside and the phloem on the outside, with the result that radial files of cells are formed (fig. 106).

These divisions are not, however, alternate; invariably much more xylem than phloem is produced (fig. 105). When division is very active, the formation of new cells is so rapid that a wide band of undifferentiated xylem and phloem accumulates on each side of the cambium, so that it becomes difficult to distinguish the cambial initials from their derivatives. The term *cambium*, however, is usually used rather loosely to include both.

In roots as in stems, secondary growth results from the formation of secondary vascular tissues due to the activity of a vascular cambium. Similarly, this cambium is initiated by divisions of strips of *procambial cells* between primary phloem and xylem that have remained undifferentiated, the number of these strips depending on the type of root. There are three present in the triarch represented in fig. 107, whereas only two occur in a diarch root but four in a tetrarch root. Moreover, since the cambium completely encircles the xylem core and follows its outline closely, in the transverse section of a triarch root it appears triangular. Because the cambium located against the concave face of this triangle divides earlier than that near the protoxylem groups adjacent to the pericycle, the cambium is moved outwards with the result that it appears circular in transverse section (fig. 107). Medullary rays are produced in the secondary xylem of roots and those originating in the pericycle opposite the protoxylem are most commonly the widest (fig. 108). In some roots, however, none of these wider rays are formed so that the xylem has a homogeneous appearance.

In the roots and stems of annuals the cylinder of secondary tissues produced by the activity of the cambium never becomes very thick. In woody perennials, however, it is often extensive, so that, in the course of many years, trees can grow to a huge girth. Both in annuals and perennials the wood, or secondary xylem, as it differentiates can be seen to be composed of vessels, tracheids, *wood fibres* and *wood parenchyma*. The nature and particularly the extent of these elements varies from species to species. In trees, the differences can be of considerable economic significance, since they give every wood its special character and value. Wood is generally classed as hard or soft. *Hardwoods* come from woody dicotyledons, and *softwoods* from gymnosperms or cone-bearing trees.

Softwoods

The secondary xylem of the *softwoods* is relatively simple in structure, and is characterized by the absence of vessels, the wood being composed principally of tracheids. Under the microscope, transverse sections appear remarkably homogeneous except for narrow rays of parenchyma, mostly one cell wide (fig. 109). These tracheids are narrow, elongate cells arranged in orderly radial series and interconnected by rather elaborate circular apertures, termed *bordered pits*. These are so-called because the secondary wall of the tracheid overarches the *pit-cavity* on each side of the primary cell wall which forms the *pit membrane*. The centre of this membrane, termed the *torus*, is usually thickened and under certain circumstances may come to lie against, and thus to close the pit opening on one side or another. The pits often occur in single

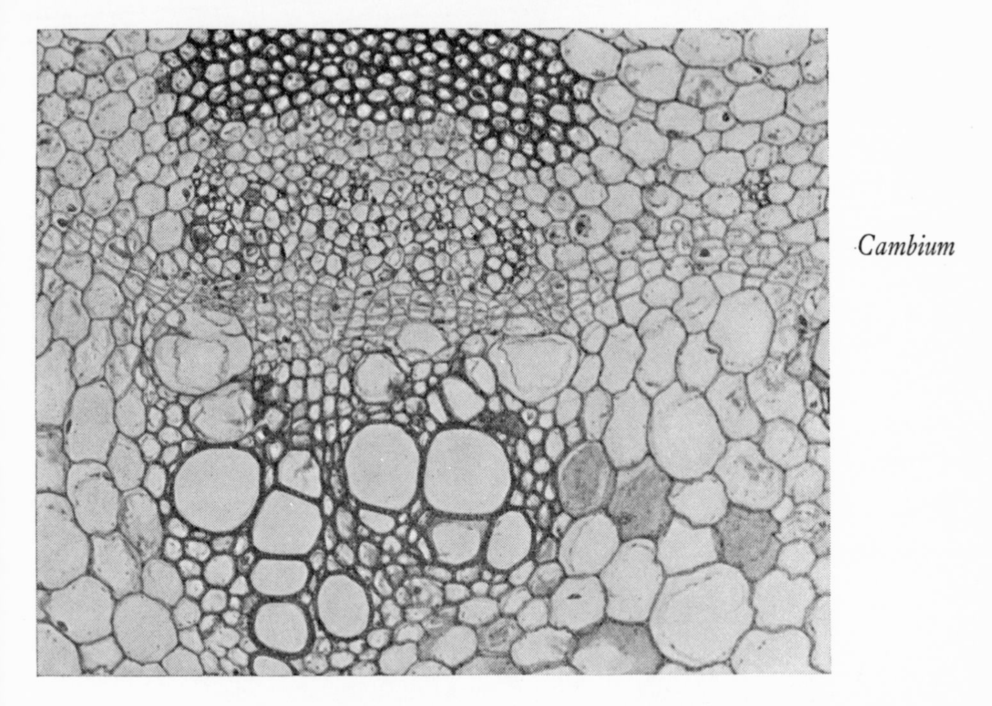

Figure 104 *T.s. of part of stem of* Helianthus *showing fascicular and interfascicular cambium.*

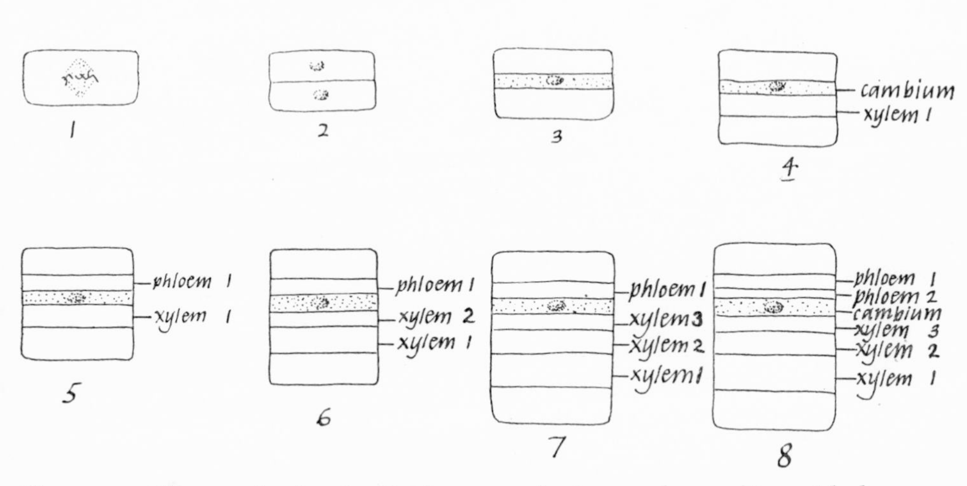

Figure 105 *Diagram showing the divisions occurring in vascular cambium with the formation of secondary xylem and phloem.*

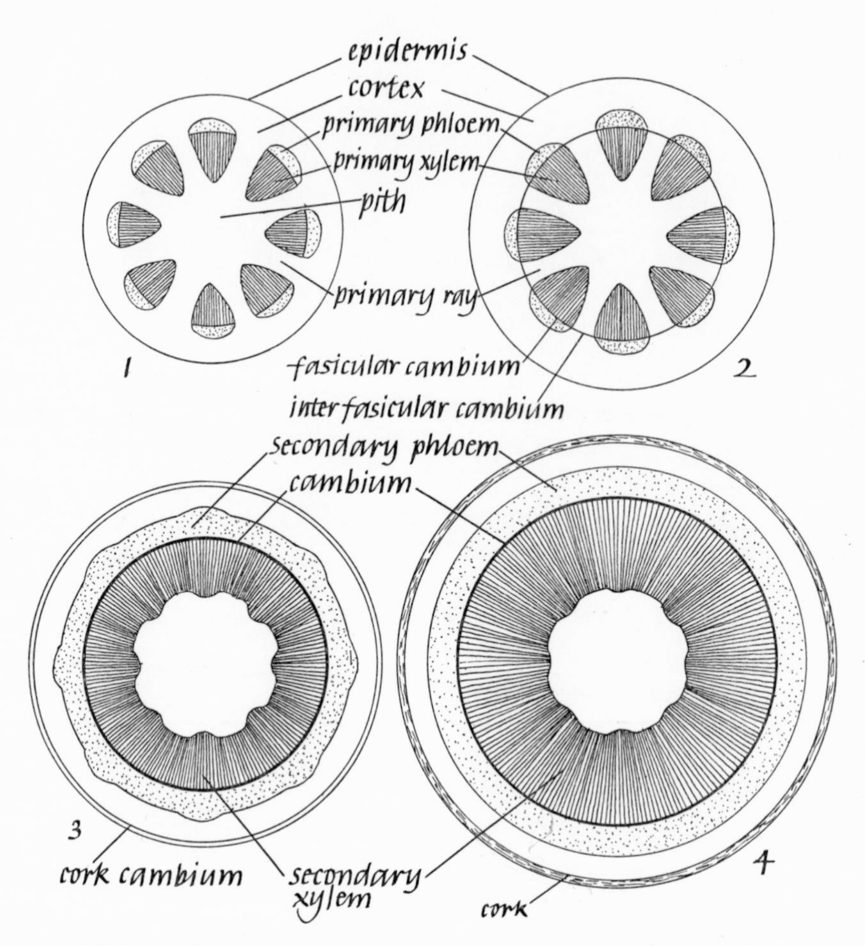

Figure 106 *Diagrammatic representation of transverse sections of a typical dicotyledonous stem taken from different levels* (*see* 1–4 *in* Figure 103) *to show stages in secondary thickening.*

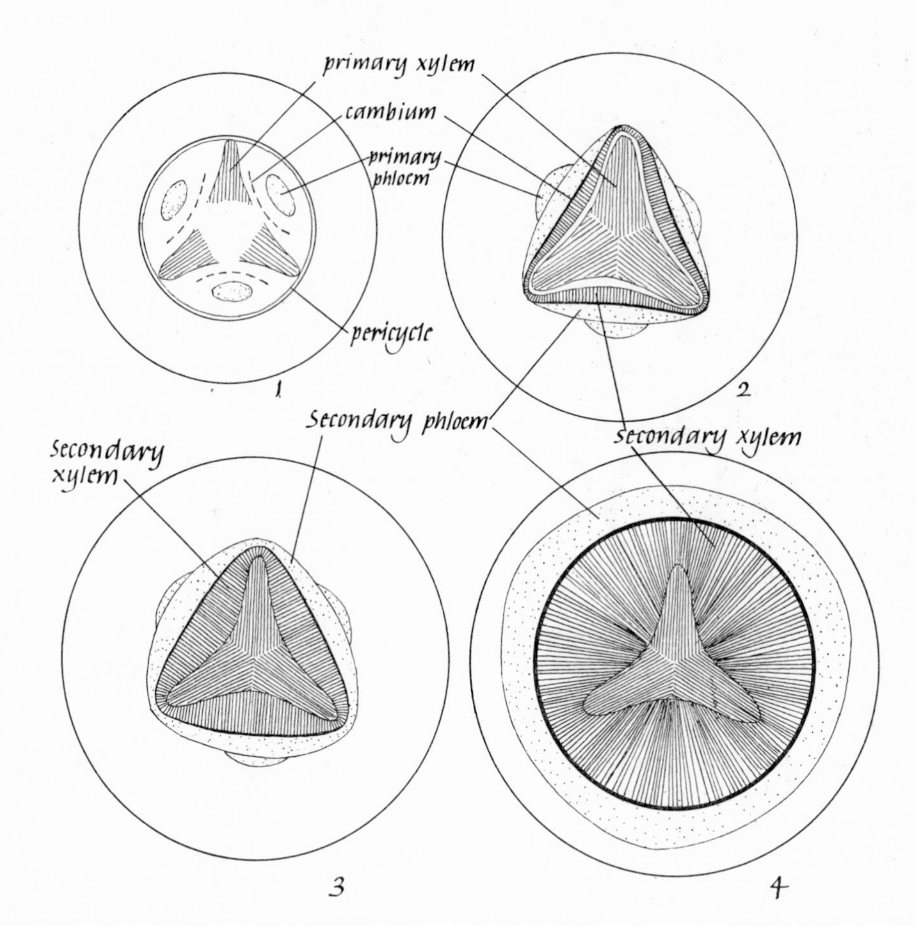

Figure 107 *Diagrammatic representation of transverse sections of a typical dicotyledonous root taken at levels of different age to show stages in its secondary thickening.*

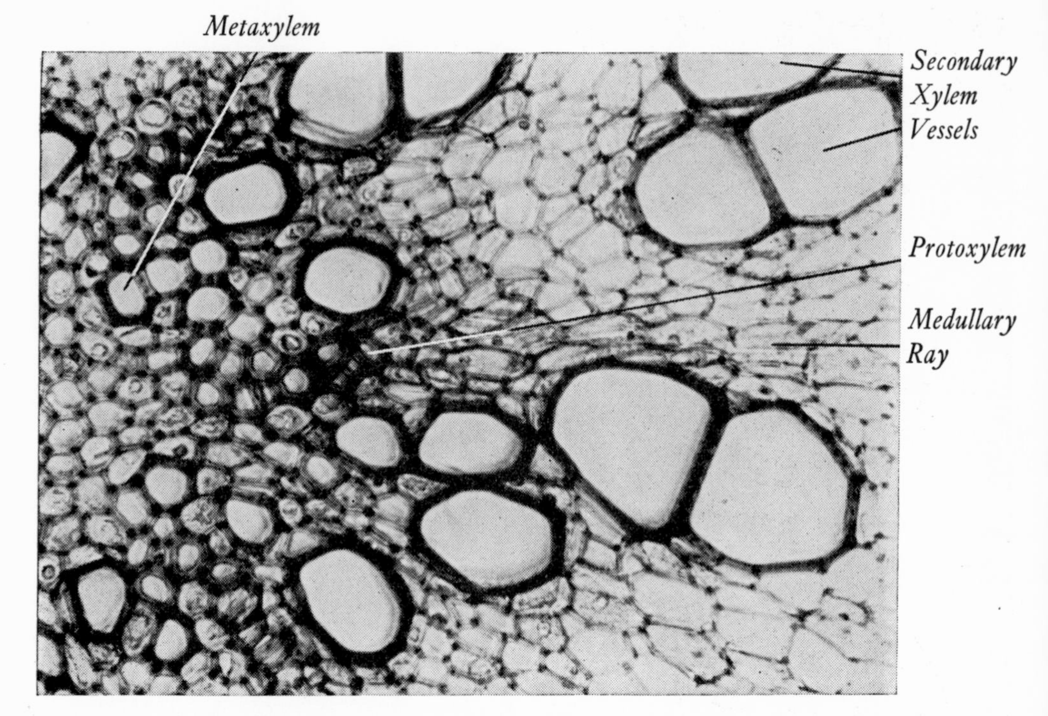

Figure 108 *T.s. of the central region of a thickened root of* Tilia europea *showing a medullary ray originating opposite protoxylem group of the primary xylem star.*

vertical rows down the length of the tracheid and are for the most part restricted to the radial walls (figs. 110 and 111).

Hardwoods

In contrast to softwoods, hardwoods exhibit much greater variety. The more or less orderly, radial arrangement of the cells (which may be vessels, tracheids, wood fibres and parenchyma) is not so pronounced; for as they enlarge, the vessels tend to displace adjacent cells. The vessels frequently bear simple or bordered pits, the number and arrangement of which is somewhat variable, even on different walls of the same element. The main factor in their distribution seems to be the nature of the adjoining cell. For example, between adjoining vessels and fibres bordered pits are closely crowded and often arranged in a distinct vertical series; between vessels and parenchyma cells the pits are simple (fig. 112) or half-bordered, the border being on the vessel side. Sometimes the vessels show reticulate or spiral thickening on their inner walls, while on the end walls of superimposed vessel elements the perforated septa are most commonly oblique. In hardwoods, tracheids are generally much less numerous than vessels and may be more or less absent in some plants. They are usually

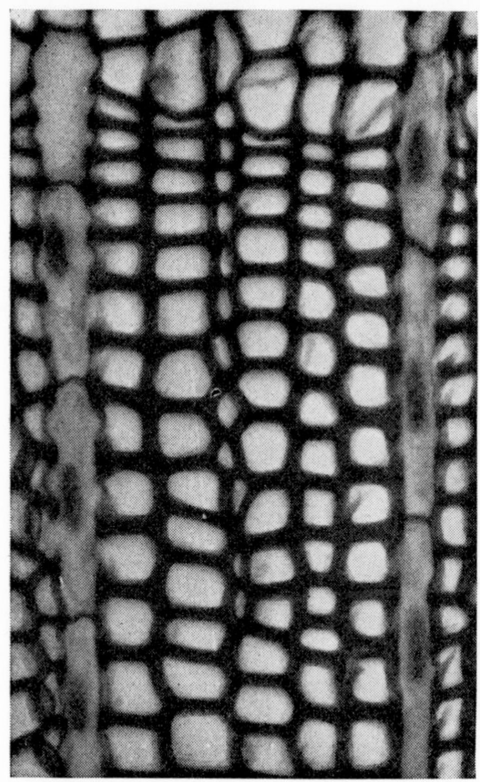

Figure 109 *T.s. stem of* Pinus sylvestris *showing the orderly radial series of tracheids interspersed with single celled rays of living parenchyma.*

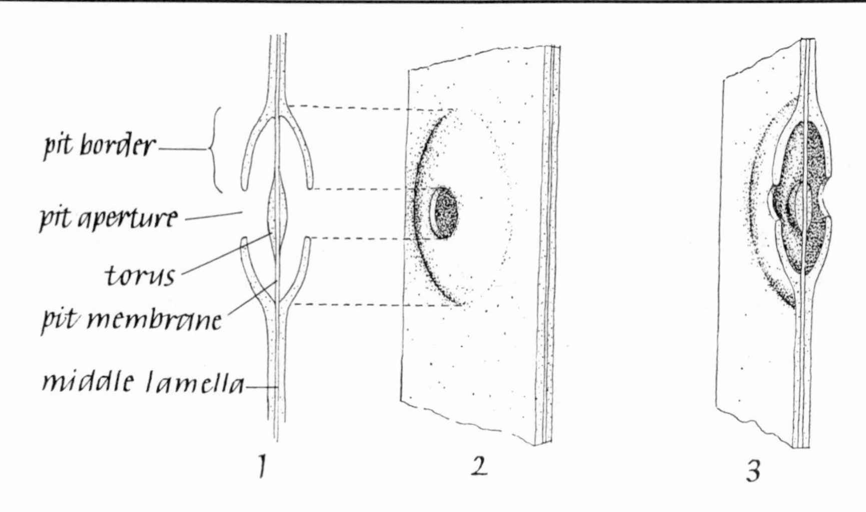

Figure 110 *Diagrammatic representation of a bordered pit*
1 *in transverse section.*
2 *as viewed obliquely.*
3 *a transverse section viewed obliquely.*

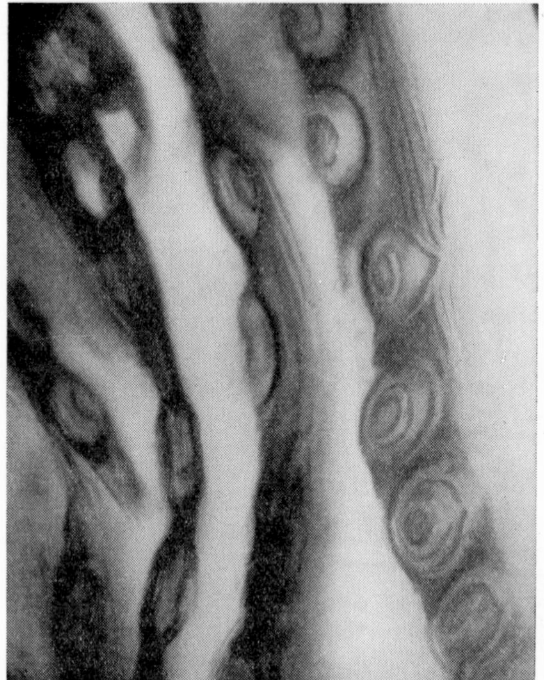

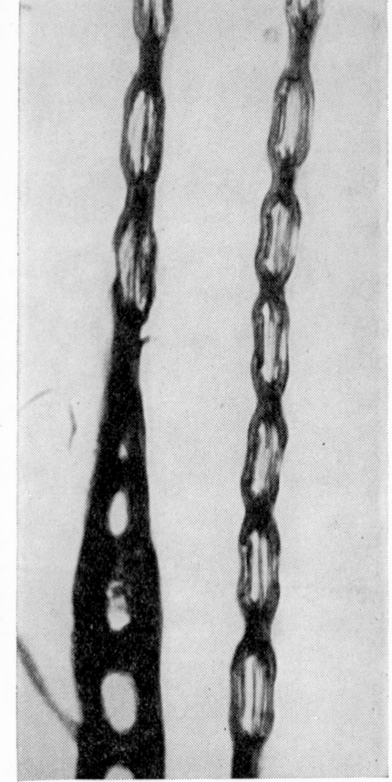

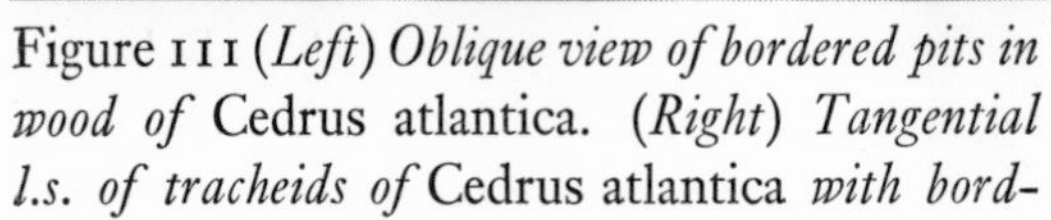

Figure 111 (*Left*) *Oblique view of bordered pits in wood of* Cedrus atlantica. (*Right*) *Tangential l.s. of tracheids of* Cedrus atlantica *with bordered pits. Note their very close grouping down the tracheid wall; also the middle lamella. There is no closing torus in these pits.*

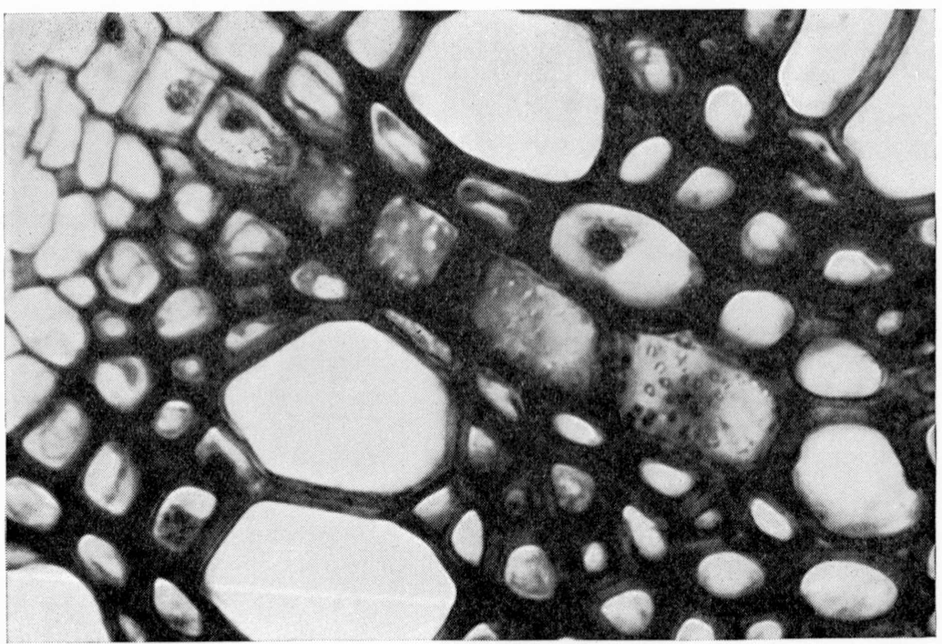

Figure 112 *Medullary ray in t.s. of the wood of* Sambucus niger. *Note the simple pits in these living cells.*

shorter than vessel elements and the communication between cells is by way of simple pit-pores with thin membranes between adjacent or superimposed tracheids.

The secondary xylem fibres are, for the most part, elongated cells with pointed ends and with lignified walls which are usually thicker than the walls of vessels and tracheids in the same wood. The walls are commonly pitted by slit-like apertures, the slits on walls of adjoining cells often being inclined in opposite directions so that in surface view these pits have the appearance of the letter X. In some woods, however, as for example beech, the fibres bear bordered pits with slit-like apertures. Most wood fibres, whose principal function is mechanical support, are without living contents, though some retain their protoplasts. Such living cells develop thin transverse walls across the cell *lumen* or cavity after the secondary wall has been laid down, hence they are termed *septate fibres*. These are quite frequent in dicotyledons, and are concerned not only with support but also with the storage of reserve materials in the wood. In structure and function they are not unlike xylem parenchyma.

The parenchyma of the secondary xylem occurs in the medullary rays and in the wood itself; in structure and contents it is the same in both. Its walls may be lignified, showing prominent pitting of simple, half-bordered or bordered type. The distribution of parenchyma in the wood appears to depend on the time of the year when it is formed. In ash, for example, it tends to be confined to wood formed in summer and then it is restricted to the immediate vicinity of the vessels, which it sometimes encircles completely. On the other hand, in birch and beech it seems to be generally distributed throughout the wood.

Medullary Rays

The parenchyma of the medullary rays tend to have rather thinner walls than other wood parenchyma and to possess simple pits which are frequently numerous on their tangential walls (fig. 112). Although the *primary rays* of herbaceous plants can be very conspicuous, being many cells wide, those of trees and shrubs are at most a few cells wide. *Secondary rays* are always limited in width to one or two cells, and, moreover, are limited in vertical extent to ten, or twelve cells at the most. This can be seen by examining tangential longitudinal sections (figs. 113 and 114). Primary rays, in contrast, usually extend through an entire internode. The vertical extent of the medullary rays can also be seen in radial longitudinal sections, where, since they are cut parallel to their flat faces, and as the cells are rectangular and elongated radially, their appearance is suggestive of a brick wall of up to twelve courses high. If such a section is cut through a primary ray, the 'wall' will extend vertically and radially across the whole (fig. 115). Although the wood consists of vessels, tracheids and fibres, for the most part without living contents, the presence of this xylem parenchyma shows it to be permeated by a continuous and quite complex system of living cells. It is possible that the function of this living system within the wood is to conduct elaborated food substances, and at certain times of the year to act as regions of storage for this food.

Annual Rings

In most woody dicotyledons the greater part of the annual addition of xylem consists of vessels and fibres. In some species, many more vessels are produced during the spring than later in the growing season, and these vessels tend to be larger and have thinner walls. Such seasonal differences in the size, form and distribution of the various xylem elements are related to the fact that every spring the increased number of rapidly expanding leaves make a very heavy demand on the plant's water supply. Later in the season, the relative increase in the proportion of fibres produced would seem to provide for the mechanical requirements of the plant. In temperate regions, cambial activity ceases in winter so that no new wood is added. Hence there is usually quite a sharp boundary between the summer wood of one season with its small vessels and higher proportion of fibres, and the spring wood of the following season with its high proportion of large vessels (figs. 116 and 117). Since such a boundary is formed yearly, the secondary xylem exhibits a succession of *annual rings* from which the age of a felled tree can be determined. Moreover, the amount of wood formed each year tends to be indicative of growing conditions during the year it was formed, so that in years favourable for growth the rings are noticeably broader than those of unfavourable years. In this way a record of climatic conditions throughout the life of the tree is preserved in its wood. Although the analysis of tree rings has its limitations with regard to long term climatic records, they nevertheless have been of value as indicators of climatic changes on the shorter time scale of a few decades. Trees growing in an equable tropical climate with no marked alternation of either warm or cold, wet or dry seasons have only vaguely defined rings, which are not necessarily annual.

Sapwood and Heartwood

As increment after increment of the secondary wood is added to the growing tree, the earliest-formed wood gradually ceases to function. Until this state is reached the wood still contains living cells and appears to be conducting, though probably less

---

Figure 113 *Tangential l.s. of* Pinus sylvestris *wood showing long tapering tracheids interspersed by medullary rays of clearly limited vertical extent. The large medullary ray in the centre of this photomicrograph is traversed by a resin canal.*

Figure 114 *Tangential l.s. of wood of lime*, Tilia europea, *showing fusiform tracheids and vessels, the latter with double spiral thickenings. The wood is permeated by long files of living cells, the medullary rays. The ray on the right is two cells wide and is probably a primary ray which may extend the entire height of the internode. Some of the secondary rays can be seen to be only* 3 *or* 4 *cells in depth.*

Figure 115 *Radial l.s. of* Tilia europea *showing a medullary ray with its rectangular, radially elongated cells lying over the vertically orientated cells of the xylem. Note the nuclei in the ray cells.*

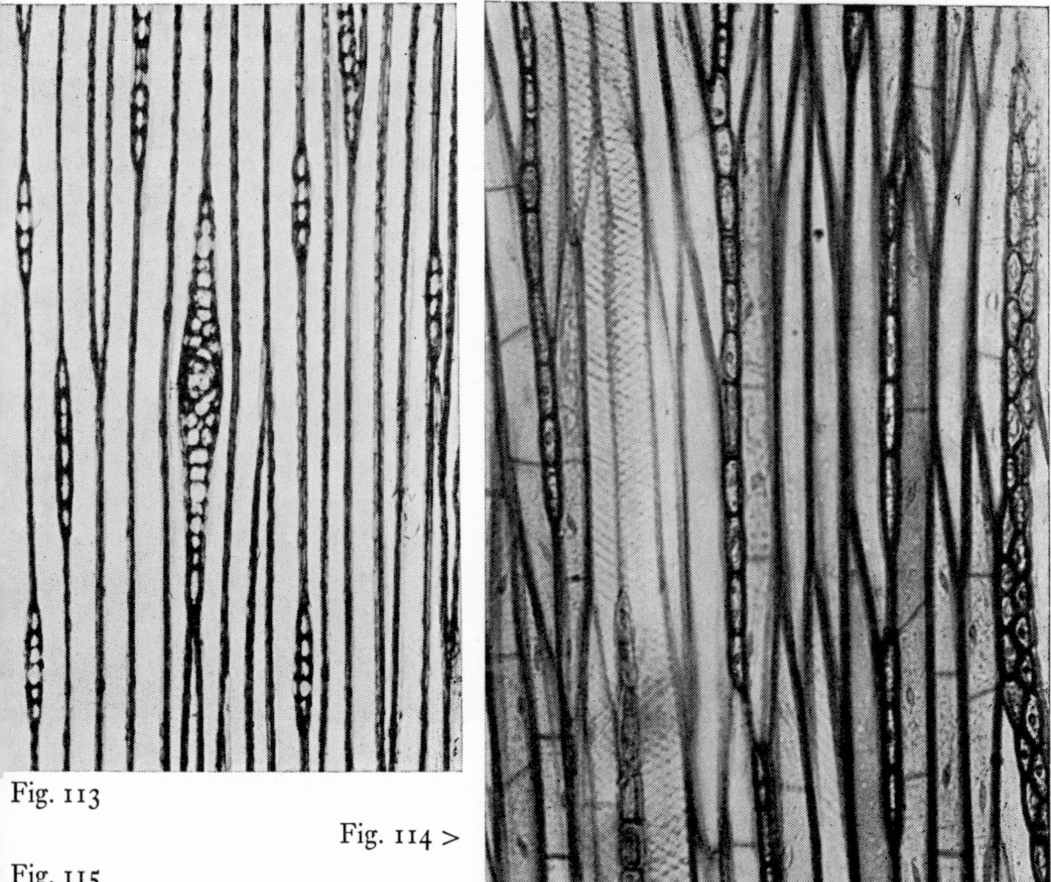

Fig. 113

Fig. 114 >

Fig. 115

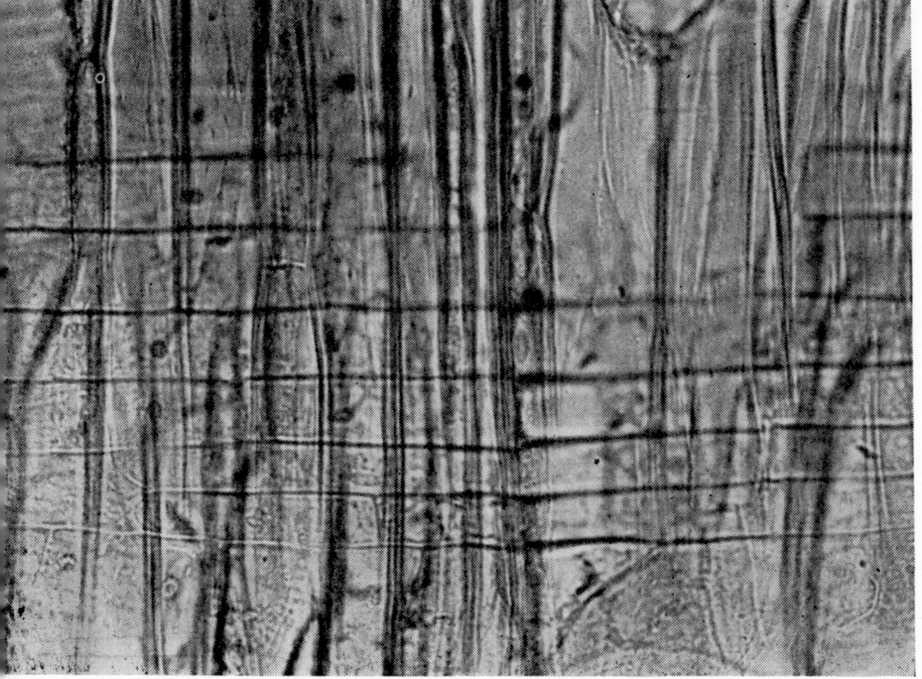

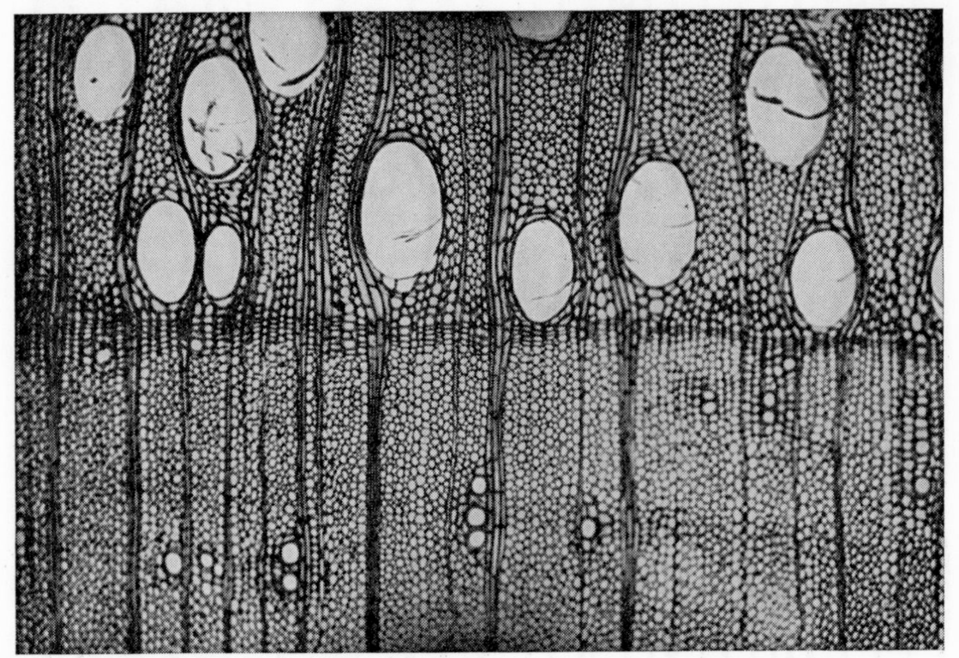

Figure 116 *Ring porous wood. T.s. of wood of ash*, Fraxinus excelsior. *Note the great difference in the size of the spring-formed vessels, in the top half of photograph, and summer-formed vessels in the lower half.*

actively than when first formed, and is known as *sapwood*. The non-functioning wood, which is frequently darker than the active wood, is termed *heartwood* (fig. 118). The relative amount of the latter seems to depend to some extent on environmental conditions and its formation involves the removal of sap and reserve food materials, and disappearance of protoplasts. At the same time the water content of the cell walls is reduced and in some wood *tyloses* are formed. These are balloon-like enlargements of the pit membrane of wood parenchyma cells adjacent to a vessel, which as they grow project into the lumen of the vessel. They are sometimes so numerous that they fill and block up the latter, completely eliminating the permeability of the wood. In sapwood, tyloses may occur beneath wounds.

Other changes from sapwood to heartwood are the formation in the changing cells or transference to them of various *oils*, *gums*, *resins*, *tannins* and other substances which tend to darken the colour of the wood. Because of these changes, heartwood is more durable as timber than sapwood of the same species.

Wood anatomists concerned with the study of timber refer to vessels in transverse section as 'pores'. On the basis of the distribution of pores, two principal types of dicotyledonous wood are recognized. These are *ring porous*, in which the vessels are distinctly larger in the spring wood than in summer wood – typified in such trees as

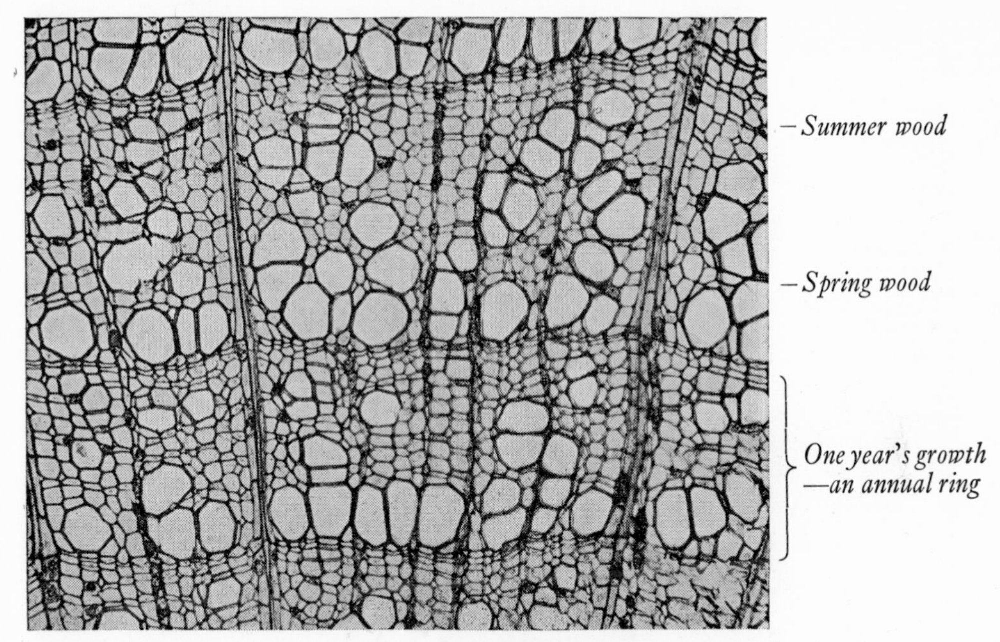

Figure 117 *Diffuse porous wood. T.s. of wood of lime*, Tilia europea, *showing the much less striking difference in pore size of spring and summer-formed vessels as compared with ash* (*cf.* Figure 116).

oak, elm and ash; and *diffuse porous* where the pores tend to be more uniform in size and distribution throughout each annual ring. Birch, beech, and lime are common examples of the latter. A series of intergrading types, however, occurs between the two extremes (figs. 116 and 117).

Secondary Phloem

The secondary phloem constitutes much less of the secondary growth in the stem than does the xylem, and as thickening proceeds the primary phloem and even in its turn the first-formed secondary phloem, may become crushed and functionless. As in the case of the primary phloem, sieve tubes, companion cells, and phloem parenchyma always occur. Although in certain cases fibres may be missing, they are generally present and indeed may be so abundant that the sieve tubes, companion cells and parenchyma may exist in the phloem only as small groups. On the other hand, it may be the fibres that are diffusely scattered. Again, fibres often appear as successive tangential strips, and give phloem a distinctly banded appearance, as in the woods of ash and lime (fig. 119).

The parenchyma rays in the secondary phloem resemble, and are in fact frequently continuous with, those of the xylem. In the older parts of the phloem in woody stems, however, the primary rays widen out by cell division and enlargement in response to

Figure 118 *Cut branches of Scots pine* (Pinus sylvestris) *showing annual rings, and central core of dark heartwood surrounded by lighter coloured sapwood.*

the gradual increase in girth of the stem, so that wide wedges of parenchyma develop between groups of phloem (fig. 119).

Cork Formation

In addition to this so-called 'flaring' response of the primary rays to the increasing girth of the stem, tissues outside the phloem are clearly subjected to even greater stresses as secondary thickening progresses. For a time the cortex and the epidermis may keep pace with expansion, by means of cell division and enlargement; but the internal pressures eventually become too great. When this happens, the protective epidermis, and cortex beneath, rupture. In place of the epidermis, however, a protective tissue of secondary origin, the *periderm*, develops. The periderm, like the secondary vascular tissues, is initiated by a lateral meristem, the *cork cambium* or *phellogen*. Like the vascular cambium, this increases the diameter of the axis by cutting off new cells both to the outside and inside. Those cut off the outside form the protective cork or *phellem*; those cut off the inside, one or two layers of living parenchyma, the *phelloderm*.

The first periderm to be formed in the stem frequently appears during the first growing season. The phellogen which produces it is always derived from the living

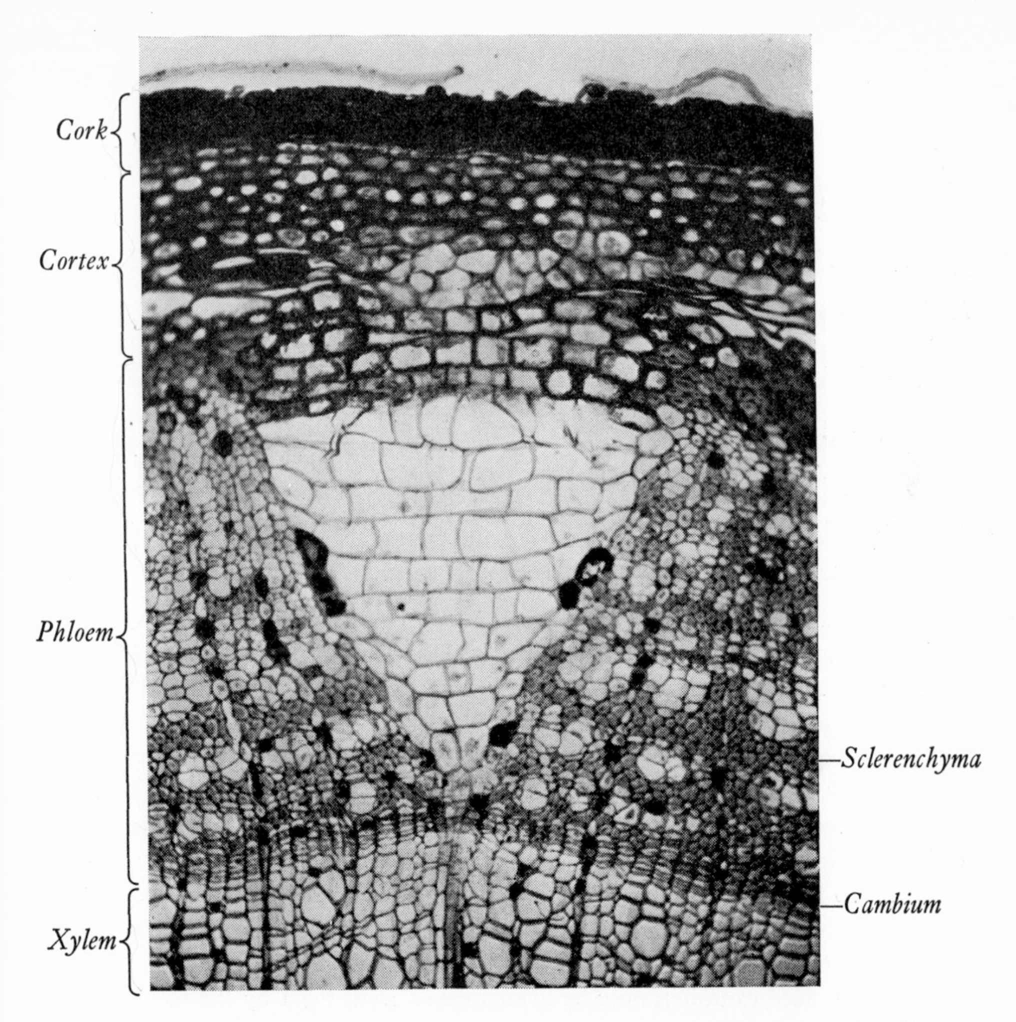

Figure 119 *T.s. of outer region of stem of* Tilia europea *showing 'flaring' produced by the development of wedges of parenchyma of the primary medullary rays. These separate the groups of phloem which are interspersed with bands of sclerenchyma fibres.*

cells, sometimes of the epidermis, but more frequently from the layer of cortical cells beneath (fig. 120). In certain plants (*Berberis*, *Ribes*, *Vitis*) it arises deeper in the stem, in the primary phloem. In shape, the cells of the phellogen are remarkably similar from plant to plant, appearing rectangular and radially flattened in transverse section, and forming a continuous ring of meristematic initials. The protoplasts of the cells from which the phellogen is formed lose their vacuoles, and the cytoplasm becomes markedly more granular; as they divide, the derivative cells are normally compactly arranged in radial rows. Unlike the vascular tissues formed from the vascular cambium, each layer of cells formed by the phellogen matures before any further

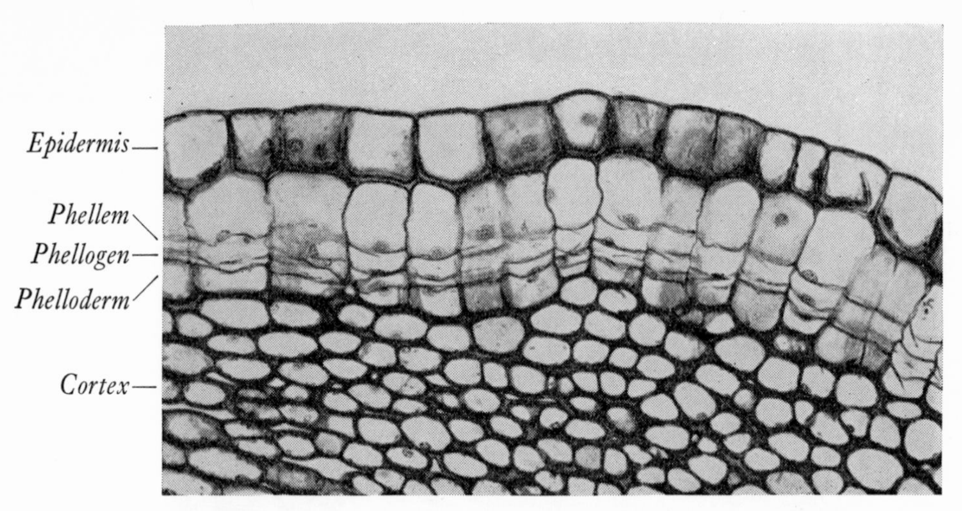

Figure 120 *Cork formation. T.s. of stem of* Sambucus niger *showing epidermis, cortex and the inception of the cork cambium – phellogen.*

division takes place, so that the phellogen is clearly recognizable. The cork cells or phellem are mostly uniform in shape; in general they are prismatic and so compactly arranged that there is an absence of intercellular spaces. The primary cell walls are of cellulose, but the secondary wall, which gives cork many of its characteristic properties, is of *suberin*, a fatty substance impervious to water and gases. The walls may be yellow or brown in colour and the cell cavity which, when the cell is mature, will have lost its living contents, may contain coloured materials related to tannins and resins. The suberization of the walls and compact arrangement of the cells of the cork prevent water-loss from the plant (fig. 121). The one or two layers of phelloderm cells cut off by the phellogen on the inside are very like the cells of the cortical parenchyma and indeed can often only be distinguished from them by the fact that they are arranged in more or less definite radial rows.

As secondary growth progresses and the girth of the stem increases, sooner or later the first formed periderm splits and thus ceases to perform its protective function. Additional periderm layers are, however, formed deeper and deeper in the stem. The first periderms are formed in the cortex, then in the pericycle, while subsequent periderms arise in the secondary phloem. Tissues to the outside of each periderm layer are cut off from the rest of the plant and, being deprived of food and water, soon die. The successive formation of periderms gives rise to a crust of overlapping layers of cork, which enclose dead tissues of the cortex and phloem. Such tissues constitute the *rhytidome*, commonly referred to as *shell* or *scale bark* (fig. 122). In everyday usage 'bark' refers to all the outer tissues that are easily removed when woody stems or logs are peeled, which, in most cases means all the tissues outside the cambium – the commonly accepted definition of bark. The term has unfortunately a somewhat loose connotation and care must be taken to distinguish 'bark' and periderm, for the two terms are not synonymous. In some plants periderm formation beneath the first periderm may take place quite early in the life of the stem, even in the first year. This protective layer may continue to function for several seasons after its formation, and in trees with smooth bark the original periderm may persist for many years. In the case of the beech (*Fagus sylvatica*) it may function for the entire life of the tree, the increase in circumference of the periderm being accomplished by radial division and enlargement of the phellogen cells, thereby keeping pace with the tree's increasing girth (fig. 124).

Lenticels

The cork ensheaths the stem in an almost impervious protective layer. To permit communication between the atmosphere and the internal tissues of the stem, however, certain limited areas of the periderm possess patches of loosely arranged cells called *lenticels*. These have small, though abundant, intercellular spaces permitting the entry of air through the periderm. On many twigs they can be seen with the naked eye as small areas of loose cells (with abundant intercellular spaces) that protrude above the surface. These fissures in the periderm vary greatly in size in different plants. They may be barely visible to the naked eye, or on the other hand be as large as one cm or more across. The rough 'specks' on apples are very familiar examples of lenticels.

Lenticels usually occur beneath stomata and are produced by the activity of the phellogen which is continuous with that of the corky periderm. The phellogen, however, bends inwards, to occur more deeply in the stem (fig. 125). On its inception, the

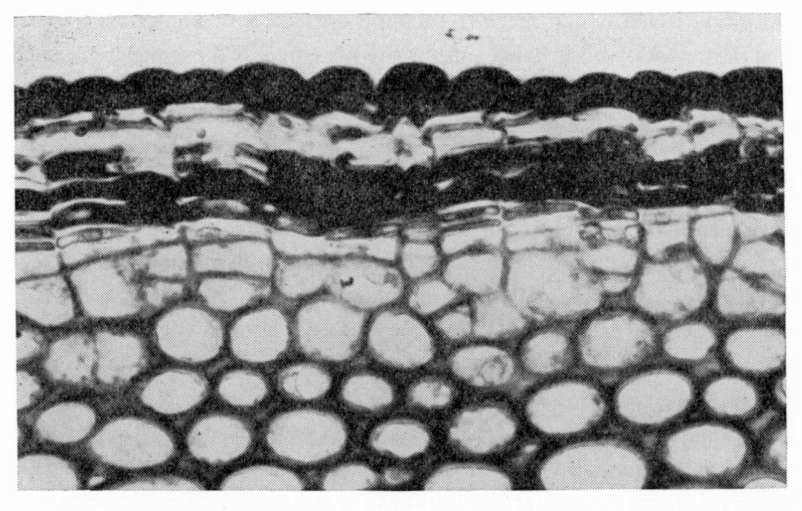

Figure 121 *Cork formation. Phellem beneath the epidermis in t.s. stem of* Sambucus niger. *Note the compactly arranged radial rows of cork cells which have become dark in colour due to the accumulation of tannins and resins.*

cells beneath the stoma divide in different planes, forming to the outside the loose mass of rounded thin-walled cells known as *filling* or *complementary tissue*. Following these divisions, the phellogen layer differentiates and begins to cut off new cells, but only in the tangential plane. As the first-formed complementary cells enlarge and lose their living contents, the phellogen forms further complementary cells beneath them. The pressure produced by this increasing mass eventually ruptures the epidermis, so that the complementary cells become exposed. Later, the epidermis around the lenticel is thrust back, allowing the mass of complementary cells, which in many cases are suberized, to protrude. In some lenticels, as for example in birch and beech, the complementary or filling tissue is formed in layers. The cells of this tissue are loosely packed and unsuberized, but at regular intervals, usually the end of the growing season, compact layers of suberized closing-tissue are formed. These layers are one or several cells deep and hold together the loose tissue, until they, like the epidermis, are ruptured by the pressure of new growth from beneath. Thus during the growing season the lenticel is open and there is an air passage from the atmosphere to the inner tissues of the organ by way of the loosely fitting complementary tissue. However at the end of the season a *closing layer* seals off the passage, except possibly for very small intercellular spaces.

In plants with persistent superficial periderm layers the lenticels may last for many years. During this time they increase tangentially in length, as the periderm increases in thickness. Such elongated lenticels form conspicuous markings on the otherwise smooth bark of birch (fig. 123), and cherry (*Prunus avium*) trees.

Lenticels are difficult to see on trees with rough bark. In the cork oak (*Quercus suber*), for example, where the cork is several centimetres thick, they form cylindrical masses of filling tissue which reach to its outer surface. In commercial cork these can be seen as dark spots, and it is because of the presence of these pervious radial pores that bottle corks are cut vertically from cork sheets so that the lenticels extend transversely through them.

Abscission

Periderm formation is an important phase in the development of protective tissue along surfaces that are exposed after the loss of various plant parts, a phenomenon of common occurence, particularly in woody plants where there is a seasonal renewal of growth. Leaves, floral parts, fruits, and foliage branches are commonly cut off from the parent plant, and the exposed surfaces are protected by the periderm.

In the case of deciduous leaves there is a narrow transverse zone where the leaf base adjoins the stem. This *abscission zone* may in some cases be visible externally as a shallow furrow or a narrow band with a somewhat different colour from the rest of the epidermis. Internally the vascular bundles are reduced in diameter, and strengthening tissues are poorly developed or absent. The immediate cause of leaf fall is to be found in the so-called *separation layer* which consists of a few layers of cells which differ from the adjoining ones in that they are smaller, and have abundant starch

Figure 122 *Shell or scale bark of sweet chestnut,* Castanea sativa.

Figure 123 *The bark of* Betula papifera *showing the persistent lenticels which have become greatly elongated round the circumference of the tree.*

Figure 124 *The smooth bark of Beech,* Fagus sylvaticus.

3

124

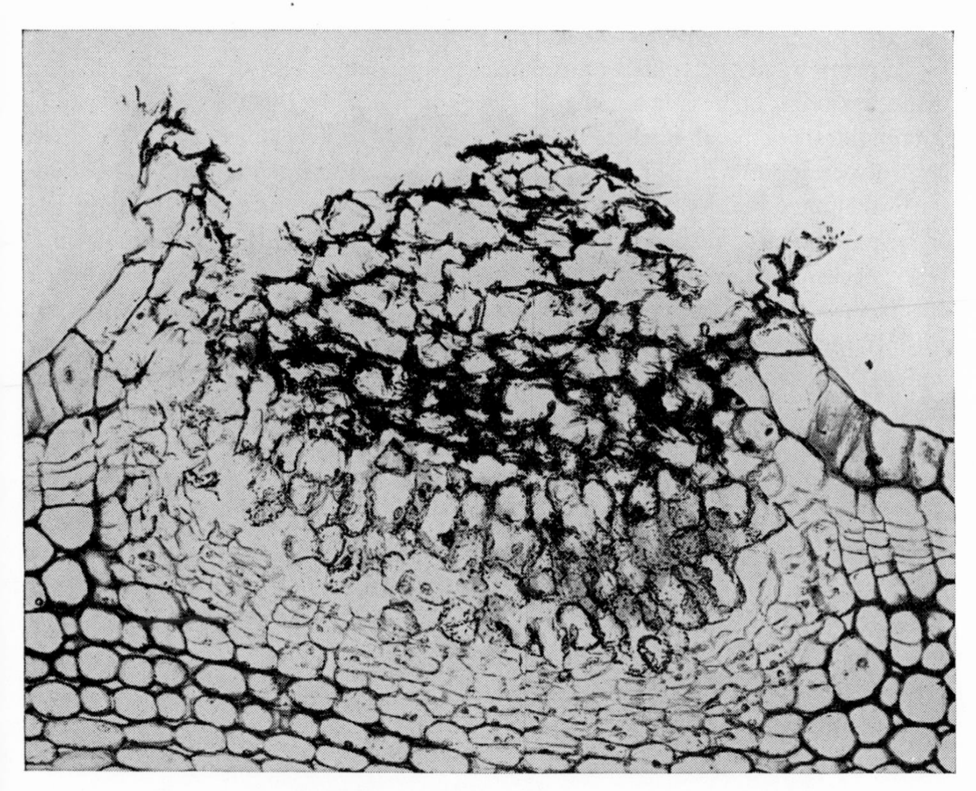

Figure 125 *T.s. of stem of* Sambucus niger *in the region of a lenticel showing phellogen and loosely packed filling, or complementary, cells.*

grains and dense cytoplasm. Just below this layer some, though not all, of the conducting elements become blocked with gums and tyloses. Shortly before leaf fall there is a dissolution of the middle lamella and part of the primary cell wall so that all the parenchyma cells of the layer become free from one another. The vascular bundles which then alone support the leaf are finally broken by the weight of the leaf or by wind action, and the leaf falls. The broken surface of the stem may be at first protected by the existing layer of parenchyma cells of the separation layer, on the walls of which there is a deposition of suberin and protective wound gum. Any later formed protective layer of secondary origin is a typical periderm layer, which develops beneath the primary protective layer and in continuity with the periderm in the branch.

It has been recognized for a considerable time that the application of auxin (see p. 44) to leaves delays or prevents the formation of the abscission layer. This finding has more recently been extended to the abscission of fruits with the result that it is now common horticultural practice to apply auxin-containing sprays to such fruits as apples, pears, and citrus fruits to delay their fall.

Wound Tissues and Grafting

In many woody perennials only a small proportion of branches persist for more than a few years. There is an automatic *pruning* of these older branches whose shedding is brought about by abscission, followed again by the development of a protective layer of periderm. When branches or trunks of woody plants are injured, however, the formation of periderm is preceded by the development of a special wound tissue or *callus*, consisting of parenchyma cells which are produced from the division of various cells near the surface of the wound (see fig. 31). There is doubt as to which cells in the wounded stem give rise to callus. However, it seems that xylem rays, and possibly the newly formed derivatives of the cambium, are amongst the principal sources. The stimulation that wounding provides has been made use of in gardening practice, especially in rose and fruit culture, and in the techniques of *budding* and *grafting*. In grafting, a piece of young stem of one plant, the *scion*, is brought into permanent contact with the cut surface of the rooted plant, the *stock*, on to which it is desired to grow, so that the xylem and phloem of both are in contact. If the graft is successful, these cut surfaces of scion and stock become intimately associated through the fusion

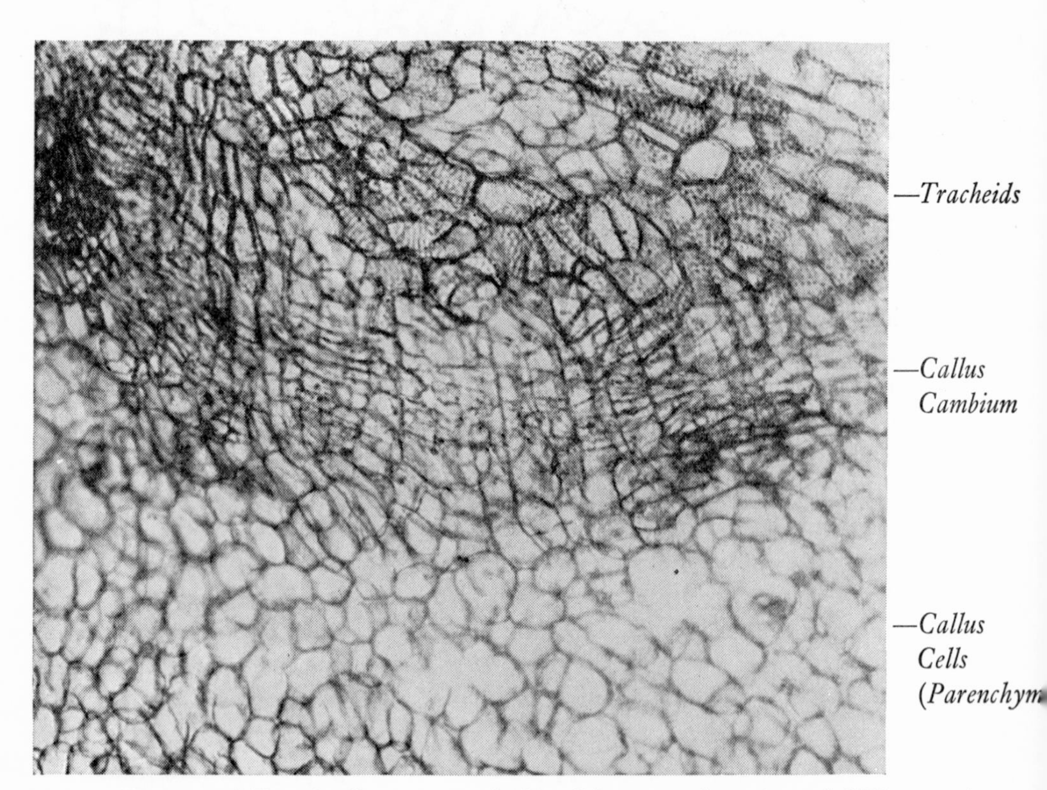

Figure 126 *T.s. of callus on stem of privet*, Ligustrum japonicum (*cf.* Figure 31).

of their cells, and the scion then grows vigorously. The establishment of *graft unions* involves phenomena similar in many ways to those associated with wound healing. Callus tissue forms from both stock and scion, so that if the graft is successful the two become so intimately joined that the vascular systems of the scion and stock become functionally united.

PART III

PLANT NUTRITION

CHAPTER 11

THE PLANT IN RELATION TO WATER

Plant growth is the culmination of a series of complex events, the visible expression of which is the increase in size of the plant's various parts. At the cellular level this growth can be observed as cell division, cell enlargement and cell differentiation. During each of these phases of growth new materials are continually being added to the plant as a result of the synthetic activities of its living cells.

The study of plant nutrition is concerned with finding out from which raw materials plants are made, and exploring just how and where these materials are taken into the plant. As with all living organisms, the bulk of the living plant consists principally of water, though woody species contain proportionately less than do herbaceous species. Clearly, a fundamental aspect of plant nutrition must relate to the entry of water into the plant and to its utilization.

If this water is driven from the plant by heating it to 100°C, then the bulk (i.e. from 90-98%) of dry matter remaining will be found to be composed of the three elements: hydrogen, oxygen and carbon. The hydrogen is derived from water, the oxygen in part from water and in part from the atmosphere, and the carbon entirely from the atmosphere. To discover how this carbon is assimilated has been the second major problem of plant nutrition.

After combustion, the remaining 2-10% of the original dry matter consists of a variety of mineral elements which are either incorporated into the cellular framework of the plant or play some vital part in various synthetic mechanisms; these elements are all supplied to the plant from the soil by way of the root system. Since water, however, is intimately connected with the entry of these elements into the plant, the consideration of water relations must precede the chapters concerned with mineral nutrition.

In germination, the life forces within the dormant seed are greatly accelerated by the absorption of water, which becomes involved almost immediately in important chemical changes. One of the first of these is the *hydrolysis* of food reserves (Chapter 17) which thereby become mobilized for use in the growing embryo. As new cells – the products of division – are added to the embryo on the renewal of activity in its apical meristems, water also becomes incorporated into their protoplasm and their walls. Growth of the embryo also involves considerable increases in cell size by vacuolation and subsequent expansion (Chapter 3). Water is essential for this *turgor enlargement*. Moreover, cell turgor must be maintained throughout the life of the plant if it is to function properly. Later, when the embryo becomes established as a seedling and begins to manufacture its own food by photosynthesis, water is directly involved in the photosynthetic reaction. Since carbon dioxide is absorbed in solution through the mesophyll of the leaf, water is also involved indirectly in photosynthesis (Chapter 18).

Mineral nutrients, which are essential components in the many complex syntheses related to the plant's growth and maintenance, are absorbed in aqueous solution from the soil, by way of the roots. Moreover, the 'raw materials' taken into the plant in this way are moved, or *translocated*, in solution through the tracheary elements of the xylem to the regions of synthesis, where water also takes part in a great variety of metabolic activities. The bulk of the water absorbed, however, is not retained in the plant but evaporates into the air, mainly by way of the stomata of the leaves, in a process known as *transpiration* (Chapter 14).

Water is therefore taken into the plant in great amounts, and is intimately involved in all aspects of its growth and development. Since it is the most abundant and at the same time the most important substance in the living plant, it is necessary to have some knowledge of the properties of water and of the way substances of biological significance occur in it.

SOME PROPERTIES OF WATER

Solutions No natural waters are pure: the clearest lake or stream contains varying amounts of a considerable number of chemical substances dissolved in it in *true solution*; that is, they are dispersed throughout the water, the *solute*, as *molecules* or *ions*. Not only do *solids* become dissolved in this way but also *liquids* and *gases*. The most common type of solution, however, is that in which a solid is dissolved in a liquid, though all substances are by no means soluble in water. Some are extremely insoluble, and there is a definite limit to the amount of even highly soluble solids which can be dissolved. When this limit is reached, the solution is said to be *saturated*. Even at that stage the solubility of certain substances may be further increased by raising the temperature of the solution. Of the gases dissolved in natural waters the most common are carbon dioxide (CO_2), oxygen (O_2), and nitrogen (N_2). Carbon dioxide is very soluble and reacts chemically with the water to produce *carbonic acid* in the following way:

$$\underset{\text{(Carbon dioxide)}}{CO_2} + \underset{\text{(Water)}}{H_2O} \longrightarrow \underset{\text{(Carbonic acid)}}{H_2CO_3}$$

Oxygen and nitrogen, which have low solubilities, do not react in this way.

Aqueous solutions of inorganic salts, acids or bases readily conduct an electric current, a property which is not possessed by solutions of most organic compounds, such as sugars, alcohols, etc. The former for this reason are called *electrolytes*, the latter *non-electrolytes*. When an electrolyte is dissolved in water it becomes dissociated into its constituent ions. For example, hydrochloric acid (HCl) dissociates into hydrogen (H) ions and chloride (Cl) ions: the hydrogen ions carry a positive charge (H^+) and are termed *cations*, while negatively charged ions (in this instance chloride ions (Cl^-)) are termed *anions*. Depending on their particular nature, anions and cations carry from one to four electrical charges, though a given ion always carries the same number and these are always of the same polarity.

In the process of dissociation, the molecules of the electrolyte do not all split up at the same time. There is, in fact, a continuous and well ordered *dissociation* and reunion of the molecules, which means that they are in a state of *dynamic equilibrium*. Not all substances are dissociated to the same extent: the so-called 'strong' electrolytes have a high degree of *ionization*; 'weak' electrolytes are poorly dissociated. The proportion of molecules dissociated depends on the concentration of the solution; it is high in very dilute solutions, becoming progressively less as the solution becomes more concentrated.

All substances which, when dissolved in water, dissociate to give H^+ ions as cations are defined as *acids*, and all those producing *hydroxyl* ions (OH^-) as anions, *bases*. The strength of both acids and bases depends on their degree of ionization, so that a high proportion of H^+ (as in hydrochloric acid (HCl)) or of OH^- ions (as in sodium hydroxide (NaOH)) gives rise to *strong acids* and to bases respectively. *Organic acids*, in contrast, are poorly dissociated and therefore are termed *weak acids*. When the anions of an acid and the cations of a base are brought together, they unite to form *salts*. In such a chemical union the H^+ and OH^- ions combine, thereby cancelling out or neutralizing the acidic or basic properties of one and the other.

Hydrogen Ion Concentration The concentration of hydrogen ions has important biological effects and may markedly influence many of the vital reactions and processes in living organisms. It is therefore essential to have some means of expressing the *hydrogen ion concentration*. Pure water shows but little dissociation of its molecules, for only one in about 500 million ionizes into (H^+) and (OH^-). It has been shown that when H^+ and OH^- ions are present in the same solution, at a temperature of 22°C the product of the concentration of these ions is constant and equals 10^{-14} gm ions per litre. In a neutral solution, which is neither acid nor alkaline, the number of H^+ ions exactly balances the number of OH^- ions and so each must be present in a concentration of 10^{-7} gm ions per litre. If this neutral solution is made alkaline by adding hydroxyl ions, the concentration of H^+ ions will decrease but the product of $H^+ + OH^-$ always remains at 10^{-14} gm ions per litre. This means that in a solution of increasing alkalinity the concentration of H^+ ions is diminishing. However, H^+ ions are always present, even in the most alkaline solutions, and it has become conventional to express *alkalinity*, as well as *acidity*, in terms of the concentration of H^+ ions. A neutral solution clearly contains 10^{-7} gm ions of H^+ per litre; an acid solution more than this concentration; an alkaline solution less. There is, in fact, an inverse relationship between the H^+ ions and OH^- ions.

The hydrogen ion concentration is, however, expressed in terms of the pH, which is the log of concentration, so that the pH of a neutral solution is log $(1/10^{-7}) = 7$. Below pH7 represents the acidic range, above pH7 the alkaline range. Thus a solution with a pH of 6 is *acidic*, with a hydrogen ion concentration of 10^{-6} gm ions per litre, and one with a pH of 8 *alkaline*, with a hydrogen ion concentration of 10^{-8} gm ions per litre. It should always be borne in mind that pH is represented on a *logarithmic scale*, so that the acidic solution with its pH6 has ten times the concentration of H^+ ions as has a neutral solution of pH7, and 100 times as has the alkaline solution with a pH of 8. Moreover, because of the differences in degree of dissociation of strong and weak acids, the pH of a strong acid of a given concentration is less than the pH of a weak acid of the same concentration.

Buffer Action Violent changes in pH are damaging to the harmonious workings of the many complex and interrelated systems within living cells. There is a mechanism in cells, however, which protects or buffers them against such changes and consists in essence of the tying up of any free H^+ or OH^- ions, more or less as soon as they are introduced into solution. This so-called *buffer action* ensures that any ensuing change in pH in the cell is relatively small in proportion to the volume of the acid or alkali introduced.

This effect can best be demonstrated by adding hydrochloric acid, which dissociates into H^+ and Cl^- ions, to a mixture of sodium acetate and acetic acid. The sodium acetate is strongly dissociated as follows:

$$CH_3COONa \rightleftarrows CH_3COO^- + Na^+$$

and the acetic acid only slightly so:

$$CH_3COOH \rightleftarrows CH_3COO^- + H^+$$

The free H^+ ions from the hydrochloric acid immediately become associated with the anions CH_3COO^- in the solution, CH_3COOH being a poorly dissociated substance. This means that the H^+ ions from the strong acid are very rapidly removed from solution: in consequence there is no marked decrease in pH. This type of buffer action is widely found in the cells of all living organisms; in plants it is probable that the salts of *phosphoric*, *malic* and *citric acid* are amongst the most important substances controlling or regulating pH changes.

Suspensions It has been pointed out that many substances, both electrolytes and non-electrolytes, will dissolve in water to produce solutions in which the molecules, or ions, become separated or dissociated from each other and evenly dispersed throughout the solvent. Solutions in fact may be defined as systems in which the molecules or ions of one substance are dispersed throughout the molecules of another. If Indian ink is stirred into water, however, the particles which make the ink appear black and which are large enough to be seen under a microscope do not separate into molecules, though they do become dispersed throughout the water. The dispersed particles in fact form a *suspension* which is *unstable* because of the size of the particles, and if left to stand these gradually settle out under the influence of gravity so that the suspension clears.

Colloids The essential difference between true solutions and suspensions is in the size of the particles of the dispersed phase. Between these two categories is an intermediate condition in which the dispersed phase consists of molecules or groups of molecules which, however, are not so large that the particles settle out under gravity, as do those of suspensions. Thus one of the essential characters of such *colloidal solutions* is that they form *stable systems*. The distinction between colloids and solutions is by no means clear cut; for some substances, such as proteins and certain organic dyes, have individual molecules that are so large that they come within the size range of *colloids*. Molecular dispersions of such substances have the properties both of colloids and of true solutions. On the other side of the range there is no sharp boundary between colloids and suspensions, and as between true solutions and colloids, there is only a gradation of their various properties and characters.

Adsorption Colloids are of great biological significance. One of their most important properties is a consequence of the small size of the molecules, or molecular aggregates, of their dispersed phase, which offers in the colloidal solution a surface area vast in relation to the actual mass of substance present. This permits the concentration or *adsorption* of molecules at the interfaces of the dispersed phase of the colloid.

Adsorption plays a significant part in most cellular activities in all living organisms. It can be demonstrated by a simple experiment with the dye, *methylene blue*, *activated charcoal*, and the organic liquid *ethanol*. A gram of the charcoal is stirred into 5 ml of 0·05% solution of the dye and it will be found on filtering that the filtrate has become colourless. The molecules of methylene blue have in fact been removed from solution and adsorbed at the carbon-water interfaces. This is because the attraction between the dye molecules and the carbon molecules is greater than that between the dye and the water molecules. If a small volume of ethanol, however, is poured over the charcoal retained on the filter paper, it will be seen that the methylene blue is released from the carbon and redissolves in the ethanol. This second part of the experiment demonstrates that there is a greater force of attraction between the dye molecules and the ethanol than existed between the dye and the carbon.

This experiment demonstrates the essential character of adsorption, that is the concentrating of molecules of a substance (in this case methylene blue) at an interface (here the carbon-water interface). Within plant cells a considerable number of such interfaces occur, not only in the various colloidal systems present in the cell sap, but at the various cell boundaries which exist, for example, between the nucleus and cytoplasm, and the cytoplasm and cell wall. At these interfaces a concentrating of solutes undoubtedly takes place.

Sols and Gels The name *sol* is often used to distinguish a colloidal solution from a true solution. If the dispersed phase is a solid, then it is termed a *suspensoid sol*, but if, as is often the case, it is liquid, then it is termed an *emulsoid sol* or *emulsion*.

Emulsions, with but few exceptions, tend to be unstable and the two components, as for example an oil in water emulsion, tend to separate rapidly, the component of lower specific gravity rising to the top. Stability can, however, be conferred on emulsions by the presence of an emulsifier such as soap or saponin. In living cells emulsions are probably most commonly stabilized by proteins.

Many sols have the property of 'setting', that is of forming a more or less elastic system, termed a *gel*. Starch, for example, forms an emulsoid sol when boiled with water, but will set on cooling into a gel. Very little solid matter will suffice to form a gel, and in the case of agar gels, which are widely used in bacteriological work, one part in a hundred of water will, if the agar powder is mixed with water, heated and then allowed to cool, set into a firm jelly. How this very small amount of matter firmly holds, in a more or less rigid state, the 99% of water presents an interesting problem, for very considerable pressures are required to squeeze any water from the gel (cf. p. 163). Some gels will return to the sol condition if further water and especially if some further heating is applied, and so their condition is said to be *reversible*. In other cases heating causes their *irreversible coagulation*, as happens when the white of an egg is hardened on boiling. Changes in hydrogen ion concentration may in certain cases convert sols to gels and vice versa, and some enzymes (see p. 201) have the same general effect.

CHAPTER 12

THE ENTRY OF WATER INTO PLANTS

In considering how plants acquire the substances – water, carbon dioxide, and mineral salts – vital for their nutrition it is necessary to have some knowledge of the physical process known as *diffusion*. The essence of this important phenomenon can best be appreciated by considering a water-filled, rectangular tank containing some solute which has been introduced at one end. Such a tank is depicted in fig. 127 and the dots in it represent the solute molecules which are clearly at a higher concentration at the left end than at the right. If the tank and its contents are undisturbed, it will be found that the concentration of the solute gradually becomes increasingly uniform throughout the water mass, which suggests that there has been a *net movement* of solute molecules from left to right. This movement, which is an example of diffusion, is not due to any repulsion between the solute molecules. It results from the fact that at temperatures above absolute zero (–273°C), the molecules in any liquid are in a state of independent, random movement. That is, each molecule of solvent and solute moves in an erratic manner with frequent changes in direction. Such random movement also means that after a given interval, any particular molecule has an equal chance of being either to the left, or right, of the position it occupied at the beginning of the interval.

This example may be further developed by considering the behaviour of the molecules in an imaginary slice of the solution which is so thin that the concentration of solute across it is virtually uniform (AA′ in fig. 127). During any short period of time, as many solute molecules will then move out of the slice to the right as move out to the left. The same conditions will obtain in any adjacent slice of equal size (e.g. BB′ in fig. 127). However, merely because there are more solute molecules (a higher concentration) in the slice to the left (AA′) than in that on the right (BB′), more solute

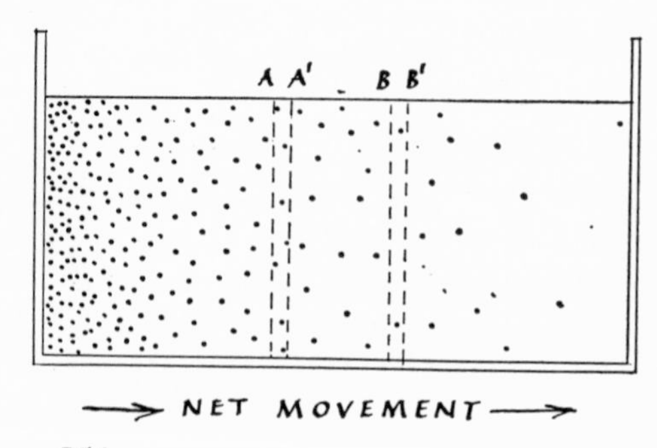

Figure 127 *Diagrammatic representation of the process of diffusion.*

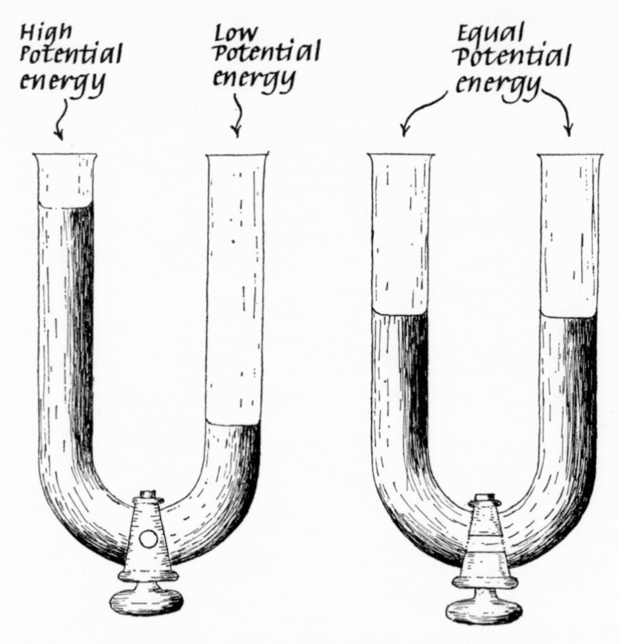

Figure 128 *Experiment to illustrate differences in potential energy.*

molecules will move from AA′ to BB′ than move in the opposite direction. As a result there will be a net movement of solute from left to right. Diffusion will continue until the concentration is uniform throughout the tank. Then, although the molecules of the solute will continue to move about in the water, there will be no net movement of solute.

It must be emphasized that in any solution there is not only a movement of solute but also of solvent. Pure water consists of H_2O molecules only a small proportion of which are dissociated at any given time, so that they are at their highest possible concentration (see p. 150). The concentration of water molecules decreases, however, even when a very small amount of some substance is dissolved in the pure water. This is because in a unit volume, a proportion of the molecules are necessarily molecules of the dissolved substance. Thus when pure water and water with a substance dissolved in it are brought together, molecules from the pure water diffuse into the less concentrated water until such time as the differences in concentration are eliminated and a state of equilibrium is attained.

An analogy can be drawn between diffusion on the one hand and, on the other, the behaviour of water in a U-tube fitted with a tap at its lowest point, as shown in fig. 128. The tap is closed and the tube filled with water in such a way that the water in the left arm is at a higher level than in the right. When the tap is opened the water will flow from left to right until the level in both arms is the same. It could be said that when the tap was closed originally, the water in the left arm had a greater *potential energy* than the water in the right. When the tap was opened an equilibrium was attained as soon as the potential energy of the water in both arms was the same. Similarly, any solute in a solution has a *chemical potential*, and at equilibrium the potential of the solute (and solvent) must be the same throughout the solution. One of the factors on which such a chemical potential depends is the concentration of the solute. In diffusion, the movement of the solute and solvent is from a region of higher chemical potential to one of lower potential – that is down a *chemical potential gradient*. Thus in the example of the tank in fig. 127, while the net movement of the solute is from left to right that of the solvent is from right to left.

In the U-tube, in order to make water move from the right arm to the left, that is from a region of lower potential energy to one of higher potential energy, it is necessary for work to be done (i.e. energy must be expended). Similarly, to move a solute or solvent against a chemical potential gradient requires the expenditure of energy.

OSMOSIS

A greater amount of water than of any other substance passes into plant cells. It does so by diffusing across the cell membranes into the vacuoles of living cells (for example the root hairs in terrestrial plants) as the result of a special diffusion phenomenon, *osmosis*. The term osmosis is derived from the Greek, meaning 'to push'.

The process of osmosis can be demonstrated with a simply constructed *osmometer*. This is made by tying cellophane (an artificial, differentially permeable membrane of viscose cellulose) tightly across the open end of a thistle funnel. The chamber so formed is then filled with a 10% *sucrose* solution, the molecules of which pass, but only very slowly, through the membrane. The funnel is then placed in a beaker of pure water. Since the membrane is permeable to water, there will be a net movement of water molecules from the beaker through the membrane into the thistle funnel, that is, down a *concentration gradient* from a region of *high concentration of water molecules* to one of low concentration. Such a diffusion, which is osmosis, will result in an increase in the volume of the solution in the funnel and this causes the solution to rise up the tube of the funnel. It is reasonable to suppose that this osmosis could be prevented by applying a pressure to the open end of the tube. Moreover, if such a pressure was applied it would be found that for any given concentration of any particular solution there would be a particular pressure at which osmosis was prevented. At this pressure the water in the system would be in equilibrium. The *equilibrium pressure* can be called the *osmotic pressure* (P) of the solution and is commonly measured in atmospheres (one atmosphere = 14 lb. per sq. inch).

When the solution in the thistle funnel is subjected to a *hydrostatic pressure* just sufficient to prevent osmosis, the water in the solution is in equilibrium with the pure water in the beaker through the semi-permeable membrane. At equilibrium, the chemical potential of the water must clearly be the same throughout the system. Therefore under these conditions, the chemical potential of water in the solution must be the same as pure water. It is thus possible to define osmotic pressure, without reference to a semi-permeable membrane, as *the excess hydrostatic pressure which must be applied to the solution in order to make the chemical potential of the solvent in the solution equal to that of the pure solvent, provided the temperature remains unaltered.* If osmotic pressure is defined in these terms, it is then not illogical to refer to the osmotic pressure of a solution when that solution is at atmospheric pressure, even in a reagent bottle. Although in such a bottle a 10% aqueous sucrose solution has an osmotic pressure of about 8 atmospheres, this does not mean that there is a hydrostatic pressure of this amount within the bottle. It merely implies that 8 atmospheres, or 112 lb. per square inch, would be the extra hydrostatic pressure to which the solution would have to be subjected to make the water in the solution behave like pure water, at atmospheric pressure. It must be added that the osmotic pressure of a solution is governed by the number of particles, molecules or ions, present in a unit volume, but is independent of the nature of these particles, at least in very dilute solutions.

Osmosis in Living Cells

In the open osmometer, the ascent of water up the tube of the thistle funnel indicates that osmosis is taking place. Such an osmometer, however, bears little resemblance to a living cell. An osmometer which has a much closer resemblance can be made by tying up the open ends of a cylinder of viscose cellulose dialysis sheet which has been filled with a 20% sucrose solution. The cylinder is then carefully suspended in a glass tank containing pure water. As osmosis proceeds, the contents of this artificial cell will increase in volume due to the hydrostatic pressure which builds up inside, and so exerts an ever-increasing pressure on the semi-permeable cellulose membrane. In consequence the cylinder becomes distended or *turgid* – a condition which it was noted (see p. 39) appears to be characteristic of all healthy cells. The pressure which the contents of this turgid cell exert on the cell wall as a result of osmosis is called the *turgor pressure* (T), and like osmotic pressure is also expressed in atmospheres. Water will continue to pass into the cell until the turgor pressure is equal to the osmotic pressure – that is until the chemical potential of the water inside the artificial cell is the same as that of the pure water outside. Living cells similarly become turgid when placed in pure water.

If a turgid living cell is allowed to lose some water by exposing it, for example, to dry air for a short time, there will be a decrease in the volume of its vacuole and an increase in the concentration of solutes, and hence in the osmotic pressure of the vacuolar sap. The reduction in vacuolar volume will also decrease the extent to which the bounding cell wall is stretched and there will in consequence be a reduction in turgor pressure. Both of these changes will cause a decrease in the chemical potential of the water in the vacuole so that it becomes less than that of pure water. Although several terms have been used to express this reduction, the one most widely used is *suction pressure* (S). This is a measure of the net tendency of water to move into a cell.

S	=	P_i	—	T
(Suction pressure in atmospheres)		(Osmotic pressure, in atmospheres of the vacuolar sap)		(Turgor pressure in atmospheres)

Clearly, when a cell is in a state of equilibrium and there is no net tendency for water either to enter or leave it, the suction pressure will be zero; or in other words, when the diffusion of water into the cell is balanced by its tendency to leave under turgor pressure. The relationship between these various values is shown in fig. 129.

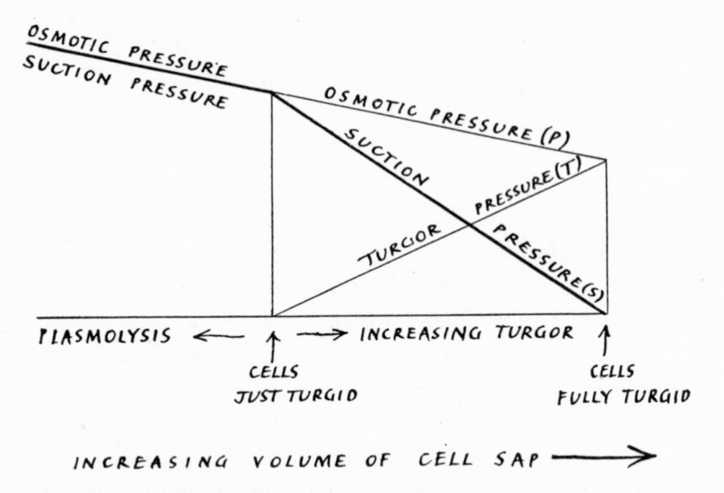

Figure 129 *Diagram to illustrate the relationship between osmotic pressure, suction pressure and turgor pressure (after Thomas).*

The rate of diffusion of water into living cells is affected not only by differences between the concentrations of diffusing substances inside and outside the cell. It is controlled also by physical factors such as temperature, but especially, since cell membranes vary considerably in their permeability, by the nature of these membranes which lie between the external solution and the vacuolar sap. Some allow neither water nor dissolved substances through them, as for example, cutinized and suberized walls. Cellulose walls, on the other hand, are readily permeable to water and dissolved solutes, though not to substances in suspension. Between these two extremes are the cytoplasmic membranes which admit water but impede the passage of many substances in solution. Thus the *semi-permeable membranes* play a decisive part in the absorption of water and solutes; indeed they govern the passage of all material into and out of living cells of all plants. In general, small molecules can pass through them, while larger ones are impeded (see, however, Chapter 15), although this *selectivity* is lost when a cell dies.

Plasmolysis

If a cell with a suction pressure (S) of x atmospheres is placed in a solution of the same osmotic pressure (i.e. x atmospheres), there will be no net movement of water into, or out of, the cell. Under such conditions of equilibrium, the cell will not change in volume, length or fresh weight; nor will the concentration of the bathing solution change. If, however, this cell is placed in a large volume of a solution of osmotic pressure (P_e) which is not equal to x, then the cell will gain water if the suction pressure (S) is greater than the osmotic pressure (P_e); or it will lose water if the suction pressure is less than the osmotic pressure. The loss or gain will continue until equilibrium is reached and $S = P_e$.

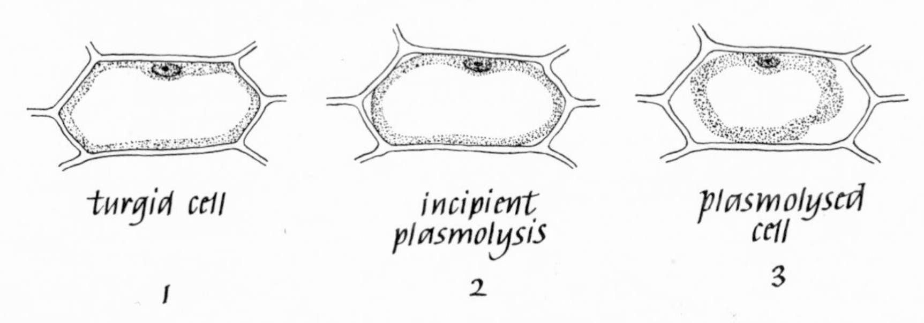

Figure 130 1-3 *Stages in the plasmolysis of a turgid cell.*

If the cell is placed in a solution whose osmotic pressure is considerably greater than its suction pressure it will lose water, and as it does so, a point will be reached, as the cell becomes less and less turgid, when the protoplast no longer exerts a pressure on the cell wall. That is, the turgor pressure is zero (T = O) and hence the suction pressure of the cell is equal to the osmotic pressure of its vacuolar sap ($S = P_1$). The water in the vacuole will therefore be in equilibrium with the water in a solution of osmotic pressure $P_e = P_i$. The cell in this condition is said to be at *incipient plasmolysis* ('lysis' is from the Greek, meaning, 'a losing'). Further loss of water results in increased plasmolysis, which is the retraction of the protoplast from the cell wall (fig. 130). Stages in the process of plasmolysis can be seen under the microscope by mounting strips of epidermal cells from the inner surface of the scale of an onion bulb, on a glass slide in 20% sucrose solution. This solution has an osmotic pressure greater than that of the vacuolar contents and so is said to be *hypertonic* (meaning 'of higher tension') to the cell sap. Plasmolysis and the shrinking of the protoplast away from the cell wall continues until the osmotic pressure of the sap is equal to, or *isotonic* ('equal tension') with that of the bathing solution. If the hypertonic solution is washed off the slide and replaced by pure water, or by a solution of lower concentration than the 20% sucrose, that is *hypotonic* ('below tension') to the sap in the now plasmolysed cell, there should be a recovery of turgor.

Plasmolysis can be used as a means of assessing the osmotic pressure of the sap in plant cell vacuoles. For example, strips of onion epidermis, or thin sections of beetroot, are placed in a series of osmotically active solutions each of known concentration – say 5, 10, 15, 20 and 25% sucrose. After a time the cells in the strips or sections are examined in turn under the microscope to discover the concentration of solution required to bring the cells just to the point of incipient plasmolysis. Since the osmotic pressure of any solution depends upon its concentration, the particular concentration causing incipient plasmolysis must be approximately equal to the osmotic pressure of the vacuolar contents being tested, when the turgor pressure of the tissue is zero. At this concentration there is no net movement of water into or out of these cells. As indicated in the diagram in fig. 129, the osmotic pressure of the sap varies with the volume, and hence the turgor of the cell, owing to dilution by the entry of water from outside.

Osmosis and the Whole Plant

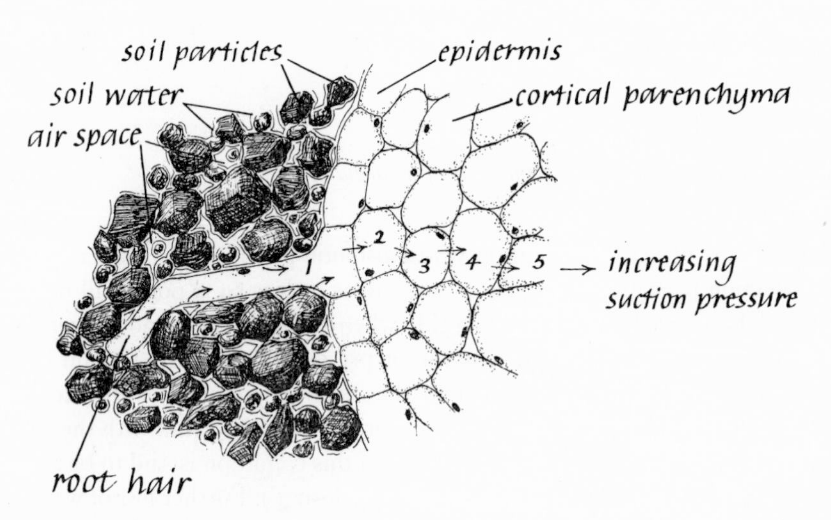

Figure 131 *Diagram to show the passage of water from the soil into the root of a plant.*

In the examples of osmosis discussed so far, only single cells have been considered. In the living plant, however, cells occur in intimate contact with one another as tissues. In these the intake of water by any particular cell depends on the difference between its own powers of absorption due to the osmotic pressure of its cell sap and those forces external to the cell which tend to remove water from it. These are the cell's own wall pressure and the pressure of the surrounding cells, which both tend to resist any increase in cell volume, and the suction pressure of adjoining cells. The latter, being osmotic systems, may also compete for any available water. Thus in the absorbing root, water available around and between soil particles diffuses from the region of higher water concentration (that is, in the soil water with its very dilute mineral solution) to that where a lower concentration of water molecules exists in the more dilute state in the cell vacuole with its high concentration of solutes. The water concentration of the sap in the root hair thus becomes greater (and solutes more diluted) than in the adjoining cortical cells, and water moves into these cells (fig. 131). As a result of the gradient of suction pressure, water passes by diffusion, often with considerable rapidity, across the cortex, through the endodermis, and so into the xylem of the vascular vessels. From there it passes upwards through the stem and into the leaves. It seems probable that the living xylem parenchyma cells, which adjoin the vessels, pass water into the vessel cavities. Since, however, measurements have indicated that the sap in the xylem vessels is most frequently of a lower osmotic concentration than in these adjoining cells, water must it seems, pass into the vessels against a concentration gradient, which suggests that respiratory energy has to be expended. Water moves within plants along suction pressure gradients and, provided the cells are turgid (as they undoubtedly would be in the root cortex), these may be independent, to a large extent, of the relative osmotic pressures of the cells. Thus water can move across a tissue having a high osmotic pressure to a region, in this case the xylem vessels, with a lower osmotic pressure but higher suction pressure. The root hairs and cortex thus act as a living multicellular, semi-permeable membrane between the soil water and the xylem. Water, it seems, will move from any region where the suction pressure is low to one where it is higher, regardless of the osmotic pressure of the cells in the two regions.

Root Pressure

That the osmotic movement of water takes place in plants can be demonstrated if the stem of a well watered, potted tomato, *Solanum lycopersicum*, or *Pelargonium*, which has been growing in sheltered, humid conditions, is cut off an inch or so above soil level. The cut stump will then exude sap, or bleed, quite profusely. This phenomenon of *bleeding*, which also occurs from wounds which penetrate as far as the xylem, has been known to man from very early times. A well-known example of bleeding is the flow of sap obtained by wounding, or tapping, maple trees, which yield a considerable flow of sugary syrup (maple syrup) in spring. The sugar exuded represents food which has been accumulated during the previous summer and stored as starch. Early during the following spring it is converted into sugar, which moves into the xylem in solution, and then drains out with the sap if any internal pressure exists in the tapped tree. In the cut off or *excised* tomato or *Pelargonium* stem, this *root pressure* can be measured by attaching a manometer to the stump, and in tomatoes, pressures in excess of 9 atmospheres may develop. This however is somewhat exceptional, and in other plants in which the phenomenon has been observed, pressures vary between 2 and 3 atmospheres. This *active absorption* mechanism of roots depends on an adequate water supply to them and being a vital process, it can be suppressed by cutting

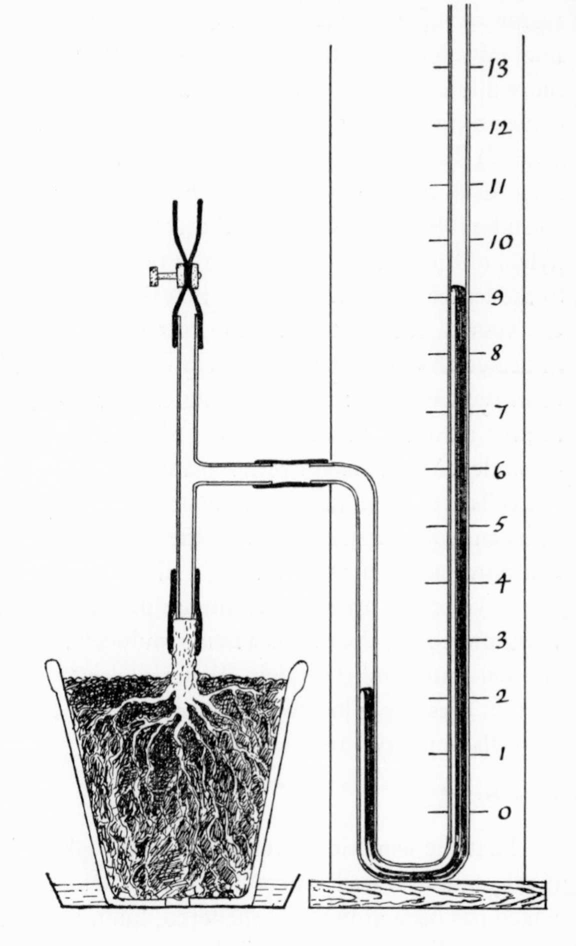

Figure 132 *Experiment to demonstrate root pressure.*

off the oxygen supply, indicating that it too is a process dependent on respiratory energy (fig. 132).

IMBIBITION

Another process basically involving the diffusion of water is that of *imbibition.* It is by this process that dried seeds take in water as the initial step in their germination (Chapter 1, p. 5). Water may be imbibed not only as liquid water but also as water vapour. Because of this, the water content of 'air dry' seeds may show from time to time considerable changes in weight which can be related to fluctuations in atmospheric humidity. Imbibition is not merely a process of diffusion, for since imbibing substances (*imbibants*) are probably all permeated by minute *capillaries*, there is undoubtedly some capillary movement through these pores. As in the case of osmosis, however, the main factor causing this type of water uptake into plants is the existence of *diffusion gradients* between the water and the imbibant which persist until a state of equilibrium is attained. It is believed that the bulk of the water imbibed is *adsorbed* on to the molecules or larger particles which make up the imbibant and which therefore has colloidal properties. Indeed, the result of imbibition is frequently the formation of a colloidal system, essentially a gel. The cellulose walls and the living protoplasm of cells possess the important attribute of being able to imbibe water.

It is well known that substances such as agar-agar and gelatine can imbibe amounts of water which are very large in proportion to their dry weight (cf. p. 153). Dried stipes of the brown seaweed *Laminaria* (see p. 377) are reported as being able to absorb as much as 15 times their own weight of water. A simple experiment can be performed to illustrate the water absorbing properties of a gel and its resultant swelling. A square of dry gelatine (a carbohydrate gel) about 4 cm × 4 cm is weighed and then placed in a dish of water so that it exactly covers a square of black paper cut to the same dimensions. After some time it will be observed that the gelatine no longer 'fits' the paper square beneath it. It has imbibed water and increased in size considerably. The accompanying increase in weight of the gelatine is indicative of just how much water has been imbibed. For example, a 4 cm square with an initial dry weight of 4·2 gms has been found to weigh 18·9 gms after twenty-four hours immersion in water at 18°C.

CHAPTER 13

WATER AND SOILS

Water is not only the most important and abundant of substances in the living plant, it is also one of the most abundant and widespread of naturally occurring substances. In addition to the great masses of water in the oceans of the world, and the smaller volumes in lakes and rivers, practically all soils and even rocks are permeated by water. It is also present in the atmosphere, often in considerable amounts, as vapour; for water evaporates from oceans, lakes, rivers, and soils in dry weather until the atmosphere becomes saturated. With any decrease in temperature, this water vapour becomes liquefied and falls as rain, so that there is a continual circulation of water.

Terrestrial plants absorb from the soil in which they are rooted greater quantities of water than anything else, hence the balance between the amount of water in the soil and in the atmosphere (as water vapour) is of the greatest importance. Until the air is saturated there is a tendency for water to be removed from the soil at the expense, and often to the detriment, of the plants growing in it.

Soil is primarily formed by the weathering of the rocks which form the earth's crust, a process brought about in part by climatic agents in the form of rain, wind, sun, and frost, but also to some extent by biological agents. These include the activities of plant root systems and such micro-organisms as bacteria and fungi. The micro-organisms break down organic matter which may accumulate within the framework of rock particles, so that eventually the soil consists of a chemical and biological complex of mineral particles and organic matter. This complex is permeated both by water in which mineral substances, so important for plant nutrition, are dissolved (the so-called *soil solution*), and by a very vital constituent, air. The fundamental character of a soil is largely determined by the nature and size of the particles which form the mineral framework. Thus soils differ in texture and can be classified either as *coarse sands*, *fine sands*, *loams*, *silts* or *clays*. The range of size of particles in this somewhat arbitrary classification is summarized below:

Particle type	Diameter (mm)	% found in typical Sandy loam	% found in typical Clay loam	% found in typical Clay
Coarse Sand	2·00 – 0·20	65	30	1
Fine Sand	0·20 – 0·02	20	30	9
Silt	0·02 – 0·002	5	20	25
Clay	below 0·002	10	20	65

The least complex soil type is a *sand* which is composed principally of simple rock particles of fairly large size. These rock particles, mainly silica, are relatively inert chemically, and since they are comparatively large there exist considerable air spaces between the fragments. This ensures good aeration and the free movement of water. Such soils therefore have a poor water-holding capacity and being loose and non-cohesive, do not compact. At the other extreme of particle size are the *clays*, which owe their most important properties to the fact that their particles are of colloidal dimensions. Hence they exhibit many of the characteristic properties of colloidal systems, the most significant for plant growth being their enormous internal surface area. Indeed, most soils owe many of their chemical and physical properties to the clay fraction they contain. Although readily compacted and poorly aerated, and therefore physically unfavourable to most root systems which must breathe, clay soils are rich in mineral nutrients and hold water tenaciously.

Loams are soils which contain a good blend of particle sizes and thereby tend to possess properties intermediate between sands and clays. For this reason they are most favourable for plant growth, holding much more available water than sandy soils, and being better aerated, and less compactable, are easier to work than clays.

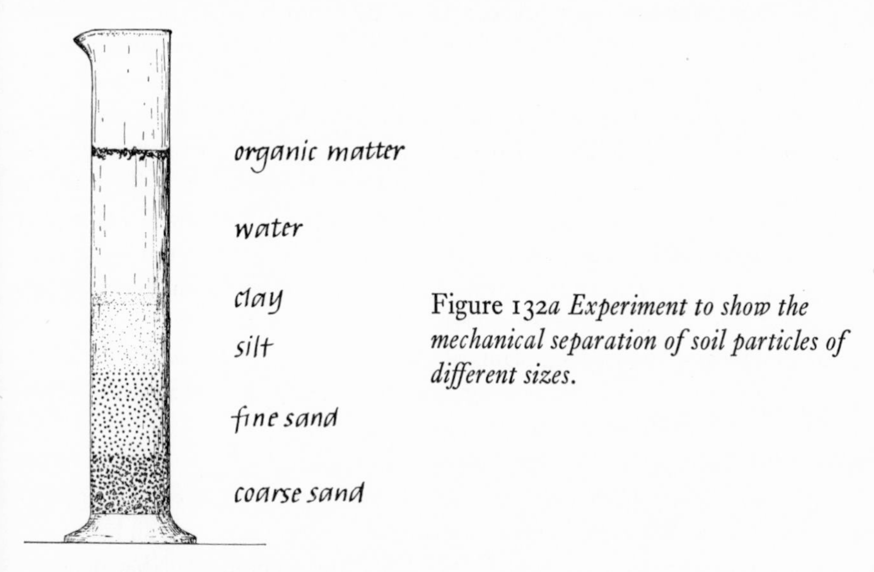

Figure 132*a* *Experiment to show the mechanical separation of soil particles of different sizes.*

Some idea of the relative proportions in which mineral particles of different sizes occur in any soil can be gained by placing a sample of the soil in a glass cylinder and filling the latter with water. After thorough stirring until completely mixed with the water the soil is allowed to settle. This mechanical separation of particles allows the largest, heaviest particles of sand to separate first and fall to the bottom of the cylinder, while the smallest, lightest particles of clay are the last to settle. Any organic matter present floats on the surface of the water. After a considerable time the clay particles form the closely compacted, uppermost layer. By this simple procedure, the approximate amounts of each broad category of particle can be determined by measuring the thickness of each layer which settles out in the cylinder (fig. 132*a*).

All soils, except those freshly formed from the parent rock, contain in addition to their mineral framework some proportion of organic matter or *humus*. When plants that live rooted in a soil die, their stems, leaves, flowers, fruits, and seeds are returned to the soil directly as vegetable remains, or indirectly in the form of animal remains or excreta. These organic remains are rapidly attacked by many types of bacteria and fungi, and are broken down so that eventually they become incorporated into the soil. It is this extremely important constituent, *organic matter*, which gives many good soils their dark brown or black colour. The organic matter is often a source of chemical elements essential in plant nutrition, especially of nitrogen and phosphorus which are commonly extremely scarce as soluble constituents of the soil solution. Equally important is the part played by humus in 'opening' the texture of clay soils, thus leading to their better aeration. Like clay, however, humus is essentially colloidal in its properties and is retentive of water, so that in a sandy soil its presence increases the water holding capacity.

A phenomenon of extreme importance in the structure of soils occurs when some of their small elementary particles become aggregated into larger granules or compound particles. As a result of such aggregation, a soil may come to combine some of the properties of clays and of soils with large particles such as sands. Without this phenomenon, which is largely a biological one dependent on the activities of soil micro-organisms and especially of earthworms, fungi, and plant root systems, many fertile soils would become considerably compacted and poorly aerated. This would result in poor root development and, in turn, poor overall growth. Since soil micro-organisms are primarily instrumental in causing soil aggregation, this important process is indirectly dependent on the presence in the soil of organic matter on which these organisms feed. Thus soil is not merely an inert mass of mineral and organic matter containing water from which plants absorb dissolved mineral nutrients: it is a highly complex system in which there is intense and varied biological activity.

Water in the Soil

For plant growth, water is the most important constituent of a soil. The amount present may vary from a mere trace in arid regions, to saturation in bogs and swamps. Not all the *soil-water* present can be used by plants; the amount available depends on the soil type. Thus in sandy soils only a very small proportion cannot be removed, whereas in a clay up to half the total water content may be held in a state unavailable to plants.

A soil may be thought of as a sponge. If water is poured over it when dry, a considerable amount will be retained even after the excess has been allowed to drain away by gravity from its larger pores. After gravitational drainage has taken place following heavy rain, the soil is said to be at its *field capacity*. Any further loss of water is then mainly due to evaporation at the soil surface, or through its absorption by plant roots. As this second phase of emptying the soil 'sponge' proceeds, a state is attained where there is insufficient water left to prevent plants growing in it from *wilting*. This point is determined empirically, and a soil is said to be at the *permanent wilting point* when a test plant collapses and will not recover from wilting without the addition of more water to the soil. Under some conditions wilting may be only temporary, and the test plant may recover if certain environmental conditions causing water-loss from the plant are modified. This may occur several times before a condition of permanent wilting is achieved. Different types of soils show considerable differences in the amount of water held at field capacity and at permanent wilting point, the extremes being clays on the one hand and coarse sands on the other. Indeed, the determination of moisture content at these two critical values are probably the most significant measurements to be made in studies of plant growth in relation to soil water.

Like a sponge, a soil contains a very great number of interconnecting spaces between its particles. These vary in size, depending on the size and shape of the particles. They are large in sands and extremely minute in clays. After a soil has been saturated and the gravitational water has drained away, the water remaining occurs as a film round individual soil particles (fig. 133), and in the smaller, capillary pores. In these, the capillary forces are strong enough to prevent further gravitational drainage. Much of this water, which is in fact the water in the soil at its field capacity, is held somewhat loosely and is readily available to, and can be drawn on by plants.

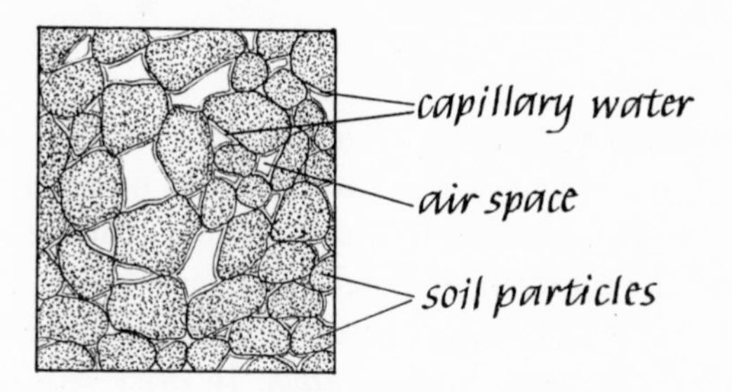

Figure 133 *Diagram of soil to show how water and air are important constituents.*

Water is still retained in an air dry soil as *hygroscopic water*, where it exists in the very finest capillaries and as a very thin film round the soil particles, probably only 15-20 molecules wide. Water may also be chemically combined in the minerals of the soil particles themselves, but like the hygroscopic water it is also unavailable to plants. Water vapour also occurs, with other gases, in the soil atmosphere, but it is unlikely that this can ever be used by plants as a source of water.

The various classes of soil water outlined above are not discrete classes, and between the three major conditions, gravitational, capillary and hygroscopic, there occurs every possible intermediate state. In general, however, the more water there is in a soil, the more readily it can be removed by plants.

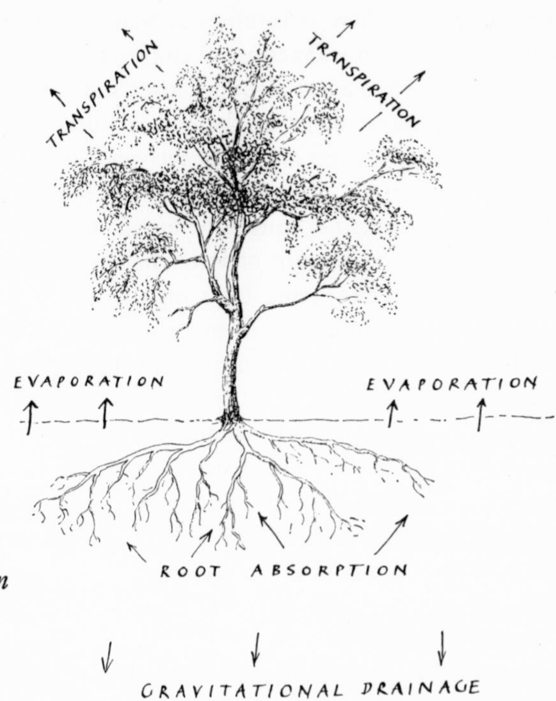

Figure 134 *The relationship between a plant and soil water.*

As a soil drys out through surface evaporation and the removal of water by plant roots, there is very little movement of water to the drier, upper layers from wetter regions (fig. 134). Only in the upper layers of soil, when it is above its field capacity after heavy rain, is there any considerable water movement. Under these conditions, as water is absorbed by roots and the soil becomes depleted, more water moves towards these drying areas by *capillary translocation*. In drier soils, however, where water movement is very slow, the roots themselves grow towards adjoining wetter regions, thereby spreading outwards and downwards, often for very considerable distances. In this way the water supply held in the soil is tapped by a plant through its expanding root system. This vital region of the plant, as described earlier, is a vastly branching system, the actively growing tips of which are potentially capable of unlimited growth. It has been estimated that the mature root systems of even quite modest sized plants bear many millions of root tips which gradually progress through the soil towards available sources of water. Some idea of the enormous extent of root systems can be gained from measurements made of 4-month-old rye (*Secale cereale*) plants. These were on average found to have a total root length of 387 miles, and the daily increase in length of a single plant was found to be 3 miles.

The exploitation of soil water is achieved not only by the continuous branching and growth of the root system but also by the production of root hairs which greatly increase the area over which the root is in contact with the soil. These provide the major portion of the absorbing region. The 4-month-old rye plant mentioned above was found to bear some 14 *billion* root hairs and, in contrast to the daily 3-mile increase in length of the root system, nearly 55 miles of new hairs were formed each day on one plant.

CHAPTER 14

TRANSPIRATION

Normally the bulk of water absorbed by plants evaporates and is lost by way of the leaves, where it is given off as water vapour. Transpiration, as this loss of water vapour is termed, may take place from any part of a plant exposed to the air, but the stomatal pores of the leaves are the organs principally concerned. Resulting from transpiration there is, under optimum conditions, a continuous flow of water through the plant. This originates around the soil particles, passes into the roots, up the stem to the branches and their leaves, and flows outwards as water vapour by way of the stomata to the air.

The loss of water occurring through transpiration can be simply demonstrated. A well watered, potted plant that has been placed in a watertight container, so that no water is lost by evaporation from the surface of the pot, is weighed, left for a period, and then weighed again. The difference in weight recorded is thus a measure of the water lost by transpiration.

A more refined method of assessment is to collect the water lost as vapour from transpiring leaves. Either a whole plant, or small areas of the leaf of a plant which can then be related to the whole leaf can be used. If a whole plant is used, it is sealed under a bell jar through which air of known moisture content can be drawn. This air, containing water vapour from the transpiring plant, is passed over tubes containing calcium chloride or phosphorus pentoxide. Any gain in weight of these tubes indicates a corresponding weight loss by the whole plant through its transpiration. Similar weight increases of tubes of calcium chloride, whose open ends are affixed to leaf surfaces, are indicative of the amount of water loss per unit area of a leaf.

Such experiments show that water loss from plants can under certain circumstances be very considerable. Under natural conditions, a hundred times its own water content may pass through a plant in a single growing season as a result of transpiration. It has been estimated, for example, that an acre of maize can use 1,300 tons of water between seed germination and fruiting.

Transpiration rates and the environmental factors controlling them can be investigated quite accurately with an apparatus called a *potometer* (fig. 135). Small entire plants grown in water, or plants whose roots are free from soil, or leaf branches, can be used. The potometer consists of a water-filled vessel into which the plant or the cut end of a transpiring branch is sealed. Attached to this vessel there is a reservoir from which the flow of water can be controlled with a stop-cock, and a horizontally placed, graduated capillary tube, the end of which is bent through 90° to dip into a second reservoir. If the second reservoir is removed for a short time, a small air bubble can be introduced into the capillary tube. This bubble will move along the tube, owing to the fact that water from the vessel which joins the tube is being removed by the transpiring plant. Thus the rate of movement of the bubble is an indirect measure of the rate of water uptake by the plant. When the bubble has travelled the length of the horizontal tube, a further set of readings can be made by opening the stopcock and allowing water from the first reservoir to flow into the potometer; this pushes the bubble back to the far end of the tube. The potometer thus gives quite rapid measurements of transpiration rates, provided absorption is equal to transpiration. With this simple apparatus it is possible to compare transpiration rates from shoots with similar leaf areas from different plants – for example between a thickly cutinized evergreen and a thin-leaved dicotyledonous shoot. Also, the environ-

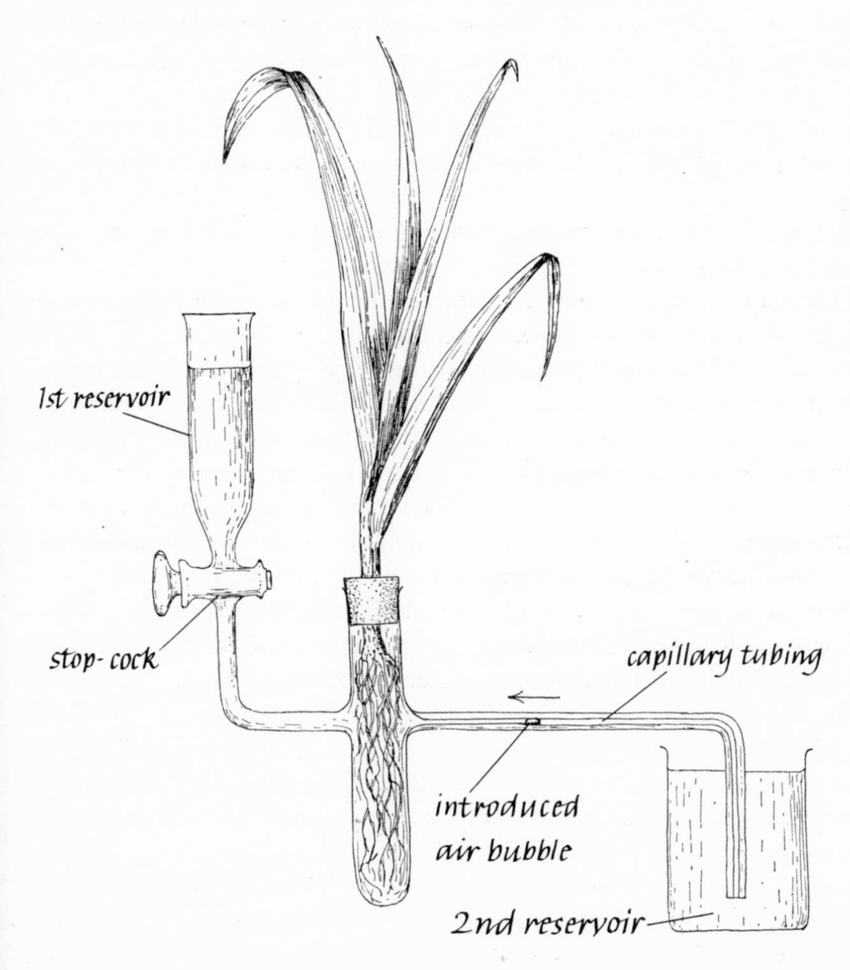

Figure 135 *A simple potometer which measures the rate of absorption of water by the root system of a small plant.*

mental factors influencing transpiration can be studied. Investigations of this nature will inevitably show that any environmental conditions which favour evaporation – warm, dry, moving air in contrast to air that is cold, moist and static – are conducive to high transpiration rates.

Measurements of transpiration made at hourly intervals over a period of 24 hours will be found to exhibit a daily rhythm. On an ideal, cloudless day the rate of transpiration increases during the day, reaching a maximum in the early afternoon, and decreases to a very low rate of water loss during the night. The differences between the maximum daylight and the minimum night time rates of transpiration can be so great that the water loss during a single daylight hour can easily exceed that during the entire night. The main environmental factors, apart from light, which operate to cause these differences are an increased daytime air temperature and corresponding decrease in relative humidity. Light, however, is the main controlling influence. It can be shown quite simply by blocking the stomata of leaves with vaseline that these pores are avenues for more than 95% of the loss of water vapour. The opening and closing of stomata is to a large extent governed by light (see p. 217); though usually wide open during the day, they close at night. This is the main reason for the observed *diurnal rhythm* in transpiration.

Stomatal transpiration is yet another diffusion process (see p. 154) resulting from the occurrence of a higher concentration of water vapour at the stomatal apertures than in the surrounding atmosphere. The intercellular spaces which permeate the spongy mesophyll and connect with the stomata through the sub-stomatal chambers are saturated with water vapour. The air outside the stomata, however, except under very exceptional circumstances, has a saturation deficit. Thus there is a movement of water vapour outwards from the stomata. Diffusion through these small, comparatively widely separated pores is more rapid per unit area than diffusion or evaporation from a free water surface. This is because as water vapour diffuses from an evaporating surface the saturation deficit of the air immediately above becomes less, and so the rate of evaporation is reduced. If, however, evaporation is from a large number of evenly distributed pores, as from the stomata of a leaf, the spaces between the pores from which evaporation is not taking place serve as 'reservoirs' for the outwardly diffusing water molecules. If the stomatal pores are sufficiently far apart, there will

Figure 136 *Diagram illustrating the effect of the distance between pores on the rate of diffusion.*

be little or no mutual interference between, or overlapping of, their so-called *diffusion shells*. The special significance of these facts is that when the stomata are open to their maximum extent, diffusion through them may be just as rapid as it would be were the mesophyll and its saturated intercellular spaces freely exposed to the air (fig. 136).

As leaves lose water vapour through the stomata, water evaporates from the walls of the mesophyll cells to the intercellular spaces. Thus a suction pressure develops in these cells and water moves into them from adjacent cells, which in turn absorb water from the xylem tracheids at the ends of the leaf veins. If the rate of transpiration is such that the amount of water lost is greater than that being absorbed, *tensions* or negative pressures will develop in the sap in the xylem. The suction produced by

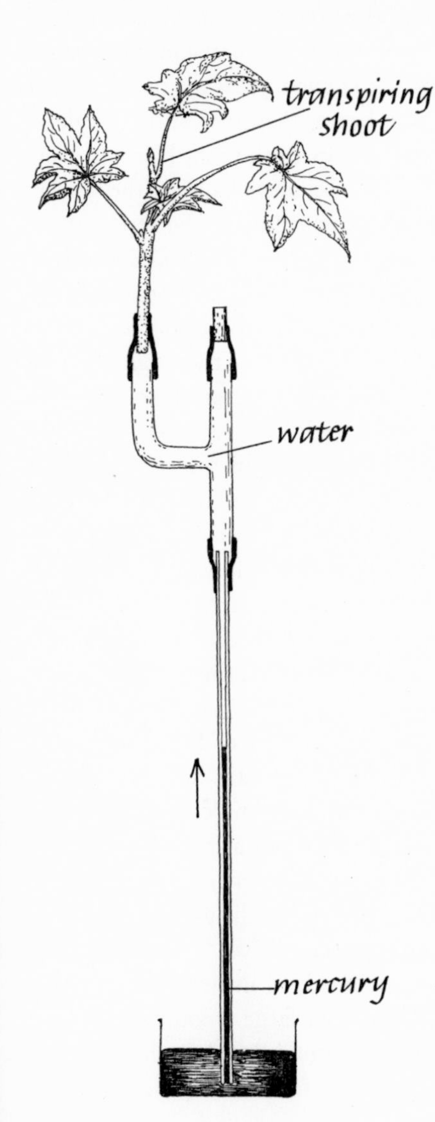

Figure 137 *Apparatus to demonstrate the pull of transpiration which causes water to ascend a vertical glass tube.*

transpiration can be demonstrated by cutting a leafy shoot under water and firmly fixing it (so that there are no air leaks) with pressure tubing into the upper end of a length of narrow glass tubing filled with water. The lower end of the tube is placed in a vessel containing mercury, which will rise gradually up the tube as it replaces water lost from the shoot by transpiration (fig. 137). If this upward water movement is allowed to continue for some time and the water in the tube contains a dye, such as *eosin*, microscopic examination of sections of the shoot will reveal that the ascent of water is by way of the xylem vessels.

When water is subjected to such tensions its diffusion pressure is lowered and this creates a suction pressure equal to the tension applied. Since, as found in the anatomical study of the xylem (Chapter 7, p. 100), almost continuous open columns extend through the xylem vessels from leaves down to the roots, this tension, and hence deficit, must be transmitted to them. As soon as the suction pressure in the xylem becomes lower than that of the adjoining cells, water begins to diffuse into the xylem. This suction pressure is then transmitted across the cortex to the root hairs; in consequence water is absorbed from the soil. If, as frequently seems to happen, the tension on the xylem sap exceeds the osmotic pressure of the cortical cells, the sap in these cells becomes subjected to tension and water then moves from the soil across the cortex and into the xylem more or less as a *mass flow*. In this way the tensions which develop in the extremities of the xylem in the leaves are transmitted downwards through the xylem vessels to the absorbing regions of the roots, the root hairs. By this process of *passive absorption* by far the largest quantities of water are taken in from the soil by transpiring plants.

This phenomenon of water movement has been explained in the *transpiration-cohesion-tension theory* of the ascent of sap. The entire validity of this theory, propounded by Professor Dixon, rested on whether it was possible for a column of water to withstand breakage when subjected to the considerable tensions comparable to those which were believed to occur in the xylem vessels of an actively transpiring plant. The maintenance of these columns would depend on the existence not only of adequate forces of *cohesion* between the molecules of water so that they would remain together as a column, but also on the strong attraction or *adhesion* between the water molecules and the xylem vessel walls. The late Professor Dixon of Dublin, and his collaborators, provided the strongest support for their now generally accepted theory with a series of elegant experiments in which columns of water and cell sap enclosed in clean capillary tubes were shown to be able to withstand, without rupture, tensions of more than 100 atmospheres. According to the theory, the energy which raises water in trees, often to enormous heights – 400 feet in the case of the giant redwoods – is provided by solar radiation as it evaporates water from their leaves.

It should now be apparent that two processes are involved in water absorption: firstly, passive absorption by transpiring plants which pass large amounts outwards through their leaves; secondly, active absorption, an osmotic process which would seem to occur only when transpiration is negligible. By the latter process water,

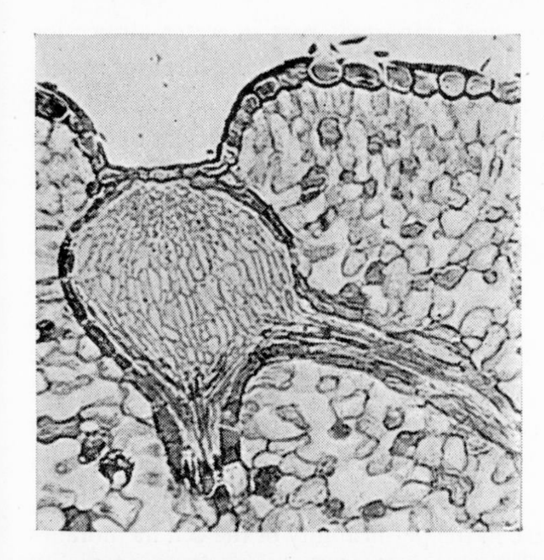

Figure 138 *T.s. of part of the leaf of* Saxifraga longifolia *showing a hydathode.*

Figure 139 *Guttation from leaf margins of poppy seedlings.*

instead of being drawn into the plant by environmental forces above, is pushed upwards by the positive action of the root system. On damp nights, however, when transpiration, and hence passive absorption, is at a minimum, active absorption can develop strongly if the soil is warm, well watered and aerated. Under these conditions considerable positive pressures may develop in the xylem vessels of many plants. In some species the resulting excess of moisture is forced out of special leaf-organs, termed *hydathodes* (fig. 138). The conditions causing this phenomenon termed *guttation* can be simulated in the laboratory by placing well watered grass or poppy seedlings under a bell jar. Small drops of liquid will be seen to collect over the hydathodes which usually occur on the leaf margins. In the poppy they occur at the ends of the main leaf veins and in grasses at the leaf tips (fig. 139).

Transpiration undoubtedly plays the most important part in water absorption and the bulk of the plant's water is acquired by this process. Moreover, water absorption is a function of the entire plant and not only the root system. When the soil water content falls to a level at which the water available is insufficient to prevent the plant from *wilting*, even though its expanding root system is continually tapping new supplies, transpiration will then outstrip absorption. This water loss causes the cells in the leaves to lose their turgidity so that the leaves as a whole become *flaccid* and begin to droop. This wilting causes a closure of the stomata thus checking further water loss. The stomatal pores, however, are also concerned with the gaseous exchange essential for photosynthesis (Chapter 18) so that the water deficit may cause a check in growth. Indeed water deficiency caused by excessive transpiration, uncompensated for by water absorption, is the most frequent limiting factor in plant growth under both natural and agricultural conditions. It is also the most frequent cause of injury and death in plants.

At low temperatures there is a decrease in the permeability of the cell membranes of roots and an increase in the viscosity and decrease in diffusion pressure of the soil water. In winter, therefore, transpiration can easily outstrip water absorption giving rise to serious water deficits in the plant. In response to this danger many plants either winter underground by the total loss of their aerial parts, or, as in woody perennials, they shed their leaves, the organs of transpiration (Chapter 4). The *deciduous habit* is thus a protective mechanism against excessive transpiration. In *evergreens*, transpiration rates are much lower because of their highly cutinized and often reduced leaves, with their specialized, sunken stomata, so that in these plants an adequate water balance can be maintained during the winter.

Xerophytic Plants

Certain plants termed *xerophytes* are specially adapted for growth in habitats where the water supply would be inadequate for the majority of terrestrial plants (*mesophytes*). Evergreens resemble xerophytes in that the form and structure of their leaves help to restrict transpiration. In typical xerophytes, the leaves are often greatly reduced in size, as in gorse (*Ulex europaeus*), or they may be rolled lengthwise so that the stomata, which occur on their inner surfaces, are protected within a cavity. This rolling may be a permanent character of the leaves, as in the cross-leaved heath (*Erica tetralix*) (fig. 140a), or temporary, the leaves unrolling when evaporation rates are low during humid weather. An example of temporary rolling is the common grass or sand dunes, marram grass (*Ammophila arenaria*) (fig. 161). Here the stomata occur only in the grooves on the upper surface and not on the intervening ridges, which are covered with short hairs. In the rolled condition the stomata, which are confined to the grooves, are well protected from the drying effects of the atmosphere (fig. 140b). Rolling occurs when water is lost through excessive transpiration from groups of large, thin walled *hinge cells* at the base of each groove. As these cells shrink, the flat edges of the ridges come together and the leaf assumes a tubular shape. In

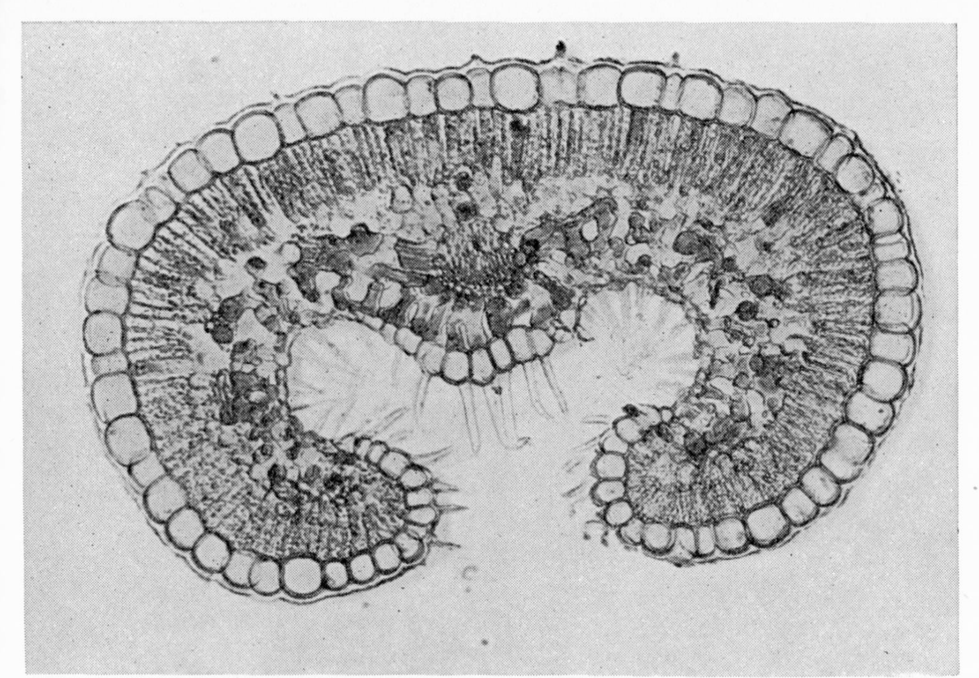

Figure 140a *T.s. of leaf of* Erica tetralix *showing rolled leaf with stomata, protected by hairs in the cavity so formed.*

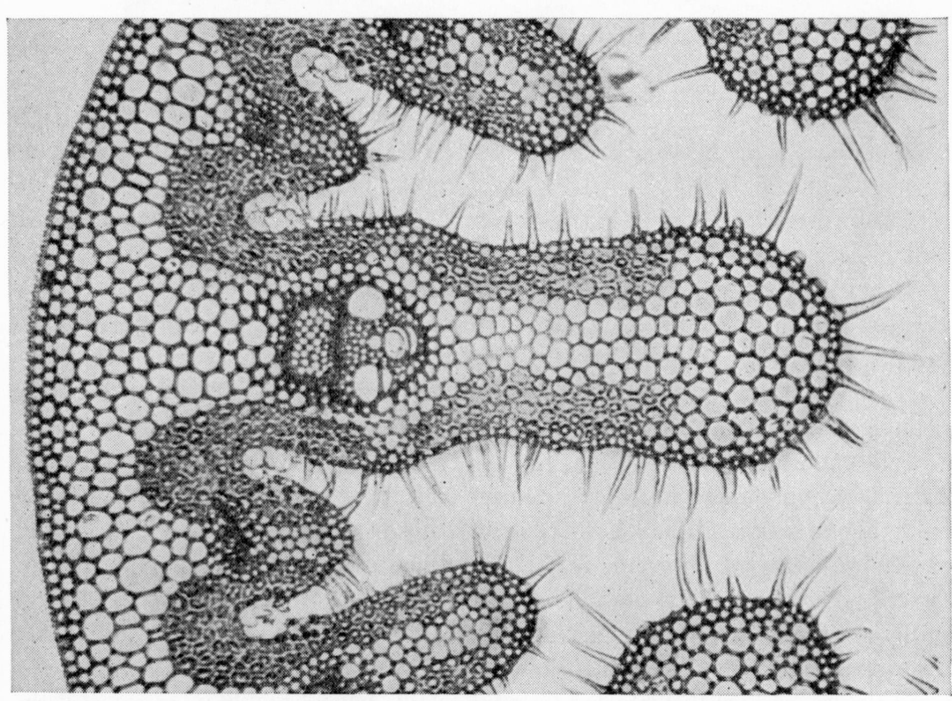

Figure 140b *T.s. of part of a leaf of* Ammophila arenaria. *Note the large hinge cells at the bases of the deep grooves in the leaf.*

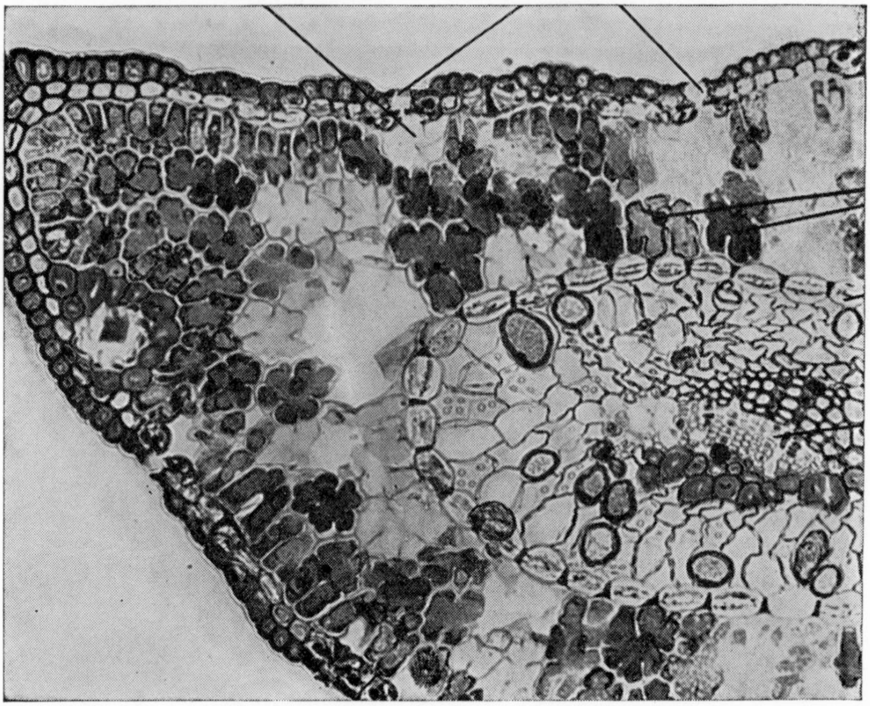

Figure 141 *T.s. of part of leaf of* Pinus sylvestris.

moist conditions the hinge cells readily take up water, the leaf unrolls and assumes an open, flattened form.

Other xerophytes, such as *Pinus*, have needle-shaped leaves in which stomata are sunk in deep pits below the level of the epidermis (see fig. 141).

It is widely, though incorrectly, believed that all drought resistant plants, because of their modified structure, are very economical in their expenditure of water and that they invariably have low transpiration rates. In fact, when there is an adequate supply of soil water available to them their transpiration rates are just as high as those of *mesophytic* plants. The distinctive feature which does, however, set many drought enduring species apart, is the ability of their cells to endure considerable water depletion without irreparable damage being done to them. The death of cells on drying is, it seems, due less to a loss of water from the protoplasm than to the mechanical injury which drying may cause to their living contents and especially to the cell membranes. Thus the cells of many drought resistant species possess very small vacuoles, which render their protoplasts less liable to injury, especially if the removal of water from the cells is slow. Indeed some mosses and ferns can be rendered air dry, and yet they recover their full vitality when brought into contact with water.

CHAPTER 15

MINERAL NUTRITION

Comparisons of the fresh and dry weights of any plant show that water constitutes the greatest part of its bulk. Although from earliest times man must have realized that plants obtained this water from the soil, it was only towards the end of the eighteenth century, following experiments performed by the Swiss physicist De Saussure, that it was recognized that the *ash* remaining after a plant is burnt consists of *mineral matter*, all of which was originally taken up by the plant from the soil. This ash represents but a fraction, often less than 1%, of the dry weight and the minerals in it occur as oxides. Chemical analyses show that marked differences occur in the composition of plant ash between different species, and even between the same species grown under different environmental conditions. All plant ash, however, will contain the following elements: aluminium, calcium, chlorine, iron, magnesium, phosphorus, potassium, silicon, sodium and sulphur. The elements carbon, nitrogen, oxygen and hydrogen, which are the most important part of the structural framework of every plant, are driven off when air-dry material is burnt.

From studies of plants grown under experimental conditions with their roots immersed in a *nutrient solution* of known composition, the chemical content of which could be varied at will, came the first contribution to the study of plant mineral nutrition. Using such *cultures*, the German physiologists Sachs and Knop established, more than 100 years ago, that plants require relatively large amounts of the elements calcium, magnesium, potassium, phosphorus, sulphur and nitrogen. These are now recognized as the *major nutrient elements* in contrast to the *minor elements* which though essential for normal, healthy growth are required only in the merest traces. The fact that these *trace elements*, which include iron, manganese, copper, boron, molybdenum and zinc, were also essential was appreciated only when methods ensuring the rigorous purification of the chemicals used in culture experiments were introduced. When culture solutions lack a particular essential element, the experimental plants grown in them show in time, symptoms characteristic of the deficient element. The early experiments of De Saussure, which demonstrated that plants take in not only water from the soil but other substances that are essential for their well-being, can easily be confirmed by growing plants in distilled water, which, of course, contains no nutrients. These plants will soon have a starved and stunted appearance and eventually they will collapse and die. In contrast, plants grown in a full culture solution show continued healthy, vigorous growth.

Soil itself cannot be used in experiments on mineral nutrition because it is quite impossible to determine how much of any nutrient element is available in it for a given plant. Thoroughly washed sand or gravel, however, can be used for studies involving major elements. These sand cultures possess the special advantage that there is, as in a soil, a diffusion of air through the spaces between the sand. The sand is irrigated with the culture medium. Aeration, essential for the proper functioning and development of root systems, must be provided in water cultures by bubbling a stream of air through the solution.

ANTAGONISM

If root hair cells, or any other living cells, are placed in a fairly concentrated culture solution containing only a single salt, it is very probable that these cells will become plasmolysed (see p. 159). If, however, a solution of the same concentration contains not one, but two salts, then there will be no plasmolysis. The plasmolysis in the presence of the single salt occurs because the metallic ions of the single salt have an adverse effect on the protein of the cell membranes, thereby greatly altering their permeability. When two salts are present, cell permeability is maintained at its normal level. The solution containing one salt is said to be *unbalanced*, the other *balanced*, and the mutual interaction between the two salts and their respective ions, which is most pronounced between ions of different valencies, is termed *antagonism*.

A very striking demonstration of this phenomenon can be carried out with small discs of beetroot. The discs are first placed in distilled water and there is a slow loss of the red pigment from the cell vacuoles into the water outside. When transferred to dilute sodium chloride solution (NaCl) the loss of colour is very muc h more rapid, owing to the increase in cell permeability brought about by the monovalent ions of sodium. On transferring the discs to a 'balanced' solution of sodium chloride (NaCl) and calcium chloride (CaCl) there is a rapid and noticeable reduction in pigment loss, because of the antagonizing effect of the divalent Ca^{++} ions on the Na^{+} ions, thereby minimizing the effect of the latter on the permeability of the beet cell membranes.

SYMPTOMS OF MINERAL DEFICIENCES

Each of the elements essential for healthy development is either incorporated into the structure of the plant or takes some part in one or other of the many metabolic processes basic to plant growth. If any one element is absent, growth is inevitably poorer than in a well balanced culture medium; in addition, other more specific symptoms characteristic of each deficient element soon become apparent. Though the exact functions and parts played by the essential elements are still far from being fully understood, knowledge of these matters is gradually being gained by detailed analyses and biochemical studies of the metabolism of plants grown in cultures deficient in particular elements.

Nitrogen is a basic constituent of all proteins including enzymes (Chapter 17), as well as of the most important of plant pigments, chlorophyll. Nitrogen deficiency is characterized by a disappearance of green colour from the leaves, which, if the deficiency continues, turn yellow. In certain plants this yellowing may be accompanied by the excessive production of red, *anthocyanin pigments*, especially in the region of the veins. An excess of nitrogen, on the other hand, causes excessive vegetative growth.

The symptoms of *phosphorus* deficiency are less obvious than those of nitrogen deficiency. Together these are the most commonly encountered deficiencies of agricultural and natural soils. Phosphorus is a constituent of many vitally important organic compounds, especially proteins and phospholipids. This element is also a component of nucleic acids (Chapter 26); thus when lacking may affect growth by limiting cell division. The main role of phosphorus is unquestionably related to the energy transfers which are involved especially in respiration and photosynthesis through the high energy chemical bonds of organic metaphosphates (Chapters 18 and 19). Plants grown in the absence of phosphate are always stunted and although their leaves may be intensely green in colour, reddish tinges may also be present.

Although *potassium* is not a component of any important plant constituents, it plays a special part in carbohydrate metabolism and when deficient has a marked effect on many parts of the plant. The leaves yellow at their tips and round the margins, and there is a poor development of those organs – roots, tubers, and seeds – where food is normally stored. Potassium deficient plants also lack mechanical strength so that their stems are easily bent or broken, they are less disease resistant, and internally there is frequently found to be a degeneration of their sieve tubes.

A lack of *calcium* in the soil is often more difficult to assess than that of other elements because of the special part it plays in relation to the absorption of other minerals from the soil (see p. 182). At the cellular level it is important not only because it helps to maintain the semi-permeable nature of cell membranes, but also because it is a constituent of calcium pectate, the cementing substance which binds cells together. The obvious effect of this is in the rapid breakdown and eventual death of the apical growing points of stems and roots, a symptom which is frequently preceded by the malformation of young leaves as they develop.

Magnesium is an essential constituent of chlorophyll and is necessary for the formation of this vital pigment. When deficient, there is a marked yellowing, or *chlorosis*, of the green parts. It is an element which seems to be very mobile within the plant and when deficient it can be readily transferred from older to younger tissues. These signs of magnesium deficiency make their first appearance in older leaves and progress systematically towards younger ones.

Iron, a minor nutrient element, is required only in traces in culture solutions. Like magnesium, it is concerned with chlorophyll formation though not a constituent of it. The symptom characterizing the absence of iron is the sudden and quite dramatic yellowing of the younger leaves, especially in the areas between the veins. Iron chlorosis differs from that due to magnesium deficiency in that leaves produced before its onset remain a normal green colour. Such plants may as a result bear young leaves which are yellow or almost white, above older, apparently healthy leaves. Iron is clearly a relatively immobile element in plants.

Large areas of the earth's surface are deficient in certain mineral elements and especially in nitrogen, phosphorus and potassium. Such deficiencies may be naturally occurring, or they may be the result of intensive agricultural cropping. Because of their wide range of nutrient requirements, many plant species can survive and even flourish in areas where these deficiencies exist or in areas where there is an excess of a particular element as in salt marshes (see p. 184). Indeed, it may be said that one plant's meat is another's poison. In agricultural practice a soil is considered to be nutrient deficient if it will not support the optimal growth of a particular crop, even though other crop plants may flourish in the same soil. Clearly, the term 'nutrient deficiency' is only relative and must be related to each particular plant species.

THE SOIL AS A SOURCE OF MINERAL ELEMENTS

All mineral elements which enter into the composition and are concerned in the metabolic activities of terrestrial plants are derived from the soil. To support good growth a soil, like a full culture solution, must have a readily available supply of major and minor elements. With the exception of nitrogen, all these nutrient elements are ultimately derived from the rock particles which form the framework of the soil. These inorganic substances which are dissolved in the soil solution exist as ions, the most important of which are as follows: the anions nitrate (NO_3^-), sulphate ($SO_4^=$), phosphate (PO_4^{3-}), carbonate (HCl_3^-) and chlorine (Cl^-); and cations ammonium (NH_4^+), potassium (K^+), calcium (Ca^{++}), magnesium (Mg^{++}) and iron (Fe_3^{++}). Some of these ions are firmly held on the surface of colloidal particles in the soil so that they are not leached out. Since there is little colloidal material in sandy soils there may be a considerable loss of ions from them in this way. Much less is lost from clays.

Cation Exchange

Clay particles which have an enormous surface area in relation to their bulk are so constituted that negative charges in excess may occur at various points on their structure. Since all electrical charges must be satisfied, cations taken from the soil solution are bound or adsorbed at these points. These bound cations may eventually pass into the soil solution, or they may be taken up directly from the clay by the process of ion exchange. In this way roots appear to give off H^+ ions in exchange for nutrient ions adsorbed on to the clay colloids which hold the main reserve of mineral elements for plant growth. These exchangeable ions are not held with equal retentiveness, so that H^+ ions are held more firmly than Ca^{++} ions, Ca^{++} than Mg^+, Mg^+ than K^+ and K^+ than NH_4^+. Indeed, there is a clear order in their retentive capacity. As a result of this type of exchange, H^+ ions accumulate on the *clay micelles* in place of other less retentive cations, which have been removed by growing plants. An excess of H^+ ions can lead to a marked and harmful increase in soil acidity. It is for this reason that calcium-containing fertilizers, in particular, are added to agricultural soils. The fertilizers induce exchanges of cations between clay particles and the soil solution and when lime is added to a soil, the Ca^{++} ions exchange with the H^{+} ions which are present in excess.

Anions in the Soil

The principal anions, nitrate (NO_3^-), sulphate ($SO_4^=$) and chloride (Cl^-), are held in the soil comparatively weakly and are therefore easily lost by leaching. A certain amount of the very important anion phosphate (PO_4^{3-}), on the other hand, gradually goes into the soil solution and may readily leach away; but some becomes tied up with soil particles in such a way that in many cases it may become unavailable to plants. The phosphorous economy of the soil therefore depends on the maintenance of a delicate balance between the soil's ability to supply growing plants with adequate amounts of this vital nutrient and the ability to resist its loss by *leaching* – the process by which nutrients are carried downwards in a soil by percolating rain water.

The Absorption and Accumulation of Ions

The plant's root system absorbs not only water from the soil but also the mineral elements which occur as ions in the soil solution. Water, a non-electrolyte, enters the plant through the root cells by the process of diffusion (Chapter 12). The protoplasmic membranes of the root cells allowing this free passage of water, which as a diffusion process continues until a state of equilibrium is maintained, slow down and often markedly impede the entry of ions in solution. The differential permeability of these membranes thus imposes a considerable degree of selectivity as to the ions that can enter a cell. Some can move in comparatively easily and in considerable amounts, while others are almost completely excluded. In general the passage of substances into, and out of, cells is governed by the size of the particular molecules involved.

There is one specially noteworthy feature characterising the uptake of ionic materials by living plant cells which does not apply to substances entering by diffusion. Plants can accumulate certain ions and pile them up within their cells, even when the concentration of ions inside the cell exceeds by far that of the external medium. This accumulation, against a concentration gradient, involves, however, the expenditure of energy by the cell. A proof of the fact that energy is a prerequisite for this important process is that active accumulation occurs only in the cells of tissues undergoing vigorous respiration: the uptake of ions can be much reduced, or even arrested, by limiting the oxygen supply or by adding to the culture medium a *respiratory inhibitor* such as cyanide. Further proof is that tissues accumulate ions only if they have an adequate reserve of food materials, such as sugars, from which respiratory energy can be drawn.

This remarkable property of ion accumulation by plant cells was first recognized when the ionic content of certain especially large algal cells was compared with that of the waters in which they grew. Thus it was shown that the stonewort, *Nitella*, accumulates monovalent potassium ions to a concentration more than 1,000 times greater than that of the surrounding medium. Although the marine alga, *Valonia*, accumulates a similar, though not quite such a proportionately large amount of potassium, it seems to restrict the entry of the divalent ions, sodium and calcium, for they occur in much higher concentrations in sea water than in its cell sap. It would seem to be therefore a principle of such selectivity that monovalent ions, whether anions or cations, are absorbed and accumulate more rapidly than divalent ions. Thus K^+ is taken up more rapidly than $Ca^=$, and NO_3^- more readily than $SO_4^=$.

Plants exhibit very marked differences in their selectivity to different ions. The common plants of a meadow or a garden, for example, take up very little sodium from the soil in which they are growing. In contrast the plants typical of a salt marsh, where unusually high concentrations of sodium chloride occur in the soil solution, may accumulate from 20 to 30 times as much sodium. This property is undoubtedly related to the ability of salt marsh plants to survive in soils where there is a very high salt content.

Another important aspect of the uptake of ionic materials is the ability of cells to absorb unequal amounts of anions and cations of a given salt. Monovalent anions, or cations, of a salt are absorbed more rapidly than divalent anions, or cations, of the same salt. In the case of $CaCl_2$, for example, Cl^- would be absorbed more rapidly than Ca^{++}. Cells cannot, however, merely take up ions of one charge and leave those of the opposite charge unsatisfied in the soil or culture solution. A perfect balance between charges must always be preserved and electrical neutrality maintained. To this end new anions are produced within the cell. These, the anions of organic acids, are produced in amounts just sufficient to balance any excess of cations taken in. At the same time, cations, in the form of H^+ ions from these acids, pass out of the cell and neutralize any unsatisfied anions in the soil solution. When there is an excess of anion absorption, the organic acids in the cell disappear proportionately to the level necessary to counteract the excess of anions absorbed. In soils a similar balance is preserved by bicarbonate (cations) and hydroxyl (anions). Thus remarkably delicate systems of adjustment maintain an ionic balance whenever differences occur in the rates of uptake of different ions from the soil solution. These may be dictated by variations in the composition of the soil solution and in the special ionic requirements of a particular species of plant.

Nitrogen in the Soil

With the exception of nitrogen, which exists either as the anion NO_3^- or the cation NH_4^+, all plant nutrients in the soil are derived from its rock framework. There are, however, no nitrogen-containing minerals in any of the rocks from which soils are formed. The nitrogen of all soils is derived in the main from biological processes which take place within it. Molecular nitrogen from the atmosphere is fixed in the soil by various micro-organisms, and by the activities of others it is changed into a form available for absorption by plants. A small though significant amount of nitrogen is also derived from the atmosphere: lightning brings about the oxidation of atmospheric nitrogen to nitrous oxide which reaches the soil in rain water as nitrous or nitric acid.

At best, a soil will contain no more than 1% of nitrogen and of this only a small proportion, from 2-10%, is water soluble. Moreover, only this fraction, which occurs either as nitrate, ammonium salts or as certain nitrogen-containing soluble organic compounds such as amino acids, would seem to be available to growing plants. The remaining 90-98% of soil nitrogen, which is insoluble, occurs as proteinaceous material in the dead remains of plants and animals in the soil humus. By processes of putrefaction, in which fungi and bacteria play a major part, these complex nitrogenous compounds are broken down to simpler ammonium compounds. A soil bacterium, *Nitrosomonas*, rapidly oxidizes any ammonium salts to nitrite, and a second bacterium, *Nitrobacter*, oxidizes the nitrite to nitrate. Thus as a result of the activity of these soil micro-organisms, which in return gain chemical energy for their own metabolism, the complex nitrogen-containing substances originally synthesized by plants and animals are broken down and simplified to an ionic form which may then be absorbed by root systems.

The first indication that molecular nitrogen could be fixed and converted into combined forms came from experiments by Berthelot in 1882 when he incubated various soils under controlled conditions and found that their total N-content increased. Some years later the French bacteriologist Winogradsky isolated a soil bacterium capable of carrying out this *nitrogen fixation*. The bacterium was an anaerobe of the genus *Closteridium* and its isolation was soon followed by that of an aerobe of the genus *Azotobacter*. The latter is probably the most important of the soil-inhabiting N-fixing organisms. Both bacteria, however, can take up molecular nitrogen from the air and by their own synthetic mechanisms incorporate it into complex nitrogen-containing compounds, bacterial proteins, which form a considerable part of the structural framework of the bacterial cell. The nitrogen bound in this way is released to the soil only on the death of the bacterium. It can, however, only be used by plants after its subsequent decomposition and oxidation to a soluble form, especially nitrate, by nitrifying bacteria, that is, *Nitrosomonas* and *Nitrobacter* (see above).

In addition to the free living nitrogen-fixing bacteria, others which occur in the root nodules of such plants as peas, beans, clover, and lupins (Leguminosae) play a significant part in maintaining the level of nitrogen of many soils. These bacteria, unlike many which live within the tissues of other organisms, are not parasitic on these plants. Although gaining food materials from the cells they invade, they confer on the host plants an unquestionable benefit in the form of a nitrogen supply. The bacteria concerned in this important type of N-fixation belong to the genus *Rhizobium*. By themselves they are incapable of carrying out the process. The *Rhizobium* will, however, invade root hairs of *leguminous* plants and as they multiply, they penetrate the cortex, moving deeper and deeper into the root until they reach the pericycle. It will be remembered that pericyclic cells can under certain conditions be stimulated

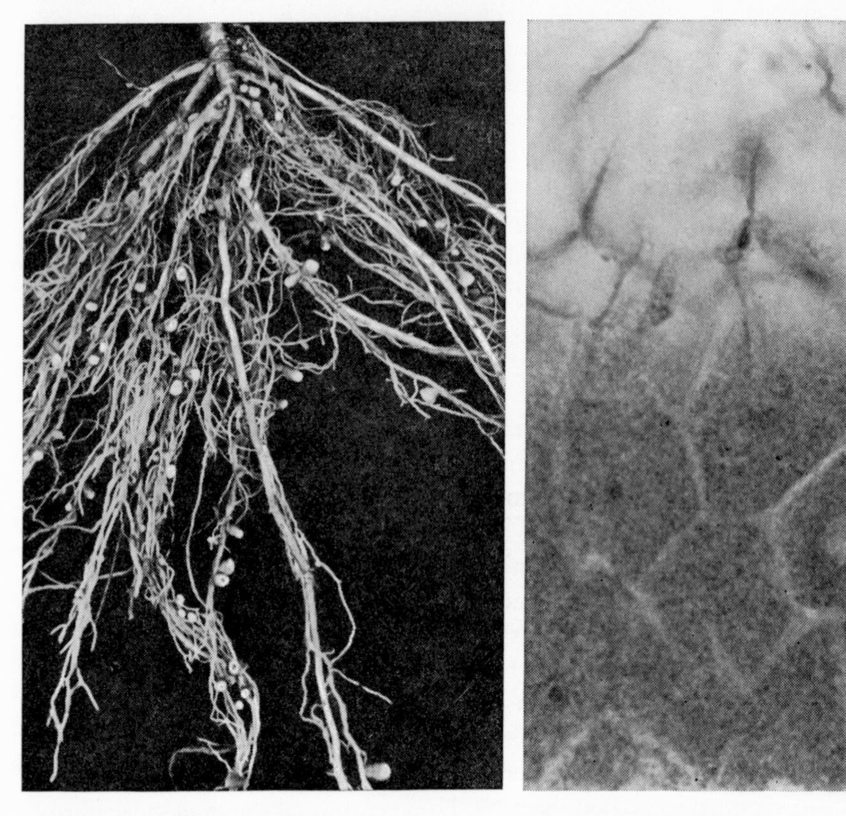

Figure 142 *The root of the leguminous plant,* Medicago lupulina, *showing root nodules.*

Figure 143 *Transverse section of part of a root nodule from* Lupulinus nootkatensis *showing vast numbers of bacteria in the cells towards bottom of picture.*

into mitotic activity, thus initiating lateral root formation (see p. 104). The presence of the bacteria stimulates the rapid proliferation of the pericyclic cells so that wart-like *root nodules* occur in the locality of the invasion. These soon become visible to the naked eye as excrescences on the side of the root and all their cells are infected with bacteria (figs. 142 and 143). Along with the host tissues the bacteria carry out the process known as *symbiotic nitrogen fixation.* A considerable proportion of the products of the nitrogen fixation are passed on to the host plant with an accompanying benefit to its growth. At the end of each growing season, however, some of the nodules with their bacterial and high nitrogen content are returned to the soil when the host roots decay. In this way the soil nitrogen content is augmented (p. 353).

The Nitrogen Cycle (fig. 144)

In the soil there is clearly a continuous circulation of nitrogen. Soluble nitrogen, mainly in the form of nitrates, is readily removed by growing plants particularly to become incorporated into proteins, the most complex of living substances. When these plants die, or are eaten by animals, all the nitrogen they have removed from the soil is eventually returned to it as the organic matter of humus, or as animal remains or excreta. All the nitrogen within these various sorts of organic matter is sooner or later converted by bacterial activity to ammonia or nitrate and so once again becomes available to plants. The *nitrogen cycle* has come full turn. At various stages in the cycle there are, however, losses of nitrogen from the soil. Some, for example, may leach away to the subsoil; some may be lost as 'run off' and so find its way by streams and rivers to the sea. There is also a loss from the soil through the activities of denitrifying bacteria, which in the process of reducing nitrates liberate gaseous nitrogen into the atmosphere. If these losses were not compensated by the process of nitrogen fixation, very soon there would be no nitrogen available in any soil for growing plants.

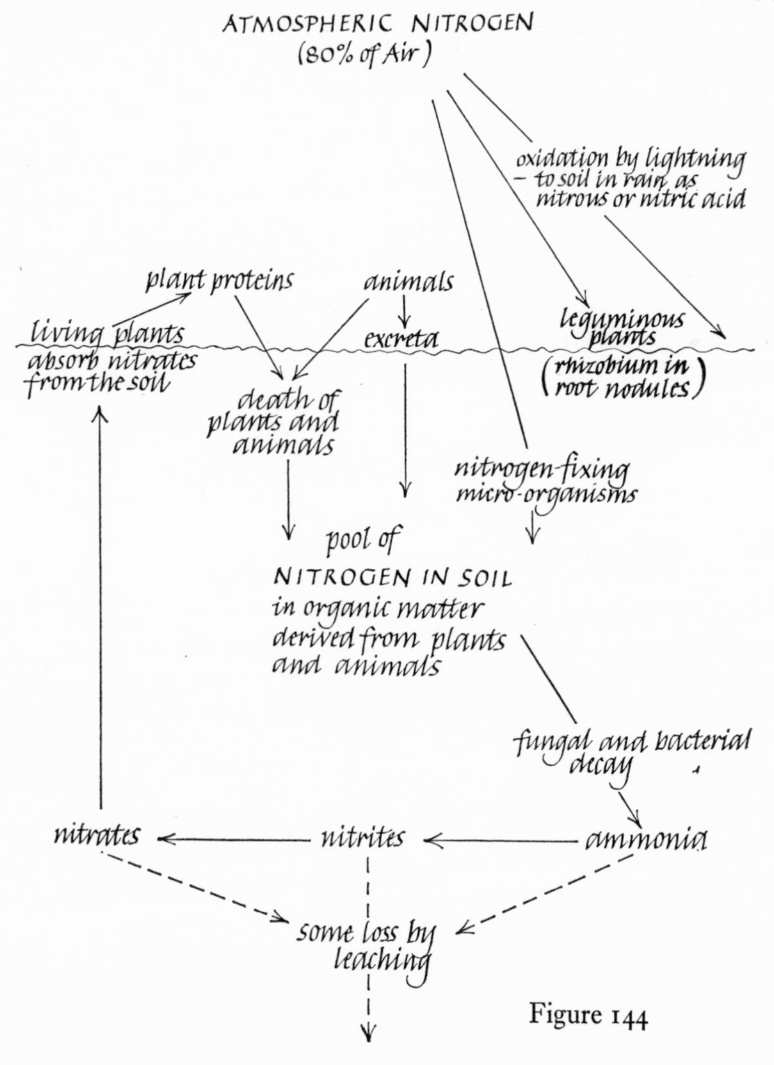

Figure 144

PART IV

PLANT NUTRITION : METABOLISM

CHAPTER 16

THE PRODUCTS OF PLANT METABOLISM: CARBOHYDRATES, FATS, AND PROTEINS

The green colour due to the presence of chlorophyll is the most significant characteristic of the vast majority of higher plants. On this depends their ability to synthesize foods from a limited number of inorganic substances obtained from their environment. Of these substances the most important is carbon, the element on which the entire living world is based. Plants in fact by their special photosynthetic mechanism provide the link between the organic and inorganic worlds (see Chapter 18). The food substances which they produce can be used by them as sources of energy (see Chapter 19) or as substances from which the basic materials essential for growth and development can be obtained. Their utilization in these ways may be almost immediate or follow a period of storage. These plant foods are, however, the very food substances ingested by animals and may be classified under the headings, carbohydrates, fats and proteins.

CARBOHYDRATES

Carbohydrates, the most important and widespread of substances in plants, are so named because in addition to carbon they contain hydrogen and oxygen in the same proportions as in water (H_2O), that is 2 atoms of hydrogen to 1 atom of oxygen. Thus in a molecule of hexose sugar there are 6 atoms of carbon, 12 of hydrogen and 6 of oxygen ($C_6H_{12}O_6$). Such molecules are the basic carbohydrates produced in the plant and from which a considerable number of much more complex compounds are formed. Some of these, such as starch and fats, constitute the principal food store and energy reserves, while others, such as the cellulose of cell walls, form the very framework of the plant. Clearly it is most necessary to have some knowledge of the chemistry of sugars and of some of the more important substances occurring in plants derived from them.

Sugars

There are various types of sugars and these differ basically in the number of carbon atoms contained in each molecule. Of the sugars synthesized by higher plants there may be from 3 to 7 carbon atoms, but only those with 5 (*pentose sugars*) and especially 6 atoms (*hexose sugars*) are important. The basic structure of a sugar molecule can be seen in the hexose sugar, *glucose*. Of its 6 carbon atoms, 5 are linked to OH or *hydroxyl* groups while the remaining apical carbon atom has an *aldehyde* grouping:

$\mathrm{C}\begin{matrix}/\!\!/\mathrm{O}\\ \diagdown\mathrm{H}\end{matrix}$. This part of the molecule can be easily oxidized, a fact which is used to identify sugars of this type; for on warming with cupric hydroxide the latter is reduced to cuprous oxide which has a characteristic brick red colour. It is for this reason that glucose is termed a *reducing sugar* – not because it keeps the waist line down! Another *monosaccharide*, as these simple sugars are termed, is *fructose*. This resembles glucose in that it is also a reducing sugar, but differs in that it has a *ketone* group ($\overset{|}{\underset{|}{C}}=O$) at carbon atom 2, in place of the apical aldehyde group of glucose.

CARBON ATOM	*GLUCOSE*	*FRUCTOSE*
1	HC = O –aldehyde group	CH_2OH
2	HCOH	C = O –ketone group
3	HOCH	HOCH
4	HCOH	HCOH
5	HCOH	HCOH
6	CH_2OH	CH_2OH

In the molecular structure of these sugars as shown in the *structural formulae* above, it must be emphasized that there is a definite spatial configuration of the hydroxyl groups about the individual carbon atoms. Thus the hexose sugar *mannose* differs from glucose only in the arrangement of the hydroxyl group about carbon atom 2, while *galactose* differs from glucose with respect to the orientation of this group at carbon atom 4:

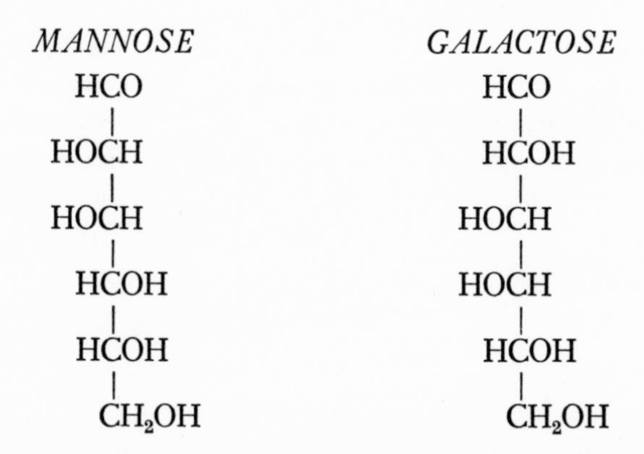

Although these differences in structure appear to be only slight they nevertheless give the individual sugars very distinctive physical and biological properties. Only glucose is readily used to any extent in plant respiration, while mannose and galactose are poor respiratory *substrates* (see Chapter 19).

The 'open chain' arrangement of carbon atoms illustrated above, applies only when these monosaccharides occur in solution. When the molecules of these sugars become linked together to form more complex molecules, the carbon atoms occur in a *ring*. Not all the six carbon atoms in a hexose sugar, for example, enter into this ring or *cyclic structure*; only the first five are involved. The ring, however, is six-membered with 5 carbon atoms, the apical aldehyde carbon atom being linked with carbon atom 5 through an *oxygen bridge*. When the ring closes, a new hydroxyl group is formed at the aldehyde end of the molecule:

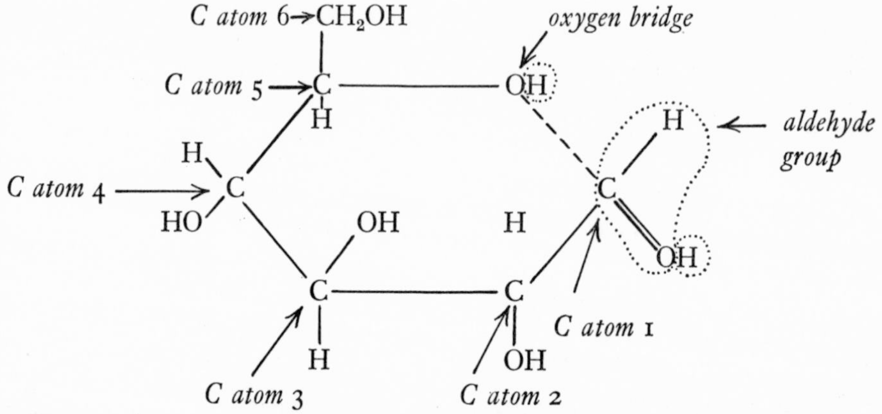

C atom 6 → CH_2OH
oxygen bridge
C atom 5 → C — OH
aldehyde group
C atom 4 → C
H
HO
OH
H
C — C
H
OH
C atom 1
C atom 3
C atom 2

When two monosaccharide molecules are linked together they form a *disaccharide* of which the most commonly occurring in plants is *sucrose*. It is this sugar, it seems, which is directly produced as a product of photosynthesis (see p. 209) and which occurs in prodigious amounts in sugar cane and sugar beet, crop plants exploited by man. The two simple monosaccharide sugar molecules in sucrose are linked together with the elimination of one molecule of water. Whereas glucose has the *empirical formula* $C_6H_{12}O_6$, that of sucrose is $C_{12}H_{24}O_{12} - H_2O = C_{12}H_{22}O_{11}$. Sucrose can be split quite easily into the two monosaccharides, glucose and fructose, of which it is composed, either by warming with dilute acid or with the enzyme *invertase*. In this *hydrolytic cleavage* one molecule of water is taken up. Because sucrose possesses neither a free aldehyde nor a ketonic group it cannot reduce cupric oxide, but on hydrolysis, these groups, which are involved in the glucose-fructose bond, are set free and are therefore capable of carrying out this characteristic reduction.

Polysaccharides

(i) Starch

Sugar residues can link together to form very much longer and more complex chains than those in the disaccharide, sucrose. These important and widely occurring sugar-containing substances are termed *polysaccharides* and of these by far the most common in plants is *starch*. Starch, it will be recalled, accumulates in great abundance

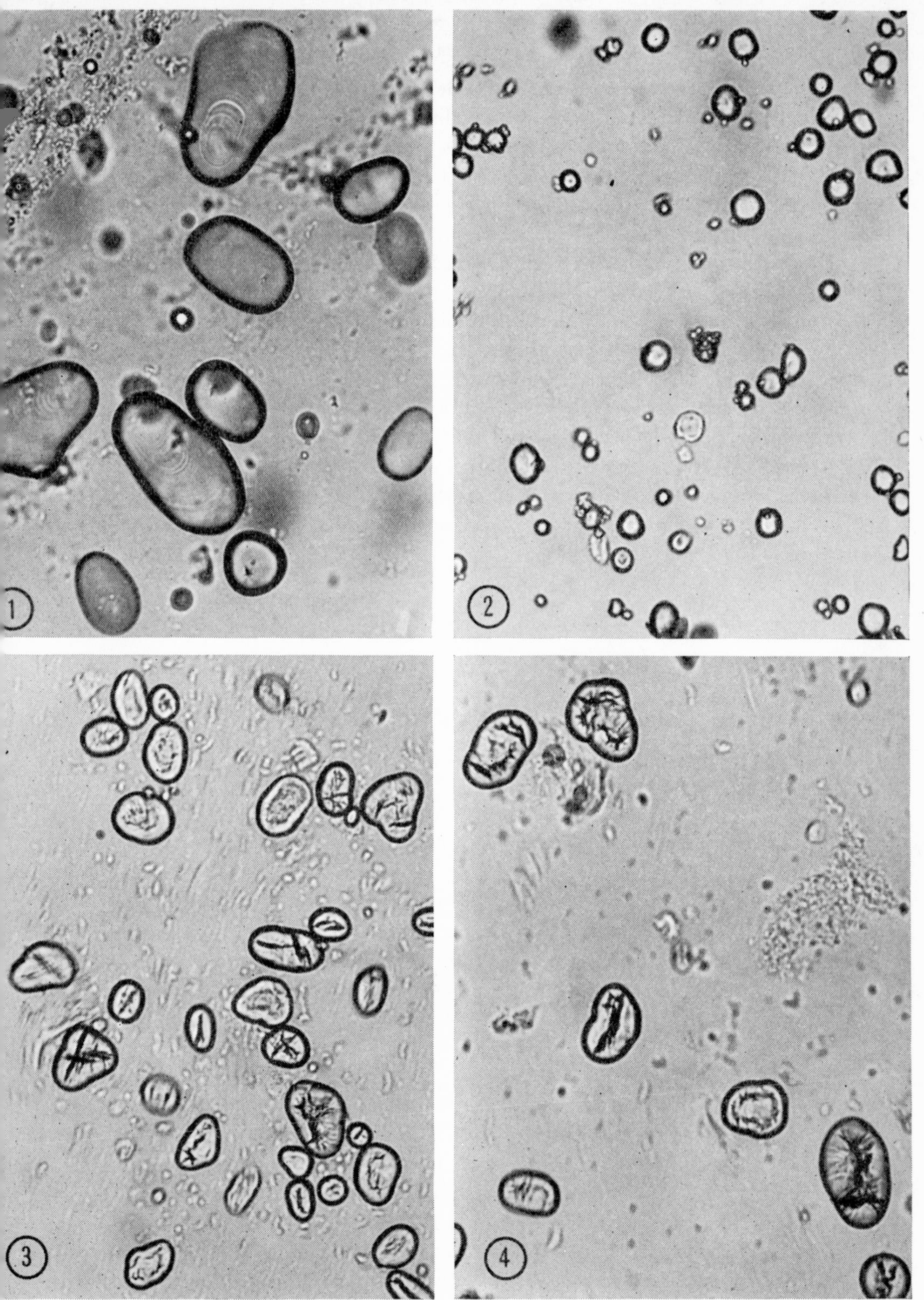

Figure 145 *Starch grains from*
1 *Potato* (Solanum tuberosum).
2 *Maize* (Zea mais).
3 *Broad bean* (Vicia faba).
4 *Garden pea* (Pisum sativum).

in the storage regions of various plant organs such as the cotyledons of seeds, in endosperm, swollen roots, and in modified stems such as rhizomes and tubers (see Chapters 1 and 4). It also accumulates in a large number of leaves in which active photosynthesis has been taking place (Chapter 18). In all of these organs this polysaccharide is stored as starch grains. On microscopical examination these grains, because of their remarkably characteristic shapes, are in many cases referable to the species from which they were obtained (fig. 145). In general, their most striking feature is their layered appearance, a fact which has been accounted for by the different way in which the starch is laid down by day and by night. Denser, more refractive starch is laid down by day, and less dense layers at night (fig. 145.1). Indeed in plants grown in continuous illumination and at a constant temperature, this layering is absent.

The starch molecule is composed of extremely long chains of *glucose residues* linked by oxygen bridges. The linkages differ, however, from those of sucrose in that the terminal carbon atom of each residue is linked through an oxygen atom to the fourth carbon atom of the previous glucose residue, so that all the residues are six-membered rings.

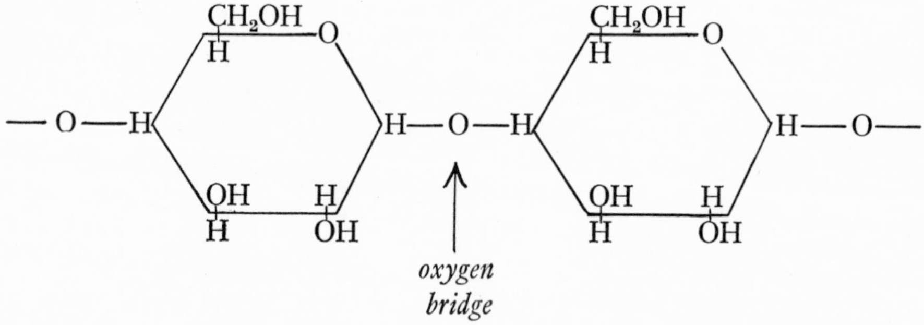

CH_2OH O CH_2OH O
H H
—O—H H—O—H H—O—
OH H OH H
H OH H OH

oxygen bridge

(ii) Inulin

Not all plants produce starch as a storage material but instead manufacture a polysaccharide, *inulin*, composed of chains of fructose residues in place of glucose. Inulin occurs in abundance in the tubers of the Jerusalem artichoke and in those of several other genera of the Family Compositae including the Dahlia.

(iii) Cellulose

Undoubtedly the most widely distributed of polysaccharides is *cellulose*, the major constituent of the primary cell walls of all plants. Like starch, cellulose is made up of long chains of glucose molecules held together by oxygen linkages between carbon atoms 1 and 4 of adjoining glucose residues. The chains which result, are of very great length and have more than 1000 links in them. The chains themselves are packed neatly together into bundles or *micelles* and these micelles are further grouped or bundled into larger *microfibrillar units* (microfibrils) consisting of many micelles.

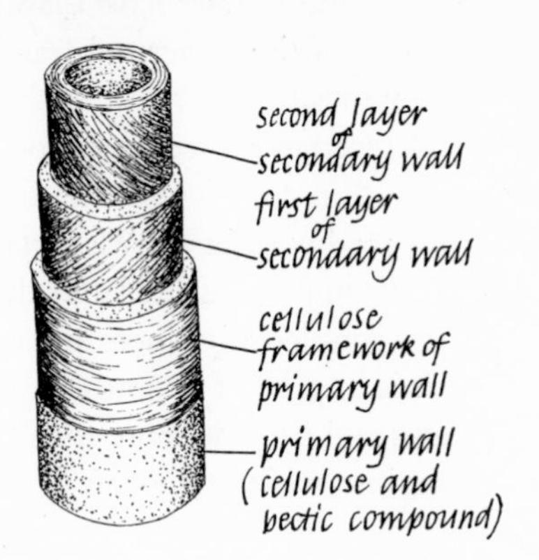

Figure 146 *Diagram of a cell showing the spatial relationship of its various wall layers and the orientation of microfibrils of these layers.*

The great diversity in cell shape in plants has been amply illustrated in the earlier chapters on cell differentiation and plant anatomy. Recent electron microscope studies on the submicroscopic structure of cell walls points to the fact that cell shape is fundamentally dependent on the arrangement of the cellulose units of the wall. Thus in elongating cells the microfibrils of the primary wall run mainly at right angles to the long axis of the cell. In spherical cells, such as the parenchyma of various storage organs and fruits, the cellulose molecules are orientated at random and extend in all directions in the wall. When secondary walls are laid down it has been found that the orientation of the cellulose chains may differ in successive layers. These layers are often laid down at characteristic angles to one another (fig. 146). The way in which succeeding layers are orientated are reflected in the mechanical properties of the cell wall. The study of the differences in the orientation of fibres such as cotton (*Gossypium* spp.) and flax (*Linum usitatissimum*) is thus of economic significance.

Of other polysaccharides occurring in the cell wall the *hemicelluloses* deserves special mention. These substances, of somewhat varying composition, are found in all woody tissues and constitute a considerable proportion of the wall material of grasses and straw, imparting strength and toughness to them. Unlike cellulose, they can be digested by specific enzymes and are used to some extent as food reserves.

FATS AND OILS

The second class of plant food substances are the fatty substances or *lipids*, which occur in considerable amounts as storage products in many seeds, for example, castor oil and sunflower, though they also occur as constituents of the living protoplasm. There are three principal groups of these substances in plants, *fats*, *waxes* and *phospholipids*, but of these only fats constitute food reserves. Waxes are fatty substances produced by the cell wall as a protective covering over various organs of the plant, thereby preventing water loss. Many fruits and flowers have these waxy coverings. Phospholipids occur within the cell as part of the structural framework of its living matter, especially the various cell membranes (p. 27).

Fats are primarily the food reserves of seeds and occur either in cotyledons or endosperm. They can be observed in cells under the microscope as droplets in the cytoplasm (fig. 17.2) and can be readily stained with certain fat-soluble dyes, such as Sudan III. The fat in the seed accumulates as the latter develops, but like starch it is *degraded* during germination into simpler substances and utilized as a source of energy and raw materials for growth. It is important to note that fats are much more efficient food reserves than carbohydrates and provide more than twice as much energy as the same quantity of carbohydrate, into which they can be fairly readily converted (see Chapter 19).

Chemically, fats are formed by the union of *fatty acids* which can be represented by the general formula $C_xH_y - COOH$, and *glycerol*, a 3-carbon atom compound:

$$\begin{array}{c} H_2COH \\ | \\ HCOH \\ | \\ H_2COH \end{array}$$

These two components are linked together by a so-called 'ester linkage' in which one molecule of water is eliminated between the acid group of the fatty acid and the hydroxyl group of the glycerol:

$$\begin{array}{ccccccc} H_2\,COH & & HOOC\text{-}C_xH_y & \xrightarrow{\text{synthesis}} & H_2\,COOC\text{-}C_xH_y & & \\ | & & | & & | & & \\ HCOH & + & HOOC\text{-}C_xH_y & \longrightarrow & HCOOC\text{-}C_xH_y & + & 3\,H_2O \\ | & & | & & | & & \\ H_2\,COH & & HOOC\text{-}C_xH_y & \longleftarrow & H_2\,COOC\text{-}C_xH_y & & \\ \textit{glycerol} & & \textit{fatty acid} & \text{hydrolysis} & \textit{fat molecule} & & \end{array}$$

This linkage can be broken on hydrolysis, or by the enzyme *lipase*, to the constituent fatty acid of the fat and glycerol (Chapter 17, p. 201).

It is of interest to note that sugar is again the basic material from which the constituents of the fatty substances in the plant are produced. Thus in the maturing seed it is sugar rather than fat which is translocated from the leaves; the synthesis of the fat takes place in the seed itself. Furthermore, as fats are used up during germination they are, in part at least, reconverted to sugar and move in this state to the growing tissues (see Chapter 20).

PROTEINS

Proteins are much more complex and in many ways more important compounds than either carbohydrates or fats, for although they occur in some seeds as food reserves, their special significance lies in the fact that they are the substances most closely associated with life. They form an integral part of all the living matter in both the cytoplasm and nucleus of all cells and in the structure of enzymes, which play such a vital role in every metabolic event. Not only are they very complex molecules, they are also very large as the following comparative table shows:

	molecular wt.
Hydrogen	1
Glucose	200
Simplest protein molecules	5,000
Complex proteins	100,000 – 1,000,000

Just as sugar residues constitute the building blocks of the more complex carbohydrates, so *amino acids* are the structural units of all proteins. Common to all the amino acids, of which 22 are recognized, is an NH_2COOH group, so that as well as containing carbon, hydrogen and oxygen, proteins also contain nitrogen as an essential constituent.

The general structural formula of amino acids is as follows:

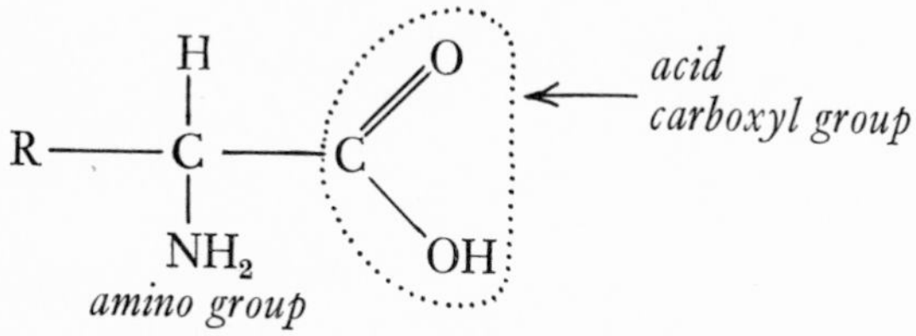

$$R-\underset{\underset{NH_2}{|}}{\overset{\overset{H}{|}}{C}}-C{\begin{matrix}=O\\-OH\end{matrix}}$$

acid carboxyl group (COOH); *amino group* (NH_2)

'R' differs in different acids and in the simplest, *glycine*, it is but a single H atom. In *alanine*, another of the simple amino acids, 'R' is a CH_3 or *methyl group*, but in other acids this group, which is attached to the carbon atom adjoining the amino group (NH_2), may be structurally very complex.

In the formation of proteins, amino acids combine with one another, sometimes in very long chains. The links which hold these chains are called *peptide bonds*, successive amino acids being joined through their amino and carboxyl groups to give *peptide chains*, after the loss of a molecule of water.

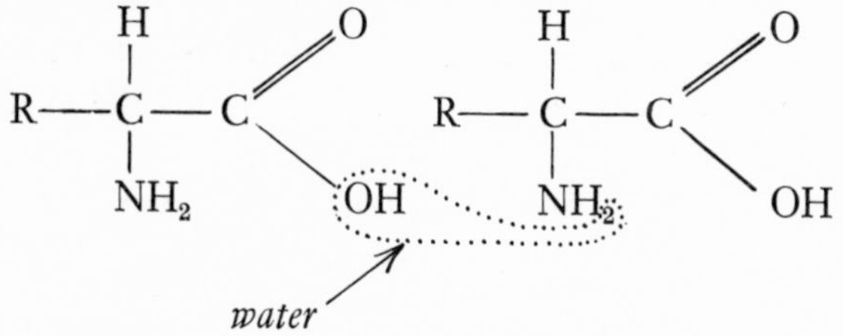

$$R-\underset{\underset{NH_2}{|}}{\overset{\overset{H}{|}}{C}}-C{\begin{matrix}=O\\-OH\end{matrix}}\quad R-\underset{\underset{NH_2}{|}}{\overset{\overset{H}{|}}{C}}-C{\begin{matrix}=O\\-OH\end{matrix}}$$

water (OH of the first acid and H of the NH_2 of the second)

The situation here is analogous to the linking of monosaccharide molecules to give increasingly complex carbohydrates, so that di- tri-, as well as *polypeptides* occur. As in the case of sugars, di- and tri- proteins are collectively termed polypeptides.

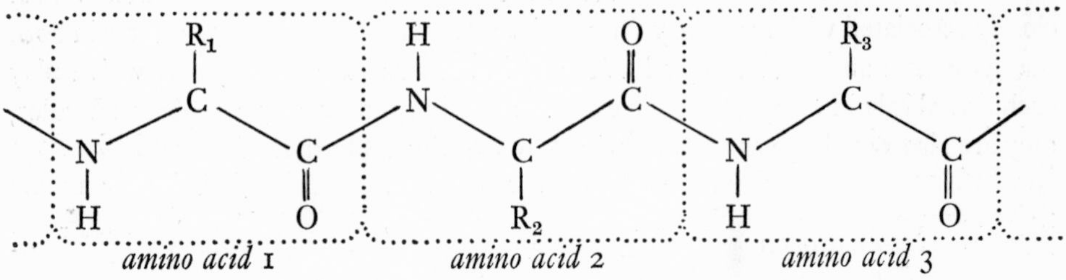

R_1 H O R_3

C N C C

N C C N C

H O R_2 H O

amino acid 1 *amino acid* 2 *amino acid* 3

Proteins are thus polypeptides and the smallest molecules consist of about 100 of these linkages, while the larger ones may contain up to 3,000 amino-acid residues. It is obvious that the number of ways in which the known 22 amino-acids can be joined together is infinite and it is this which gives proteins their strong individuality. The amino-acid constituents of a given protein can be obtained by hydrolysis, which may be brought about by heating with dilute acid or by treatment with *proteolytic* enzymes (see Chapter 17). Thus for any given protein it is possible to determine its constituent amino acids. However the crucial factor which gives each protein its individual and inimitable properties is the spatial arrangement of these amino acids in the chain. Recently, as a result of elaborate X-ray analysis of certain simple animal proteins, the first picture of a protein molecule has been constructed – one of the greatest scientific achievements of the century. This picture reveals the fact that proteins are not simple chains but complexly coiled, folded, and branched three-dimensional structures (fig. 147).

The formation of proteins is one of the most characteristic properties of living cells, and the very special and noteworthy feature in this connection in their construction is that the sequence of amino acids is rigidly and inflexibly maintained. Thus every organism is able to make very large numbers of highly specific and very precisely constructed proteins each with a special place and function in its life.

In the synthesis of proteins in plants, carbohydrates produced as a result of photosynthesis are the source of carbon, hydrogen, and oxygen, while the essential nitrogen of the amino acid residues comes from nitrates absorbed from the soil. In the formation of amino acids the nitrate is reduced, by the activity of certain enzymes, to ammonia and this combines with certain products of the breakdown of sugars. The small molecules of amino acid can be readily translocated to those parts of the plant where protein synthesis is active. Here there occurs the final and crucial step, where the amino acids are linked up in their very orderly and highly specific way through peptide bonds to form proteins. Although this synthesis can, and probably does, take place in every living cell, it seems to occur especially in regions of active growth.

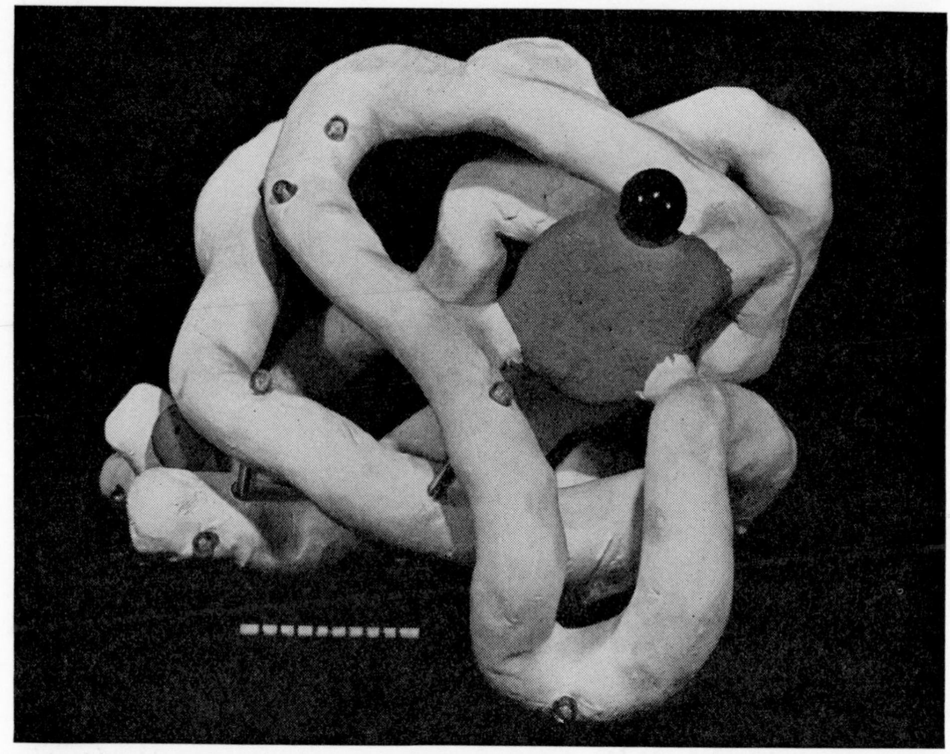

Figure 147 *A model of a protein molecule, myoglobin, a simple protein present in animal muscle and other tissues. The polypeptide chains are represented in white and the grey disc is a haem group. The marks on the scale are* 1 *Angstrom Unit* (10^{-8} *cm*) *apart.* (*Photograph by Dr J. C. Kendrew*, FRS.)

Simple proteins also occur as *nitrogenous food reserves* of certain cells, especially in storage organs. Here the proteins may be dissolved as colloids in the cell sap, or they may occur as crystal-like bodies (crystalloids). In the outer layers of the cells of certain oil containing seeds such as castor oil and Brazil nut (*Berthelletia excelsa*), especially large granules arise from the contents of the vacuoles, which are rich in protein as the seeds dry out on ripening. These granules, termed *aleurone grains*, are relatively complex structures. Each consists of an outer membrane enclosing ampor-phous protein in which a large, angular, crystalloid protein grain and a much smaller, globoid grain is embedded.

CHAPTER 17

ENZYMES

It should be evident from the previous chapter that living cells are involved in intense and varied chemical activity. In order to survive, to grow and to reproduce, all cells must be provided with a variety of so-called food substances. In the green plant these are basically derived from sugar, the product of its photosynthesis. This sugar may be rapidly moved away from the cells where it has been made and then transformed and stored away for future use in the form of much larger and more complex molecules such as starch, fats or proteins; or the sugar may be utilized as the basic structural material from which new cells with their walls, cytoplasm and nuclei are built; or it may be broken down, or degraded, to provide the energy necessary to drive these complex synthetic activities of the living cell.

The most remarkable feature of these various metabolic activities, whether in synthesizing new materials or in breaking down and extracting from storage products the energy necessary for such synthesis, is that these highly complex processes, which do not occur spontaneously, are carried out in plant cells with great speed and efficiency. If a chemist, even with unlimited apparatus, was to attempt to transform sugar into alcohol by purely chemical means, the task would take a considerable time and involve a series of complex stages. When the cells of a unicellular fungus (*Saccharomyces*) (yeast), are introduced into a solution of sugar, alcohol will very soon appear in the solution accompanied by the evoluton of carbon dioxide. This biological process has been used from ancient times. In the making of bread, the carbon dioxide produced leavens the dough; and the alcohol so formed has been used in the manufacture of intoxicating drinks, even by primitive man. Until the mid-19th century it was thought that only living cells could bring about this degradation or *fermentation* of sugar. However, the German chemist Büchner demonstrated that the contents squeezed from living cells were alone capable of splitting sugar in this way. To the substance extracted from yeast and possessing this property he gave the name '*en-zyme*', meaning 'in yeast'.

A very considerable number of enzymes, which have been termed *bio-catalysts*, are now known to occur in all plants and animals. Like the catalysts used by the inorganic chemist, they are capable of greatly accelerating the rate of chemical reactions, or of causing reactions to proceed which do not occur spontaneously. Moreover, they are not consumed during the course of the reaction, nor do they appear to be chemically combined with any of the end products. Very minute amounts of enzyme can bring about dramatic changes to very considerable amounts of reactant. Thus one molecule of the enzyme *catalase*, which is capable of splitting hydrogen peroxide into water and oxygen, is said to be able to decompose at least 2 million molecules of peroxide per minute at 0°C.

Unlike inorganic catalysts, enzymes are very sensitive to temperature. Low temperatures retard their rate of action, while high temperatures do likewise. Between 0° and 35°C their activity increases; above 35°C their activity shows a pronounced decrease, and they are completely inactivated at 70°C. They are destroyed, or rapidly denatured, at 100°C. This temperature sensitivity is in part a reflection of their colloidal nature, as is also the fact that, because of their high molecular weight, they are unable to pass through semi-permeable membranes (see Chapter 12). The majority of enzymes are soluble in water, and after extraction from the tissues in which they occur they can usually be precipitated by adding alcohol to the extract. The precipitate can be filtered off and if carefully dried at a low temperature can be stored almost indefinitely without loss of activity. Since 1926, a considerable number of enzymes have been isolated in a pure crystalline state. It was in this year that the first pure enzyme *urease*, capable of splitting *urea*, was prepared from Jack Beans by the American biochemist, Professor J. B. Sumner. All enzymes isolated in this pure state have so far been found to be proteins, and indeed many of their properties, such as temperature sensitivity and their colloidal nature, would seem to be associated with this fact. Thus proteins, as well as being important structural elements and food reserves of the living cell, are at the centre of all metabolic activity. Indeed, since it has been said that 'Life is largely a matter of enzymes', this is the supreme role of proteins in the cell.

All organisms are endowed with large numbers of enzymes working together in harmony to bring about the synthesis of some substances and the breakdown of others. Although highly specialized substances, even the simplest organisms possess enzymes which are very similar to those occurring in the most highly evolved organisms. In all organisms there appear to be separate enzymes concerned with each distinct metabolic change which takes place in its cells. Urease, for example, acts only on urea; *catalase* only on hydrogen peroxide. A very special and valuable property of many enzymes is that they can cause certain reactions to proceed either in the direction of synthesis or breakdown, depending on conditions within the cell. Thus under some conditions fats can be split into their constituent fatty acids and glycerol by hydrolysis in the presence of the enzyme *lipase*. Under a different set of conditions, however, the same enzyme will bring about condensation of these same fatty acids and glycerol to bring about the formation of fat. A further remarkable feature of these biocatalysts is that an enzyme of one species may not be structurally the same as the enzyme performing a similar function in a different species of plant or animal. This implies that they have a strong individuality, a fact which is not so surprising when it is remembered that enzymes are proteins, and that the amino-acid units of which the latter are constituted can in their formation be combined in an almost unlimited number of ways.

Enzymes are in many cases distinguished from the type of substance, or *substrate*,

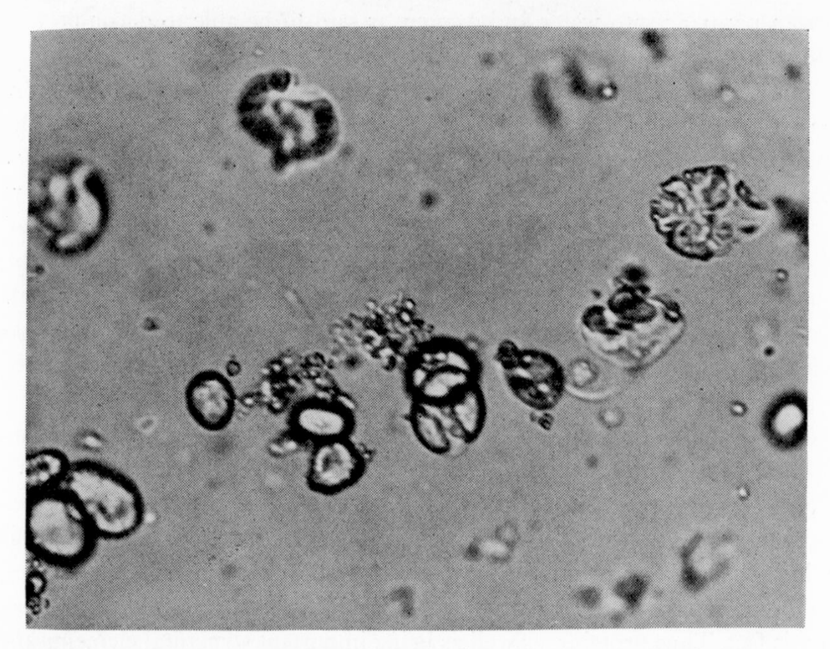

Figure 148 *Disintegrating starch grains from barley after digestion by the enzyme amylase in human saliva.*

on which they act by a change in the name ending of the latter to 'ase'. They have been classified into broad categories depending on the types of reactions they catalyse; thus *hydrolases* are concerned with hydrolyses; *oxidases* with oxidations involving the addition of oxygen; *dehydrogenases* with those in which there is a removal of hydrogen. It should be remembered that a number of enzymes were discovered before this system of nomenclature was adopted and that their original names, as for example *pepsin*, *rennin*, *trypsin*, have been retained. Some of the most commonly occurring plant enzymes, their source, substrate, and some indication of their special activities, are outlined in the tables on the opposite page.

Although some enzymes probably consist of only a protein molecule, as for example the proteolytic enzymes which break down proteins, many are also coupled to a non-protein portion. The latter, termed a *coenzyme* or *prosthetic group*, may in some cases consist merely of a single metal atom, as in the case of the copper atom of the enzyme *tyrosinase*. If this copper is removed, then the enzyme becomes inert and is unable to split the amino-acid *tyrosin*. Zinc, manganese, magnesium and iron are all known to function as prosthetic groups of various enzymes though they do not all occur (as copper in tyrosinase) as single atoms. They mostly form an integral part of a quite complex coenzyme molecule. It is almost certain that the heavy metals required only in minute traces for successful plant growth are in fact essential because of the vital part they play in the structure of coenzymes. The complex organic molecules,

1. HYDROLASES: enzymes concerned in hydrolyses and condensations

	ENZYME	*SOURCE*	*REACTION*
at- or lipoid- splitting (ESTERASES)	LIPASE	Many germinating seeds, especially Castor Oil	HYDROLYSIS ⇄CONDENSATION⇄ FATS ⇄ GLYCEROL and FATTY ACIDS
:arbohydrate- plitting RBOHYDRASES)	INVERTASE	Leaves Yeast	SUCROSE⇄GLUCOSE (INVERT and FRUCTOSE SUGAR)
	DIASTASE { AMYLASE (see fig. 148)	Germinating seeds Leaves	STARCH⇄MALTOSE
	DIASTASE { MALTASE	,,	MALTOSE⇄GLUCOSE
	CYTASE	,,	HEMICELLULOSE⇄GLUCOSE
'rotein- splitting (PROTEASES)	BROMELIN PAPAIN etc.	Pineapple *Papaya* leaves	PROTEINS⇄AMINO-ACIDS and POLYPEPTIDES

eakdown of A, B, and C goes on particularly in regions where food is stored. The products are transported in r form to growth regions for building new cells or to supply energy for growth and other physiological functions.

2. OXIDIZING and REDUCING ENZYMES

ENZYME	*SOURCE*	*SUBSTRATE*	*PRODUCT*
IDASE	Broad Beans	PHENOLIC SUBSTANCES	Dark coloured OXIDIZED SUBSTRATE
TALASE	*Mesembryan- themum*	HYDROGEN PEROXIDE	WATER + MOLECULAR O_2
.HYDRO- GENASE	All respiring cells	ALCOHOL	OXIDIZED SUBSTRATE (Alcohol – Aldehyde) + H attached to H acceptor
DUCTASE	Most roots	NITRATES	NITRITES

3. FERMENTATION ENZYMES

MASE	Yeast and plants generally	HEXOSE SUGARS	ETHYL ALCOHOL + CARBON DIOXIDE

vitamins (which first came into prominence as essential requirements in human and animal foods, though in minute amounts), are now known to be the prosthetic groups of various plant enzymes.

There is still much to be discovered about the way in which enzymes bring about their remarkable and highly specific reactions. Much, however, seems to depend on their surface properties on which the reacting substances can be adsorbed or chemically combined. Thus in reactions where molecules of specific substances, fats for example, are split by an enzyme, it is believed that the initial step in the process is the close fitting together of the enzyme and the substrate about to be changed. It is probable that this fit is a very tight and intimate one, so that the union between enzyme and *substrate* is stronger than that existing between the constituent molecules of the latter. The bond joining the constituents is in fact weakened and eventually splits. In enzymatic synthesis, which is much more difficult to demonstrate outside the cell, it seems that the surface pattern of the enzyme molecule provides a highly specific jig, or cradle, which holds together the constituent molecules of the substance to be synthesized. The chemical bond between them can then be formed, the structural features of enzyme or coenzyme enabling the required energy to be adequately provided.

It is now recognized that enzymes mostly occur in the living components of the cell, that is in the cytoplasm and nucleus; few, if any, occur in the cell wall or vacuole. In fact, most of the proteins of the cytoplasm and nucleus are probably intimately concerned in enzymatic activities. The various *organelles* which occur in the cytoplasm are known to contain specific enzymes; the chloroplasts, for example, possess a number which are concerned in the complexities of photosynthesis and starch formation, whilst the mitochondria, the main centres of cell respiration, contain respiratory enzymes; less is known about enzymes in the nucleus. Recent genetical studies have revealed that a change in the genetic material of an organism (a mutation in the chromosomes) may cause a change or loss in its ability to carry out certain syntheses (Chapter 25, p. 310). These mutations are believed to be associated with changes or losses of a particular enzyme in the organism. *Heredity* is, in fact, now thought to be largely a question of passing on from one generation to the next the ability to make the right enzymes. Although these always occur in minute amounts, they are nevertheless the very machines of metabolism, controlling and integrating the complex chemical reactions in the cell which are life itself. Life is indeed, 'largely a matter of enzymes'.

CHAPTER 18

PHOTOSYNTHESIS

Photosynthesis is the process by which plants containing chlorophyll convert *light-energy* into physiologically-useful *chemical energy*. This chemical energy is accumulated in the plant as complex compounds of carbon carbohydrates (see Chapter 16). Almost immediately after being formed or, alternatively, after a period of storage the carbohydrates are used to provide respiratory energy, and also some of the materials essential for growth. It has been estimated that, by the process of photosynthesis, some 200 billion tons of carbon per year are fixed or incorporated within living plants throughout the world and its oceans. Moreover, the vast majority of living organisms in the world depend for nutriment either directly or indirectly on the products of photosynthesis. The understanding of the means whereby green plants accomplish this all important transformation of the sun's energy, is one of the fundamental problems, not just of botanical science, but of all biology.

When animals and plants breathe, or respire, they absorb oxygen from the air, and give off carbon dioxide with a slow and controlled release of stored energy (see Chapter 19), much of which is channelled into the performance of cellular work. When wood or coal burns, there is a similar absorption of oxygen and release of carbon dioxide, but this is accomplished by a violent release of energy, so that much heat is liberated. During both respiration and combustion, however, carbon compounds are broken down, and it is the energy contained in them which is released. During photosynthesis this process is reversed and a synthesis of carbon compounds takes place. The English chemist, Joseph Priestly, in 1771, first showed that plants have the ability to 'improve' air from which the oxygen had been used up in combustion, though he failed to realize that light played any part in the process. It was in fact Ingen-Housz who first stated that sunlight was essential to enable plants to purify air, and the Swiss physicist De Saussure who demonstrated that green plants absorb carbon dioxide from the air in the presence of light and give off oxygen. De Saussure also recognized that water entered into the 'purification' process. From these early investigations of photosynthesis it gradually became clear that there existed an inverse relationship between this process and respiration. In the process of photosynthesis the CO_2 of the atmosphere is consumed, while there is a complimentary replenishment of CO_2 from the respiration of living organisms. This very important relationship is summarized in the following reversible equation:

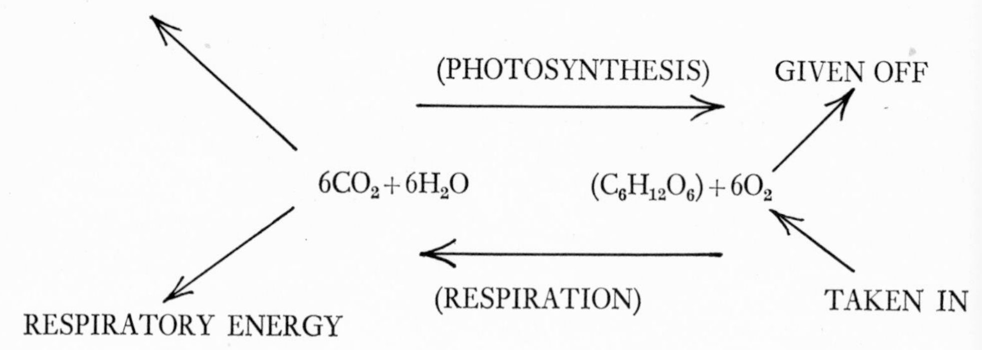

It is noteworthy that water, originally absorbed by the plant's root system, is involved in both reactions; also that the chemical energy released in respiration is derived entirely from solar energy held within the molecules of the carbon-containing compounds elaborated by the plant during photosynthesis.

THE CARBON DIOXIDE CYCLE (fig. 149)

Although carbon dioxide is of such vital importance for the growth and functioning of all living organisms, it is one of the minor constituents of the atmosphere, of the total volume of which it comprises only 0·03%; whereas nitrogen, which as a gas is useless to the majority of plants, represents 78%, and oxygen about 21%. Despite this, carbon dioxide plays the leading role in the metabolism of plants and is of the greatest biological significance, being continuously consumed (except in the hours of darkness) by the vast assemblage of plants both on the earth and in its oceans. It has been estimated that the annual turnover of carbon dioxide represents about one-thirtieth of the total amount present in the earth's atmosphere. How then is this apparently scarce but biologically vital gas replenished, so that its concentration is maintained at a constant level?

As already stated, some carbon dioxide is derived from the respiration of living plants and animals. But even after their death and return to the soil, the carbon within their decaying bodies, through bacterial and fungal activity, is in a large measure released as carbon dioxide – the process measured as 'soil respiration'. Some carbon dioxide is also released from volcanoes and mineral springs, and in the combustion of wood as well as from the burning of coal and oil. These latter substances are the heritage of photosynthetic activity from past geological ages.

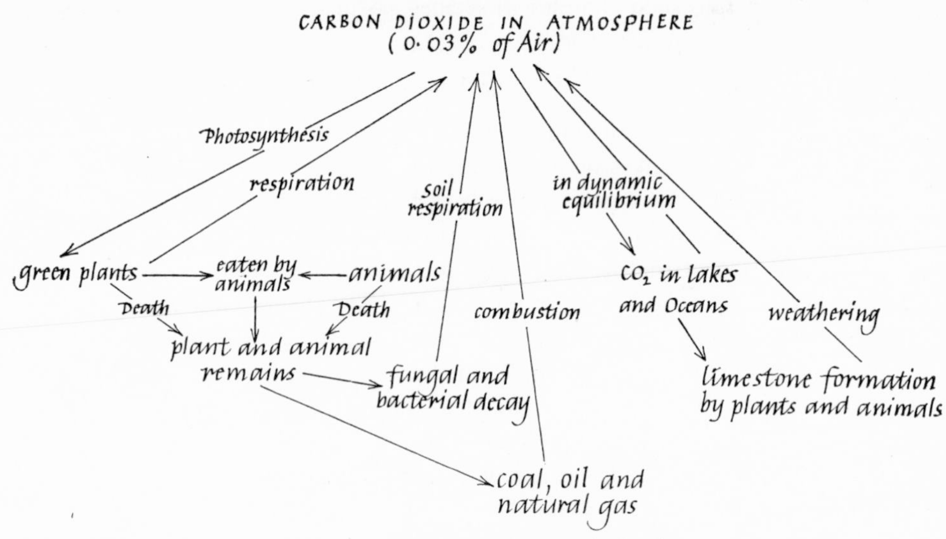

Figure 149 *The Carbon Dioxide Cycle.*

The most important reserves of carbon dioxide, however, are the world's oceans, which occupy three-quarters of its surface and whose vast volumes of water teem with floating plant and animal life. These waters are believed to contain as much as eighty to a hundred times more carbon in forms available to plants than does the atmosphere. Although the bulk of the plants in the oceans are microscopic single-celled *algae* floating freely in the waters, they are, like terrestrial plants, photosynthetic (see Chapter 32). The carbon assimilated by the *phytoplankton*, as these microscopic floating plants are collectively termed, occurs not only as dissolved carbon dioxide but also as *carbonates* and *bicarbonates* which exist in complex equilibrium with this all important gas. Carbonates are precipitated in the formation of the shells of many marine animals and by both plants (algae) and animals (coelenterates) in the formation of corals. Both shells and corals are involved in the formation of limestone rocks and these in the course of geological time may become raised above the seas in which they were produced. On their subsequent weathering the carbon dioxide bound in them as carbonate may be released once more into the atmosphere.

There is in fact a constant exchange of carbon dioxide between the oceans and the atmosphere, and indeed it is probably through the maintenance of a dynamic equilibrium between them that the remarkably constant concentration of carbon dioxide in the atmosphere is preserved.

THE PROBLEM OF PHOTOSYNTHESIS

The crux of the photosynthetic problem is to determine how carbon dioxide, having diffused into a leaf and on reaching the chloroplasts, becomes synthesized in the presence of light into such complex molecules as sugar and starch. The somewhat arbitrary photosynthetic equation,

$$6CO_2 + 6H_2O + \text{light energy} \longrightarrow C_6H_{12}O_6 + 6CO_2,$$

apart from showing that equal volumes of carbon dioxide and oxygen are respectively consumed and evolved, gives no indication of the steps that bring about so complex a transubstantiation. The equation merely indicates that for every six molecules of the raw materials CO_2 and H_2O utilized, one molecule of hexose sugar is synthesized.

The elucidation of the probable steps in this synthesis has engrossed not only botanists but many of the world's finest chemists. The theory most widely accepted, until the recent employment of minutely sensitive analytical techniques using radio isotopes, was essentially that propounded in 1870 by the German chemist Von Baeyer. He suggested that the principal intermediate substance involved was *formaldehyde* (CH_2O) and that a union of six molecules of the latter resulted in the formation of one molecule of glucose ($C_6H_{12}O_6$). It is now almost certain that formaldehyde plays no part in photosynthesis; and it is abundantly clear that there are several distinct steps, involving many enzymes.

The initiation, or first phase, of photosynthesis involves the absorption of light (mostly from the red region of the spectrum) by chlorophyll. The energy from the absorbed light causes an excitation of a part of the chlorophyll molecule. This 'light reaction' is the essence of the whole process, for it results in the conversion of light-energy into physiologically useful chemical-energy. In its excited or activated state the chlorophyll splits water into its component elements, hydrogen and oxygen. The hydrogen is held by the chlorophyll, or by some *hydrogen-acceptor*, until required, but the oxygen is set free. That the oxygen evolved in this first crucial step in the process comes from water has been established beyond doubt by photosynthetic experiments in which water labelled with radio-active oxygen (O_2^{18}) was used in place of normal water. By supplying an air mixture containing similarly labelled CO_2 to photosynthesizing plants it has been confirmed that the oxygen is not derived from the oxygen of CO_2. Under the latter conditions no O_2^{18} was liberated.

The equation conventionally written to represent the overall photosynthetic reaction, which shows one molecule of O_2 evolved for the uptake of one molecule of both CO_2 and H_2O, viz.,

$$6CO_2 + 6H_2O \longrightarrow (C_6H_{12}O_6) + 6O_2,$$

must be revised in the light of the evidence about the origin of the O_2 given off. Clearly two molecules of water must be decomposed for the evolution of one of oxygen. Thus consideration of the experiments using labelled water indicates that the equation should be written as follows:

$$6CO_2 + 12H_2O^{18} \longrightarrow (C_6H_{12}O_6) + 6O_2^{18} + 6H_2O.$$

Sooner or later the 2 [H]atoms resulting from the *photolysis* of water must be 'harnessed' or directed into doing some metabolically useful work. Certain coenzymes, amongst which is the *pyridine nucleotide*, TPN, are essential for this process. These act as carriers of hydrogen and in so doing are converted from the oxidized TPN to the reduced form-TPNH. In this process of forming a stable reduced compound, some of the light energy absorbed is utilized in the production of an energy-rich phosphate bond of ATP. The production of ATP, the most important holder of chemical energy in all living cells, is called a *photosynthetic phosphorylation*. Non-green plants, all animals, and the respiring parts of green plants produce some ATP by the oxidation of stored carbohydrate – *oxidative phosphorylation* (see Chapter 19). It must be stressed that the vital and outstanding event in the photosynthetic reaction is the production of ATP without the utilization of any stored carbohydrate or other food reserve. Green plants can in fact manufacture an excess of energy-containing substances beyond their own needs. The supply of this energy is the prime necessity for the continuance of life in all non-photosynthetic organisms.

The second major phase in photosynthesis is the reduction of carbon dioxide. Before this can occur, however, the CO_2 must be taken up within the cell by some *carbon dioxide-acceptor*. It seems probable that this is a 5-carbon, or pentose sugar, and that the addition-compound so formed immediately splits into two molecules of a simple substance containing 3 carbon atoms, *3-phosphoglyceric acid* – the first stable product of photosynthesis. This stage may be regarded as the final one in the strictly photosynthetic process. The conversion of the 3-phosphoglyceric acid to the level of a carbohydrate requires TPHN and ATP, which, as has been shown, are the most important products of the 'light reaction'. Thus the two phases, the 'light' and the 'dark', are interrelated and not readily separated. The carbohydrates finally resulting from the conversion differ in different groups of plants. Thus they may be the monosaccharides, glucose and fructose, the disaccharide sucrose, or polysaccharides such as starch (see fig. 150). These latter transformations may take place in living cells in any part of the plant. They commonly occur in storage tissues to which the smaller molecules of glucose or surcose have been translocated (see Chapter 20).

The Light and Photosynthesis

The foregoing summary of the probable mechanism of photosynthesis has emphasized that the process is initiated by the absorption of light and that the so-called 'light reaction', which brings about chemical transformations, is the critical stage. The induction of chemical change by light is not, however, limited to photosynthesis. It occurs when the colours of such materials as paints, textiles or wall-papers fade; and all photographic processes depend on this phenomenon. Indeed it occurs to some extent whenever light falls on a substance which absorbs it. Dark objects absorb more light than bright ones, which reflect it. In the cases of reflecting materials the energy absorbed is very unstable and most of it is usually liberated immediately as heat.

Solar energy appears to be propagated across space in the form of undulating waves, and different categories of energy have different wavelengths. The wavelengths detectable by the human eye, which produce the sensation of light, range from 300 mμ (millimicrons) to 760 mμ. 'White light', when passed through a prism, appears as a spectrum of colours (the colours of a rainbow), red, orange, yellow, green, blue, indigo, violet – each corresponding to a different range of wave-lengths between these values. Wave-lengths greater than those of visible light are known as infra-red or 'heat' waves, while radio waves are longer still. The wave-lengths shorter than those of visible light include ultra violet, X-rays, and gamma rays.

A satisfactory explanation of the conversion of radiant energy into chemical energy requires the added assumption (for which there is strong evidence) that light is also propagated as a random emission of minute particles, called *photons*. When photons strike any suitable substance their energy may be transferred to it by inducing a photochemical reaction. In this the most significant effect occurs within the atoms, which are the ultimate units comprising the substance on to which the light falls. All atoms consist of a positively-charged nucleus with a number of negatively-charged electrons moving as closely as possible in orbit round it. When light particles (photons) and their associated energy are absorbed, electrons are displaced outwards. This causes them to travel in an orbit further from the centre of the atom than their original path and the potential energy of the atom rises accordingly.

The energy of light is contained in indivisible packets called *quanta*, whose energy-content varies inversely with wave-length. For example, a quantum of ultra-violet radiation with a wave-length of 100 mμ has six times the energy of yellowish-orange light of wave-length 600 mμ. If the light absorbed carries sufficient energy, an electron may become displaced to such an extent that it is lost from the atom altogether, and the atom gains energy. When an electron is displaced to a higher energy level it sooner or later reverts to its normal position and in so doing energy may be released, so bringing about a chemical change. It is a *photochemical* change of this nature that is the crucial part of photosynthesis. As a result, chlorophyll, the essential cog in the photosynthetic machine, becomes activated or excited by absorbing light energy.

Starch Formation

Once hexose sugar (see p. 190) has been formed, the photosynthetic process may be regarded as complete. However, starch is subsequently and rapidly produced in a very large number of plants, by condensation in assimilating organs exposed to light. As carbohydrate is produced it is taken out of circulation in this way, and stored for future use. The presence of starch in leaves resulting from photosynthetic activity, can be readily demonstrated with iodine, with which the starch reacts to give a typical blue-black colour. Since this colour is masked by the pigments of the leaf chloroplasts, the chlorophyll must be removed before the *iodine test* is applied. To accomplish this, the leaf is plunged into boiling water which kills the cells, leaving their protoplasm highly permeable. The chlorophyll must then be dissolved out with warm alcohol until the leaf appears almost white. The decoloured leaf is finally transferred to a solution of iodine in potassium iodide, and if starch is present it almost immediately gives the characteristic blue-black reaction. The starch-iodine test thus provides an easy and rapid indication of photosynthetic activity in many plants – though not in all, for in many monocotyledons starch is never formed in assimilating organs.

If potted plants, of species known to form starch in their leaves as the end-product of photosynthesis, are kept in the dark, all the starch will disappear from their leaves so that they give no iodine reaction. These destarched plants can then be subjected to various environmental conditions in order to demonstrate some of the factors necessary for photosynthesis. It can be shown, for example, that *carbon dioxide* is essential, by illuminating a destarched plant in an atmosphere from which all the CO_2 has been removed with caustic soda (NaOH). Under these conditions, no starch will form in the plant's leaves, although there is rapid and abundant starch-production in a comparable destarched control plant similarly illuminated in an atmosphere where there is a normal CO_2 supply.

That *chlorophyll* is a prerequisite for photosynthesis can be shown by applying the starch-iodine test to variegated leaves, such as privet, or *Pelargonium*, which have been supplied with all the conditions known to be necessary for the process to occur. The test will indicate that starch is formed only in the green, chlorophyll-containing areas of the leaves. Yellow or whitish areas give no reaction with iodine.

That *light* is essential can be quite neatly demonstrated by covering a leaf of a destarched plant with a stencil or an opaque paper cover with a hole cut in it and then exposing the leaf to light. It will be found on testing for starch that the covered regions of the leaf give no iodine reaction, only the open areas exposed to light turning blue-black. This experiment also serves to demonstrate that there is no lateral movement in a leaf of the products of photosynthesis.

The Measurement of Photosynthesis

These simple demonstrations of some of the factors necessary for photosynthesis, utilizing the iodine reaction, can give only the most general indication of the rate of the process, and of course can be applied only to starch-forming plants. Precise quantitative measurements of photosynthesis are most frequently based on determinations of the amount of carbon dioxide absorbed by a leaf or leaves of known area, or even a small, entire plant. The amount of oxygen evolved can also be used, since, as shown by the photosynthetic equation, the volume of carbon dioxide absorbed is the same as the oxygen liberated. The measure of carbon dioxide absorbed is, however, more frequently used because, it will be remembered (see p. 206), normal air contains only 0.03% of carbon dioxide compared with 20% by volume of oxygen. Thus even if all the carbon dioxide in the experimental environment were taken up by the photosynthesizing plant, this would lead only to a very insignificant increase in the normally large amount of oxygen present in the atmosphere; these measurements would therefore be liable to considerable inaccuracy.

Much valuable quantitative work on photosynthesis has been performed with the unicellular green alga *Chlorella* (see p. 359). Large cultures of this alga can be rapidly grown under standard conditions, and, for experimental purposes, split up into considerable numbers of more or less identical portions. These *replicate cultures* can then be subjected to various environmental influences appropriate to the particular aspect of photosynthesis under investigation. All such experiments are carried out in closed vessels which make it possible to measure gas exchange due to photosynthesis by estimating internal pressure changes, instead of measuring alterations in the concentrations of CO_2 or O_2 themselves.

In making quantitative measurements of photosynthesis it must be remembered that, even when the process is proceeding at a rapid rate and CO_2 is being absorbed, there is a parallel evolution of the same gas, owing to respiration. The assumption is generally made that the amount of respiration in photosynthesizing tissues is identical to that occurring in the same tissues in the dark. To determine the true rate of photosynthesis, therefore, it is first necessary to determine the rate of respiration of the plant material in the dark, and then to add this amount to the experimentally determined rate of photosynthesis. An increase in carbohydrate in the photosynthesizing cells or tissues may itself however, cause an increase in respiration, owing to the presence of a greater quantity of *respiratory substrate* (see Chapter 19, p. 223).

Under certain environmental conditions, as for example at low light intensities or low temperatures, the rate of photosynthesis may be reduced to a level just equal to the plant's respiration. In such circumstances no exchange of CO_2 or O_2 between the plant and its environment will take place, and in consequence no loss or gain of carbohydrate. This point of zero gas-exchange is termed the *compensation point.*

Limiting Factors in Photosynthesis

If light intensity is increased gradually so that the rate of photosynthesis rises above the compensation point, it can be shown that over a considerable range the rate is directly proportional to the intensity. Eventually an intensity is reached beyond which the photosynthetic rate will not increase, no matter how much the light is intensified. At this point the plant is said to be *light-saturated.* A similar relation is obtained when the rate of photosynthesis is measured against an increasing concentration of CO_2. As with light, a point is reached where no further increase can be detected. If the experimental plant is photosynthesizing in weak light, the level of CO_2 at which any increase in rate ceases is lower than at higher light intensities. This is because the light energy falling on the chloroplasts can only utilize a limited amount of the CO_2 entering its leaves.

Experimental observations of this nature emphasize that it is essential to take account of other factors known to be involved when a study is being made of the effects of one particular factor in photosynthesis. In the case of observations on the effects of CO_2 concentration, for example, the intensity of illumination can clearly *limit* the process, no matter how great the concentration of gas supplied. In other words, at low light intensities any increase in CO_2 concentration can induce an increase in the rate of photosynthesis only if there is a corresponding increase in light intensity. This concept of *limiting factors* was the outcome of studies by the distinguished British plant physiologist F. F. Blackman. Mainly as a result of his work, it has been recognized that three external factors, light, CO_2 concentration and temperature, in association with certain internal factors – of which chlorophyll is the most important – ultimately determine the rate of photosynthesis.

Thus it can be shown that light intensity, or CO_2 concentration, may limit the process and that at low concentrations of CO_2 the maximum possible rate is produced at quite low light intensities. Attempts to increase photosynthesis by increasing the illumination will under these conditions not succeed, because CO_2 concentration is the limiting factor. Clearly the rate of photosynthesis is a function of CO_2 concentration at different light intensities.

The effect of temperature on photosynthesis depends on whether the limiting factor is the CO_2 concentration or the light intensity. If light intensity is the limiting factor, increases in temperature do not increase photosynthesis; when CO_2 is the limiting factor the rate is markedly increased by temperature increments. This differential influence of temperature is a direct reflection of the fact that there are two main phases to the overall photosynthetic reaction (see p. 208). The initiating photochemical phase, in common with other photochemical reactions, is not sensitive to temperature changes; but the second phase, involving the uptake and reduction of carbon dioxide, is markedly so.

CHLOROPLASTS AND THEIR STRUCTURE

In the majority of higher plants the leaves contain most of the chlorophyll, and are therefore the main organs of photosynthesis. The extent of their surface area in proportion to their volume, and also their orderly arrangement, which results in very little overlapping, allows them to intercept large amounts of light. The photosynthetic pigments responsible for their green colour are (see p. 214) localized in small, flattened, ellipsoidal or disc-shaped bodies, called *chloroplasts*. There are many of these in each cell of the palisade and of the spongy mesophyll of the leaf (see fig. 150). When photosynthesis is proceeding rapidly, the chloroplasts in many plants may become packed with starch grains polymerized from the hexose sugar produced during the photosynthetic reaction.

It is a fairly simple matter to prepare a suspension of chloroplasts which is more or less free from the other parts of the cells (such as walls, cytoplasm and nucleus) in which they were originally contained. Spinach leaves are very suitable for such a preparation. They should be immersed in a sugar solution, and ground with coarse sand, which helps to break up the cells. The sugar prevents the disintegration of the chloroplasts, which would occur if water alone were used. The resulting green homogenate is then filtered through cheesecloth to remove the larger tissue debris, such as unbroken clumps of cells and vascular elements, and then centrifuged at 500 × gravity for 5 minutes. In recent years isolated chloroplasts have been made to carry out

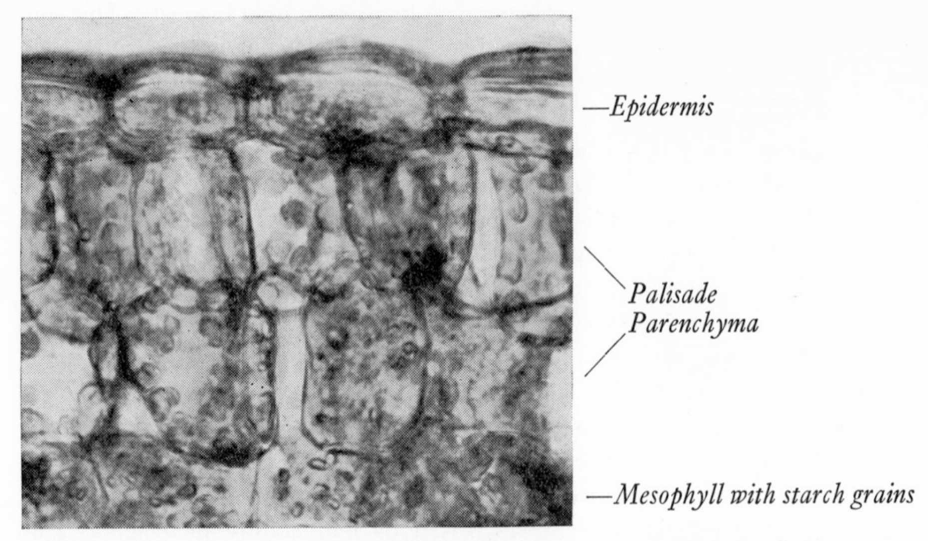

Figure 150 *T.s. of upper part of living leaf of* Pachysandra terminalis *showing chloroplasts in palisade layers. Starch grains can be seen in some of the cells beneath the palisade parenchyma.*

photosynthesis, though to achieve this it is essential to add to them substances which stabilize their activity. When chloroplasts precipitated in this way are examined under the light microscope, each can be seen to consist of closely packed bodies, the *grana*, up to 50 of which may be contained within the bounding membrane of the chloroplast.

Much more intimate details of the internal structure of chloroplasts have been obtained from electron microscope studies of sections of chloroplast-containing cells. These have revealed that all chloroplasts are composed of regularly spaced, flat plates or *lamellae*. The lamellae are, however more closely packed in some regions than in others, and these denser areas, which tend to be circular when viewed from above, correspond with the grana which can be seen with the light microscope. Between the closely set lamellae it is probable that the all important chlorophyll molecules are held, several million within each granum (figs. 151 and 152).

The Photosynthetic Pigments

Chlorophyll, which represents only about 8% of the total dry weight of the chloroplast, can quite readily be extracted from leaves. The rest of the chloroplast consists in a large measure of proteins, which form the framework of the lamellae. Very strong solutions can be obtained from spinach, grass cuttings, elder and ivy leaves in such organic solvents as alcohol or acetone. Much information about the nature and properties of the photosynthetic pigments has been gained from such extracts. If, for example, they are shaken up with benzene, which is then allowed to separate out from the alcohol or acetone, it becomes apparent that the extract con-

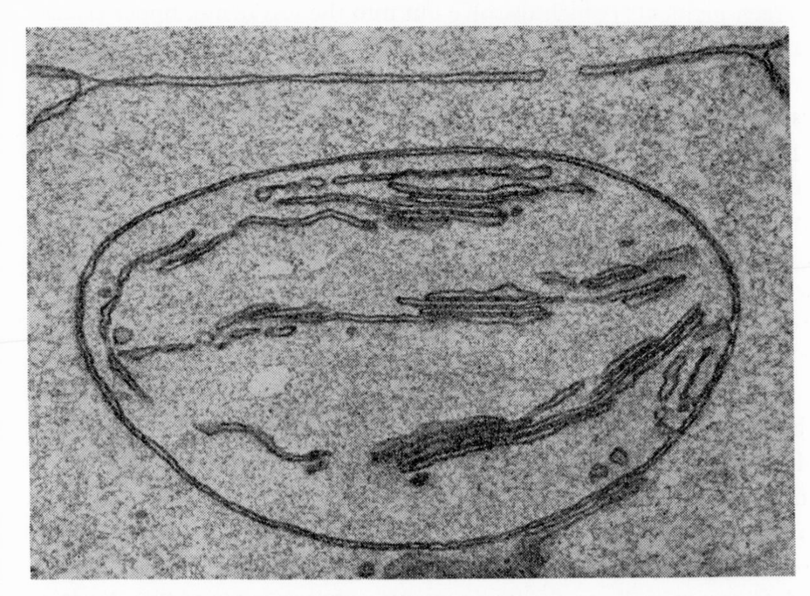

Figure 151 *Electron micrograph of a section through a chloroplast of* Lupinus albus *showing lamellae and grana.* (*Photograph by A. J. Tullett.*) × 60,000.

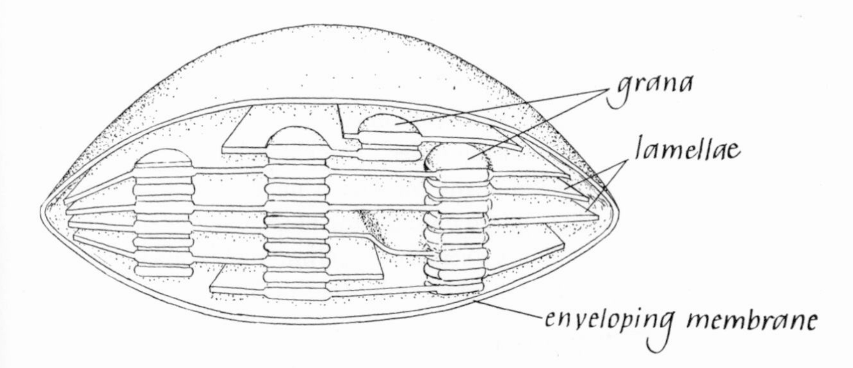

Figure 152 *Diagram of the internal structure of a typical chloroplast as seen with the electron microscope.*

tains not only green pigments (which dissolve out into the less dense, upper layer of benzene) but also yellow. Yellow pigments can of course be seen in organs normally green but in which chlorophyll for some reason has failed to develop, as for example when seedlings are grown in the dark, or in culture solutions lacking iron or magnesium (see Chapter 15, p. 181). These pigments also become apparent in the golds and yellows of autumn leaves, for at this time the chlorophyll in them degenerates. One of these yellow-orange pigments also occurs abundantly in carrot roots, hence its name *carotin*. Related to it chemically are several types of another yellow pigment, *xanthophyll*, which also occurs in leaves.

A number of different kinds of chlorophyll have been found in the plant kingdom, each differing slightly in chemical composition. The basic unit of all chlorophyll molecules, however, is the *porphyrin ring*, which consists of four simple *pyrrole nuclei* joined by carbon linkages, the centre of each molecule being occupied by a single atom of magnesium. It is of some interest to note that the porphyrin ring is also the fundamental unit of the red pigment of blood, *haemoglobin*. In haemoglobin, however, iron occurs at the centre of the molecule in place of magnesium. The chloroplasts of all green plants, including green algae (Chlorophyceae), mosses, liverworts, and ferns, as well as flowering plants, always contain two types of chlorophyll which differ only in the nature of a particular side chain of their molecules. The most abundant, *chlorophyll a*, has a methyl or -CH_3 group in contrast to the other, *chlorophyll b*, which contains an aldehyde (-CHO) group in the equivalent position. Thus an alcoholic leaf extract contains chlorophylls a and b, carotin and xanthophyll.

Although it has been shown that, with the use of benzene, the yellow pigments together can be separated from the green, all four pigments can be separated by employing the knowledge that they are differentially absorbed on a solid substrate. To achieve this, leaves are ground up with acetone and the pigment extracted thereby is transferred to petroleum ether (B.P. 60 – 80°C). The latter is then washed with distilled water to remove the acetone, dried with sodium sulphate, and then applied to a glass column tightly packed with cellulose powder. The chlorophyll pigments will now form a distinct band across the top of the column. A mixture of 3 parts petrol ether and 1 of chloroform is carefully poured onto the top of the column and allowed to filter slowly through. Its passage causes a series of superimposed layers to separate out, or 'develop' in the column in the following order (fig. 153):

1. Yellow-green = degredation products
2. Olive-green = chlorophyll b
3. Blue-green = chlorophyll a
4. Yellow = xanthophylls
5. Colourless
6. Orange-yellow = carotenes

A less complete separation of pigments can be effected simply by standing a piece

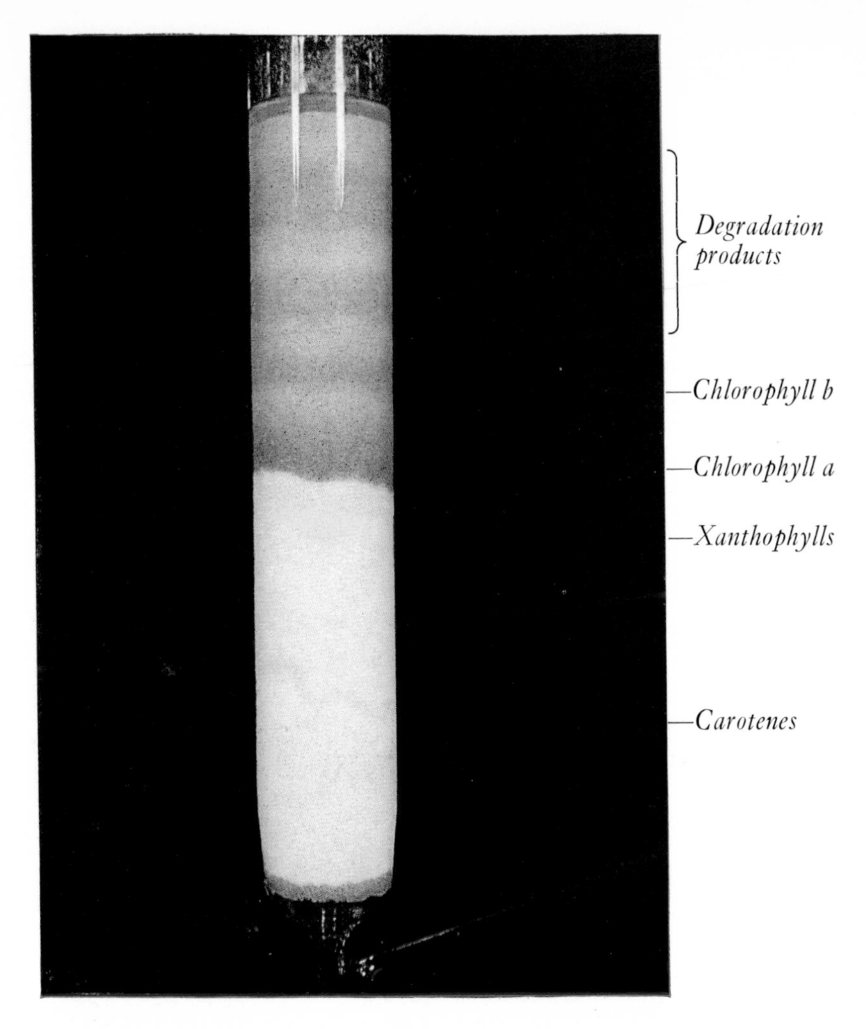

Figure 153 *The separation of chlorophyll pigments from the leaves of* Vicia faba *in a cellulose column. (Prepared by Dr J. K. Hayes; photo, courtesy Royal Botanic Garden, Edinburgh.)*

of white black-board chalk in a leaf pigment extract, or by placing a strong, freshly prepared chlorophyll solution in an evaporating dish and hanging a strip of filter paper above it so that one end is just dipping into the solution. In both experiments it should be observed that a yellow coloured zone, mainly of carotin which is but little absorbed, advances into the chalk or paper more rapidly than the green. If the green zone is carefully examined it may be possible to discern that its upper edge is bluish-green in colour (chlorophyll a) while the lower part is much more yellow (chlorophyll b). The principle involved in the above separation of photosynthetic pigments is essentially that used in *paper chromatography*, which depends on the differential rates of absorption of organic substances by filter paper.

A strong alcohol, or acetone, leaf pigment extract appears bright green when held up to a light source which passes through it. If, however, the extract is held up against a dark background and illuminated, it takes on a distinctly reddish hue. This property of re-emitting light, of a wavelength different (usually longer) from that principally absorbed by it, is termed *fluorescence*. When a chlorophyll extract is interposed between a source of white light and a spectroscope, which splits white light into its component colours, it can be seen that certain wavelengths are more completely absorbed than others. As a result of this *differential absorption*, dark bands occur in the red and blue-violet portions of this spectrum, while the colours orange-yellow and especially green pass through. Because of this, chlorophyll appears green (fig. 154a).

Bearing in mind that different wavelengths of light have different energy values (see p. 210), it is possible to determine which colours are most active in photosynthesis. This can be done by measuring the rate of photosynthesis of a green leaf, or a *Chlorella* culture (see p. 212), illuminated successively by equal quantities of light energy (quanta) of different wavelengths. Each photosynthetic rate is then plotted against the wavelengths tested in the experiment. The resulting graph is called an *action spectrum* and shows a maximum of photosynthetic activity at those wavelengths which earlier spectroscopic examination has shown to be most strongly absorbed by the photosynthetic pigments (red and to a lesser extent blue). The close correspondence between the absorption spectrum and the action spectrum provides the strongest evidence that the light absorbed by chlorophyll is that which provides the necessary energy for photosynthesis (fig. 154b).

The Entry of Carbon Dioxide into Leaves

Carbon dioxide enters the leaf by diffusion through the stomata. The stomata open in response to light and thus their movement seems to be related in a large measure to the photosynthetic activity of the guard cells, the only chloroplast-containing cells of the epidermis (see Chapter 9, p. 116). The CO_2 content of the sub-stomatal cavities is also believed to be of significance, for even when leaves are well illuminated, the stomata only open when the CO_2 concentration of these cavities is less than that of the atmosphere outside, and they are always closed when the CO_2 concentration is equal to that of the atmosphere. Movements of the stomata depend on

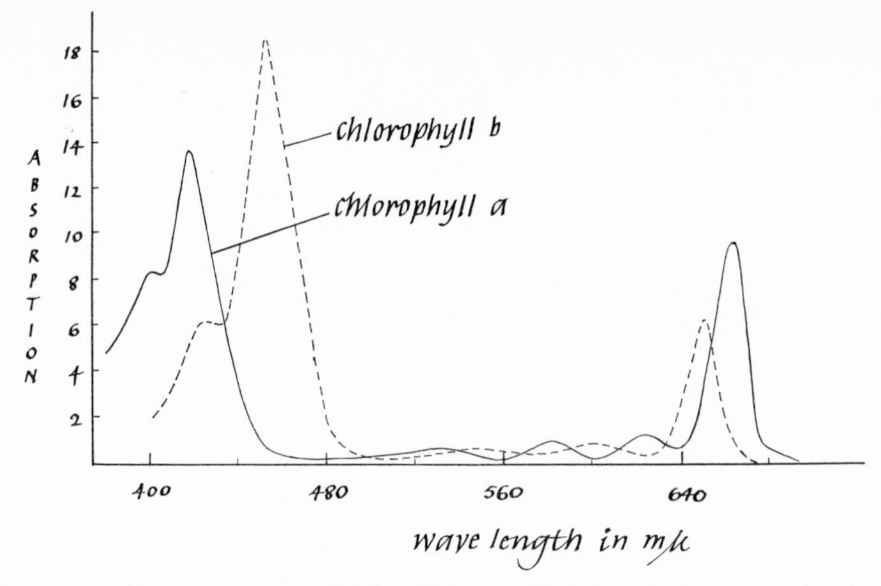

Figure 154a *Absorption spectra of chlorophylls a and b dissolved in an ether ethanol mixture (after Zscheile and Comar).*

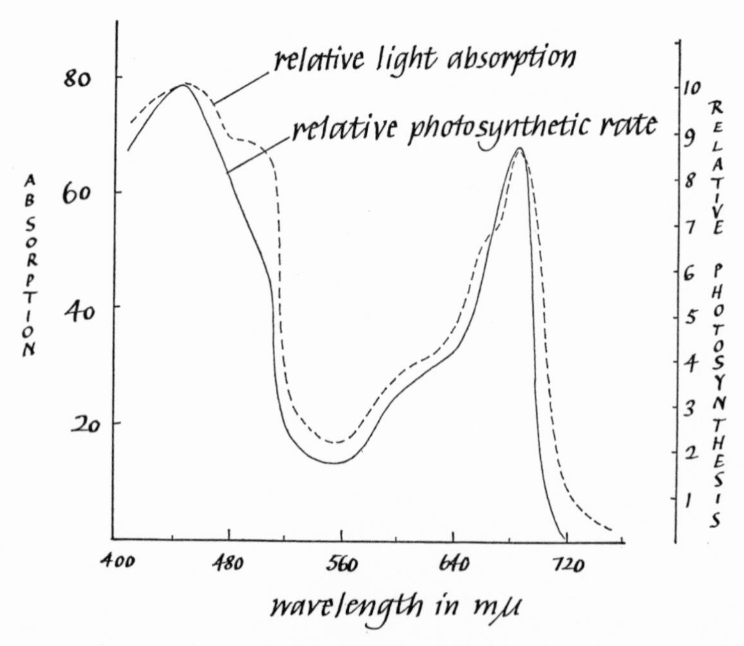

Figure 155b *Absorption and action spectra for the marine alga* Ulva *(after Haxo and Blinks).*

turgor changes of the guard cells. When the latter are flaccid the pores remain closed, but open as turgidity increases. Guard cell turgor is thought to be made greater by increases in the osmotic pressure of their contents. This results from the production of osmotically active sugars by the photosynthetic activity of the cell. Thus there is a diurnal stomatal opening and closing, related to the hours of day light and darkness. But in times of drought when leaves may suffer from water deficiency, regular diurnal stomatal movements may be modified so that they fail to open properly during the day; photosynthesis is consequently impeded (see Chapter 14, p. 176).

When fully open, the stomatal apertures normally occupy less than 1% of the leaf surface, yet the rate of entrance of CO_2 can be as much as 50 times as fast as its diffusion into an efficient absorbing surface, such as caustic soda. As pointed out in connection with the loss of water vapour from leaves by transpiration (see Chapter 14, p. 172), this is because many more molecules of a gas can diffuse through a small number of large pores of the same total area.

Within each leaf there is a very extensive labyrinth of intercellular spaces (fig. 155). This means that practically every chloroplast-containing cell is in contact with the leaf's internal atmosphere. The palisade and spongy mesophyll in fact present a tremendous internal surface for gaseous exchange, which in the case of lilac leaves has been estimated to 13 times the external surface. The walls of the mesophyll cells are normally saturated with water so that the vapour pressure of the internal air spaces is usually higher than that of the atmosphere outside. The carbon dioxide forms carbonic acid (H_2CO_3) with this water, and some diffuses to the chloroplasts in this form, though probably some also does so simply as dissolved carbon dioxide.

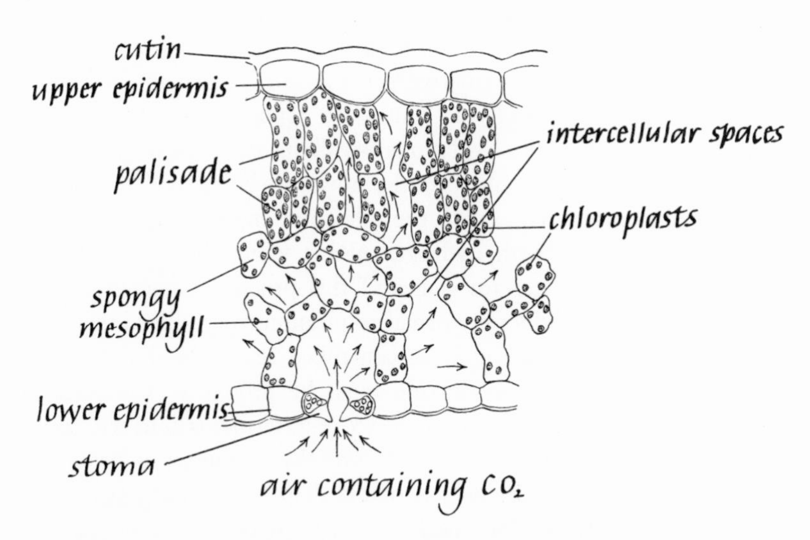

Figure 155 *Diagram showing the passage of carbon dioxide through a leaf to the chloroplasts.*

CHAPTER 19

CATABOLISM AND RESPIRATION

Photosynthesis involves not only the elaboration of carbohydrates from the carbon dioxide of the air, but also the fixation, within these compounds, of energy derived from sunlight. Moreover, these high energy containing carbon compounds form the basis of all food materials made by the plant, and from the site of their synthesis in the leaves they are largely translocated to regions where they are transformed and stored away in an insoluble, non-diffusible form (see Chapter 20). Before these stored foods can be utilized in the general metabolism of the plant, however, they must once more be rendered soluble and diffusible. This is brought about by processes of *enzymatic digestion* (see Chapter 17). In this way starch, for example, is hydrolysed to soluble sugars, fats to glycerol and fatty acids, proteins to their constituent amino acids. Each of these various digestive, or splitting up, processes is catalysed by an appropriate enzyme and the resulting products used either as materials for the synthesis of other organic substances required by the plant, or as the raw materials for the construction of new cells (i.e. for growth). In all of these digestive processes, however, there is very little release of energy. Just as animals require energy for the performance of their vital activities such as blood circulation, muscular activity, etc., so plants require energy for the maintenance of life. Such energy is released when some of the products of digestion are still further degraded. This more complete breakdown of food substances is termed *respiration.*

Respiration is essentially an oxidative process and is normally accompanied by gas exchange. This is why most living things are dependant for their survival on a supply of molecular oxygen. In oxidations involving molecular oxygen, the latter combines with the constituent elements of the substance being oxidized, which is then converted to its appropriate oxide with the release of energy. In all cases molecular oxygen ultimately combines with hydrogen atoms which come from the respired substances, and it is during certain stages of this process that energy is released. Carbon dioxide, the other product of normal respiration, is produced through various intermediate substances by other enzyme-controlled reactions. Thus oxidations do not necessarily imply that carbon dioxide must be produced. Conversely carbon dioxide may be produced in anaerobic processes (e.g. fermentation) without the consumption of oxygen. In these circumstances virtually no energy is produced. Thus in respiration, hexose sugar ($C_6H_{12}O_6$) is oxidized to CO_2 and water, and energy is released. This energy can also be released from sugar with some violence by burning it, but here again the sugar is oxidized to CO_2 and water. Both reactions can therefore be represented by the equation:

$$C_6H_{12}O_6 + 6O_2 \longrightarrow 6\ CO_2 + H_2O + \text{energy}$$

In burning sugar, the process is very rapid and uncontrolled, and energy is lost as heat. In respiration on the other hand, the oxidation of the sugar is slow and controlled, being catalysed by enzymes in the cells of the plant, and a large proportion of the energy is conserved as a special type of chemical energy which can be used by the plant.

Even in the plant, however, this transformation of respiratory energy is not completely efficient and a small proportion of it at least is liberated as heat. That heat is liberated from respiring vegetable material can be readily demonstrated by allowing seeds (e.g. peas or wheat) to germinate in a thermos flask into which a thermometer has been inserted. Within a few hours it should be found that there has been a significant rise in temperature within the flask as compared with a control.

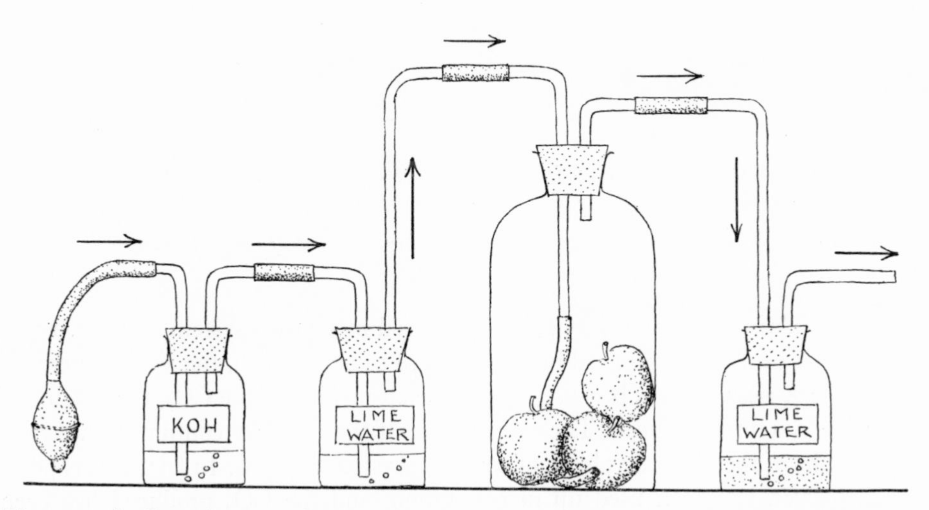

Figure 156*a* *Experiment to demonstrate that carbon dioxide is produced from respiring plant tissues. Air, freed from carbon dioxide, having passed over the respiring tissues, turns lime water milky due to the precipitation of calcium carbonate.*

That carbon dioxide is produced from respiring plant tissues such as germinating seeds, flower heads, fruits, etc., can be readily demonstrated by drawing air made free of CO_2 (by passing it over caustic potash) over the respiring tissue and then allowing it to bubble through a solution of lime water, $Ca(OH)_2$ (see fig. 156a). That the air passing over the tissue is free from CO_2 can be confirmed by bubbling it through lime water – it should remain clear. However, the lime water through which the air bubbles after having passed over the respiring tissue will turn milky, owing to the precipitation of $CaCO_3$. If leaves are used in this experiment, they should be placed in a darkened bottle to prevent the CO_2 produced by respiration from being immediately utilized in photosynthesis.

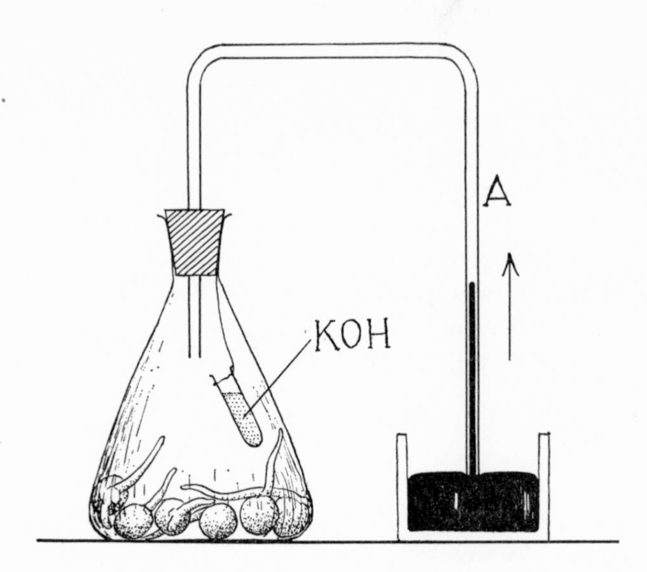

Figure 156*b* *Experiment to demonstrate that one of the gases of the air (oxygen) is utilized when aerobic respiration takes place. Note that the level of mercury will continue to rise until only about 4/5ths of the original volume of air remains.*

If germinating (respiring) pea seeds are placed in a closed system as in fig. 156b, and the CO_2 evolved is absorbed by a solution of caustic potash, the level of mercury in the tube A rises. This is because, due to the absorption of the CO_2, the volume of gas in the system is reduced. The rise in level of the mercury continues until only about 4/5ths of the original volume of air in the system remains. In fact, at this point all the oxygen has been used up in respiration, and the CO_2 produced has been absorbed by the potash, At this point *aerobic respiration* ceases. If a similar experiment is set up without the potash to absorb the CO_2, there will be no change in gas pressure in the system and the level of mercury in the tube will remain at its initial level. This clearly points to the fact that in the respiration of barley seeds, the volume of CO_2 produced is equal to the volume of O_2 absorbed, as shown in the equation above representing the aerobic respiration of hexose sugar. For every molecule of sugar burned in respiration, six molecules of oxygen are absorbed and six of carbon dioxide are evolved.

Respiratory quotients

The ratio of CO_2 evolved to O_2 consumed in respiration is termed the *respiratory quotient* or R.Q. Clearly in the case of the respiration of germinating barley, and other tissues utilizing hexose sugar, the R.Q. is unity $\left(\frac{CO_2}{O_2} = 1\right)$. Plants can use *substrates* (as the substances respired are termed) other than sugar as sources of energy. Higher plants, however, most commonly use glucose or fructose, though in many germinating seeds, fats are commonly the respiratory substrate; while in other tissues amino acids and other organic acids may be utilized. In the case of respiration in oily or fatty seeds, since fats are poorer in O_2 and richer in H_2 than are sugars, correspondingly more O_2 is needed for the oxidation of their fat store to CO_2 and water. Thus the determination of the gas exchange of germinating fatty seeds gives an R.Q. of less than unity. On the other hand, plant acids are richer in oxygen and poorer in hydrogen than is sugar and so proportionately less oxygen is absorbed, with the result that the R.Q. during the respiration of these acids is greater than unity. To the plant physiologist, the R.Q. is indicative of the nature of the substrates being used in respiration – though it gives no more than an indication, for frequently several substrates may be broken down as energy sources at the same time. In such cases the R.Q. will obviously represent only the overall respiration of the plant tissue under investigation.

Respiration takes place in every living cell of every organism, plant or animal, and the process is very similar in both divisions of the organic world. Sometimes, however, in dormant seeds and in hibernating animals, it is so slow as to be almost undetectable. Once respiration ceases completely, however, either in a cell, or in all the cells of an organism, that cell or that organism must be regarded as dead. Unlike animals, plants have no special organs of respiration, though in higher plants the paths of exchange of the O_2 taken in and CO_2 given out are by way of the stomata and lenticels, and the intercellular spaces associated with them (fig. 155).

Factors influencing respiration

In germination (Chapter 1), which is essentially a process in which food stored in the seed is mobilized and used as a source of respiratory energy and raw materials for the growth of the developing embryo, several factors, both internal and external (environmental), may influence the rate of respiration. Of the environmental factors, *temperature* is very important. Respiration is very slow around 0°C and increases to a maximum somewhere between 30-40°C. At temperatures in excess of this, the rate of respiration decreases quite sharply owing to the damaging effects of the higher temperatures on the enzymes which catalyse the process (see Chapter 17). Since respiration is essentially an oxidative process, a second important environmental factor is an adequate *oxygen supply*. Oxygen is not usually limiting in the respiration of aerial parts of plants, though in polluted waters it may seriously limit the growth of aquatic plants. It may be very critical, however, in the soil, for roots must respire actively as they grow and take up nutrients (see Chapter 15). In heavy or waterlogged soils oxygen may be so deficient in the soil atmosphere that root growth and salt uptake are severely limited, to the detriment of the whole plant.

One of the internal factors of special significance is the amount of *available respiratory substrate*, especially carbohydrates. Thus plants grown in low light intensity for long periods may show reduced rates of respiration. If such plants or plant tissues are then artificially supplied with sugar, their rate of respiration immediately increases. Also important is the activity of the plant's *enzymes*; not only those directly concerned with respiration, but also the hydrolysing enzymes mentioned previously. There are concerned with the initial splitting up or digestion of food reserves into simpler substances which can then be oxidized in respiration.

Respiration and the Mitochondria

Originally it was believed that the respiratory oxidation took place generally throughout the living cell. It has now been shown, however, that many of the enzymes concerned in these oxidations, and the very oxidations they catalyse, are located in the *mitochondria*, the small, spherical or rod-shaped bodies which are scattered throughout the cytoplasm (see Chapter 3). Techniques of centrifugation have been developed whereby these mitochondria can be separated from the rest of the cell, and careful experiments have shown that some of the most important respiratory enzymes are in a fully functional condition in the extracted mitochondria. Thus it may be said that whereas the site of *energy fixation* in the plant cells is the chloroplasts, the site of the *release* and *transformation* of this energy is the mitochondria. The very special and significant property of these cell *organelles* is their ability to carry out this energy transformation in a series of gentle stages. Coupled with this control of the process there is built into the mitochondria a very important system, enabling them to utilize certain very special properties of phosphate-containing organic substances, the *organic metaphosphates*. Of particular importance in this connection is *adenosine diphosphate* (ADP), for when the phosphate chain of this compound is lengthened by another phosphate unit to *adenosine triphosphate* (ATP), it acquires a package of energy. When ATP is hydrolysed by an appropriate enzyme it quite readily gives up its additional third phosphate unit to another molecule. The additional energy acquired with this phosphate is not, however, lost as heat, but is mostly transferred to the molecule which accepted the phosphate, the so-called *phosphate-acceptor*. This energy is used in the many synthetic reactions in the plant.

Respiration, in terms of energy, is essentially a process which produces energy-rich, organic phosphates (ATP). These substances in fact constitute the connecting link between the energy liberated from the high energy containing substrates consumed in respiration and the energy required in the various biological activities – growth, synthesis and ion accumulation – which must take place if the living plant is to survive and prosper.

CO_2 evolved
↗
Respiratory substrate e.g. hexose sugar ⟶ *Respiration* ⟶ *Energy* into energy-rich organic metaphosphates
↗
O_2 absorbed

1 mol. glucose ⟶ 38 mols. ATP

Biological Work

↙ ↓ ↘

Growth Synthesis Salt accumulation

This process of energy transformation is remarkably efficient – 70% compared with 15% in a power station.

Biochemical Phases of Respiration

The mitochondria cannot bring about the oxidation of carbohydrates, fats or proteins, or even the products of their digestion. They play their part only when these substances have been degraded into keto, hydroxy, or other organic acids, the most important of which appears to be *pyruvic acid*. The biological combustion, or respiration, of sugar to CO_2 and water, as in the synthesis of carbohydrates during photosynthesis, is in fact a very complex process. Many steps are involved, each of which is catalysed by a particular enzyme. The process as a whole, however, can be divided into two major phases. In common with many metabolic transformations, there is initially a *phosphorylation* of the hexose sugar to the 6 carbon atom compound, *fructose diphosphate*. The latter is then split into two molecules of a 3 carbon compound, which is then transformed into pyruvic acid on which the mitochondria act:

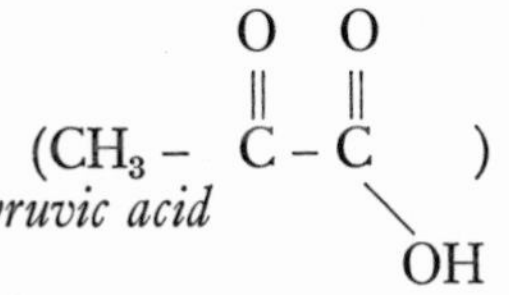

$$\left(CH_3 - \overset{\overset{\displaystyle O}{\|}}{C} - \overset{\overset{\displaystyle O}{\|}}{C} \diagdown OH\right)$$

pyruvic acid

This *glycolosis* can proceed in the absence of oxygen, and alcohol accumulates.

The second major phase in the process is the oxidation of the pyruvic acid through a series of steps in which various simple organic acids, in particular *citric acid*, are involved, until it is degraded to CO_2 and water. This second phase, the intricate steps of which were unravelled by the Oxford biochemist Sir Hans Krebs, is now termed the *Krebs'* or *citric acid cycle*. That the mitochondria are in fact the seat of this oxidation has been proved by the fact that extracted mitochondria, fed with radio active or *labelled pyruvate*, rapidly oxidize it through the Krebs' cycle. Whereas the first phase may not require oxygen, this second phase is very dependant on its presence.

Many plants, or plant tissues, when deprived of free oxygen may still continue to give off carbon dioxide, though at the same time they produce alcohol. This *anaerobic respiration*, which is the same process described already in the consideration of enzyme action in the unicellular fungus, *Saccharomyces*, is the normal source of respiratory energy in numerous fungi and bacteria. That it occurs in higher plant tissues may be shown by placing germinating peas without air above mercury in an inverted boiling tube. After several hours it will be observed that the gas given off by the peas has pushed some of the mercury out of the tube. It can be confirmed that the gas evolved is CO_2 by introducing a little caustic potash into the tube, for it will be rapidly absorbed by the potash and the mercury will once more fill the tube (fig. 157).

The first phase of anaerobic respiration is the same as in aerobic respiration; there is a cleavage of sugar to pyruvic acid. The pyruvic acid produced, however, is in the

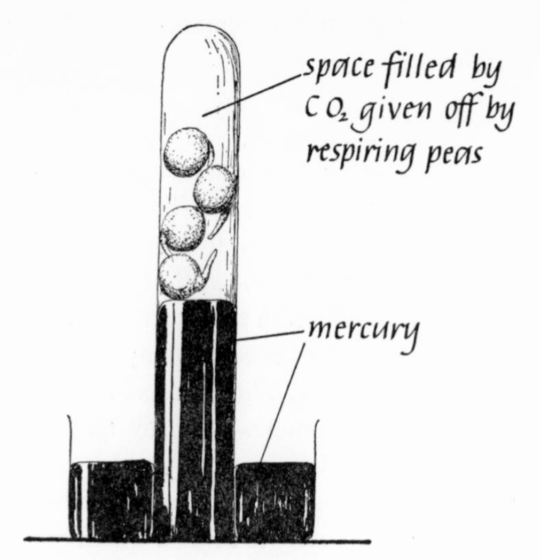

Figure 157 *Experiment to demonstrate anaerobic respiration.*

second phase reduced rather than oxidized. It loses a molecule of CO_2 through the action of the enzyme *carboxylase* on it to become *acetaldehyde*; following this *decarboxylation*, the acetaldehyde is reduced by the action of yet another type of enzyme, *alcohol dehydrogenase*, to ethyl alcohol. Much less energy is liberated in anaerobic respiration than when sugar is completely oxidized to CO_2 and water in aerobic respiration. In the latter more efficient process, 673,000 calories of energy per molecule are liberated compared with 21-28,000 in fermentation.

CHAPTER 20

TRANSLOCATION

The vessels of the xylem are the elements principally concerned with the conduction of water and inorganic salts from the soil to the leaves. The sieve tubes of the phloem, on the other hand, are the elements mainly involved with the redistribution to various parts of the plant of the sugars and other products of metabolism formed in the leaves. In the other organs of the plant, such as roots, developing fruits, stems, and regions of active growth, these food substances may be transformed and stored for future use. Some may be utilized immediately in the various syntheses associated with growth and development; some is broken down to provide the energy required for these vital processes.

That the structure of the sieve tubes indicated conduction to be their main function was first suggested by the German physiologist Hartig, who provided experimental support for his thesis with *girdling experiments*. He removed from leafy shoots of trees, a complete ring of bark, that is all the tissues external to the cambium, leaving the xylem intact. Resulting from this treatment there occurred after a time a swelling of the bark above the girdle and within this wound tissue, sugars were found to accumulate. When, however, a shoot without leaves was treated in the same way, there was no sugar accumulation. Hence he concluded that food elaborated in the leaves must pass down the bark, the sieve tubes of the phloem being the only elements through which this could take place; also that this downward movement can be interrupted by girdling. Experiments of this sort at the same time confirm the fact that the supply of water to the leaves is by way of the xylem, since the leaves on girdled shoots usually show no signs of wilting.

Translocation through the phloem takes place not only downwards from the leaves to regions of growth and storage, there is also translocation upwards and outwards to any region and organ of the plant where there may be growth or storage. Thus it is considerable to all shoot meristems, to developing flowers and fruits, and to unfolding leaves. This fact is recognized in horticultural practice when in spring, fruit trees are girdled. Such treatment is said to increase the production of flower bud formation, and hence of fruit, for the following season; the numbers of fruit buds which develop would seem to be related to their carbohydrate supply. When such trees are girdled, the downward flow of carbohydrate to the roots is at least temporarily prevented.

An indication of the quantity of materials translocated from leaves can be gained from the fact that they lose more weight overnight when attached to the plant than when removed. For example, sunflower leaves may lose as much as 12% of their dry weight in a 10 hour night when attached to the plant. Although some of this loss, probably only one-fifth, is due to respiration, it is in the main a result of translocation. In these experiments, analyses carried out to determine the nature of the substances lost from the leaves have indicated that sugars represent some 98% of the total.

Other chemical analyses of the contents of sieve tubes have shown them to contain, as well as those large amounts of dissolved carbohydrates, amino-acids and certain other nitrogen-containing substances. Recent developments in the analysis of sieve tube contents have made use of the fact that certain plant-feeding insects (aphids) can direct their tube-like, sucking mouth parts with unerring accuracy into these elements, so rich in food substances (fig. 158). When the insect is seen to have inserted its *stylet*, as its mouth part is termed, into the plant, the experimenter then carefully cuts it off. The contents of the sieve tube can then be collected for analysis as they flow from the open end of the stylet. Most of the carbohydrate in the phloem of stems is the sugar, sucrose, and this has been found to show marked diurnal fluctuations in amount. Values are highest when the leaves are actively photosynthesizing during the day and producing large amounts of sugar. They decrease towards the end of the night, by which time all the carbohydrate reserves in the leaf have been used up.

There has been a considerable conflict of ideas about how the transport of substances through the phloem comes about. Probably the most widely accepted hypothesis is that there is a *mass flow* of this carbohydrate-rich solution brought about by differences in turgor pressure between the source of its production, the photosynthetic cells of the leaves, and the tissues or regions to which it is being translocated. Sugar is thought to be the solute primarily responsible for the turgor pressure gradients which develop between various regions of the plant. Other solutes, however, may be passively carried through the sieve tubes.

Figure 158 *An aphid feeding on a lime tree. The aphid's stylet can be followed in this transverse section from the cork through the parenchyma wedge of a medullary ray to the phloem.* (*Photo kindly provided by Dr M. Zimmermann and reproduced by permission of 'Science'.*)

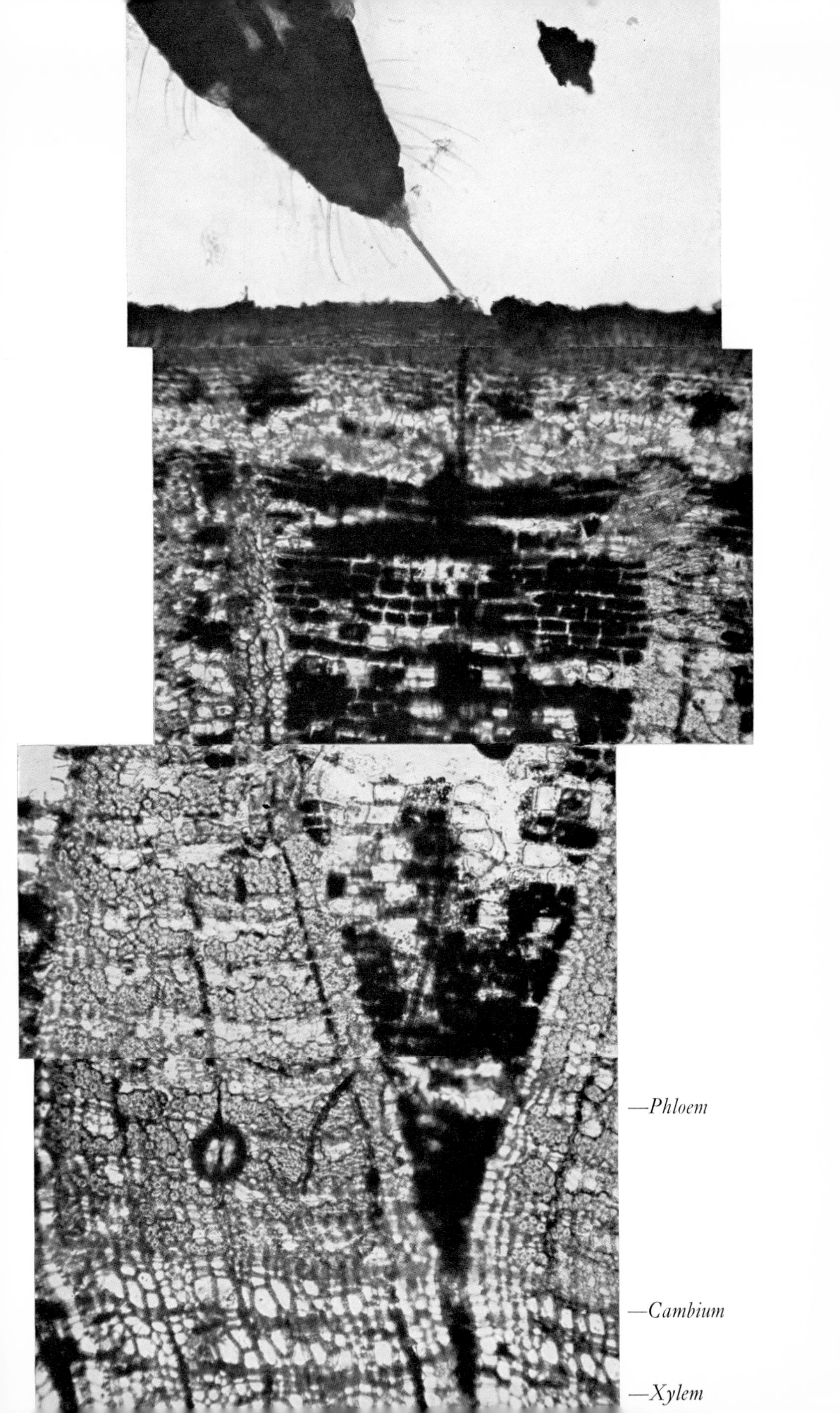
—Phloem
—Cambium
—Xylem

CHAPTER 21

THE PLANT AND ITS ENVIRONMENT

Various aspects of the physiology of plants such as germination, growth and development, nutrition and metabolism, have been studied mainly in the context of individual plants growing in pots or culture solutions in the laboratory. Under natural conditions, however, plants grow together in closely associated and integrated groups, which not only tolerate the variety of physical and chemical conditions imposed on them by climate and soil, but they must also survive the biological conditions produced by the presence of other plants, and by animals. These physical, chemical and biological conditions, which may be classified as *climatic*, *edaphic* (soil), and *biotic* (animal and plant) *factors*, together constitute the environment of the plant in the particular place where it lives – that is, its habitat. The study of any organism in relation to its environment is *ecology*.

The main aim of plant ecology is to analyse the composition of the vegetation in a given *habitat* and examine the conditions under which this vegetation lives. The environment under natural conditions is invariably complex, and thus in ecological investigations one must, wherever possible, first analyse the many components of the environment and then observe the effects of varying the intensity of each particular factor in turn, while keeping all other environmental influences as constant as possible. There are many difficulties in the experimental approach to ecology for the closer one succeeds in simulating natural conditions, the less can the various environmental factors be controlled; it also becomes increasingly difficult to measure these factors and the plants' reactions to them. Indeed, the experimenter having established very finely controlled, and therefore inevitably artificial, conditions, soon questions to what extent his investigations is providing any real indication of the performance of the plant under natural conditions.

The problems of ecology are far from simple, the principal reason being that there is complex interaction between the major habitat factors, each of which can be further subdivided into particular climatic, edaphic, and biotic factors. Moreover, every plant species inherits not only morphological or structural characters, which the taxonomist uses to separate one species from another, but also certain physiological characters which may determine the species' range of *tolerance* to environmental conditions. Each species will in fact flourish and reproduce itself only in those situations or habitats where its particular physiological requirements are satisfied, and where the environmental conditions lie within its range of tolerance. The study of individual species from this point of view (*autecology*) is of the greatest importance, for it provides the only basis on which the study of vegetation as a whole (*synecology*) can be adequately founded.

Climatic Factors

Of the three major habitat factors, climate is without question the most important, for not only does it act directly on vegetation, it also acts indirectly by its influence on edaphic and biotic factors. The individual climatic factors which must be considered are temperature, precipitation, atmospheric humidity, wind, and light.

Plant species differ greatly in their abilities to withstand differences in climate; thus there are marked differences in the composition of the vegetation of the world's major climatic regions. These run parallel to the equator and are broadly as follows, passing from the equator to the poles:

a. Tropical and sub-tropical
b. Warm temperate
c. Cold temperate
d. Sub-arctic and arctic

Vegetational types correspond in a general way with these divisions, and so they too occur as belts lying parallel to the equator. Temperature, and light in terms of day length, are the most important climatic influences bringing about these major vegetational differences. In any one area they may, of course, be greatly modified by factors such as the relation of the particular land mass to the sea and the direction of the prevailing winds from the sea. Altitude also changes the climate and vegetation in a manner remarkably similar to the changes observable from the equatorial to arctic regions. Thus in ascending an equatorial mountain one may pass through vegetational zones from *tropical rain forest* at its base to *tundra* on its snowcovered heights, in many respects similar to that of the arctic.

Differences in climate must not therefore be conceived only in terms of the four broad climatic divisions outlined above, nor yet in the rather more restricted sense of a particular country such as Great Britain with its *oceanic climate* dominated by the moisture-laden, south-west winds which prevail from the Atlantic, so tempering both the summer heat and the winter cold. The ecologist must also study the influence of local climates such as exist in a sheltered valley or on the top of a hill as well as the very smallest differences in climate, the *microclimates*, which occur on different sides of a tree or rock. Even the slightest differences in climate can be reflected in the occurrence and distribution of vegetation.

The great range of temperatures existing between the polar regions and the tropics has a very significant effect on the distribution of the world's vegetation. Temperature exerts its influence on all the physiological activities of the plant and every physiological function has *temperature limits* above or below which it ceases. Thus there are maximum, minimum and optimum temperatures for seed germination and for all subsequent phases of plant growth up to and including the development of flowers and fruits (see Chapter 23). If, therefore, the temperature in a given area is unsuitable for any one of these phases of development the plant in question may not survive, or if it does it may be unable to reproduce itself.

The climatic factors, *rainfall* and *humidity* are closely interrelated with temperature, for the *saturation deficit* of the atmosphere is directly proportional to temperature. Humidity is especially important in that it exerts a direct action on transpiration (see Chapter 14) and this factor may therefore virtually determine the character of the vegetation in all but the wettest of habitats. Rain, except in a few cases, is the principal source of water for terrestrial plants. The effect of the annual rainfall on the vegetation of a given area is not so much in its total annual amount, but in its annual distribution. Obviously rain is most beneficial to the plant during its growing season, though the adequacy and effectiveness of rainfall also depends on the extent of water loss by transpiration from the plant and by evaporation from the soil. The natural vegetation of an area with a marked wet and dry season is very different from an area with the same total amount of rain spread out fairly evenly over the whole year. In general, regions with an even distribution of rainfall support a richer type of vegetation than those with well marked wet and dry seasons.

Wind affects water loss from both plants and soil. Its most important influence is its drying action, which increases evaporation and thus emphasizes the effects of any water shortage. Also, a dry atmosphere is known to modify the form of plants during their growth: in general they are squatter, with shorter internodes; they have larger root systems; internally there is a greater development of sclerenchyma; and, their usually smaller leaves may be more hairy and possess more stomata.

Light as an ecological factor is mainly related in its effects on photosynthesis. Though the intensity of light is comparatively uniform over much of the surface of the earth, even on a cloudless day, plants are exposed to a continuous variation in intensity from dawn to dusk. There is also a marked variation in the duration and intensity of sunlight with latitude and from one season of the year to another. Such differences in the relative lengths of day – light and darkness during the growing season, *photoperiodism*, exert a marked effect on the flowering and fruiting of many plants (see Chapter 23). This in turn plays an important part in controlling the reproduction and hence the distribution of species, many of which have very critical *day-length requirements.*

In certain habitats shading by other plants can cause a diminution in light intensity at certain seasons. In woodlands, for example, light intensity may be at a minimum in mid-summer and a maximum in winter, following leaf fall. There is undoubtedly a minimum survival intensity of light for each plant species and this must exceed the compensation point so that carbohydrate production exceeds its loss in respiration. The amount of light necessary for survival, however, differs very greatly. The shade plants of woodlands can tolerate much lower intensities than those whose normal environment is open country, such as moorland or mountaintop. There may also be a close interrelation between *topography* and light, as for example in the different amounts of illumination received on opposite sides of an east-west valley. In terms of *land utilization* this fact is emphasized in the different heights to which crops can be grown on the north and south slopes.

Other light effects of ecological significance relate to its influence on seed germination (see Chapter 1) and, more important, on the way it affects the distribution and activity of growth hormones (see Chapter 4). Thus growth is retarded by light and in its absence in shady situations, longer stems and reduced leaves are produced. Differences in the shape and texture of leaves may be observed even on different sides of the same trees, *shade leaves* being produced on the north side and *sun leaves* on the south side exposed to maximum light.

Edaphic Factors

Soil is a habitat factor whose influence is second only to climate in determining the distribution of vegetation, though soil development and hence soil type is largely dependent on climatic factors. Indeed, as with the major division of the world's vegetation, so there are world groups of soil, for even though the mineral basis of a soil may differ considerably, there is a tendency towards the formation of a uniform *soil type* throughout a particular climatic region. For example, in the high rainfall regions of the tropics, *laterites*, which are generally red in colour owing to the presence of iron oxides, are the typical soils. Climate therefore has an indirect effect on plants through its influence on the soil, though by the same token vegetation itself can influence, and may in time greatly modify, the character of a given soil.

Although soil type depends in the first instance on the parent rock types from which it was derived, climate plays a very important part in shaping its final structure. It can be seen by cutting deep trenches in soils that nearly all show *stratification*, with a number of layers or *horizons* occurring from the surface down to a given depth. Soil scientists distinguish three major horizons in a *soil profile*. The *A horizon* contains most of the root systems of plants as well as most of the soil organic matter (humus). Below this the *B horizon* is distinguished by the fact that it is less weathered than the upper layer, but in addition, it usually contains accumulations of matter, principally clay particles, carried down from the A horizon by percolating rain water. In the lowest or *C horizon*, there occur the parent materials from which the upper layers of soil have been derived by the physical and biological processes of *weathering*. These horizons are principally formed by the action of water, frost and sunlight acting on the surface, though an important additional influence is the vegetation growing in the soil itself with its contribution of humus. The rate of decay of plant remains which form this humus is also dependent on climatic and other environmental conditions (fig. 159).

In Britain it is possible to distinguish three major types of soil which owe their character to climatic influences – *podsols*, *brown earths* and *moss peats*. Podsols, which are ashy-grey in colour and derive their name from the Russian word for 'ash', are soils typical of wet regions such as the west of Ireland and Scotland. In these areas heavy rainfall and low evaporation rates cause a movement of water downwards with the consequent leaching of exchangeable cations. This leads to a marked increase in acidity due to the replacement of these cations by hydrogen ions (see Chapter 15).

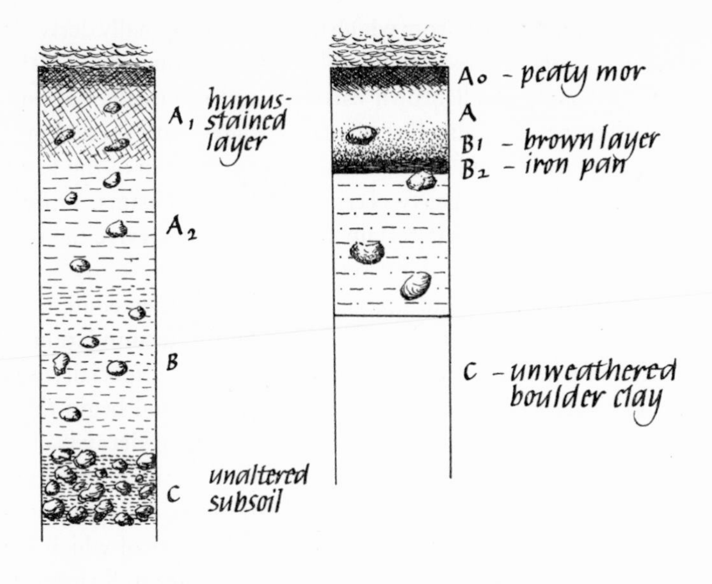

Figure 159 *A Brown Earth and Podsol soil profile (after Tansley).*

At the same time there is only a slow breakdown of plant remains because the prevailing cold, wet, acid conditions are unfavourable to soil micro-organisms. Below the strongly leached upper layer, the A horizon, impoverished of basic salts and typically greyish in colour, there is often a dark band, the B_1 horizon, formed by soluble humus material washed down from above. A reddish band of iron oxides, the B_2 horizon, may occur below the *moor* or *humus pan* and give rise to a *hard pan*. This layer may be so compacted, and so thick and strong, that it prevents the downward growth of tree roots. This B_2 horizon lies immediately above the unaltered subsoil or C horizon. The natural vegetation of podsols is most frequently heath and moorland, though pine and birch woods do survive on them.

In the drier and somewhat warmer regions of the British Isles, particularly in the midlands and southern parts of England and in eastern Ireland, where leaching is not so intense as in podsol areas, the characteristic soils formed, especially on clays and loams, are the 'brown earths'. These are the areas of the finest agricultural land. In these soils, if any lime happens to be present in the surface layers, it is inevitably leached away, yet the humus of the A horizon is well broken down and not raw, as in a podsol. In the B horizon there is an accumulation of materials leached out of the surface layers, and in the same middle zone, there is frequently a concentration of fine, insoluble mineral particles. Stratification is less marked in brown earths than in podsols, so that horizons are less easy to distinguish. Brown earths may vary in character from a clay to a sandy loam, depending on the rock from which the soil was originally derived; and indeed the nature of these soils differs considerably in the various parts of the British Isles. In their natural condition all brown earths would eventually support deciduous woodland, in particular oakwoods. The plants associated with these dominant trees, that is other trees, shrubs, and herbaceous plants, are often of the same species regardless of whether the soils are heavy clays or light sandy loams. Differences that do exist may be due to the fact that certain species cannot survive in cold, wet clays, while others cannot tolerate a dry, light soil.

Moss peats differ sharply from podsols and brown earths in that they contain no parent rock but are entirely organic in content, being formed by the accumulation of the partially decayed remains of generation upon generation of plants, especially bog mosses (*Sphagnum* spp.). Typical peats are strongly acid in reaction and begin their formation on waterlogged soils. As these first plants die, and since their decay is only partial, due to oxygen-lack in the waterlogged soil, they form the substratum on which succeeding generations of mosses grow. Repetition of this process leads to the production of a purely organic soil, many feet in thickness, the lower layers of which are gradually compressed and compacted by the weight of the layers above to form peat.

Podsols and brown earths are both *mature soils*. Other soils however may not be so fully developed, either because they have been laid down too recently, or because climatic and other environmental influences severely retard their maturation. The most striking examples are provided by *maritime* and *mountain soils*. Mountain soils in many cases are exposed to violent *erosion* and so always remain to a large extent merely as loose *mineral debris* (fig. 160); maritime soils may occur as shifting sand dunes, their form being constantly changed by wind action (fig. 161), or as in salt marshes, continually subjected to the action of tides. These *immature soils*, however, support a specialized and highly characteristic vegetation.

Biotic Factors

Plant ecologists consider as biotic factors any of the actions and reactions which animals and plants might impose on the particular plants being studied. It is often difficult to separate the effects of individual biotic factors because the majority of organisms in nature commonly form closely knit, and mutually dependent, units. Indeed, the study may have to be confined to those animals and plants which have a very marked influence on the vegetation. Moreover, because of the very diverse and often subtle influences of one living organism on another, it is much more difficult to obtain quantitative data about their effects than in the case of climatic and edaphic factors, where physical and chemical measurements can in most cases be made. For these reasons, biotic factors in ecology present a difficult field of study and one still requiring much detailed investigation.

With regard to the effects of plants on plants, there can be no doubt that the major factor is *competition*, by which is meant the tendency for one plant to suppress the growth of another. Competition operates at all stages of the plant's development

Figure 160 *Screes composed of loose mineral debris in Coire Garblach, Glen Feshie, Inverness-shire. These areas support a very specialized type of vegetation. (Photograph by Dr J. D. Dodds.)*

Figure 161 *An immature, maritime soil: sand dunes at Aberlady, East Lothian. In foreground a young plant of* Ammophila arenaria *and* Honkenia peploides (*dark patches on sand*). *The dunes in the background are mainly colonized by* Ammophila. (*Photograph by Dr J. D. Dodds.*)

and, in assessing its influence, questions such as the conditions and speed of seed germination, the effects of shading, competition by root systems for water and mineral salts, *reproductive capacity*, including possible methods of rapid vegetative multiplication, must be considered. Some plants, too, produce certain chemical substances which pass into the soil where they may inhibit seed germination or the root development of other plants.

Parasitism is, of course, another and often very striking way in which certain plants may affect others sometimes with drastic results. At present, however, knowledge is in most cases limited to the extent of parasitism, especially by fungi (see Chapter 33), and little is known about how parasites may limit the range of distribution, or the abundance of plants in the wild.

Animals as biotic factors are in general destructive in their effects on vegetation, for in most environments plants are consumed as food by a considerable variety of animals. Seeds, seedlings and all later stages of the developing plant may be eaten and so destroyed. An extreme example is the devastation of tropical areas by locusts. In Britain, mice, voles, deer, squirrels, various birds, such as wood-pigeons and jays, and various leaf-eating insects, do untold damage to trees. Before the virus-disease *myxomatosis* reduced rabbit populations so drastically, these rodents kept large areas of Britain eaten down to the condition of a closely grazed turf. The disappearance of the rabbit allowed quite a lush vegetation to develop, and even shrubs and trees regenerate in areas now rabbit free. Agricultural yield in the country as a whole, it has been estimated, has increased by an amount comparable to the production of a county the size of Yorkshire, such was their destructive effect. Some animals, however, confer a positive benefit on the plants, as for example in the pollination of flowers by insects, the dispersal of certain seeds by animals; and earthworms have an important role in the economy of the soil.

It must not be forgotten that man is the biotic agent who has exerted the greatest influence, in a measure destructive and in a measure constructive, on plant life in many areas of the world. By clearing forests, by draining rivers and marshes and by converting these areas into pasture and arable land he has enormously modified vast areas of natural vegetation and thus altered for ever much of the earth's surface. Moreover, in the pasturing and herding of sheep and cattle – and in certain parts of the world, goats – he has likewise brought about most strking and far-reaching changes in natural vegetational cover. In Britain, for example, his influence has been so far reaching that, except for certain maritime areas, some bogs and marshes, and certain habitats in regions above 2000 feet such as mountain tops, screes and ledges (fig. 162), few areas can be said to be entirely natural. Much is completely artificial, being either agricultural land or forestry plantations.

Plant Communities

Except in arid regions, or under conditions of instability as in sand dunes or on mountain tops where soil cannot develop, plants tend to grow together to form a continuous carpet over the earth. In this extensive cover it is usual to find particular species of plants growing so well and so abundantly that they dominate all others. Typical examples are woods dominated by oak, beech or birch (hence oakwoods, beechwoods or birchwoods), moors dominated by heather (heather moors), or bogs by the moss *Sphagnum*. Closely associated with these dominants and growing in any spaces left between them there are always other plants whose ecological requirements appear to be fulfilled in these particular situations. These together with the dominants form *plant communities*. Although the particular species associated in a given community, for example in a birchwood, differ to some extent according to the edaphic and climatic factors operating in it, many of them are nevertheless common to, and are in consequence typical of, all such communities.

The dominant plants in a natural plant community, because they overshadow other vegetation, tend to be the largest or tallest which can establish themselves in that particular habitat. By cutting off light below, their presence may prevent the establishment of some species; or by the shade they afford they may favour the growth of certain others. In a woodland community there are often several distinct layers or *strata* of *vegetational cover*, each with its own dominant species. The plants of each layer moreover control, at least in some degree, the composition of the layers below. In an oakwood beneath the tree layer, dominated of course by oak, is a hazel-dominated *shrub layer*, then a herbaceous or *field layer* containing wood anemones, primroses, or bluebells (*Endymion non-scripta*), and finally a *ground layer* of mosses. In studying such a community the ecologist attempts to analyse its structure and composition, to determine how it has developed, to note to what extent it differs from similar communities elsewhere, and where possible, to relate his observations to various environmental influences.

Plant communities are not always well defined or distinctive entities. In extreme cases it may be difficult, or even impossible, to designate the plants of a particular area as a definite community. Even a well defined community may show a gradual transition to an adjoining one, either because intermediate habitat conditions occur towards its margins, or because one community is in the process of ousting an adjacent one. In the main, however, there is a strong tendency for plants to form characteristic communities, showing remarkable stability and fitted to the prevailing conditions of climate and soil.

Plant Succession

Close observation of an area of vegetation over a period of years will reveal that it is constantly changing. The oakwood community existing now has not always existed, for like individual plants or animals, it has a beginning and a finite existence and therefore a *developmental history*. In the course of the development of any community, one group of plants has succeeded another as environmental conditions have changed. Excellent material for the study of *plant succession* can be gained by following the *invasion* of an area of bare ground by plants. By such a study it will be found that the types of plants which arrive first, and the speed with which they establish and spread themselves, vary with the existing climate and the nature of the substratum. Often the first colonizers, especially on damp, bare rocks, are algae, lichens, and mosses. On loose soil, such as alluvial silt or tidal mud, the *pioneer colonizers* are usually annuals whose seeds are readily dispersed from surrounding areas with an already existing plant cover. The important contribution made by these first colonizers to the progress of succession is on their death. Their decaying bodies add the first humus to the raw mineral soil, so altering its physical and chemical properties. The first colonizers may reproduce and spread, but at the same time an increasing number of perennials begin to invade the area; and, since many of these can spread rapidly by vegetative means, they tend to oust and replace the annuals. In this way a closed carpet of vegetation sooner or later becomes established. At even later stages in the succession, provided the soil with its ever increasing humus content remains undisturbed, the seedlings of trees and shrubs may appear. Where these establish themselves they will eventually overshadow many of the lower growing plants to the detriment of those requiring full illumination. In general, as a succession progresses the dominant species tend to increase in size. Moreover, throughout the process, fundamental changes are occurring in the soil with respect to its composition and structure, and these changes are closely related to changes observable in the vegetation.

In some communities the dominant species may from time to time degenerate. On high mountain slopes, large masses of the woolly fringe moss (*Rhacomitrium lanuginosum*), which constitutes the *vegetational climax* of a succession in the colonization of bare mountain-top debris, is periodically stripped away by wind (fig. 162). Colonization of these bare areas then begins over again with mountain crowberry. This is succeeded by bilberry, (*Vaccinium myrtillus*), and bog whortleberry, (*V. uliginosum*), until *Rhacomitrium* re-establishes itself and then once more becomes dominant. This sort of *cyclical change* occurs in a variety of vegetation types and may result from the destruction of the dominant type either through age, or some factor prevalent in the particular habitat such as wind erosion or flooding, or even by the action of antagonistic species, which may in turn be destroyed.

Clearly, ecology involves not merely the study of the organism in its environment but 'the study of the *reciprocal relations* between organisms and environment'.

Figure 162 *Mountain top vegetation in the Cairngorms, Inverness-shire, showing the climax of a succession in the colonization of mineral debris by* Rhacomitrium. *The pock-marked appearance of the surface is the result of the vegetation being stripped away by wind. Other plants present are* Juncus trifidus *and* Carex bigelowii. (*Photograph by Dr J. D. Dodds.*)

PART V

REPRODUCTION, HEREDITY, EVOLUTION

CHAPTER 22

REPRODUCTION

One of the outstanding attributes of all living organisms is their ability to reproduce their own kind. For example, in unicellular plants such as the alga *Chlamydomonas*, each division of the cell leads to an increase in the number of individuals. In flowering plants, cell division in meristematic regions is a fundamental aspect in the growth of the whole plant (Chapter 3). Many examples have already been described in which, after the plant has grown to a certain size and reached a certain stage in its development, there may be a separation, from the parent, of specialized stems, roots or leaves (Chapter 5). From these vegetative parts new plants develop.

The essential feature of such vegetative or *asexual reproduction*, in both simple or complex multicellular plants, is cell division. Sexual reproduction, in contrast, involves not only cell division, but the union or *syngamy* of special sex cells or *gametes*, one derived from each of the parents. There is, however, a very special type of cell division concerned in the formation of these gametes, termed *meiosis*, or *reduction division*. The particular significance of this division is that it leads to a halving of the number of chromosomes normally present in the nuclei of these cells compared with those elsewhere in the plant. The somatic or body nuclei of a plant, or any other organism, contain a constant number of chromosomes (Chapter 3). When the chromosomes are large, as for example in *Crepis pulchra* (fig. 21), they can be grouped in homologous pairs, so that the members of each pair are identical in length, in the position of their centromeres and therefore in the relative lengths of the chromosome arms. That it is possible to pair somatic chromosomes in this way, emphasizes the fact that each complement in each nucleus comprises two complete sets: one derived from the male, the other from the female parent. If there was no means of halving this double, or *diploid*, number ('diplöos', double; 'eidos', likeness) during the formation of gametes to the *haploid*, or single, number ('haplöos', single), the chromosome complement in successive generations, resulting from sexual reproduction, would increase in geometrical progression. Thus one essential feature of meiosis is the regulation of chromosome numbers, thereby counterbalancing the effects of syngamy. It is most important to have a fairly detailed knowledge of this remarkable process since it is such an essential part of sexual reproduction. Moreover, this knowledge is a very necessary prerequisite to the understanding of heredity (Chapter 23).

MEIOSIS

The time at which meiosis takes place varies considerably in different organisms. In most animals, for example, it occurs at the time when the gametes are being formed, that is immediately before fertilization. In many algae and fungi the first cell division immediately after fertilization is a meiotic division. This means that only the *zygote*, the cell resulting from the union of male and female gametes, is diploid; all subsequent divisions which lead to the development of the new plant, including the formation of its gametes, are mitotic.

In some algae, and in liverworts, mosses, and ferns, the first division of the zygote is not meiotic but mitotic, and subsequent divisions give rise to the *sporophyte*, or spore-bearing generation of the plant. Meiosis occurs in the formation of these spores, which are therefore haploid. When disseminated these spores germinate to produce a haploid plant, sometimes identical, but often very different, in appearance to the sporophyte generation. The haploid generation is termed the *gametophyte*, since it produces the gametes. Thus in the life history of these plants there is a clear *alternation of generations*, haploid gametophyte alternating with the diploid sporophyte.

One of the significant trends during the course of the evolution of seed plants has been that the gametophyte has become progressively reduced in complexity. Instead of being the dominant phase in the plant's life history on which the sporophyte was almost entirely dependent for food, as it still is in present day liverworts and mosses, the gametophyte appears to have gradually lost its independence until in the seed plants it has become reduced to only a few cells. Associated with this reduction in size and complexity of the gametophyte there has been a corresponding increase in the dominance and independence of the sporophyte generation.

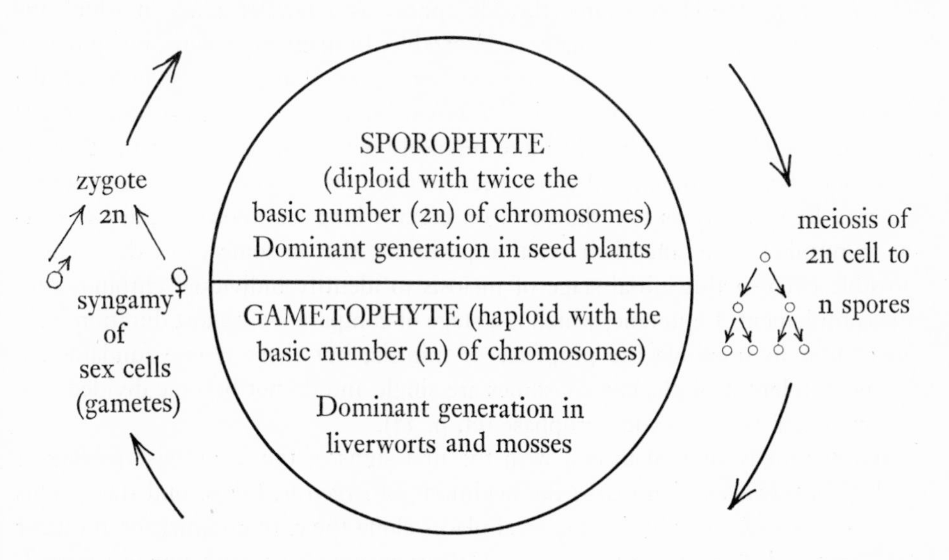

Essentials of Meiosis

Meiosis consists of two nuclear divisions, the one following almost immediately after the other. The first division involves the random separation of the maternal and paternal chromosomes, which have paired in an earlier stage of the process. The two nuclei resulting from this separation each contain half the number of chromosomes originally present; thus they are haploid. The second division, which follows this *reductional* division, is *equational* and involves the longitudinal separation of chromatids in each haploid nucleus formed by the first division, with the result that four haploid nuclei are produced. This means that although there have been two divisions of the nucleus there has been only one division of the original chromosomes. These nuclear divisions are accompanied by divisions of the cytoplasm, so that depending on the organism, four haploid spores, or sexual gametes, are formed from the original diploid cell that went into meiosis.

Stages in Meiosis (figs. 163 and 164)

Meiosis, like mitosis, has for obvious reasons been separated into stages, each of which can with practice, be fairly readily recognized, since each possesses certain characteristic features. Like mitosis, meiosis is a continuous process, so that there is a gradual transition from one stage to the next, and each may be further described as being in an early, mid, or late condition.

The nuclei of cells about to undergo meiosis are generally larger than those of the surrounding tissues (fig. 165). When the chromosomes first appear in the *meiotic prophase* they are longer and more slender than those in a mitotic prophase of the same organism. Prophase is the most protracted, complex, and significant stage in meiosis and can be further subdivided into five distinctive stages. In the first of these stages, *leptotene*, the chromosome threads appear as a tangled mass in which individual chromosomes are not usually recognizable. In many organisms, it is possible to detect, at leptotene and during later stages, a series of granules, or bead-like structures, the *chromomeres*, at irregular intervals along the length of these threads (fig. 166). The chromomeres stain more intensely with basic dyes than the thread-like portions between them, and it has been shown that the chromomeres, of which there may be as many as two thousand on certain long chromosomes, are so constant in number, size, and their relative positions, that in some cases they render it possible even in this initial stage of meiosis to identify individual chromosomes of the complement. Leptotene, which is a stage of comparatively short duration, may seem at first to resemble the prophase of mitosis, but there is one fundamental difference; in leptotene the chromosomes are single and do not become divided into two chromatids as in a mitotic prophase (cf. p. 33).

Leptotene may be said to end with the first signs of the lengthwise pairing of homologous threads which marks the beginning of *zygotene*, the second stage. This pairing, or *synapsis*, may begin at several places along the chromosomes, or at one or other of the ends (fig. 166). Once initiated, these chromosome pairs, one of paternal, the other of maternal origin, come close together usually along their entire length in a manner rather reminiscent of the closing of a zip fastener. Unlike a zip fastener, however, a point to point attraction of the threads causes homologous chromomeres to come to lie side by side when zygotene pairing is accomplished. This pairing is usually

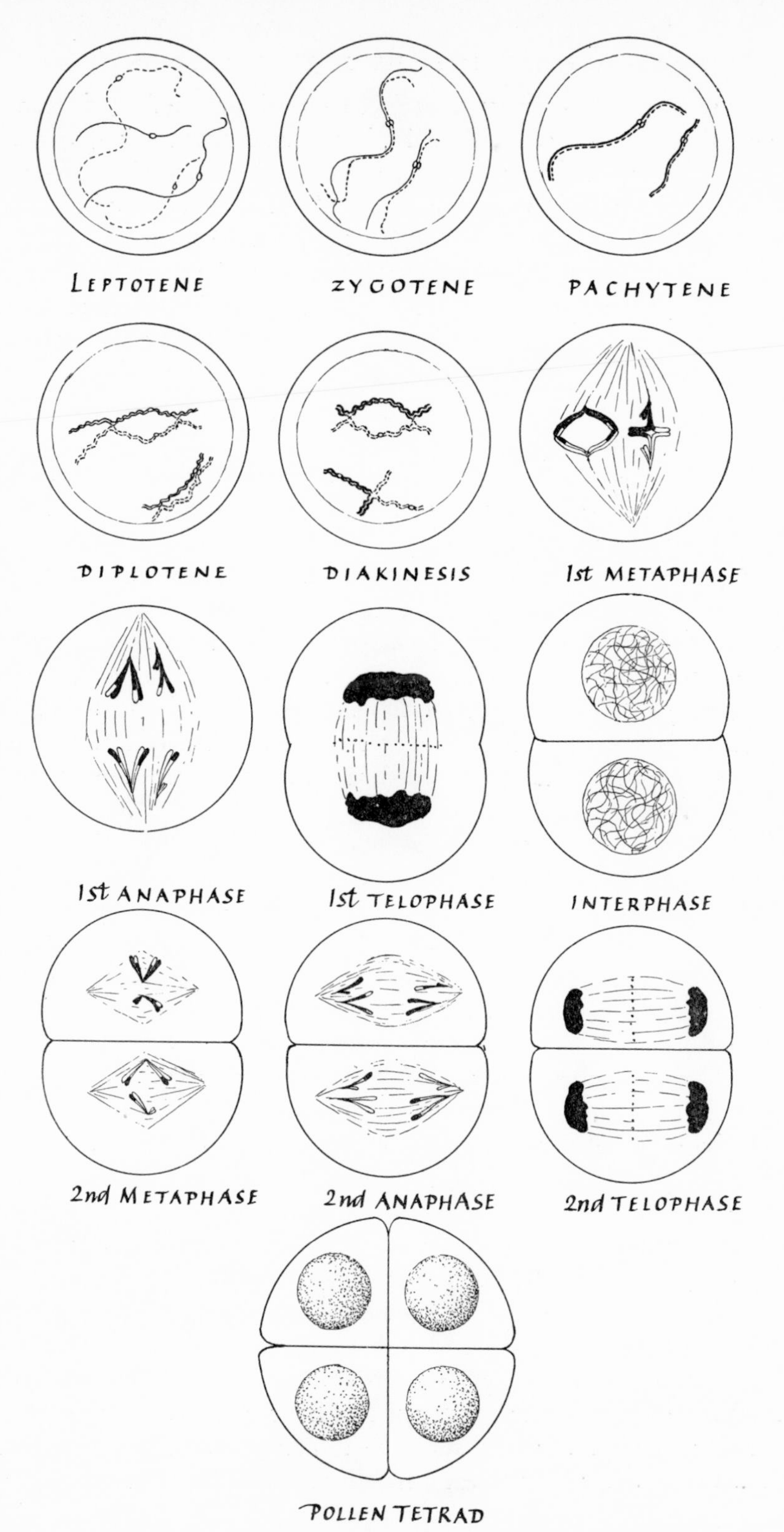

Figure 163 *A diagrammatic representation of the principal stages of meiosis. For simplicity only two chromosome pairs are shown.*

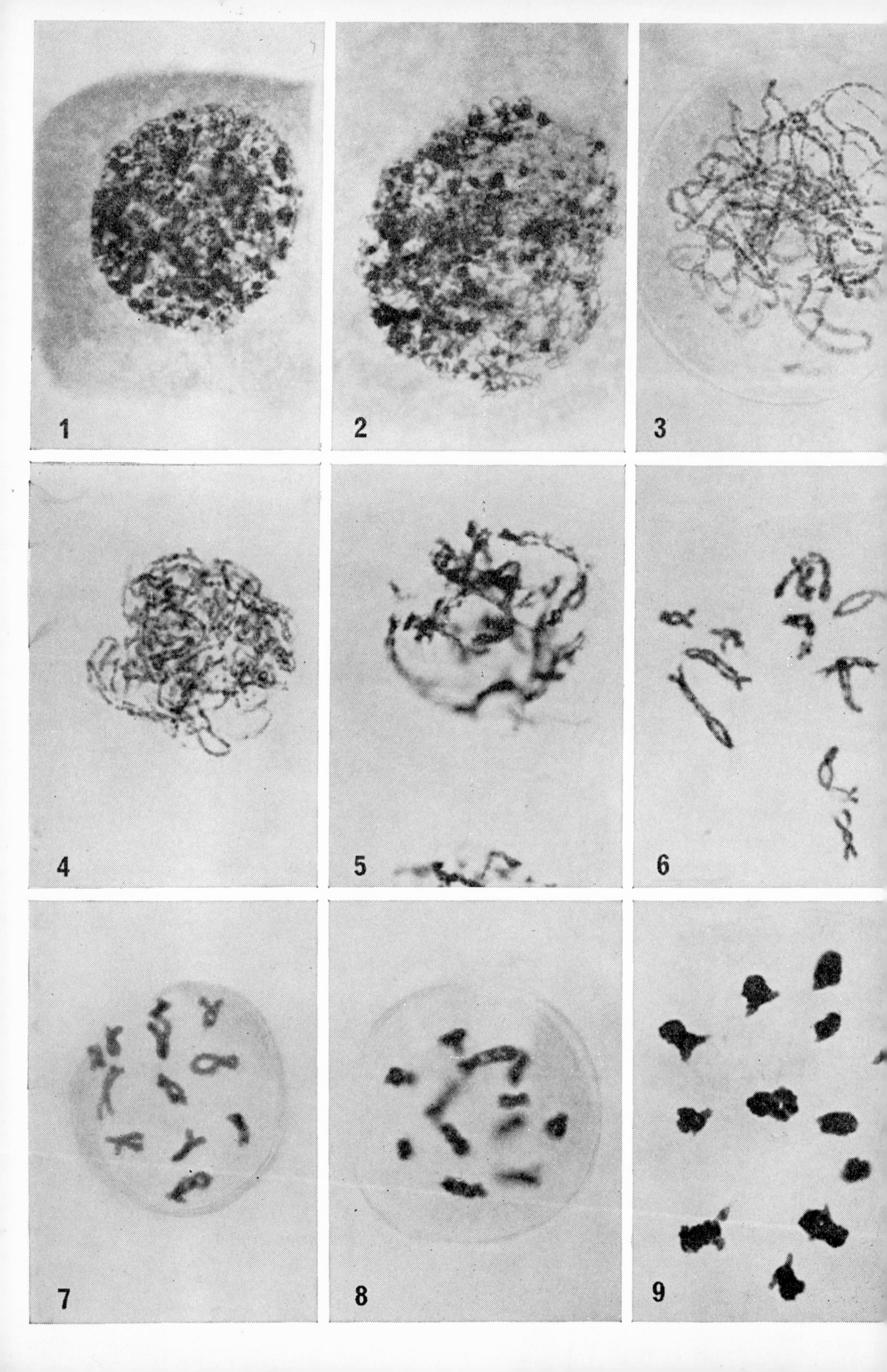
1
2
3
4
5
6
7
8
9

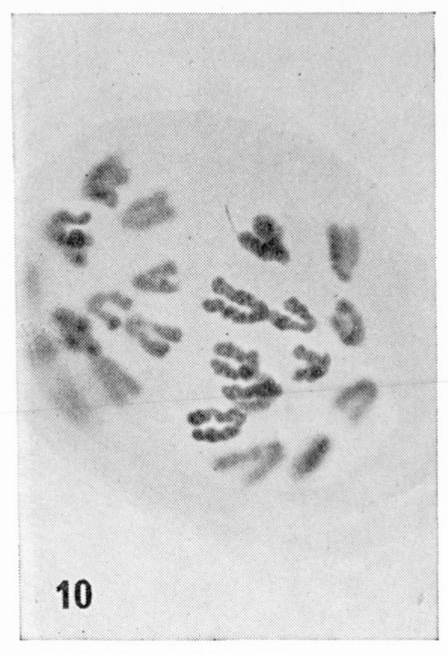

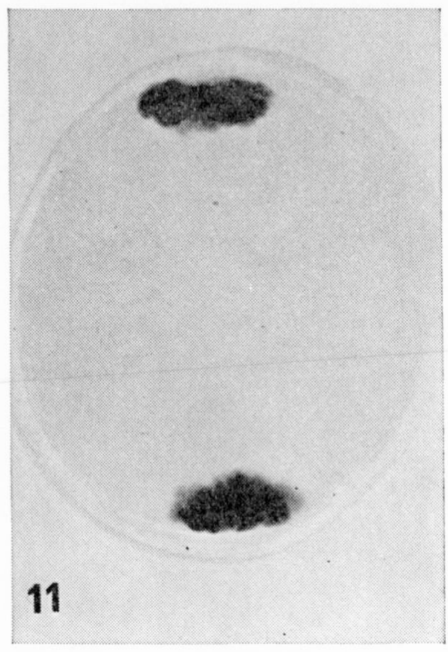

Figure 164 1–13 *Stages of meiosis in pollen mother cells of* Lilium auratum

1 *Leptotene, during which the very long chromosome threads (chromonemata) become apparent.*

2 *Zygotene, when the twenty-four homologous chromosomes begin to associate in pairs along their length.*

3 *Pachytene, the stage when zygotene pairing is complete (the paired condition can be clearly seen in the loop of thread at the bottom of this nucleus), and when chromosome contraction and thickening becomes much more obvious. The bead-like appearance of the threads is due to the presence of chromomeres along their length.*

4 *Late Pachytene – the contraction of the chromosomes continues and leads to*

5 *Diplotene, when each chromosome thread has divided longitudinally. This event causes the attraction between the paired chromosomes of each bivalent to lapse, except where they are held together by chiasmata.*

6 *Diplotene at a later stage showing still further contraction of the bivalents so that twelve can now be distinguished. Note the loops between the chiasmata which are the result of repulsion between chromosomes.*

7 *Diakinesis, during which the twelve bivalents contract still further. Their arrangements round the periphery of the nucleus is apparent in*

8 *Late Diakinesis.*

9 *First Metaphase in which the coiling of the bivalents is very obvious. The more lightly stained portions of these bivalents which extend outwards in opposite directions from them are the regions where the centromeres are being drawn towards the poles of the spindle.*

10 *First Anaphase showing the separation of half of each bivalent to opposite poles. The major coils can still be distinguished.*

11 *First Telephase and the formation of two nuclei which will soon become separated by a cell wall.*

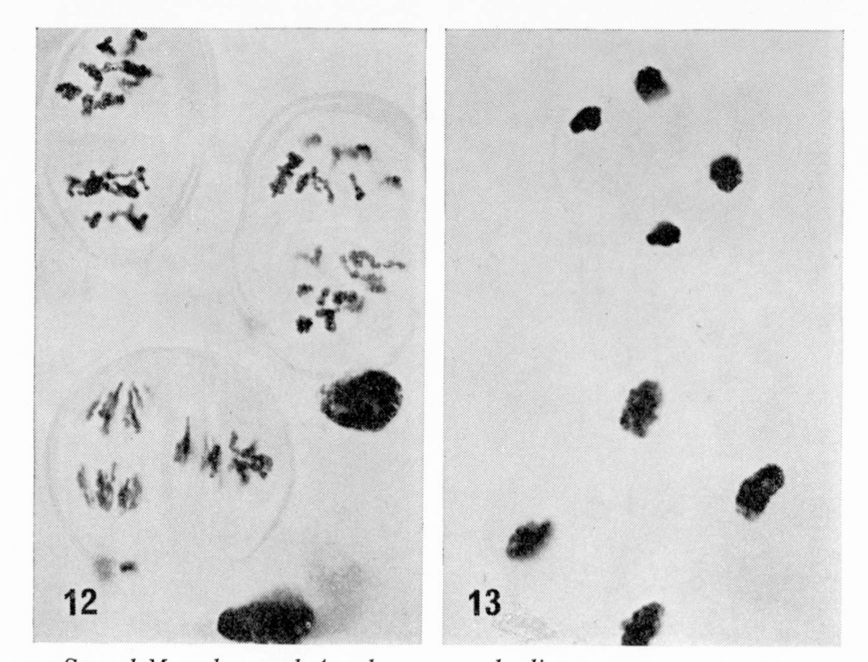

12 *Second Metaphase and Anaphase, stages leading to*

13 *Second Telophase where the chromosomes have reached the poles and four haploid nuclei are forming. The resulting cells become a tetrad of pollen grains.* (*From preparations and photomicrographs by Dr A. F. Dyer.*)

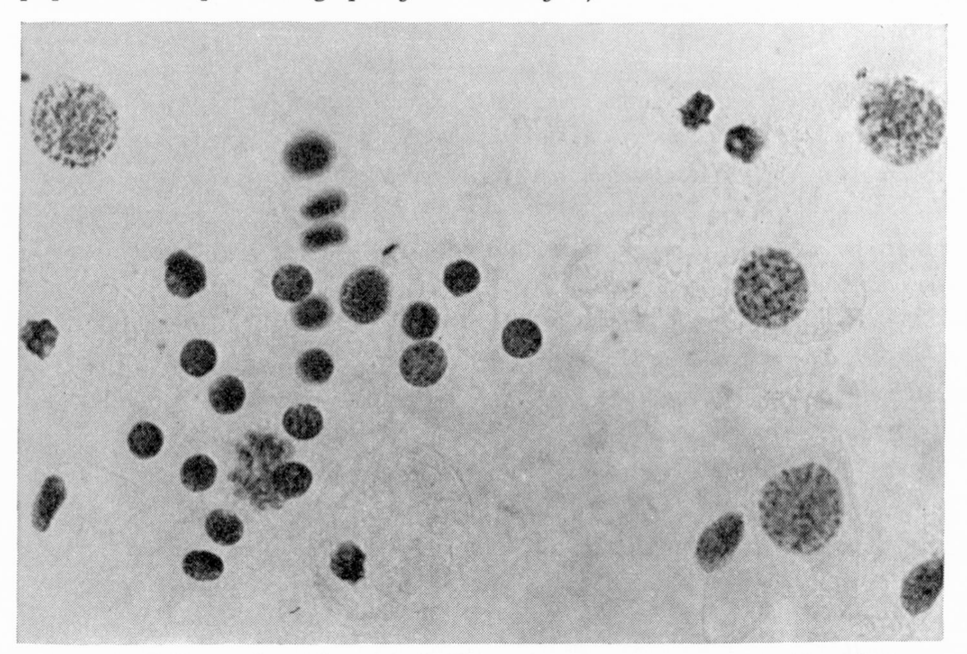

Figure 165 *Pollen mother cell nuclei of* Lilium auratum *entering meiosis. Note the considerable difference in size of the nuclei.* (*From a preparation by Dr A. F. Dyer.*)

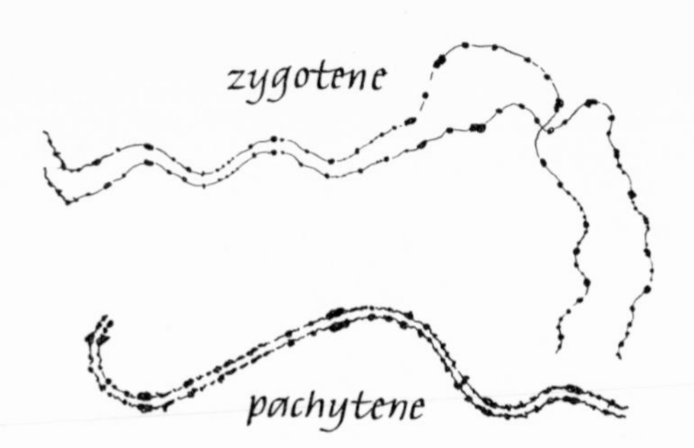

Figure 166 *Parts of pairs of homologous chromosomes at zygotene and pachytene. At zygotene the pairing between homologous regions, chromomere by chromomere has begun, while at pachytene it is complete.*

so intimate that the chromosome threads now appear to be present in the haploid number. Since, however, each thread consists of two closely paired homologous threads, each pair is referred to as a *bivalent*.

The chromosomes throughout zygotene gradually shorten and thicken and, when the forces of attraction which draw the leptotene threads together have been satisfied, there follows a comparatively quiescent period, the third prophase stage, termed *pachytene*. The paired homologues of each bivalent, however, continue to contract and thicken and often appear to be wound, or *relationally coiled*, round one another like the two wires in a piece of flex. At some time during pachytene a more vital change occurs in the chromosomes of each bivalent, though evidence of this change is not usually apparent until the next stage in the meiotic prophase. This is the longitudinal splitting of the chromosomes into two equal parts, except at the centromeres which remain undivided. With this splitting, the strong forces of attraction in the threads, which drew the maternal and paternal chromosomes together during zygotene, relapse, and the force appears to be satisfied instead by an attraction between the daughter chromatids formed at the pachytene splitting of each chromosome. As the pairing relationships lapse, the homologous chromosomes start to be repelled by one another, and so move apart. Pachytene may be said to end once this movement becomes apparent. The nucleus has then entered *diplotene*, the fourth stage of the meiotic prophase.

The diplotene separation of homologous chromosomes is rarely, if ever, complete, for the now double threads of each bivalent appear to be held together at one or more points along their length. Each such point of contact is termed a *chiasma*, meaning a cross, for at these points there is an exchange, or *crossing over*, of chromatid parts. In general, long chromosomes have more *chiasmata* (the plural of chiasma) than short ones, and some very long chromosomes may have ten or more of these points of crossing over along their length (fig. 167).

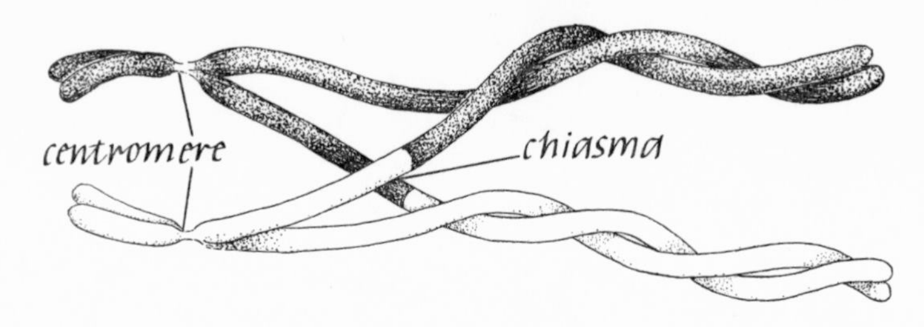

Figure 167 *A bivalent at diplotene of meiosis with a single chiasma. Crossing over has taken place between one white and one black chromatid. The chiasma is beginning to terminalize.*

The mechanical basis of chiasma formation has been the subject of considerable study, and speculation, not only for its inherent interest but because of its profound genetical implications (see Chapter 25). Although there is still much controversy about this complex subject, the theory widely held for the past thirty years is that at the end of pachytene, where there are four threads coiled round one another with strong forces of attraction existing between daughter chromatids and forces of repulsion between homologous chromosomes, considerable stresses are set up within each bivalent. Under such stress it seems that any break which may occur along one of the chromatids will tend to relieve the tortional stress within the chromosome of which it is a part. This, however, will increase the stress in the partner chromosome of the bivalent to such a degree that one of the chromatids of this chromosome will break at the corresponding point along its length. As soon as these breaks occur, the chromatids concerned will begin to unwind in their immediate vicinity and with a half twist come to lie opposite the broken ends of their partners. The broken ends of each chromatid then immediately unite with those of the homologous chromosome so that there is an actual exchange or crossing over of chromatid parts.

An important aspect of chiasma formation is that when more than one chiasma occurs in a bivalent, adjoining chiasmata may not necessarily be between the same chromatids as were involved in the first. Indeed along the length of a bivalent all four chromatids are very often involved in crossing over.

As a result of their continued coiling or *spiralization*, the chromosomes become progressively thicker and shorter throughout diplotene. This contraction, coupled with the movement which forces the homologous chromosomes apart towards the poles, causes the chiasmata, but not the points of exchange, to pass towards the ends of the chromosomes. The consequence of this process of chiasma *terminalization* is that the chiasmata, one by one, move to the free ends of the bivalents. Thus the number of chiasmata present apparently decreases throughout the remaining stages of the meiotic prophase. Chiasmata, however, never terminalize over the centromere, so that bivalents with centromeres situated in the middle of the chromosome and with

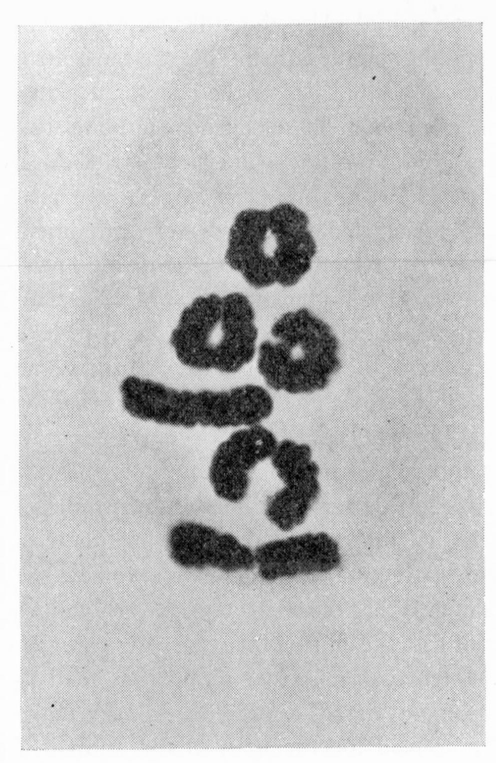

Figure 168 *Ring and rod bivalents in metaphase* 1 *of meiosis in* Trillium. *The major coils are very prominent.* (*Photo by Dr A. F. Dyer.*)

chiasmata on either side form a *ring-like configuration* when terminalization is complete (fig. 168). There is only one chiasma, the arms of the bivalents rotate through an angle of about 90° during terminalization and come to lie in different planes so that a cross-like configuration results. When several chiasmata are present, this same 90° rotation between chiasmata causes the bivalents to appear like the links in a chain with successive links lying at right angles to one another.

The change from diplotene to *diakinesis*, the fifth and final stage of the meiotic prophase, is gradual and not clearly defined. In early diplotene the bivalents still tend to be closely grouped together, but as diakinesis proceeds they become evenly distributed around the periphery of the nucleus. During diakinesis the chromosomes continue to contract, becoming shorter and thicker, thus acquiring a more regular and smoother outline. Also during this last phase, terminalization may bring about a reduction in the number of chiasmata. In addition the nucleoli, which were prominent in all earlier prophase stages, disappear or become detached from their associated chromosomes.

Diakinesis, and therefore the meiotic prophase, ends with the disappearance of the nuclear membrane and the appearance of the spindle. The bivalents then take up their positions on the spindle and the nucleus has passed into the *metaphase* condition. The meiotic metaphase differs from a typical mitotic metaphase especially in that the chromosomes are much shorter and they are paired. Also the still undivided centromeres of the chromosomes do not lie along the spindle equator; instead the centromeres of each bivalent take up positions on opposite sides of the equatorial plane. The distance between homologous centromeres at metaphase depends on the relative lengths of the chromosomes and the *proximal* (end) position of their chiasmata. Also, in the meiotic metaphase chromosomes of some plants, the (*major coils*), which produce the final shortening and thickening of the chromosomes, are very prominent (fig. 168). Moreover, in mitosis, the centromeres of each chromosome divide at the end of metaphase, while in meiosis they do not do so until the metaphase of the second meiotic division. During the first meiotic metaphase, however, there seems to be a strong repulsion between homologous centromeres, for a region of each chromosome on both sides of the centromere frequently appears to be under tension and is thereby stretched out in the direction of the poles.

The repulsive force which was clearly apparent at metaphase continues to exert its influence throughout the *anaphase* which follows, when the undivided centromeres of each chromosome migrate towards the poles, dragging the two chromatids with them. Up to this stage, because of chromatid attraction, the chiasmata have held the homologous chromosomes together as bivalents. At the onset of anaphase this binding force suddenly seems to lapse, with the result that the ends of the separating chromosomes become freed from one another. Moreover, even sister chromatids tend to separate, giving the ends of each chromosome a 'flared' appearance as they move polewards. Sister chromatids are in fact now held together only at the undivided centromere. Herein lies the essential difference between this, the *first meiotic anaphase*, and a typical mitotic anaphase. In the mitotic anaphase, it is the chromatids that segregate following the division of the centromeres at the end of metaphase; in the meiotic anaphase, whole chromosomes, consisting of two chromatids and an undivided centromere, move to each of the poles.

During the *telophase* which follows the first meiotic anaphase there may be a reappearance of the nuclear membrane and a relaxation of the coiling of the chromosomes as the nucleus rounds up and passes into the interphase condition. Accompanying this transformation there is commonly a cytokinesis which causes the two newly formed haploid nuclei to be separated by a cell wall. In certain organisms, however, telophase, and the succeeding interphase, may not occur. After the completion of their anaphase movements the chromosomes in such cases undergo no apparent change until the *second meiotic division* begins. There is then no prophase in the second division.

Prophase of the second meiotic division, when it occurs, is usually of short duration, for the chromosomes soon come to arrange themselves across the equatorial plane of the spindle as a metaphase plate. The characteristic features of the *second metaphase* of meiosis which distinguish it from the first are as follows. Firstly, there is only the haploid number of chromosomes present; secondly, the chromosomes show the *relics* of the major coils apparent in the first metaphase; thirdly, there is a repulsion of chromatids, not chromosomes as in the earlier metaphase; fourthly, the spindles are at right angles to each other and both are at right angles to the spindle of the first meiotic metaphase. Anaphase movements begin when the centromeres of the metaphase chromosomes divide and the daughter chromosomes are free to move to each pole. With the reorganization of the nuclei at the second telophase and the subsequent cytokinesis, four haploid cells are produced from the diploid cell which entered meiosis.

Although this second meiotic division resembles in certain respects a typical mitosis, there are significant differences – quite apart from the fact that there may be no prophase. These are that the chromatids retain the 'flared' appearance originally seen during the first anaphase and hence relational coiling is often absent. Most important, however, is the fact that, as a result of chiasma formation and crossing over, there will have been an interchange of chromatid parts in many of the bivalents, and each haploid nucleus differs therefore in the constitution of its chromosomes. This phenomenon is of the greatest significance when meiosis is studied in relation to heredity (see Chapter 25). Although the second meiotic division is sometimes referred to as the *meiotic mitosis*, the differences in these processes make it more desirable to refer to the first, the reductional, and the second, the equational, divisions of the meiotic chromosomes as *meiosis I* and *meiosis II* respectively (fig. 163).

CHAPTER 23

FLOWERS

In higher plants the cytological processes which are the essence of sexual reproduction – meiosis and gamete formation and the later union of these gametes in the act of fertilization – occur in highly specialized shoots called flowers. Indeed, a flower may be regarded as a stem, the internodes of which remain short, and whose leaves are modified to serve as the various floral organs, that is sepals, petals, stamens, and carpels, and whose functions differ radically from those of normal leaves.

The production of flowers is, in many plants, the final phase of their development, and once the resulting seeds are shed the life of the plant ends. This is especially the case in many annuals, for example shepherd's purse, though it also applies to certain very long lived species of which the century plant, *Agave americana*, provides a striking example. This may take as long as 70 years before it forms flowers, but when reproduction is accomplished and its seeds are shed the *Agave* dies. In bulbs such as tulip (*Tulipa*) and crocus, the formation of both sexual and vegetative organs of reproduction, that is flowers on the one hand and bulbs or corms on the other, terminates vegetative growth. Many perennials, and in particular trees and shrubs, have definite phases of vegetative and reproductive growth and in quite a number of plants, for example coltsfoot (*Tussalago farfara*), flowers are produced before the renewal of vegetative growth for the season.

It may be asked what great advantage has sexual over vegetative reproduction, especially when many plants seem to be able to propagate themselves, so that the survival of the species is assured purely by vegetative means. In sexual reproduction the characters of the parents are mixed as a result of meiosis and fertilization; this confers benefits of the greatest biological significance to the offspring (see Chapter 22). Of secondary importance is that whilst the products of vegetative reproduction cannot be disseminated to any great distance away from their parents, seeds, the ultimate products of sexual reproduction in flowering plants, may frequently be carried for great distances from their parents, a feature of considerable biological advantage.

PHYSIOLOGY OF REPRODUCTION

It has been recognized for a considerable time that plants must attain a certain size and, therefore, reach a certain stage in their vegetative growth before flowers can be initiated. The condition of vegetative development, which must be attained before flowers can form, is termed *ripeness to flower*, and it has long been recognized that this may depend on the balance of carbohydrates to nitrogenous substances in the plant.

Because of its practical implications, considerable research has been directed towards the study of the factors involved in the control of flowering. Although reproductive development may follow immediately, and it seems automatically, once the stage of ripeness-to-flower is reached, certain special environmental conditions must be fulfilled before many plants actually flower. During flower formation profound changes in the growth pattern, shape of the apex, and morphology of the primordia invariably take place. It is usually a fairly simple matter to ascertain whether such events have taken place by stripping the leaves from a growing point and examining the apex, even under a quite low magnification of the microscope (cf. p. 123).

The main problem of floral initiation is to discover the factors involved in causing apical growing points to form floral organs instead of leaves. It is now known that most important in this respect is light and that its determinative influence is through the relative lengths of daylight and darkness to which the plant is exposed. Flowering plants can be placed into one or other of three broad categories with regard to their *photoperiodic* requirements; these are termed *short day*, *long day* and *day-neutral* plants. Day-neutral plants flower under a wide range of day lengths, provided that other environmental conditions leading to their ripeness to flower are fulfilled. Short day plants initiate flowers only when the day length is less than a certain period, and although mostly natives of the tropics, these plants when grown in northern latitudes, flower in late summer or autumn. Long day plants, in contrast, will flower only when the daily amount of illumination they receive exceeds a certain critical duration and, as such, are mostly natives of northern latitudes where the flowers are initiated during the long days of summer.

Research has shown that the response of plants to photoperiodic stimuli is through their leaves and, as in vegetative growth and development, hormones are intimately involved. For example, in the case of short day plants the response is not so much to a short period of illumination as to a long period of darkness during which a hormonal substance or substances are formed in the leaves. These substances travel through the phloem to vegetative buds which in some unexplained way are stimulated to develop floral primordia. By contrast, in long day plants substances unfavourable, or antagonistic, to flower initiation are produced if the plants are exposed to long periods of darkness, so that flowers are in fact initiated by short nights. Photoperiodism is clearly just as much a response to periods of darkness as it is to day length.

It is important to recognize that flower initiation does not inevitably lead to the production of flowers; it may happen that subsequently the conditions necessary for their successful development are unfavourable. Thus it is important not to use flowering itself as an indicator of a plant's photoperiodic requirement. A clear distinction must be drawn between these two aspects of flower production, for it is now known that in certain plants floral primordia are formed only during certain day lengths, while their subsequent development is promoted by a quite different day length. For example, there was for some time considerable doubt whether the aster (*Callistephus chinensis*) was a short or long day plant. It is now known that its flower buds form and rosettes start elongating during long days. If the plants continue to receive long day treatment, stem elongation persists for a long time before the plant eventually flowers. Short day treatment given immediately after the rosette begins to elongate, however, stops further elongation, and flowers appear very much earlier than if long day treatment had been continued. The requirements of strawberries are quite the opposite; their flower buds are formed during short days, but actual flowering occurs during long days. Clearly with regard to floral initiation, the aster is a long day plant and the strawberry short day, but from the point of view of the whole flowering process the aster might be termed a long day/short day plant, the strawberry a short day/long day plant.

Knowledge of the photoperiodic requirements of plants is of considerable practical importance to horticulturalists, for by means of quite low intensity artificial illumination it is possible to bring long day plants into flower out of season.

Temperature, like light, is a very variable factor of any plant's environment and all normally experience annual as well as diurnal fluctuations. Like light, temperature often seems to play some part in establishing the relative lengths of the vegetative and reproductive phases of development. Cauliflowers, for example, will flower sooner if subjected to the low temperatures of a normal winter environment than if protected, in the early stages of development, in a greenhouse. Winter wheat sown in spring usually does not flower at all during that season. If sown in the previous autumn, however, so that the seed is exposed to the following winter's cold and frost, it flowers during the next growing season. From such observations and a great deal of experimental work, much of it carried out by Russian workers, including Lysenko (whose name is also linked with more controversial biological topics), it has been concluded that the seed has to pass through a particular developmental phase requiring a definite temperature for its successful completion. If this phase, known as the phase of *vernalization* (a word derived from the Latin 'vernalis', pertaining to the spring), is not completed, further development will not take place. Findings of this sort have been turned to practical advantage by exposing wheat in an early phase of germination to temperatures between 0 and 5°C for a few weeks. These seeds can then be stored until soil conditions are suitable for spring sowing, but they will flower in that growing season. Not all plants requiring a *temperature stimulus* for reproductive development respond to cold treatment. The vernalization of maize requires a temperature of between 20 and 30°C; cotton (*Gossypium*) also requires a high temperature before the onset of flowering. Also, many plants requiring vernalization will flower successfully only if later subjected to a day-length appropriate to their needs. It has been suggested that the particular cold or heat requirements demanded before the onset of flowering are of ecological significance, in that they guarantee that the plants' reproductive phases will occur at the appropriate season (see p. 230).

THE FLOWER

The individual flowers of any inflorescence begin their development in the same way as leaves are initiated, that is, by periclinal divisions of meristematic cells situated beneath the outer layers of the bud apex. By the continued growth and differentiation of the protuberances so formed, the various floral organs eventually develop. However, unlike a developing vegetative bud which elongates into a shoot with nodes and internodes, each individual flower is a compressed shoot whose various parts when fully developed are not separated by internodes. These various parts always originate in a definite sequence on the meristem, usually from the outside inwards; that is in *acropetal succession*. There may, however, be considerable differences in their relative rates of development; consequently one organ, though originating before another, may yet develop much more slowly (fig. 169).

The first floral primordia to develop are small, leaf-like organs called *bracteoles*. There are generally two bracteoles in Dicotyledons and only one in Monocotyledons. They are therefore the oldest and outermost members of the flower and protect the floral parts within in the early phases of their development. Often buds arise in the axils of bracteoles, so their position determines the points at which the flower stalk or *pedicel* branches. In Dicotyledons, the two bracteoles are usually inserted symmetrically to left and right of the flower-stalk, with an angle of about 137·5° between them on the side towards the main axis bearing the flower-stalk. The single bracteole of the Monocotyledons occurs on the side of the pedicel next to the main axis. It is often very broad, completely enclosing the rest of the flower until shortly before opening. These bracteoles or *spathes*, are found in many cultivated Monocotyledons of gardens such as *Narcissus* and snowdrop (*Galanthus nivalis*).

After formation of the bracteoles the next floral organs to be produced constitute the *perianth*, which usually consists of sepals and petals. These are commonly much larger than the bracteoles but still leaf-like in form. The *sepals*, the outer members of the perianth, together comprise the *calyx* and are commonly green, while the inner *petals* constituting the *corolla* are frequently brightly coloured. After the formation of the perianth, the male organs, the *stamens* which constitute the *androecium*, and finally the female organs or *carpels*, are initiated successively towards the centre of the flower. The female organs of the flower together are termed the *gynaecium*.

During the development of these floral parts the axis of the flower elongates both above and below the two bracteoles, though it does not elongate appreciably between any of the other floral parts. The result of these changes is that the bracteoles appear to be separated on the flower stalk, the swollen terminal region of which is called the *receptacle*. The term 'flower' is usually restricted to the terminal cluster of organs arising from the receptacle; the last-formed organs (the carpels) occur near its apex. In some flowers it can be seen that the floral parts are spirally arranged so that when fully developed, the floral organs appear to be attached at different levels on a rather elongated receptacle. Many flowers, however, seem to have their different organs occurring as three or more concentric whorls arising from a somewhat flattened receptacle.

The petals and sepals, which envelop the organs of reproduction, are commonly

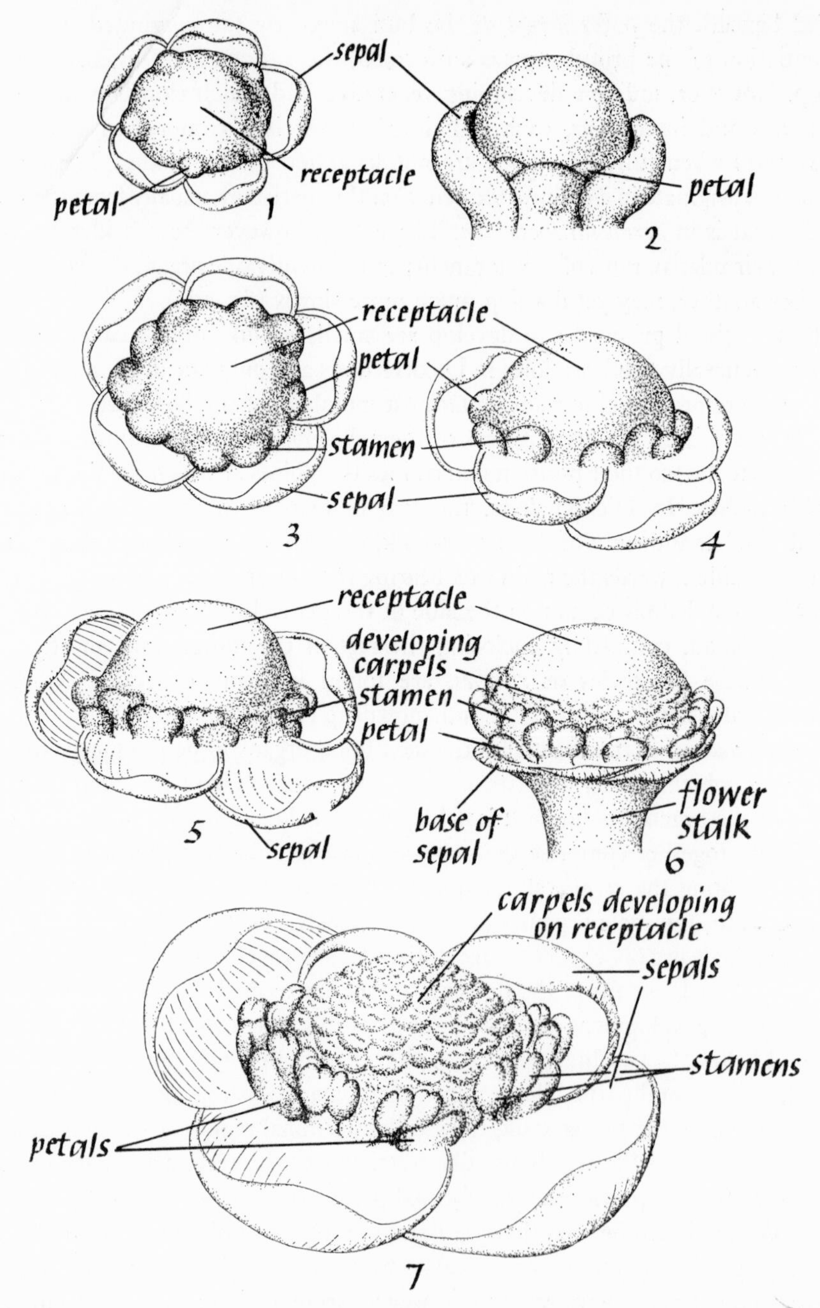

Figure 169 1-7 *Stages in the development of a flower bud of* Ranunculus bulbosus (*after Payer*).

Figure 170 *Male and female flowers (catkins) of an alder* (Alnus viridis). *The large pendulous catkins on the right are the male flowers. The female catkins which are much smaller stand erect towards the upper left of the photograph.*

referred to as accessory, or *non-essential floral* parts, for they are not directly involved in the actual reproductive processes. They are, in fact, organs principally concerned with the attraction of insects and with protection. In certain *naked* flowers, as for example those of certain trees (ash), only the essential organs, the stamens and carpels, are present. When all four sets of floral organs are present, a flower is said to be *complete*. It is *incomplete* if any one set is absent. A special distinction is also drawn between flowers lacking either stamens or carpels. When both of these male and female organs are present a flower is described as *perfect*, even though the calyx or corolla may be absent. It is said to be *imperfect* if either stamens or carpels are absent. There are therefore two categories of imperfect flowers: those with carpels or *pistils*, but without stamens and thus termed *carpellate* or *pistillate*; and those without carpels termed *staminate* flowers. In some plants both staminate and pistillate flowers are produced on the same plant as in the catkin-bearing trees – alder (fig. 170), birch, and hazel (*Corylus avellana*), which are therefore termed *monoecious* (meaning 'one household'). In *dioecious* ('two households') plants, male and female flowers are produced on different individuals.

Perianth

The sepals and petals, which in the majority of flowers form the two outermost

Figure 171 *The apetalous flower of* Caltha palustris *in which the large coloured sepals function as petals.*

Figure 172 *A flower of* Helleborus orientalis *with its tube-like petals.*

whorls of floral organs, are constant in their number and arrangement not only for a given plant species but also, generally, for whole families. When both sets are present they alternate in their positions of attachment to the receptacle. Thus in Monocotyledons each flower has three sepals situated to the outside of and midway between three petals, and they are usually alike in colour, e.g. *Galanthus*. In Dicotyledons, which most frequently have 4 or 5 sepals and petals, the sepals are frequently green, while the petals are white or brilliantly coloured. Quite a large number of fairly common plants possess only one perianth whorl and, since this is always considered to be the *calyx*, such flowers are termed *apetalous*. It has been suggested that primitive flowers had only one kind of perianth member like those of the present day marsh marigold (*Caltha palustris*) (fig. 171), and that the corolla evolved later as a ring of organs developed from the outermost whorl of stamens, just as the additional petals in *double flowers* replace some or all of the stamens. In the Christmas rose and its allies (*Helleborus* sp.) small trumpet-shaped structures occur immediately within the calyx: these seem to replace some of the stamens and, although they are very different from typical petals, they are commonly referred to as such (fig. 172).

The essentially protective function of the calyx can be demonstrated quite strikingly in some flowers (e.g. the field poppy, *Papaver rhoeas*) if it is removed before the flower buds open. Following this treatment the petals, especially, will be found to be withered and damaged when the flower eventually opens. Although in some plants (e.g. poppy), the sepals are shed like scale leaves as the flower opens, in most cases they are persistent organs and may in fact serve to protect the fruits, which subsequently develop after fertilization. Although sepals are commonly simple, leaf-like and distinct from one another, in many plants they are fused together to form a cup or tube at their base. The unfused portions appear as teeth, corresponding in number to the number of sepals composing the tube. When the sepals are free, the calyx is described as *polysepalous*; when joined together as *gamosepalous*. The latter are usually regular in form but many polysepalous calyxes are markedly irregular, as for example in the garden nasturtium, where one side is developed as a conspicuous *spur* (fig. 173).

Great diversity of form is encountered in the shape and arrangement of petals, which like the sepals may not be separate structures throughout their length but may be fused to form a tube. The terms *polypetalous* and *gamopetalous* are used to refer to free and fused corollas respectively. Gamopetalous corollas like gamosepalous calyxes originate when there is meristematic activity between the individual primordia, thus forming the continuous ring on which the primordia are raised. As this ring grows, it gives rise to the corolla tube, while the original primordia produce its free lobes. These lobes vary considerably in size in different plants. They are very large in the primrose (*Primula vulgaris*), but hardly perceptible in the bindweed (*Convolvulus arvensis*) (fig. 174).

In many flowers all the floral parts are arranged with perfect symmetry about a vertical axis, so the flowers are star-shaped or *actinomorphic*. This means that no matter how the flower is halved longitudinally, each half will be a mirror image of the

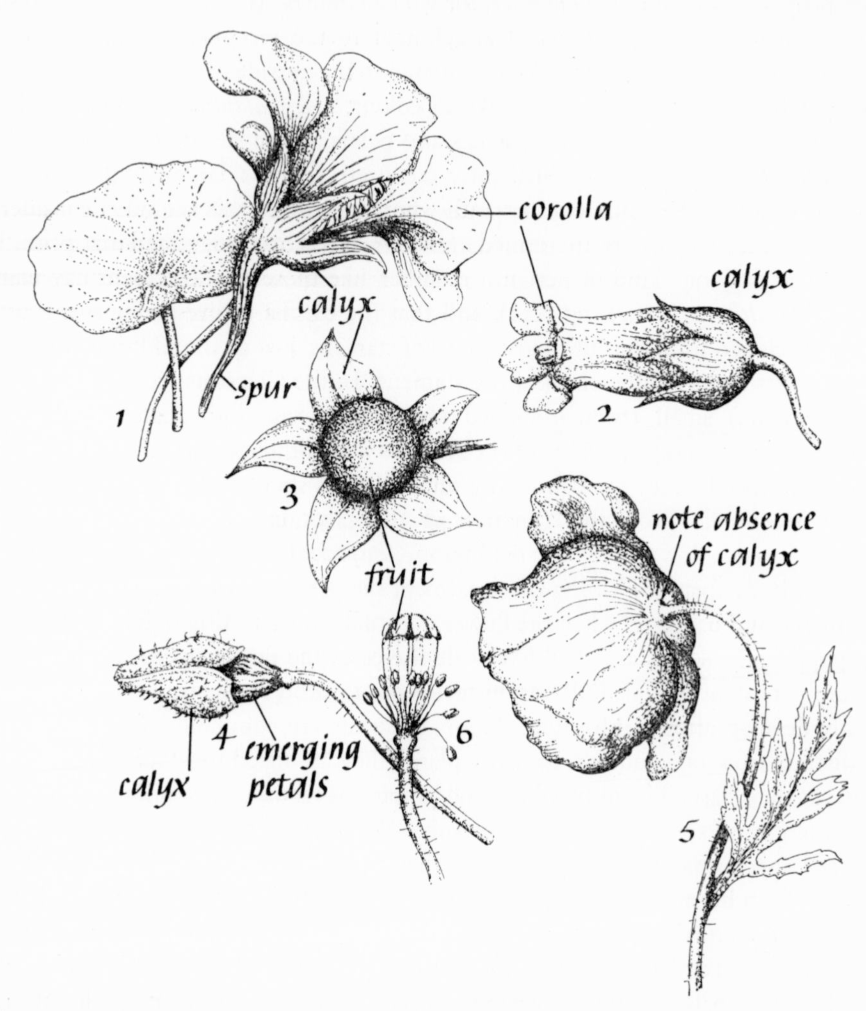

Figure 173 *The calyx*

1 *Flower of* Tropaeoleum *showing calyx developed as a conspicuous spur.*

2 *and* 3 *Flower and fruit of* Atropa belladonna *showing persistent calyx round fruit.*

4 *Flower bud of* Papaver rhoeas *showing petals emerging from calyx.*

5 Papaver *flower open with calyx cast off.*

6 Papaver *fruit without sepals or petals, though stamens are still retained.*

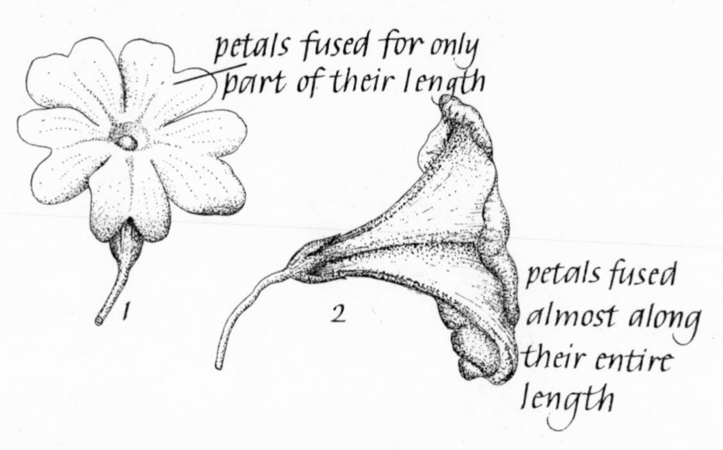

Figure 174 *Gamopetaly* (1) *in* Primula *and* (2) Convolvulus.

other (e.g. *Ranunculus* spp.). Unequal growth of the various primordia leads to the production of flowers of irregular form. The petals in particular are often conspicuously different in size and shape, producing, for example, the two lipped or *bilabiate* corolla of the Family Labiatae, or the butterfly-like or *papillonaceous* corolla of the Leguminosae. In these irregular flowers, there is only one longitudinal plane through which the flower can be cut so that two symmetrical mirror images are obtained. Bilaterally symmetrical flowers of this type are termed *zygomorphic*, which means joined forms (fig. 175).

Inflorescences

Once the physiological conditions for the change from the vegetative to the reproductive phase of development are satisfied, the resulting flowers are produced in a more or less definite and characteristic position on a given plant. Indeed, in many cases their mode of occurrence is of significance for the recognition of tribes or genera of Flowering Plants (e.g. *Galium*, *Malus*) and even for entire families, as for example the Umbelliferae, Compositae, and Gramineae. Sometimes the flowers are *solitary*, the buds from which they arise being initiated singly at the end of a shoot or in the axil of a foliage leaf, as in the scarlet pimpernel (*Anagalis arvensis*) (fig. 176). In many cases, however, they occur in groups, being confined to special branch systems called *inflorescences*. There is great variety in the form of inflorescences: they may terminate the main axis of the plant or be axillary to a foliage leaf, and each may consist of a branched or unbranched axis bearing a number of stalked or unstalked flowers. The central axis of any inflorescence is termed the *rachis* and the primary stem which supports it the *peduncle*, while the stalks arising from the rachis which bear the individual flowers are called *pedicels*. The rachis usually bears leaves, much smaller and simpler than those produced in the vegetative parts of the plant, and it is in the

Figure 175 *The zygomorphic flower of the orchid* Cymbidium walton setonii. *There is only one plane of symmetry, so that if the flower is cut longitudinally down the middle two symmetrical mirror images are obtained.*

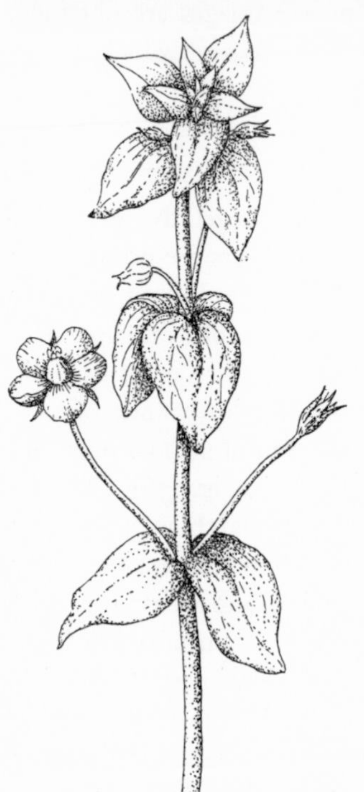

Figure 176 *The solitary flowers of scarlet pimpernel* Anagalis arvensis.

axils of these *bracts*, as they are termed, that each flower or floral axis arises. In some quite common plants, such as wallflower (*Cheiranthus cheiri*) and other members of the family Cruciferae, bracts are absent. Occasionally bracts are large and very conspicuous as in poinsettia (*Euphorbia pulcherrima*), while the striking hood of the cuckoo-pint (*Arum maculatum*) is a single large bract, a spathe.

Although it is frequently impossible to draw an absolutely clear distinction between them, two main classes of inflorescence are recognized – *determinate* and *indeterminate*. In determinate inflorescences, the first flower bud forms at the tip of the rachis; there can therefore be no further terminal growth. Any subsequent development of the shoot must occur with the production of a branch. The simpler type of determinate inflorescence is the *solitary*, terminal flower as found in the tulip, though it is believed that this may have been derived in the course of evolution by reduction from more complex types. The other type of determinate inflorescence is the *cyme*, the axis of which also always terminates in a flower which is the first to open. Branches arise in the axils of bracts beneath this flower, but these too end in flowers and themselves branch in a similar manner. According to their mode of branching, *cymose inflorescences* may be subdivided into *monochasial* (one-branched), or *dichasial* (two-branched) cymes. Typical of the former are the inflorescences of members of the family Boraginaceae, of which the forget-me-not (*Myosotis palustris*) is a common example. Successive alternate branching occurs on opposite sides of the parent stem to produce a progressively incurving *scorpioid* cyme. In the *helicoid* or spring-like cymes, commonly but erroneously described as scorpioid, the successively produced flowers all arise on the same side (fig. 177).

In dichasial cymes the branches often arise on either side and below each of the flowers as they are produced, though the development of one of these branch pairs may be suppressed. However, when both develop, their successive production results eventually in the formation of a flat-topped or somewhat convex cluster, in which the flowers at the centre develop first. The pink family, Caryophyllaceae, provide examples of these. It should be noted that the branching of cymose inflorescences is always sympodial (see p. 71 and fig. 177).

The mode of branching of indeterminate inflorescences is monopodial. In indeterminate inflorescences the terminal bud of the shoot does not normally initiate a flower, so that the axis is potentially capable of indefinite growth. The simplest inflorescence of this class is the *raceme* where the flowers are borne on an elongated axis having along its length a series of bracts within the axils of which the individual flowers arise. Successively younger flowers are produced, and open one by one from the base of the raceme upwards. Thus if any *racemose inflorescence* is viewed from above, the oldest flowers can be seen to be towards the outside (centrifugal) with the youngest in the centre (fig. 178). This contrasts with cymes in which the oldest flowers usually occur towards the inside (centripetal) and the youngest to the outside.

In some racemes, termed *spikes*, the flowers are sessile, having no pedicels, and they arise directly from the rachis. At the other extreme of pedicel development is

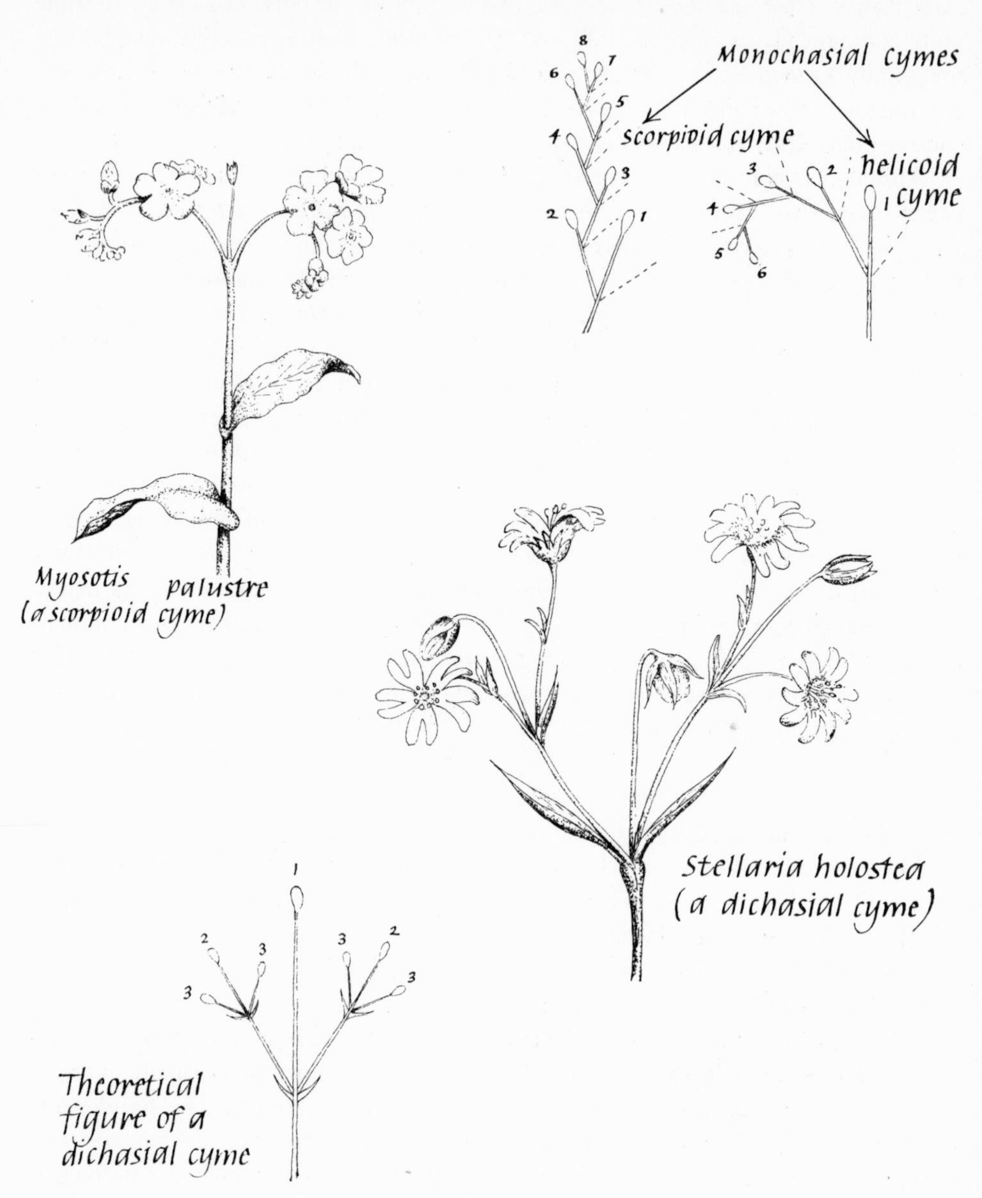

Figure 177 *Cymose inflorescences*

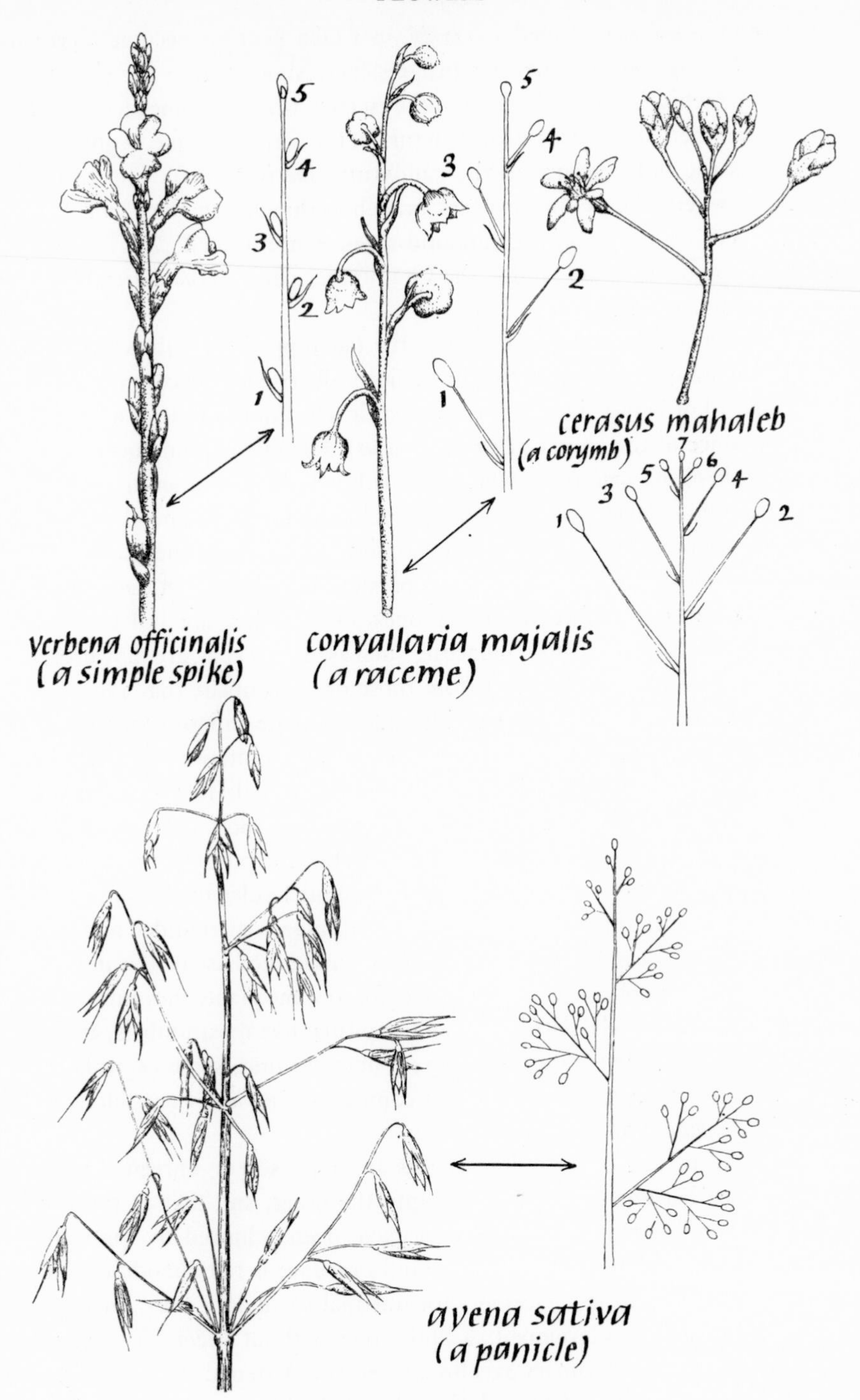

Figure 178 *Racemose inflorescences*

the racemose inflorescence termed a *corymb*, in which pedicels become increasingly elongated as they age so that they are progressively shorter from the base towards the apex of the rachis. This results in an inflorescence which is somewhat flat-topped in outline, in contrast to the pyramidal structure of the simple raceme. A good example of a corymb is the inflorescence of the candytuft (*Iberis amara*). The raceme-like inflorescences, where the peduncle bears branch peduncles in the form of simple racemes, are very complex. Such compound racemes are termed *panicles* and occur in some members of the grass family, the Gramineae: oats, *Avena sativa*, provides a good example (fig. 178).

An inflorescence superficially similar to the flat-topped corymb is the *umbel*. It differs fundamentally, however, in that its pedicels all arise from a common point on a peduncle, instead of being given off at different levels. An example of a *simple umbel* is the inflorescence of the cherry (*Prunus cerasus*). Of much commoner occurrence, however, are *compound umbels*, in which the peduncle bears numerous branch peduncles all at the same level, each branch peduncle producing an umbel of pedicels at its end. This inflorescence, as its name implies, typifies members of the family Umbelliferae, such as parsley, carrot, fool's parsley, and chervil. In most umbels the outermost flowers open before the inner ones so that they are indeterminate inflorescences. Umbels of the Amaryllidaceae, such as *Allium* spp., are, however, determinate, for the central flowers open before those on the outside (fig. 179).

A very characteristic and unmistakable indeterminate inflorescence typifies the family Compositae, to which the daisy, dandelion, and sunflower belong. This is a *capitulum* or *head*, with a large number of very small, sessile flowers, *florets*, tightly grouped on the broad, flattened apex of the peduncle (fig. 180). The youngest flowers occur at its centre, the oldest round its margins. Each capitulum normally has the appearance of a single flower because the conspicuous ligules of the larger marginal florets look like a whorl of petals. The flattened peduncle is surrounded and protected by a whorl or whorls of *involucral bracts* which encircle the base or the inflorescence (fig. 181). Capitula are not always recognizable, for in some plants they intergrade with spikes, racemes, and umbels. Although most capitula, like most umbels, are indeterminate inflorescences, their outermost flowers opening first, some capitula must be classed as determinate, since they are in fact compact cymes and their florets open in groups, as in *Scabious* spp.

It is essential to realize that inflorescences are not discrete, unrelated morphological entities but that one category grades into the other, and that in the course of evolution very similar groupings of flowers have been achieved by quite different developmental paths. Thus every indefinite inflorescence is but a modification of the raceme, so that a corymb is a raceme with unequal secondary axes; an umbel one whose primary axis is undeveloped; a spike one without secondary axes; and a capitulum a spike with the primary axis broadened and flattened. In certain species of plants the occurrence of capitulate, spiked, and umbelled flowers depends on environmental conditions during development.

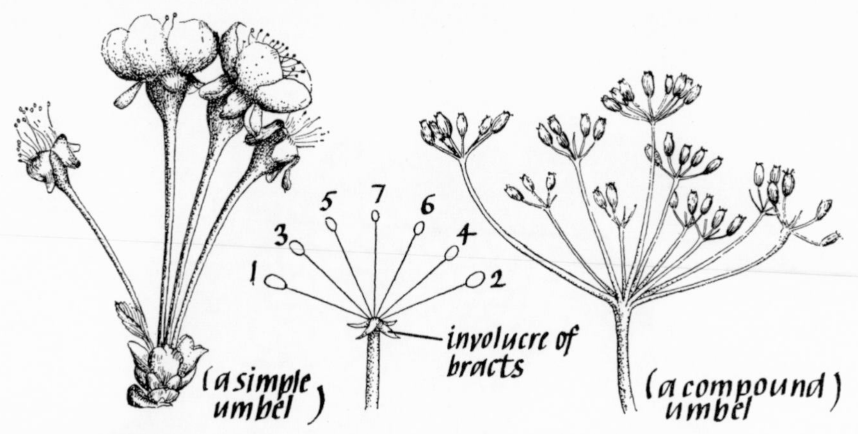

Figure 179 *Umbels*

(*left*) *A simple umbel of* Prunus cerasus.

(*right*) *A compound umbel of* Foeniculum vulgare.

(*centre*) *Diagram showing order of opening of flowers in an umbel.*

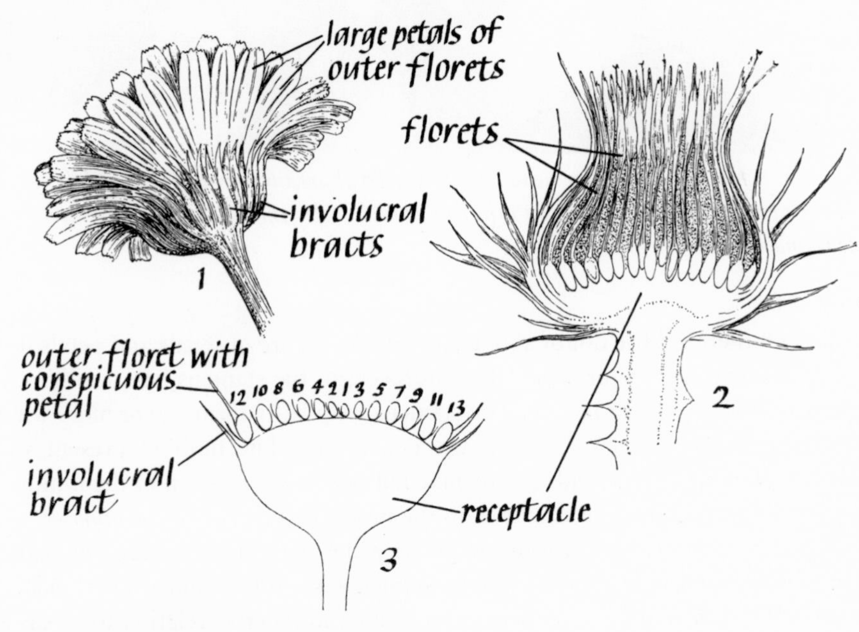

Figure 180 *Capitulums*

1 *of* Calendula *showing petals of outer florets and involucral bracts* (*after La Maout and Descaine*).

2 *Vertical section through a capitulum of* Onopordon *showing crowded florets borne on a flat receptacle.*

3 *Diagram showing order of opening of florets.*

Figure 181 *A fruiting sunflower head. Note the spiral arrangement of the seeds which have developed from florets borne on a flat receptacle; also the protective involucral bracts round the outside of the head.*

Androecium

Although there is little doubt about the leaf-like nature of sepals and petals it will become apparent that the organs of the androecium, the stamens, seem to have few features pointing to a foliar nature. The stamens frequently form one or more whorls, or spirals, between the perianth and the gynaecium. The number present varies greatly in different flowers, and may or may not bear some relation to the number of sepals and petals present. For example, in the meadow cranesbill (*Geranium pratense*) the five outer stamens are opposite the petals while the inner ones are opposite the sepals. Some flowers contain only a single stamen while others contain very many.

Careful examination of discrepancies in stamen number in relation to sepals and petals may reveal that one or more stamens have failed to develop properly. Very often their place is taken by sterile stamens or *staminodes*. In the storksbill (*Erodium cicutarium*) five staminodes occur opposite the petals and five fertile stamens opposite the sepals (fig. 182).

As in the case of sepals and petals, the stamens of certain flowers are all fused to one another to form a tube, as in the gorse (*Ulex europaeus*); in other flowers only some are joined together while others are free, as in the sweet pea (*Lathyrus odoratus*). There are also differences in the relationships of stamens to other floral parts in different flowers. Commonly they arise directly from the receptacle, but in the case of tubular corollas (hyacinth and daffodil) the *filaments*, the slender stalks of the stamens, often appear to arise from, and may be in certain cases almost completely fused with, the petals. Such stamens are described as *epipetalous*, meaning 'on the petals' (fig. 183).

The stamens themselves are remarkably constant in form, usually consisting of a slender stalk or *filament*, which in some plants may be very short, bearing at its apex an *anther*. The anther may be firmly attached at its base to the filament, or it may arise from the filament near its centre; it is thus able to swivel with a rocking motion as in liliaceous plants (fig. 184). Each anther when fully developed consists of two pairs of elongated sacs, *locules*, each pair being joined along their full length by a tissue called the *connective*. When mature the sacs, termed *pollen sacs*, are full of *pollen grains* (fig. 186).

In the initial stages of their formation in a developing flower, each stamen appears as a small, four-angled outgrowth from the receptacle. The differentiation of the stamens from these initials can best be followed by examining transverse sections of flower buds at various stages (fig. 185). At first they appear as trapezoids of un-

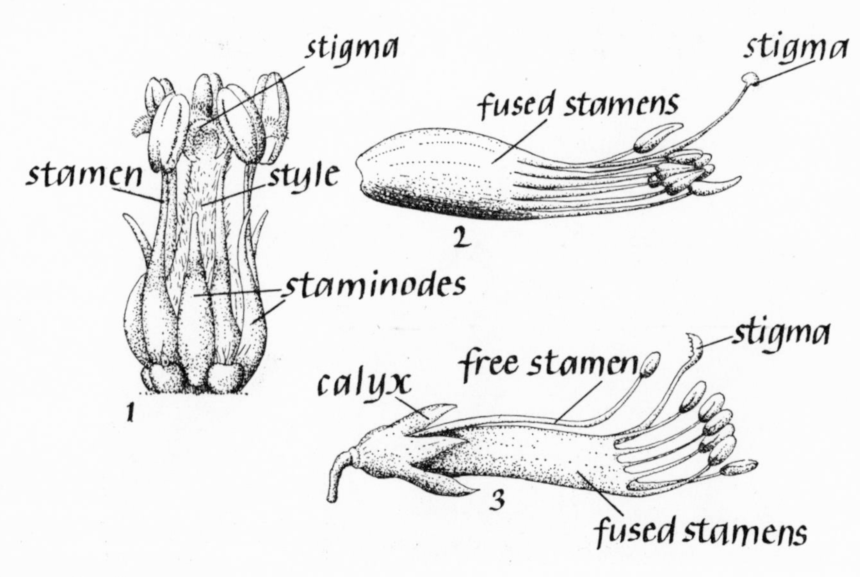

Figure 182 *Stamens*

1 *Stamens and staminodes of the flower of* Erodium cicutarium (*sepals and petals have been removed*) (*after S. Ross Craig*).

2 *Fused stamens of Ulex europaeus* (*after S. Ross Craig*).

3 *Fused and single free stamen of* Lathyrus odoratus.

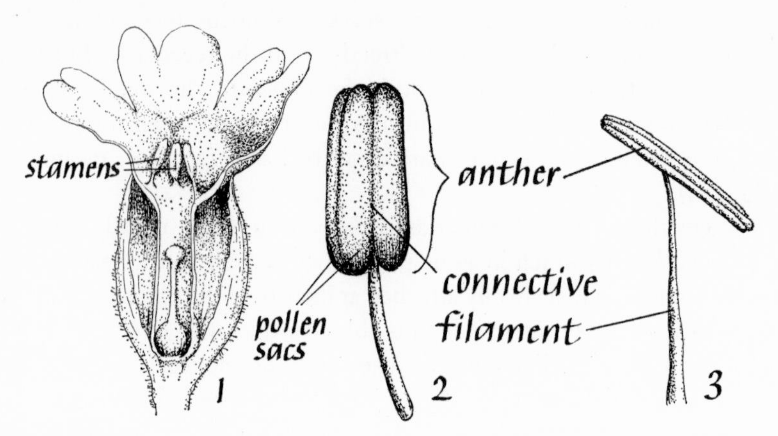

Figure 183 *Stamens*
1 *Epipetalous stamens of thrum-eyed flower of* Primula vulgaris.
2 *A generalized picture of a single stamen.*
3 *Rocking stamen of* Colchicum *sp.*

Figure 184 *Centrally pivotted, rocking anthers in the flower of the amaryllid* Crinum moorei. *The stigma and style can be seen to the left of the stamens.*

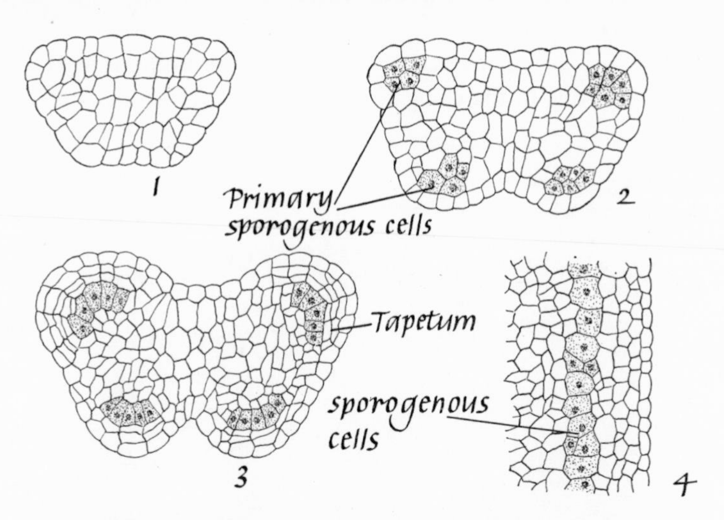

Figure 185 1-3 *Transverse sections of anthers at different stages in their development showing the sporogenous cells from which pollen grains are produced.*
4 *L.s. of an anther at a similar stage in development as* 3.

differentiated parenchyma bounded by an epidermis. Soon, however, each developing stamen shows a slight lobing of its outline, a change of shape which foreshadows the future pollen sacs. Towards the corners of each lobe, strips of one or two cells, extending as a narrow band almost down the entire length of the anther, become active. The nuclei of these previously undifferentiated parenchymatous cells become more prominent and their cytoplasm becomes more dense and granular. Each of these cells becomes meristematic and divides tangentially to give groups of inner cells, the *sporogenous cells*, surrounded by several layers of narrow, flattened cells which ultimately form the rather specialized wall cells of the pollen sacs. The four inner groups of cells form the actual pollen-producing tissue, the *pollen mother cells*, by repeated mitotic divisions.

Transverse sections through still later stages of the developing anther show the differentiation of a small strand of vascular tissue. This runs down the centre of the largely parenchymatous cells of the connective which lies between the two pairs of anther lobes. Each anther lobe can be seen in successively older sections to be more conspicuously divided into pollen sacs, almost circular in outline. The central cells of each, now the pollen mother cells, stand out quite distinctly because of their larger size, prominent nuclei, and dense protoplasmic contents. Surrounding each group of pollen mother cells is a layer of large, slightly vacuolated cells, elongated at right angles to the surface of the pollen sac. This, its innermost layer, is called the *tapetum* and is nutritive in function. The epidermal cells of the pollen sacs are relatively flat and tabular, while immediately beneath these there frequently occurs a layer of large cells packed with starch (fig. 186).

By the time these various regions have differentiated, the anther usually undergoes a fairly rapid extension, due to the elongation caused by the vacuolation of the cells

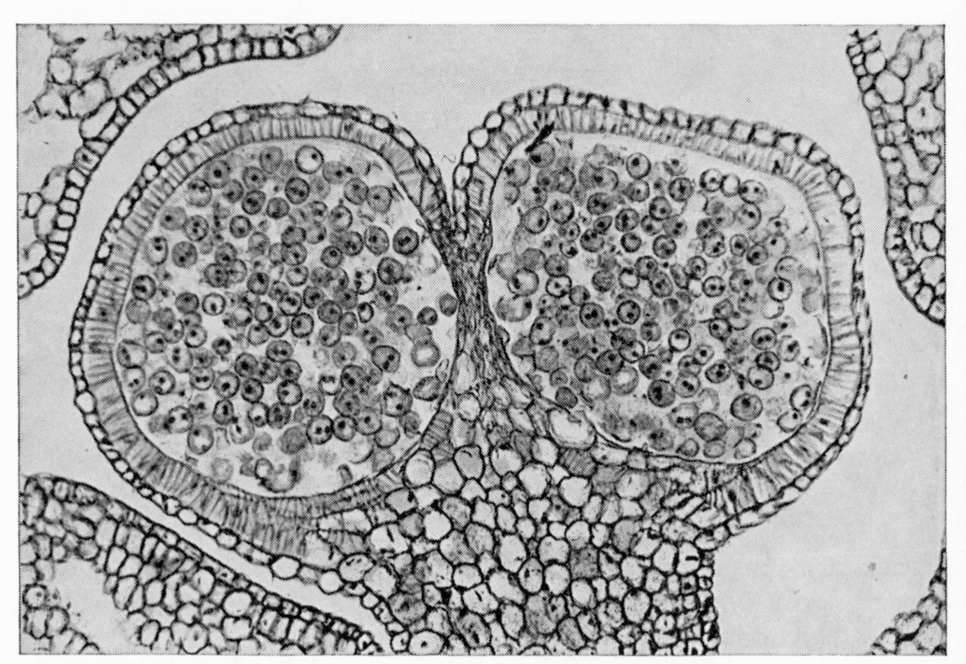

Figure 186 *T.s. of part of an anther of* Lilium *sp. Pollen grains with their vegetative and generative nuclei are enclosed within the two layered walls of the pollen sacs. The inner fibrous layer has characteristically thickened radial walls. The thinner lip cells or stomium can be seen between the two pollen sacs.*

forming the walls of the pollen sacs. As a result of this elongation, the pollen mother cells no longer fill the entire pollen sac but begin to round off as individual cells lying in a liquid medium. It is at this stage that the nuclei of these cells undergo meiosis (see p. 242), resulting in the production of four haploid nuclei each of which is surrounded by a wall so that a tetrad of pollen grains is formed. If an anther is crushed at this stage and the contents of the pollen sacs are smeared on a clean microscope slide and stained with *aceto-carmine*, or preferably *acetic orcein*, excellent preparations can be produced showing all stages of the meiotic divisions of the pollen mother cells and the subsequent formation of the pollen grains (fig. 164). This important division takes place at various times in different plants. In *Lilium* spp., from which excellent results can be obtained, meiosis occurs from May to July; in the spiderwort *Tradescantia virginiana* some flower buds will often be found in a suitable condition from June to early October; in many bulbous species such as tulips and *Fritillaria* spp. meiosis takes place while the developing flowers are still enclosed in the bulb between September and November.

While these changes have been taking place in pollen sacs, significant changes also occur in the pollen sac walls. First, the tapetum, and sometimes two or three layers of the wall beyond, disorganize, and their contents augment the nutritive liquid already within; this liquid is soon absorbed into the developing pollen. With the disorganization of the tapetum and inner wall layers, only three or four layers remain to form the pollen sac wall. The walls of the sub-epidermal layer become lignified by radial bars of a characteristic fibrous thickening, and in some cases these are connected by similar thickening on the inner tangential walls of the cells. During this transformation these cells, which constitute the *fibrous layer*, lose their living contents. Where the walls of adjacent pollen sacs meet there is a line of weakness marked by long rows of spindle-shaped cells, termed the *lip cells* or *stomium*, which are somewhat enlarged. At this stage the pollen sacs of each pair become confluent beneath the stomium owing to the breakdown of the partitions separating them. Also during this period the *pollen tetrads* begin to separate and the individual grains become two-walled; the outer wall grows considerably in thickness and develops a characteristic form, which differs in different species of plants. In insect-pollinated plants particularly, the outer walls of the grains may be ornamented with spines, ridges, or furrows, though the surface may be smooth, especially when the grains are normally disseminated by wind or water (fig. 199).

During the ripening of the pollen the wall layers of the pollen sacs lose water, either through environmental influences or through competition for water by adjoining tissues of higher osmotic pressure. In this way the cells of the fibrous layer begin to contract, but because of their thickening they can only shrink tangentially and therefore fold like the bellows of a camera. This folding exerts tensions on the stomium which eventually ruptures longitudinally so that gaping splits appear down each side of the anther; the pollen is now released. Under damp atmospheric conditions, which would be unfavourable for the dispersal of pollen, the pollen sacs may close by the swelling of the fibrous layer. Not all pollen sacs open in the manner described above, for some open or *dehisce* by means of apical pores and others by means of apical valves, which on bending back allow the pollen to escape.

Sometime before the anther dehisces and often before the flower opens, the single haploid nucleus within each pollen grain divides mitotically to give a large *vegetative*, or *tube cell*, and a smaller *generative cell*. The nucleus of the latter is surrounded by denser cytoplasm than the tube cell nucleus and it is this cell which ultimately gives rise to the male gametes (fig. 187 and 188).

Gynaecium

The basic units of the female reproductive part of the flower, the *carpels*, arise from the central region of the receptacle. Some morphologists have suggested that

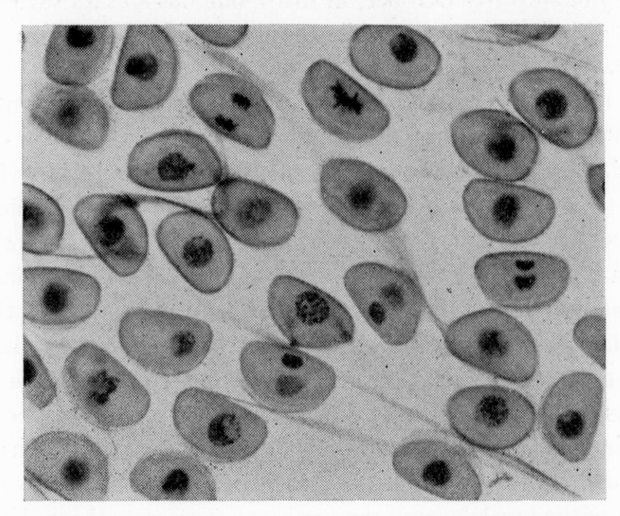

Figure 187 *Stages in pollen grain mitosis in* Tradescantia virginiana. *Prophase, metaphase, and telophase nuclei can be seen in addition to some grains in which the division into vegetative and generative cell is completed.* (*From a preparation by Dr A. F. Dyer.*)

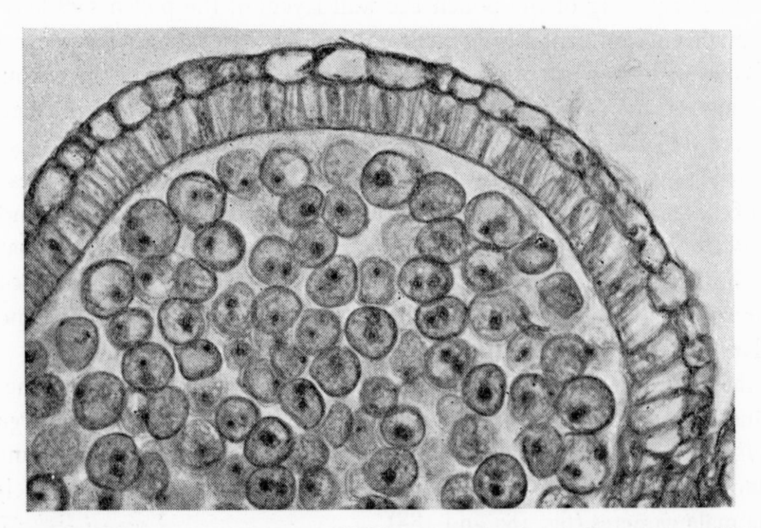

Figure 188 *T.s. of part of a pollen sac of* Lilium *sp. showing pollen grains which have undergone pollen grain mitosis. Note the fibrous layer with its thickened radial walls.*

Figure 189 (*left*) *Fertilized flower of* Helleborus orientalis *which has begun to produce seed showing enlarged carpels. The lateral veins can be clearly seen on the carpel walls. The outer edge of the carpel is the mid rib.*
(*right*) *One carpel of the same flower opened to show inside of ovary with its double row of developing ovules attached down its inner surface, the placenta.*

Figure 190 *Flower of* Helleborus orientalis *with two carpels cut transversely to show double row of ovules attached by placenta to the ovary wall.*

the carpel too is to be looked upon as a highly specialized leaf. Currently, however, it is believed to have evolved from a non-photosynthetic, leaf-like appendage rather than from a foliage leaf. The foliar nature of the carpel can be appreciated from the examination of the flower of *Helleborus* spp., especially if it has begun to produce seed (fig. 189). As in a leaf, a prominent midrib occurs down one side of the carpel from which lateral veins arise. Thus it is not difficult to envisage this as a leaf which has become inrolled and whose originally free edges have become joined to protect the *ovules*, which develop in two rows down the edges (fig. 190). The enclosed cavity within the carpel, with its typically enlarged basal region, is the *ovary*. The inner surface of the ovary to which the ovules are attached, usually the inrolled, united edges of the carpel, is termed the *placenta*. In a transverse section of some simple ovaries, the two rows of ovules occur so close together that they appear to be in a single row.

The free, upper end of a carpel terminates in a special receptive region, the *stigma*, which is very commonly borne on a considerably elongated, slender *style*. The stigma receives pollen set free from the ripe stamens and in consequence its surface may be grooved or furrowed or it may exude an adhesive fluid to facilitate the pollen's reception. In some carpels, however, the style is absent so that the stigma is sessile on the ovary (e.g. *Ranunculus* spp.).

Some families of plants, such as the Ranunculaceae and Rosaceae, have a gynaecium consisting of several, or many, individual carpels. These are described as *apocarpous* (fig. 189) and contrast with the *syncarpous* condition of very many flowers in which, as the ovary consists of two or more united carpels, the gynaecium appears as a compound structure (fig. 191).

The cavity containing the ovules within each ovary is termed a *locule*; hence those of apocarpous flowers are said to be *unilocular*. In most syncarpous ovaries it is usually possible to distinguish the same number of loculi as the carpel initials from which the ovaries developed, and so there are also *bi-* and *tri-locular* ovaries. In these, the walls separating each locule are the contiguous walls of the individual carpels. In some syncarpous ovaries, however, these separating walls do not develop, so that although they are derived from several carpel initials, they consist of only one locule. Moreover, they cannot be described as simple ovaries, as in larkspur. Unilocular ovaries are only simple if there is an apparently single row of ovules down the length of one of the inner walls.

The manner in which the ovules are borne on their placentae within the ovary, their *placentation*, differs considerably. The placentae occur on the supposedly inrolled, united margins of the ovary wall, and so in apocarpous ovaries the placentation is described as *parietal*, meaning 'against a wall'. In syncarpous ovaries, because of the way in which the carpels unite during their development, the placentae are commonly situated along the central axis of each locule. Such *axile* placentation is typical of the family Liliaceae, the members of which have trilocular ovaries derived from the fusion of three carpel initials (figs. 191 and 207.3).

In the flowers of the Primulaceae and Caryophyllaceae the ovules arise from a

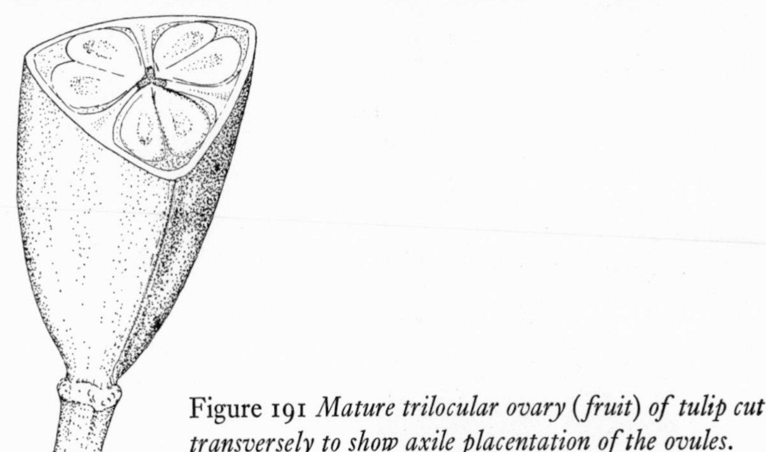

Figure 191 *Mature trilocular ovary (fruit) of tulip cut transversely to show axile placentation of the ovules.*

central axis which does not reach the roof of the ovary. Hence their placentation is described as *free central.* In some members of the latter family there is a combination of axile and free central placentation, for the ovaries may be basally 3-5 loculed, with the axile placentation in the lower third and the free-central placentation above.

The number of ovules within each ovary or its loculi varies considerably. In the Umbelliferae, for example, there is usually one in each locule, often suspended from its base or apex; while in the poppy family, Papaveraceae, many hundreds are produced in each. Even within the same family the numbers of ovules differ from species to species. Thus in the Ranunculaceae the apocarpous ovaries of the winter rose (*Helleborus niger*) contain numerous ovules borne parietally in two rows down the ventral suture of the ovary wall; in the meadow buttercup (*Ranunculus acris*) each unilocular ovary of the 30 or more free carpels contains a single basal ovule (fig. 207.2).

Position of the Ovary

The position of the ovary in relation to the other floral parts shows marked differences in various flowers, so that a considerable range of ovary types have been distinguished. These different types are, however, by no means discrete and as will be shown, one grades into the other.

The simplest condition, and what is considered to be the most primitive, is where there is a conical receptacle bearing either separate (*apocarpous*) ovaries over its surface or a *syncarpous* ovary as a terminal structure. The other floral parts thus are situated below the gynaecium and so are termed *hypogynous.* The buttercup (*Ranunculus*) and foxglove (*Digitalis purpuralis*) respectively provide excellent examples of *superior* apocarpous and syncarpous ovaries (fig. 192).

Some hypogynous flowers, for example *Viola*, have slightly concave receptacles

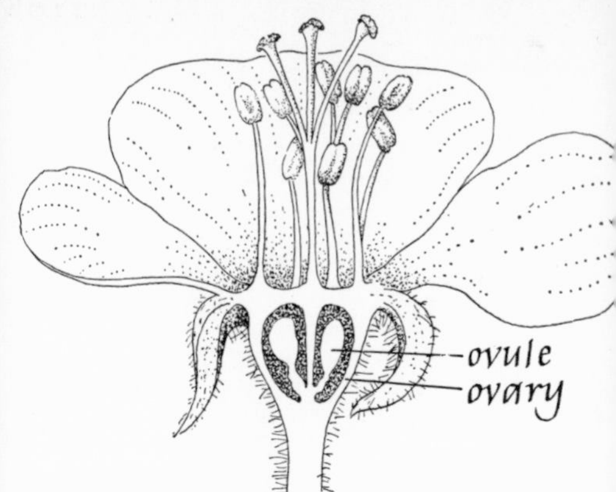

Figure 194 *L.s. of flower of* Malus *sp.*

Figure 192 *Ripening ovaries of flowers of* Digitalis purpurea *from which the petals and their attached stamens have fallen. These syncarpous ovaries occur above the other floral parts and consist of two fused carpels. The line of fusion is marked by the shadow down the right of the two ovaries on the left of the picture.*

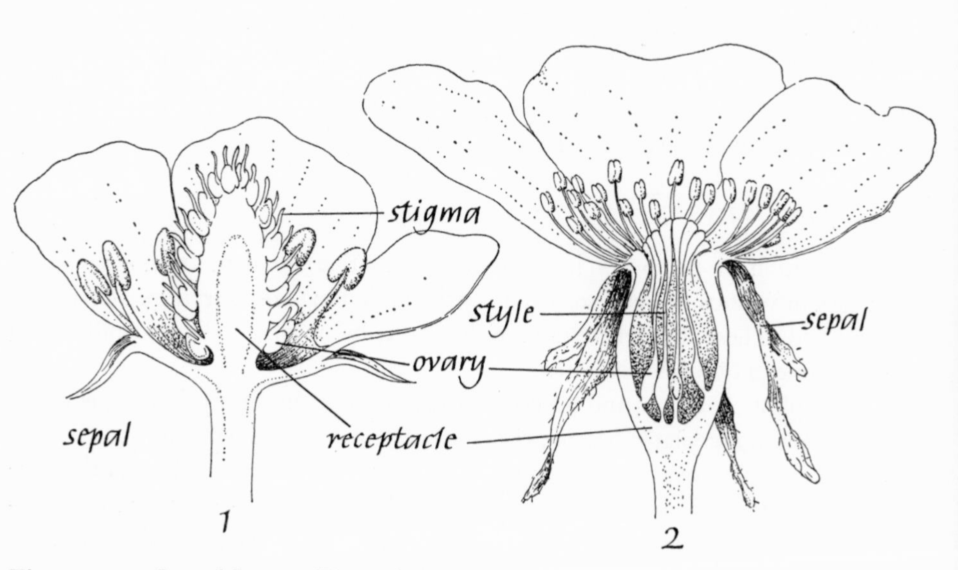

Figure 193 1 *L.s. of flower of* Fragaria *sp.*
2 *L.s. of flower of* Rosa *sp.*

with the result that the other floral members are inserted at a somewhat higher level than the ovary. Related to this condition is that found in flowers of the Rose family (Roseceae): during development, in addition to a concave receptacle, meristematic activity occurrs in the recepticular region situated between the bases of the stamens and the ovaries. This produces a so-called *perigynous zone* between these organs, the effect of which is to further increase the concavity of the receptacle and at the same time to separate the other floral parts from the gynaecium (fig. 193). Considerable differences in the width and concavity of this zone are apparent in different members of the family. For example, although the flowers of strawberry (*Fragaria*) and avens (*Geum*), as well as those of blackberry and raspberry (*Rubus* spp.), seem to be hypogynous, since the receptacle of each is a prominent cone bearing numerous carpels, they in fact exhibit a certain degree of perigyny. At a late stage in the development of these flowers, meristematic activity of the region of the receptacle between the outer ring of carpels and the stamens gives rise to a narrow flange of tissue, which pushes outwards the floral parts external to the gynaecium. More marked perigyny is apparent in flowers of the genus *Prunus* which includes the plum and cherry. The perigynous zone of these is distinctly cup-shaped and a single carpel, the young ovary of which is thereby afforded some extra protection, occurs in the base of the cup. Extreme perigyny is to be found in *Rosa* spp., where a very extensive perigynous zone forms a deep flask with a narrow neck, rather than a cup. Protruding through the neck are the styles of the carpels enclosed within (fig. 193).

If the ovaries are completely enveloped by tissues which are either perigynous or recepticular in origin, so that the other floral organs are situated above them, the flower is said to be epigynous and its gynaecium *inferior*. As with perigyny there is a wide range of conditions which may be described as *epigynous*. Moreover, it should be realized that they may also possess a perigynous zone (e.g. *Malus*), a feature which serves to deepen the cup formed by the receptacle, though it does not form part of the ovary. During an early stage in the development of epigynous flowers there is always a marked deepening of the recepticular cup. At the same time the bases of the carpels become much broader and in so doing often come to occupy a considerable area of the cup-wall. Eventually they may meet laterally and as a result almost fill the inside of the cup. The rapidly extending apical regions of the carpels give rise to the styles, and these may also fuse. They project above the rim of the cup and are surrounded by other floral parts (fig. 194).

Ovule

The first sign of the developing ovules on the placenta is as small projecting domes of thin-walled cells. Each enlarging mound of tissue, a *nucellus*, becomes surrounded early in its development by one or more, usually two, rings of tissue called *integuments*. When fully developed the latter almost completely envelop the nucellus except for a small apical pore, the *micropyle* (fig. 195).

All ovules initially grow erect, so that the micropyle is situated at the opposite

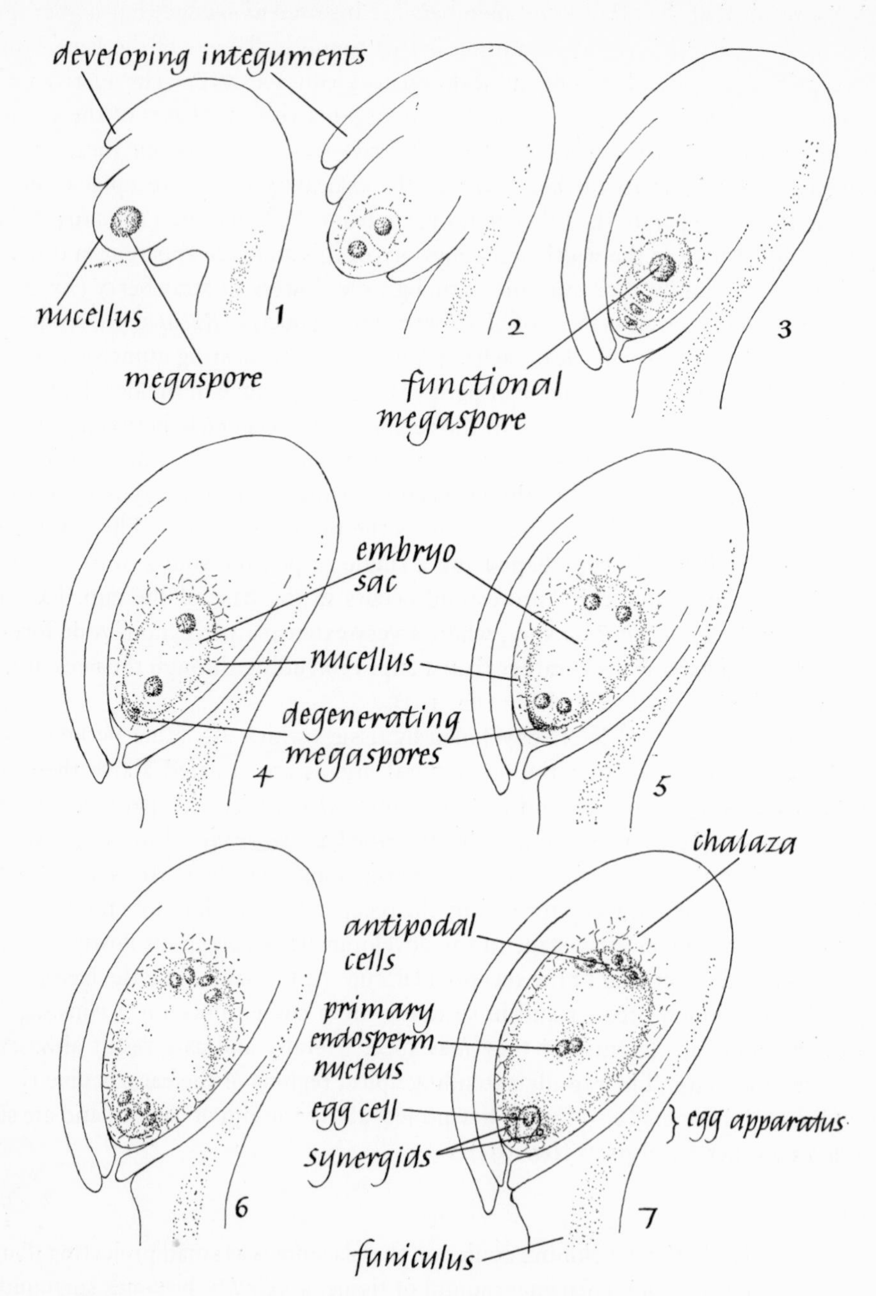

Figure 195 *Stages in the development of a typical anatropous angiosperm ovule.*

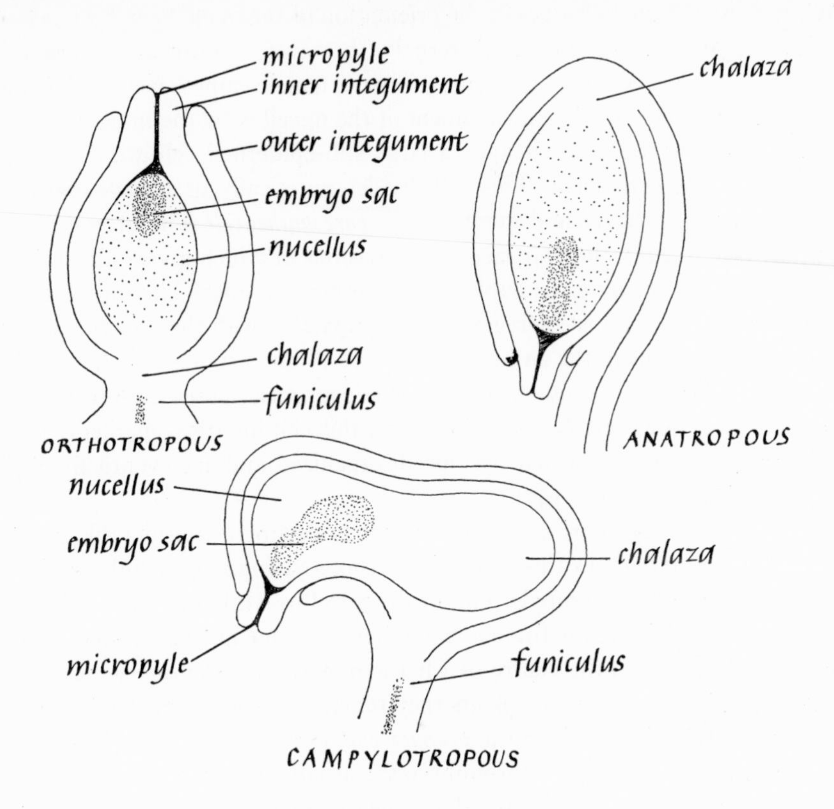

Figure 196 *Types of ovules*

end to the placental stalk or *funiculus*, and in *orthotropous* ovules this attitude is maintained throughout development. The majority of ovules, however, are *anatropous*, a condition produced by the one-sided growth of the basal region of the nucellus, the *chalaza*. This causes the main part of the body of the ovule to become bent down against the funicle so that the micropylar end points towards the placenta. In other flowers there is even greater asymmetry in ovule development, and the nucellus and integuments become so bent round that the micropyle is approximately at right angles to the funiculus. Ovules of this type, which are not uncommon, occurring for example in shepherd's purse, are termed *campylotropous*. Since curvature is initiated at a very early stage in the development of anatropous ovules so that the nucellus and funiculus lie side by side, the outer integument is often suppressed, or at best difficult to distinguish (fig. 196).

The funicle in each type of ovule is traversed by a vascular strand which enters from the placenta and extends to the chalazal region. This strand supplies the ovule with the food materials necessary for its development.

While these external changes in the orientation of the ovule have been occurring, the whole organ increases in size. Internally, however, a more important series of vital changes concerned with the formation of the female gamete begins to take place. Thus at an early stage in the envelopment of the nucellus by the integuments, there appears just below the nucellar apex a large sub-epidermal cell with a prominent nucleus and dense cytoplasm. This cell divides mitotically in a tangential plane to produce an outer *tapetal cell* and an inner *megaspore mother cell*. The latter then divides meiotically (see p. 244), the two successive divisions of which give a file of four cells each with nuclei containing the haploid chromosome number. The formation of this row of four *megaspores* must be regarded as comparable with the meiotic divisions of the pollen mother cells in the anthers into tetrads of microspores which later become pollen grains. Commonly only one of the file of four megaspores, however, functions as a gamete (see, however, *Lilium* below), and this cell increases markedly in size at the expense of its sisters, which become disorganized and are eventually absorbed during its development (fig. 197).

The surviving megaspore eventually comes to occupy a considerable part of the nucellus. It then undergoes three mitotic divisions giving rise to eight nuclei. Four of these migrate to the micropylar end of the nucellus while the other four move to the chalazal end adjoining the funicle. Soon, however, one nucleus from each of these groups of four moves to the centre of what is now termed the *embryo sac*, and here these *polar nuclei* meet. In some plants they remain as separate nuclei for some time but commonly they fuse to form the *primary endosperm nucleus*. The three nuclei remaining at the funicular end of the embryo sac usually become enclosed by cell walls and, as the *antipodal* cells, may later play some part in nourishing the developing embryo. The three nuclei remaining at the micropylar end constitute the *egg-apparatus*, consisting of a naked *egg cell* and two accessory cells or *synergidae* (fig. 195).

Although the above account of ovule development leading to the development of the embyo sac with its egg cell in a state ready to be fertilized by the male gamete from a pollen grain outlines the sequence of events in the majority of flowers, it is by no means universal. In fact three major developmental types, depending on the number of megaspore nuclei taking part in the formation of the embryo sac, have been recognized. The most common or 'normal' type, with only one nucleus involved has already been described. In the other two categories, two or four nuclei respectively may participate. In *Lilium* spp., which are often used to demonstrate embryo sac development, as well as other stages in reproduction because of their prominent nuclei and large chromosomes, four megaspores take part in embryo sac formation. It must also be pointed out that, especially in this latter category, there are considerable differences in the final appearance and arrangement of the cells and nuclei in the embryo sac (fig. 201).

Pollination

Before the male gamete, eventually produced within the ripe pollen grain, can fuse

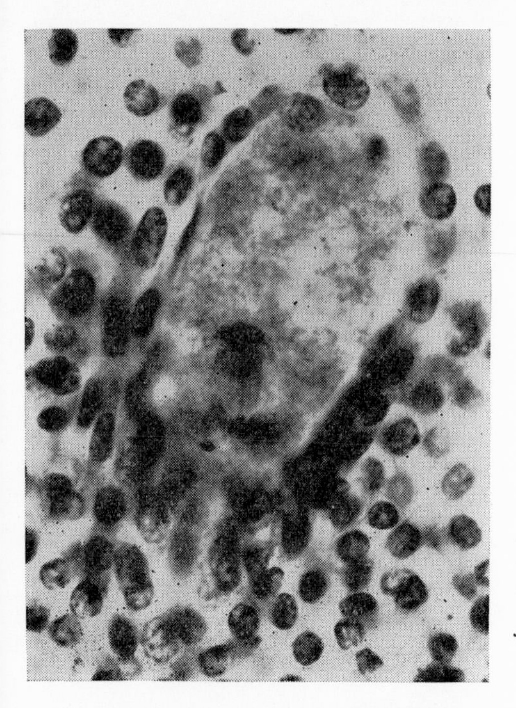

Figure 197 *Megaspore mother cell in l.s. of* Lilium *embryo sac undergoing its first division.*

with or fertilize the egg cell formed within the ovule, pollen must be transferred from the anther to the receptive stigma of the ovary. This is the process of *pollination*. Although pollen from the ripe anthers of a given flower may reach its own stigmas so that it is *self-pollinated*, it has been shown by experiments with many plants that usually a larger number of seeds which give rise to more vigorous offspring are produced if the pollen comes from the stamens of different individuals of the species. This ensures a mixing of the genetical material from separate individuals – the 'biological rationale' for sexual reproduction. Such *cross-pollination* may be brought about by various agencies but the most important are wind and insects. *Wind pollinated* plants commonly have numerous, exposed, inconspicuous flowers, as for example many grasses and trees, since the arrival of the pollen on the usually much branched or feathery stigmas, is largely a matter of chance. The dry pollen is usually produced in very considerable amounts. By contrast, *insect pollinated* flowers are usually very showy, with a compelling smell. They are visited by the insects for the pollen or sugary *nectar* which arises from a special tissue, or from hairs localized in *nectaries*. The most commonly occurring type of nectary is an entire or interrupted ring round the base of the ovary. The insect visitors obtain part or all of their food from the pollen, which is fatty and rich in protein; or from the nectar; or both. In many *entomophilous* (insect loved) flowers there are elaborate mechanisms which favour cross-pollination following such feeding visits by insects. Some of the most perfect of these are to be found in the zygomorphic flowers of the Leguminosae, Labiatae and Scrophulariaceae.

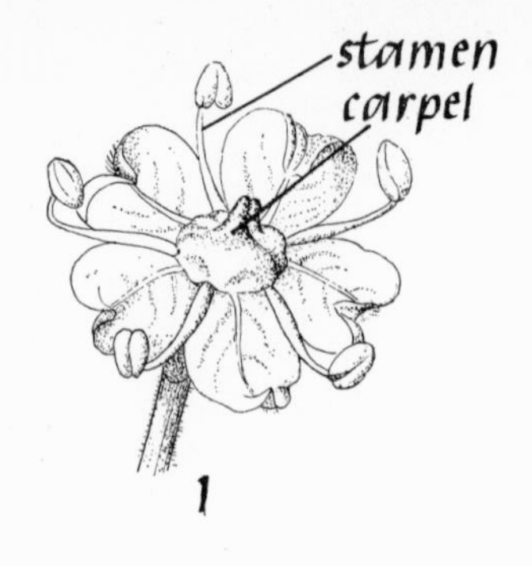

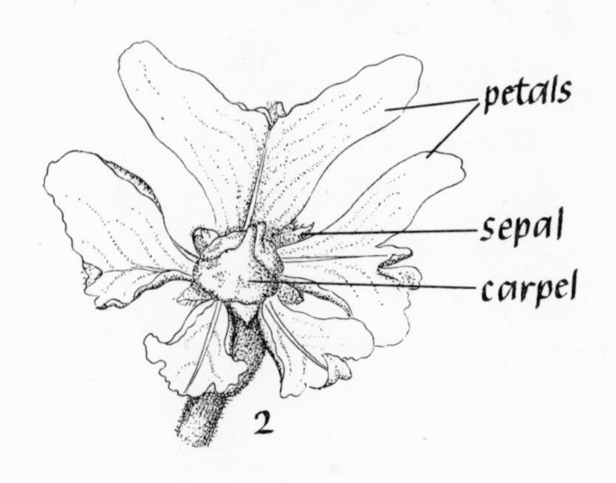

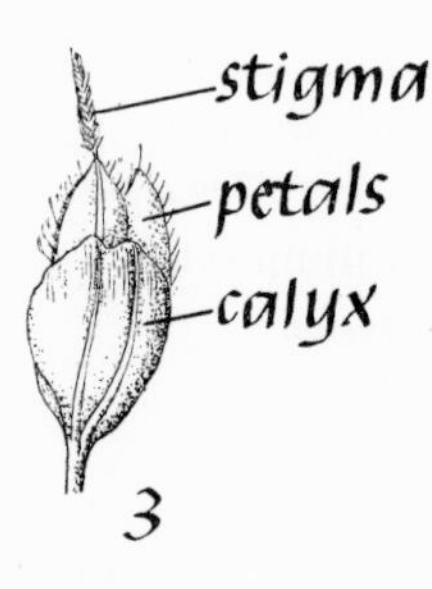

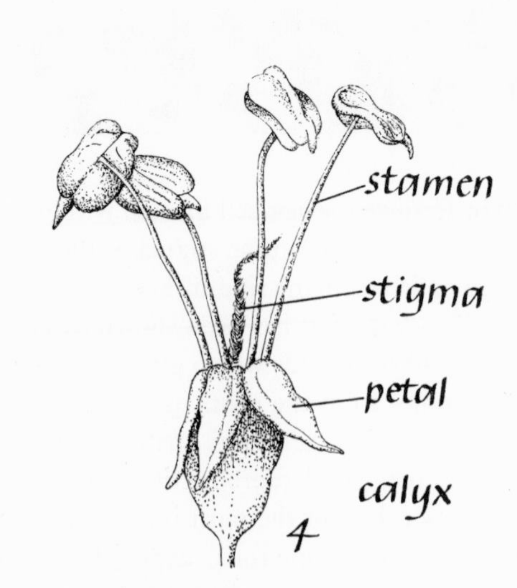

Figure 198 *Cross-pollination mechanisms*
1 *and* 2 *Protandry in* Heracleum sphondylium.
1 *Inner floret from inflorescence with mature stamens and immature carpels.*
2 *Outer flower from which stamens have been shed to prevent self-pollination* (*after S. Ross Craig*).
3 *and* 4 *Protogyny in* Plantago lanceolata.
3 *Flower of female stage with petals and stamens still enclosed in calyx.*
4 *Older flower in male stage with stamens fully developed* (*after Muller*).

Apart from possessing complex morphological adaptations, many flowers also show another mechanism ensuring cross-pollination. This is the separation in the time of maturation of the pollen and stigmas of a given plant. The most common type of this *dichogamy*, as it is termed, is *protandry*, in which the anthers mature before the stigmas. *Protogyny* is the reverse condition. In some flowers, such as the hogweed, *Heracleum sphondylium*, dichogamy is so pronounced that the stamens fall before the stigmas mature, though in many plants there is commonly a period of overlap during which both organs are mature so that self-pollination is also possible (fig. 198).

Not all insect-visited flowers are dichogamous, and instead self-pollination is impeded by the relative positions of anthers and stigmas. In dioecious plants, which have staminate and carpellate flowers on different individual plants, the possibility of self-pollination is completely excluded. In other plants, self-pollination is prevented by the phenomenon of *self-sterility* whereby pollen, even if it does reach a stigma of its own flower, fails to germinate; or if it does, it fails to develop properly and fertilization is never effected.

Some cross-pollinated plants may, however, be self-pollinated towards the close of their flowering season either by curvatures of the stamen filaments or of the styles, so that anthers and stigmas come into contact. In shepherd's purse, although insects may visit its small white flowers, self-pollination is automatic and inevitable, for of the six stamens the two outer ones are short and four inner ones long. The latter are in contact with the stigmas which are mature when the anthers are ripe so that there is no dichogamy. Another class of self-pollinated flowers are those which do not open at all. Thus sweet violet (*Viola odorata*), wood sorrel (*Oxalis acetosella*) and sundews (*Drosera* spp.) produce these closed or *cleistogamous* flowers in addition to those opening normally. Their corollas are usually very poorly developed and their anthers do not dehisce, but instead the pollen grains germinate inside, the pollen tubes eventually growing through the anther wall to reach the stigma.

On reaching a mature stigma, which in many flowers is specially modified to receive it, the pollen germinates. Germination is thought to be induced by the sugar-containing solution secreted from the stigma, though other substances may also be involved. Indeed, in certain species the stigma is believed to have a specific controlling influence on *pollen germination*. Thus while the pollen from some plants can be readily induced to germinate in a sugar solution of the appropriate strength, in others, germination can only be effected by adding crushed stigmas to the solution. The time taken for germination varies considerably in different plants and may be only a few minutes or as long as several days (fig. 199).

As in the germination of a seed, the initial step in pollen germination would seem to be the absorption of water from the stigma, an event which is soon followed by the protrusion of the inner wall of the grain, the *intine*, through one of the germ pores of the thick, outer *extine*. The resulting, narrow *pollen tube* continues to elongate and soon penetrates the tissues of the stigma. The pollen tube grows rapidly and travels either down the moist inner wall of the style if the latter is hollow, as in *Viola* spp.,

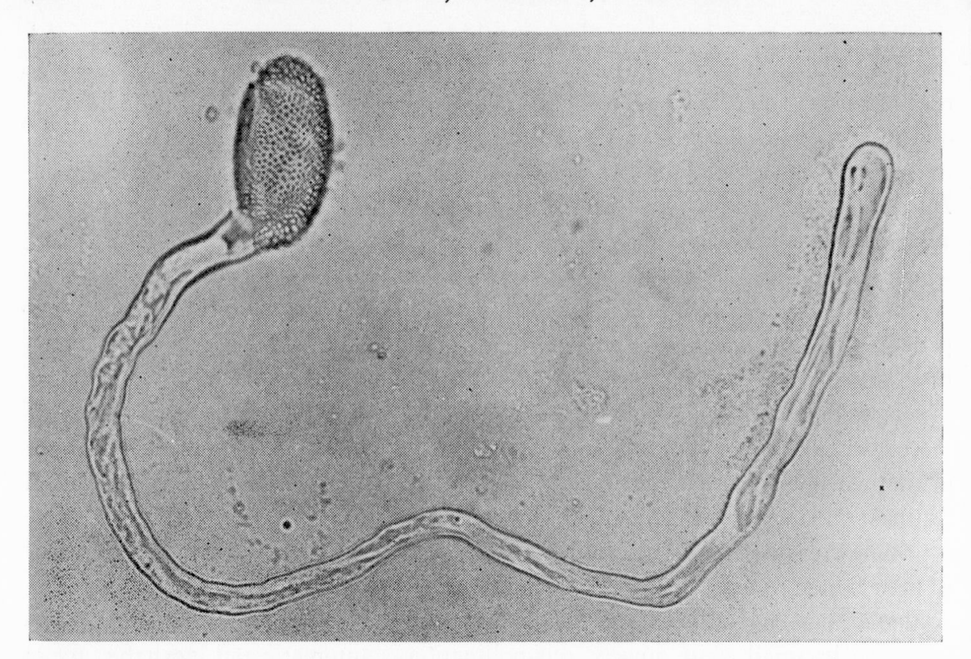

Figure 199 *Pollen grain of* Tradescantia virginiana *germinated on a glass slide covered with agar containing a 5% sucrose solution. The pollen tube has grown to this length in less than two hours. Note the granular contents of the tube and the sculptured wall of the pollen grain.*

or down a canal filled with mucilage, as in *Rhododendron*. Commonly, however, the style is a solid core of tissue. The pollen tube then penetrates the intercellular spaces between its cells. This is facilitated by the secretion of appropriate enzymes.

Gamete Formation in Pollen

Sometimes before its germination, but more commonly at an early stage after, the nucleus of the generative cell of the pollen grain divides mitotically to form two male gametes. These gametes, which are cells and not merely nuclei since they are always surrounded by a thin layer of cytoplasm, progress down the tip of the pollen tube as it grows, together with the vegetative nucleus. The latter was at one time believed to play some part in controlling the growth of the pollen tube, but this now seems open to doubt since there is considerable evidence that it soon degenerates. Thus as the pollen tube approaches the ovary, only the two male gametes are present (fig. 200).

On reaching the ovary, the pollen tube either continues its growth towards the ovule between the cells of the ovary wall or it enters the loculus and grows down the inner surface of the wall. On reaching the ovule the pollen tube usually enters through the micropyle (*porogamy*), though in some instances entry is by way of the chalaza (*chalazogamy*). The cells of the micropylar canal are stated, at least in some cases, to

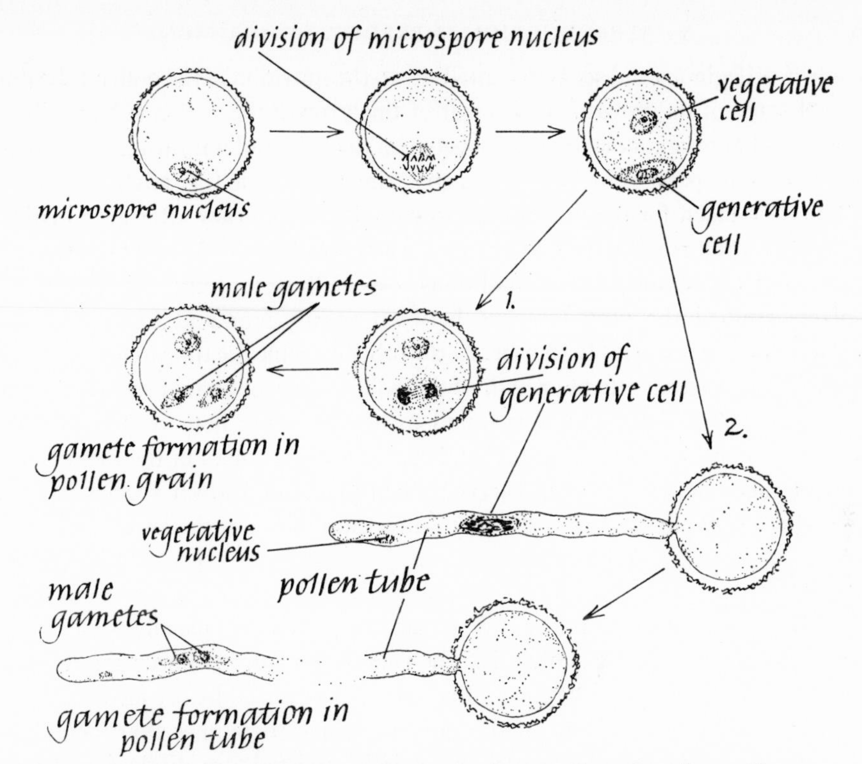

Figure 200 *The development of the male gametophyte in flowering plants. Gamete formation in the pollen grain* (1) *and in the pollen tube* (2) *are illustrated.*

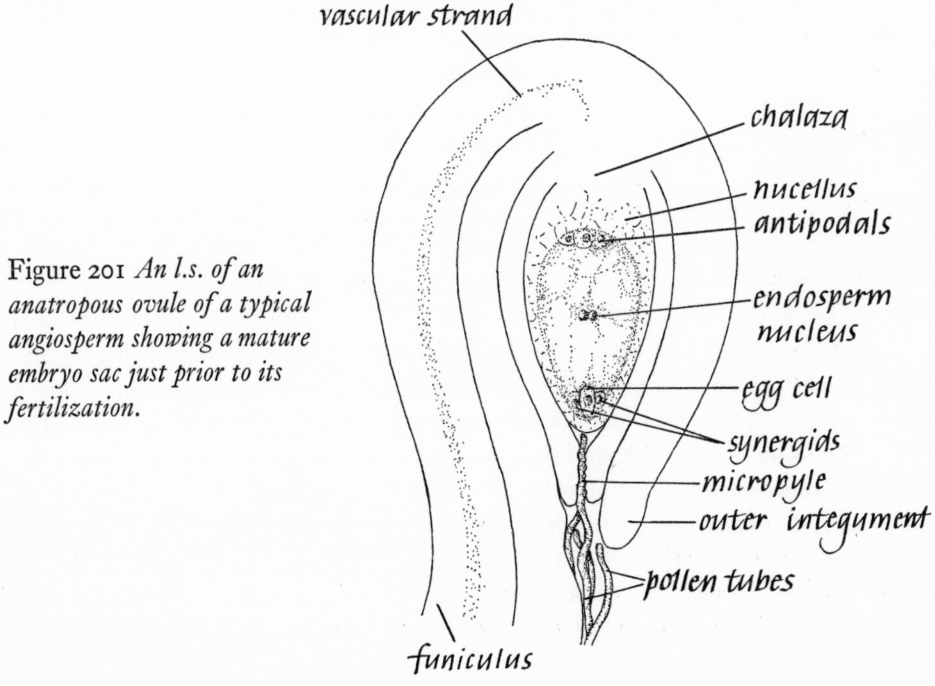

Figure 201 *An l.s. of an anatropous ovule of a typical angiosperm showing a mature embryo sac just prior to its fertilization.*

become mucilaginous and seem to contribute to the nutrition of the pollen tube during the final stage of its growth. As a result of this growth the pollen tube reaches the nucellus and here again makes its way between the cells and not through them on the final phase of its passage to its ultimate goal, the embryo sac (fig. 201).

The time taken for the pollen tube to complete its journey after germinating on the stigma until it reaches the embryo sac varies considerably. Although it depends to some extent on environmental conditions, especially temperature, in the majority of plants studied the period ranges between twenty-four and forty-eight hours, though it can be considerably shorter. At the other extreme the time must be measured in months. The actual rate of growth of the pollen tubes of certain species have been measured. In *Iris versicolor* it was found to be 4 mm per hour compared with 35 mm per hour in *Taraxacum kok-saghys*. Significant differences in the rate of growth of pollen tubes have also been observed when plants of a given species have been self- and cross-pollinated, growth being much more rapid in the latter case.

Fertilization

On penetrating the wall of the embryo sac, the pollen tube usually passes between the egg cell and one of the synergids. The role of the latter is uncertain and indeed they may have no specific function and become disorganized before fertilization takes place. Once within the embryo sac the gametes, which sometimes alter their shape at this stage becoming spindle-shaped and spirally twisted, are discharged from the pollen tube. The latter may bifurcate at its end. One of these gametes effects fertilization by fusing with the haploid egg nucleus. The other fuses with the already diploid primary endosperm nucleus, which hereafter possesses three sets of the basic complement of chromosomes and thus is triploid. This latter fusion may be completed simultaneously or in certain cases some time before *syngamy*, as the fusion of the gametes is termed, is accomplished (fig. 202).

The diploid cell resulting from this fertilization of the egg by the male gamete is termed a zygote. The subsequent development of the ovule and of this zygote contained within leads to the formation respectively of the seed and its embryo.

Endosperm Development

The triploid endosperm nucleus eventually gives rise to the nutritive endosperm tissues within which food reserves are stored for later use by the developing embryo. Divisions of the endosperm nucleus, which initiate the formation of this nutritive tissue, almost always precede those of the fertilized egg nucleus, the zygote, in the formation of the embryo. This triploid nucleus divides repeatedly so that the embryo-sac contains numerous free nuclei usually distributed uniformly throughout its mass, or in some plants round its periphery (fig. 203). Later, these nuclei become separated from one another by cell walls and subsequent divisions are accompanied by cytokinesis. Usually the resulting cells are isodiametric and contain large amounts of food materials, which may be starchy, fatty or proteinaceous in proportions which vary in

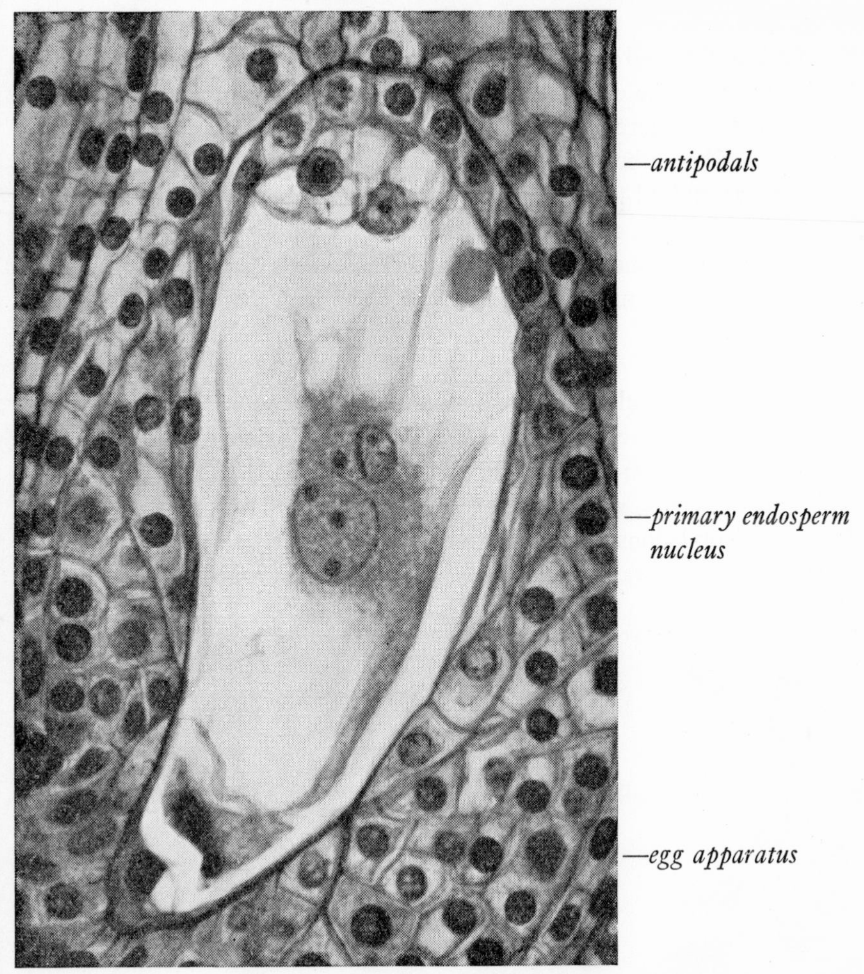

Figure 202 *L.s. of the mature embryo-sac of* Tradescantia virginiana *at fertilization. The pollen tube has entered the embryo sac and one of the gametes will fuse with the egg. The other has travelled to the central diploid endosperm nucleus with which it will also fuse.*

different species. Commonly their cell walls are thin and without pits, but when, as in some plants, hemicellulose (see p. 195) is the principal food reserve they are often greatly thickened, pitted, and show distinctive stratification.

The food reserves in the endosperm may gradually pass into the embryo as the developing seed matures. Here it is stored in the cotyledons as for example in the non-endospermic seeds of broad bean and castor oil (see Chapter 1, p. 3). In endospermic seeds, such as maize and all grasses and cereals, the endosperm persists as a food-storage tissue utilized on the germination of the seed.

As a result of its development the endosperm in most seeds displaces the nucellus, though in some a small amount persists as *perisperm* in which some food is stored.

Embryo Development

After fertilization the resulting zygote does not divide for some time, though it is not inactive, for it undergoes certain changes, especially in the extent of its vacuolation. The length of this period varies under different environmental conditions, but the initial division rarely occurs, as stated above, before that of the primary endosperm nucleus. In most Dicotyledons this first zygote division is nearly always accompanied by the formation of a cross wall. The two cells so formed are termed respectively the

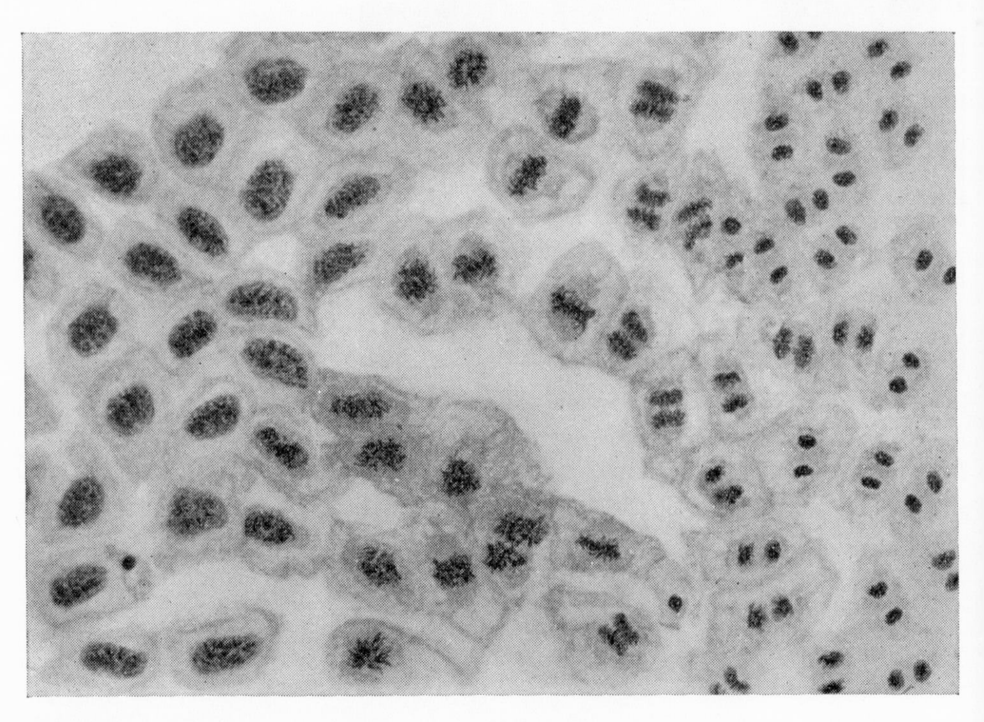

Figure 203 *Stages in mitosis of the triploid endosperm nuclei of* Trillium. *Nuclei in prophase to telophase can be seen from left to right of the picture* (*from a preparation by Dr A. F. Dyer*).

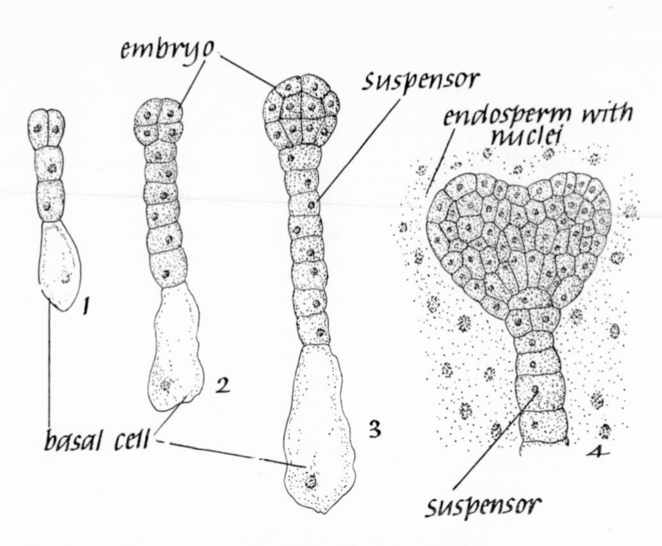

Figure 204 *Embryo development in* Capsella bursa-pastoris.

basal cell, which lies towards the micropylar end of the embryo sac, and the *terminal cell* to the inside. In general the basal cell gives rise to the *suspensor* of the embryo, which attaches the latter in the embryo sac and through which it probably absorbs food. Subsequent divisions of the terminal cell give rise to the embryo proper (fig. 204).

The terminal cell first divides longitudinally, the basal cell transversely, so that a 4-celled *pro-embryo* is produced. The two upper cells of this pro-embryo, derived from the basal cell, then divide to give a row of 6 to 10 suspensor cells, the outermost of which becomes markedly swollen and probably has some absorptive function. While the suspensor has been developing, the two terminal cells become divided by vertical walls at right angles to the wall laid down at the first division of the terminal cell. This results in the formation of a *quadrant stage*, the cells of which are later divided by transverse walls forming a group of eight cells. The lower four cells of this *octant* are destined to become the cotyledons and plumule, the upper four the hypocotyl.

Periclinal divisions of each of these eight cells produce a sphere of sixteen cells, the embryo proper, consisting of eight central cells surrounded by eight peripheral cells. The latter by subsequent division give rise to the epidermis, while the inner group of eight eventually become the cortical and vascular tissues of the future adult plant.

The lowest cell of the row of suspensor cells gives rise to the initials which eventually form the radicle of the embryo, the tip of which is directed towards the micropyle. Many further divisions take place in the embryo, especially at the two points in the lower tier of cells which eventually form the cotyledons. The extent to which the embryo develops within the seed before the latter is shed varies in different plants.

In some it proceeds so that the cotyledons, with the plumule between them, the hypocotyl and the radicle are clearly distinguishable. In others development does not proceed far beyond the pro-embryo stage and is completed away from the parent plant before the seed germinates.

In Monocotyledons, the pattern of embryo development is not fundamentally different from that described above for a typical Dicotyledon. Generally, however, the suspensor is a more bulky structure and the single cotyledon occupies a terminal position with the plumule arising from one side of it.

CHAPTER 24

SEEDS AND FRUITS

Seeds and their Developments

Fertilization not only sets in motion the developmental changes in the zygote which result in the formation of endosperm and the embryo within the ovule. Its effects also become apparent in other parts of the flower and these lead ultimately to the formation of *seeds* and *fruit*.

The formation of the seed is intimately connected with the development of the embryo, and as the latter grows within the embryo sac the integuments surrounding the ovule keep pace with its enlargement. When it has ceased increasing in size, the ovule begins to lose water and the outer integument especially forms a mechanically resistant and impervious layer of cells, the seed coat or *testa*. While the inner integument commonly dries out and persists as a thin, papery layer, the outer integument may undergo profound structural alteration from the several layers of thin-walled cells of which it was originally formed. The considerable range of form of the mature *seed coat* of different plants depends on the mode of development and differentiation of these cells.

The most familiar seeds are those with dry coats, usually hard and leathery. These are formed by the lignification of the walls of some of the layers of integument cells which at the same time become variously coloured and impermeable to water. These hard, resistant coats afford protection from dessication, mechanical injury and in some cases from the digestive juices of animals which may consume as food the fruits in which the seeds are contained. The impervious testa also prevents germination from taking place too soon, so that the essential internal changes which must take place during a seed's obligatory dormancy can be completed (see Chapter 1). In some seeds the epidermal cells of the outer integument elongate into hairs, papillae, hooks or even wings, which are structures associated with their *dispersal*. In other seeds, the epidermal cell walls are hygroscopic and thus become mucilaginous when they come into contact with moisture.

Wholly external to the integuments proper, though in some cases being rather like a third integument, there occurs in certain seeds an investment or *aril* which arises usually from the funicle, or from the placenta when no obvious seed stalk is present. This investment may develop, as in *Asphodelus*, before fertilization of the egg cell within the ovule, but more commonly the appearance of an aril is associated with other post-fertilization developments. The mature arillar envelope may not cover the seed completely and may consist only of a ring of tissue round the funicle. In other cases it may almost completely envelop the seed. It may be fleshy and brightly coloured, dry and somewhat wrinkled as in the so-called *mace* of nutmeg; or as in the willow it may bear a tuft of well developed hairs which completely envelop the seed. The white water-lily, *Nymphaea alba*, has an aril consisting of a thin, cellular bag containing many air bubbles. These enable the seed to float and assist in its dispersal (fig. 205).

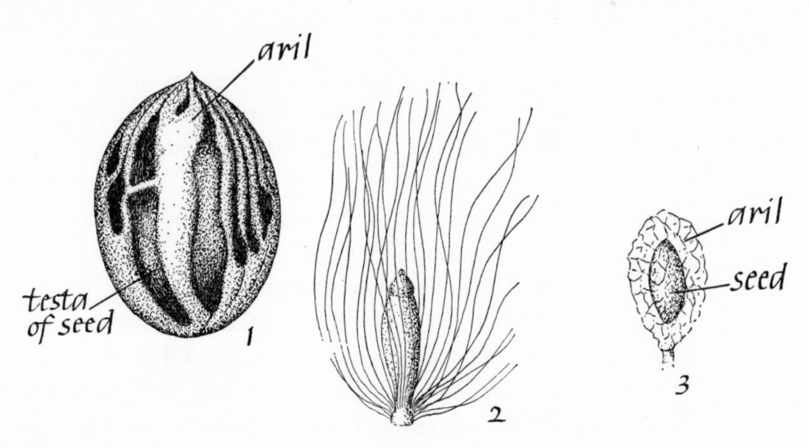

Figure 205 *Arils*

1 *Aril surrounding seed of nutmeg* Myristica fragrans (*after Wettstein*).
2 *Arillar hairs of the willow*, Salix pentandra.
3 *Bag-like aril of* Nymphaea alba.

Of different origin to the funicular arils are those which develop at the micropylar end of the seed. Such arils are termed *caruncles* (see p. 11) and they arise by proliferation of the integumentary cells in the region of the micropyle, thereby obliterating this pore. Commonly caruncles are simply small, warty outgrowths as in the castor oil seed (see fig. 4), though in some seeds, as in *Careye arborea*, this proliferation assumes the form of a backwardly directed process looking, in the later stages of its development, like a funicular aril.

Arils and caruncles, especially when hairy or wing-like, usually play some part in seed distribution, though in certain plants they may help in the opening of the fruit and so assist in the liberation of the seed.

When most of the developmental changes have taken place in the fertilized ovule, the vascular strand in the funicle, which has been supplying it with food material from the parent plant, becomes severed and the seed separates from the placenta. At the point of separation a scar becomes apparent on the seed coat, the *hilum*. In seeds derived from anatropous ovules, in which the ovule is bent over so that it lies against the funicle, the hilum is adjacent to the micropyle, whereas in orthotropous types these two features of the testa occur at opposite ends of the seed. Also in anatropous seeds, there is commonly a ridge, the *raphe*, on the testa marking the region where the tissues of the funicle were continued onto the integument of the ovule.

A seed at maturity thus consists, in brief, of an embryo, with or without endosperm, surrounded by a papery inner integument and a protective testa externally. The latter may be variously coloured and ornamented and may itself be more or less invested in an aril of one sort or another. On the testa wall the relationships of hilum, micropyle, and raphe if it occurs, can be referred back to the type of ovule from which the seed was derived.

Fruits and their Development

In addition to the changes in the ovule which lead to the formation of the seed, other parts of the flower, especially the ovary, enter a new phase of development after fertilization (fig. 206). The result is a structure exclusive to flowering plants, the fruit. After fertilization, the ovary enclosing the ovule becomes the fruit enclosing the seed. The biological significance of fruits is that they afford greater protection, and possibly improved nutrition, to the maturing seed, while later they provide some specialized means of dispersal for the seed.

Although the simplest fruits are derived from the ovary alone, many include in their structure parts derived from the style, the receptacle, parts of the perianth, the pedicel and peduncle, or even bracts and bracteoles. Thus a fruit may be defined as a structure developed from a flower, usually after it has been fertilized. It consists of one or more mature ovaries, together with any accessory structures derived from other floral parts, and is concerned with the protection and commonly the later dispersal of the seeds contained within it.

Fruit formation may occur in some instances without the stimulus of fertilization and without the accompanying development of seeds. This *parthenocarpy* (meaning 'virgin fruiting') is normal in several plants of economic value, such as bananas, some oranges, and seedless grapes. Moreover, parthenocarpy can be artificially induced by the application of growth substances (see p. 48) to the stigmas or even the ovary walls of unfertilized flowers. By such treatment seedless tomatoes, cucumbers, and other edible fruits have been produced in recent years.

The enormous diversity in the structure of flowers is associated with a comparable diversity of fruit form. This is in part a reflection of the fact that fruit development is not restricted to the ovary but commonly involves other floral members, and in part that a fruit may develop from one carpel or from the aggregation of carpels into compound structures. The latter may be derived from one flower, in which case the fruit is termed an *aggregate fruit*, or from several flowers, when it is termed a *multiple fruit*.

Because of the complexity and diversity of fruit form it is difficult to classify fruits satisfactorily, but one of the most rational approaches is that which conceives the fruit as the product of the entire gynaecium and of any associated floral parts. In this the basic distinction between fruit types is determined by whether the original flower was apocarpous or syncarpous.

Figure 206 *Flowers of* Helleborus orientalis *showing the considerable enlargement of the carpels of the lower flower following fertilization. The upper flower has not been fertilized.*

In *apocarpous fruits* a single carpel may be involved, as in the *legume* of the pea or the *ear* of oats; or there may be many separate carpels each of which is considered to be an individual fruit, as in *Ranunculus acris* or *Helleborus* spp. These examples are all derived from the superior ovaries of hypogynous flowers and so are termed *aggregate free fruits*. Other apocarpous fruits, termed *aggregate cup fruits*, are derived from perigynous flowers, a common example being the hip of the rose.

In *syncarpous fruits*, the carpels are consolidated or united into a single body. This category, like the apocarpous fruits, can be sub-divided into *united free fruits*, derived from a syncarpous, hypogynous flower, as for example in the tulip (fig. 207), and *united cup fruits*, derived from a syncarpous, epigynous flower, as in *Cornus*.

Coupled with these fundamental differences in the form of the gynaecium, which determines the basic structure of the fruit, are further striking differences in form caused by the mode of differentiation of the fruit wall or *pericarp*. This usually consists of three more or less distinct regions, an outer *exocarp*, a middle *mesocarp* and inner *endocarp*. Depending on the nature of the pericarp at maturity, two structural types of fruit walls are recognized. These are the sclerenchymatous walls of *dry fruits* and the parenchymatous walls of *fleshy* or *succulent fruits*.

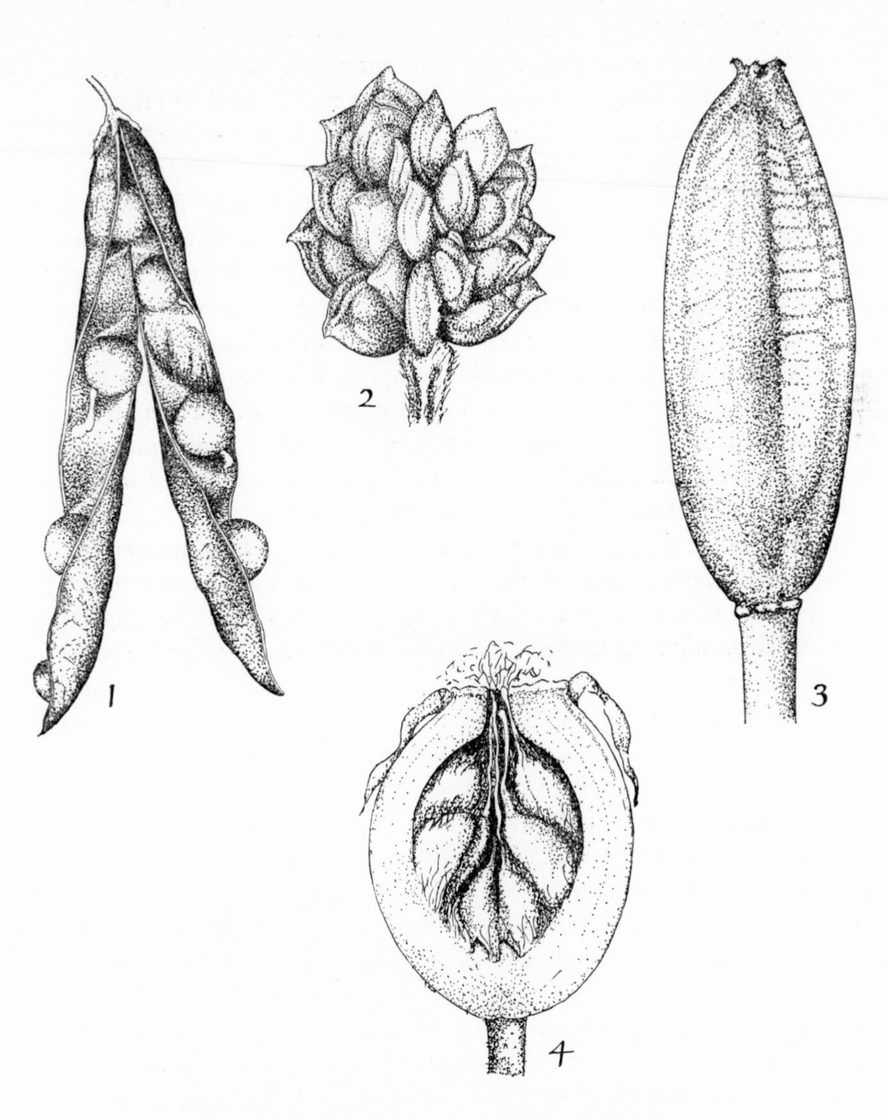

Figure 207 1 *Legume of pea.* 2 *Achenes of buttercup.* 3 *Trilocular capsule of tulip.* 4 *Hip of rose.*

Dry fruits may be *dehiscent* or *indehiscent* depending on whether or not the fruit wall splits open at maturity. Dry dehiscent fruits usually contain numerous seeds and may be derived from single, unfused carpels (apocarpous), as in the *legumes* of the pea family and the *follicles* of *Delphinium*, or from several united carpels (syncarpous) as, for example, the trilocular *capsules* of *Iris*. Follicles are distinguished from legumes in that their dehiscence is along the cohering edges of the carpellary leaf, the *ventral suture line*, where there is no vascular bundle. In legumes, dehiscence occurs along both the ventral suture line and median bundle of the carpel, often with explosive violence accompanied by a spiral twisting of the original carpel walls (fig. 207).

The dehiscence of capsules may be longitudinal and occurs either along the line where the carpels are united so that, as in *Convolvulus*, they separate into individual carpels, or, as in *Iris*, separation is down the middle of the bundle of each locule. In some capsules, for example the bladder campion, *Silene inflata*, this longitudinal rupture extends for only a short way down the ovary wall, and in other fruits such as the poppy, the zone of dehiscence is even more localized and only small pores occur at the distal ends of the fruits. The minute seeds within are liberated when the wind is sufficiently strong to shake them out (fig. 208).

The fruit wall of dry indehiscent fruits usually develops from an ovary containing only one ovule. The special feature of these fruits is that the pericarp usually resembles a seed coat in its appearance and structure, and in many cases the actual seed coat acquires no thickening but becomes more or less obliterated during the course of the fruit's development. Moreover, the successful dispersal of these fruits automatically brings about the dispersal of their seeds. If in such fruits the seed is attached to the pericarp only at one point, the fruit is termed an *achene*. Achenes derived from hypogynous flowers occur in the Ranunculaceae (fig. 207). Noteworthy are the achenes of *Clematis* which has a long, hairy, persistent style which assists the dispersal by wind of these fruits. The bicarpellate fruits of the Compositae are also termed achenes, but these are derived from flowers with inferior ovaries so that the pericarp is confluent with the floral tube. Other dry, indehiscent, one-seeded fruits are the wind-dispersed *samaras* of ash or elm, and the double samara of sycamore in which the pericarp develops as a wing (fig. 209).

When the pericarp and testa are adherent, the fruit is termed a grain or *caryopsis* such as occurs in the majority of the grasses and cereals, the Gramineae.

Fleshy fruits are also derived from various types of gynaecia, though accessory parts of the flower may also be involved. They exhibit a great variety of both external form and internal structure, the latter in particular being related to differences in the manner and extent of differentiation of the various layers of the pericarp. In some fleshy fruits even the placentae and the partition walls separating the locules of syncarpous ovaries may become fleshy in addition to the ovary wall. These fleshy fruits may be one-seeded, as in the plum or cherry, and the seed itself is inclosed in hard sclerified endocarp (the stone). Outside this is the fleshy mesocarp (the succulent, edible portion) covered by the relatively thin exocarp consisting of epidermis and

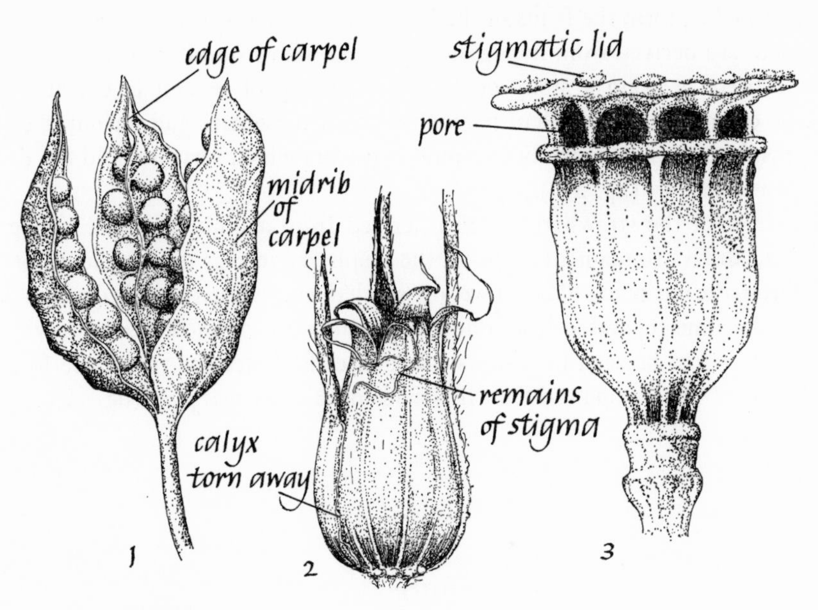

Figure 208 *Capsules of*
1 Iris *sp.* 2 Silene inflata. 3 Papaver *sp.*

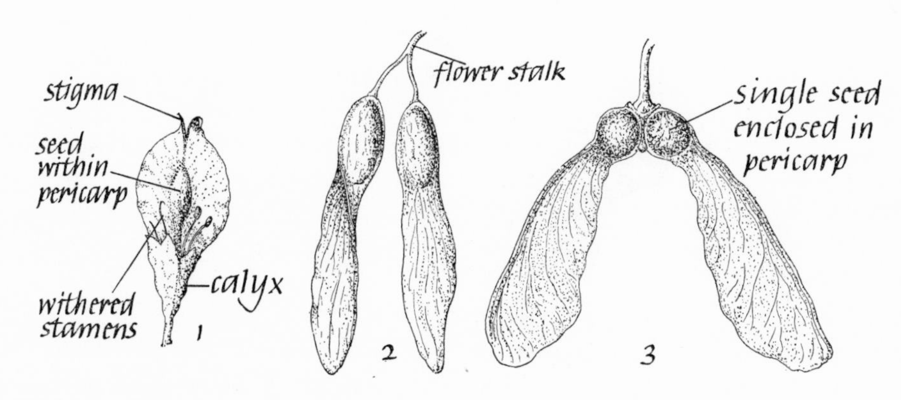

Figure 209 *Samaras of*
1 *wych-elm* (Umus glabra) 2 *ash* (Fraxinus excelsior)
3 *sycamore* (Acer pseudoplatanus)

some sub-epidermal collenchyma. Such fruits are called *drupes*. Collections of drupes, termed *drupelets*, form the fruits of the blackberry (*Rubus* spp.) and raspberry (*Rubus idaeus*) and are derived from hypogynous flowers with a number of separate carpels. In these there is again a stony endocarp consisting of several layers of sclereids variously orientated, a succulent parenchymatous mesocarp, and an outer exocarp. In the raspberry, the exocarp bears epidermal hairs which serve to hold the druplets together at maturity (fig. 210).

The fruit of the strawberry is also derived from a multicarpellate hypogynous flower, but differs fundamentally from the raspberry in that its succulent portion is formed from the receptacle of the flower on which the individual carpels develop. These gradually become separated from one another as hard, dry achenes from which the original styles can be seen to arise as black threads. Since the receptacle forms the greater part of this compound fruit it is said to be a *spurious fruit* (fig. 210).

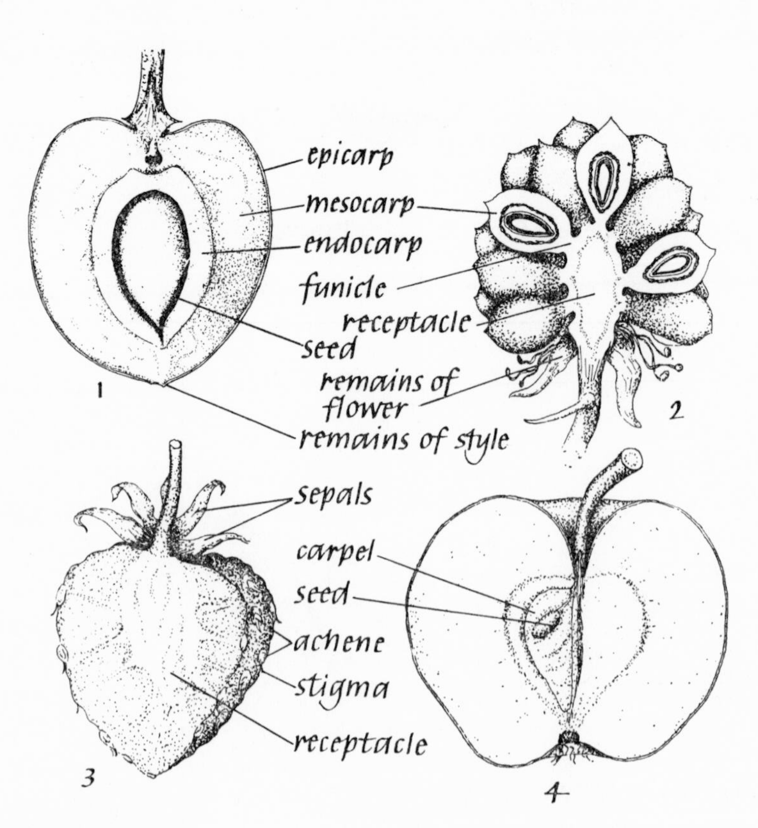

Figure 210 *Types of fruits*

1 *Drupe of cherry.*
2 *Drupelets of blackberry.*
3 *Spurious fruit of strawberry.*
4 *Pome of apple.*

The flower from which the fruit of the apple, a *pome*, is derived is syncarpous and epigynous since its receptacle is deeply cup-shaped and fits closely round the five, several seeded carpels. During the development of this united cup fruit, the carpels become almost completely fused with one another and with the receptacle. Much of the 'flesh' of the fruit is derived from the latter and consists of parenchymatous cells, while the 'core' is formed by the horny development of the inner layers of the pericarp. The rose hip is derived from the cup-shaped receptacle of an apocarpous, perigynous flower (fig. 207).

Differing from drupes and pomes in possessing a pericarp which is entirely fleshy are the true berries, and in these the testa forms the hard, protective layer of the seed. The tomato is such a berry derived from a syncarpous flower with a superior ovary and axile placentation. Much of its flesh is placental in origin. The gooseberry (*Ribes uva-crispa*) on the other hand is a berry originating from a syncarpous flower with inferior ovary, as can be seen from the remains of the perianth which persists at the other end of the fruit from the stalk.

CHAPTER 25

HEREDITY

Most plants closely resemble one or both of the parents which produced the original seed from which they developed. Something within the embryo must, therefore, dictate the pattern of its subsequent development. Since the male and female gametes are the only physical link between one generation and the next, it must be assumed that this something is passed on to the embryo during sexual reproduction in these gametes.

The central feature of sexual reproduction is the union of two gametic nuclei whereby each new individual derives half of its nuclear substance from each parent (Chapter 23). The physical link from one generation to the next is the nucleus. Indeed, it is a basic tenet of heredity that the nuclei of the male and female gametes are endowed with the physical materials of heredity so that an unbroken continuity of *germinal substance* between successive generations of all living organisms is maintained.

The central problem of *genetics*, the scientific study of heredity, is to discover how the individual characters of organisms are transmitted to their offspring. Inherited characters, however, often show marked discontinuity; some remain hidden for several generations and then reveal themselves again unexpectedly. Thus genetics is also concerned with exploring the reasons for the reappearance in a descendant of characters which were present in more remote ancestors. Also, this branch of biology deals with the study of *variation* and is as much concerned with investigating the causes of differences between related organisms as with studying their similarities. Indeed the crucial experiments on which genetics is founded were performed with plants which *differed* markedly in particular inborn characters. These were cross-pollinated and the appearance and breeding behaviour of their offspring were studied through several generations.

Mendelian Inheritance

Although for over two thousand years thinking men have speculated about the similarities and differences which are everywhere so apparent between parents and offspring, and about their causes, it was only at the beginning of the present century that certain fundamental 'laws' of heredity became accepted and the foundations of the science of genetics laid. In 1900 several biologists recognized that a series of breeding experiments with garden peas (*Pisum sativum*) performed some forty years earlier by an Austrian monk, Gregor Mendel, provided a simple and valid explanation for certain hereditary phenomena. The results of these experiments were published in the Transactions of the Natural History Society of Brünn in 1866 but went unnoticed until 1900 when independently Correns, De Vries, and Von Tschermak rediscovered the paper and realized its immense value and significance.

In these experiments Mendel cross-pollinated pure-bred strains of peas differing in particular, strongly contrasting characters, such as stature, flower colour or seed shape. For example, he crossed a strain producing round seeded peas with one producing angular, wrinkled seeds; a strain which produced purple flowers with a strain with white flowers, and so on. In his experiments using plants of different stature, all the plants (the F_1 generation) resulting from an initial cross between tall and dwarf plants, were invariably tall in stature. When these F_1 tall plants were *self-pollinated*, the next generation (the F_2) produced tall and dwarf plants in the ratio of approximately 3 : 1. That is, three-quarters of the plants were tall and the remaining quarter dwarf. These results suggested to Mendel that the 'egg and pollen cells' (the *germ cells*) of each parent plant carried a factor which determined stature. Such inherited factors were subsequently termed 'genes' by Johanssen in 1911. The germ cells of the tall plants would thus carry the factor (T) causing the appearance of tall plants in the next generation; likewise the germ cells of the dwarf plants would carry a dwarf producing factor (t). When purple and white were crossed, both factors (T and t) would be present in the F_1 (hybrid) generation. Mendel stressed that these factors do not blend, but maintain their identity throughout the F_1 generation. Moreover, tallness (T) dominates, or is *dominant* to and prevents the expression of, the dwarf factor (t), which he thus described as *recessive*. This term 'recessive' was used because 'the characters designated withdraw or entirely disappear in the hybrids but nevertheless reäppear unchanged in their progeny. . . '. When the F_1 plants flowered and their germ cells were formed, the two contrasting flower-colour factors, or *allelomorphs*, which would be present in all the somatic cells of the F_1 plants, separate or *segregate*, so that half the gametes receive the tall factor and the other half the dwarf. This segregation of factors in germ cell formation is one of the fundamental principles of Mendelism and is embodied in Mendel's 'Law of Segregation'.

In the F_2 generation the 3 : 1 ratio of tall to dwarf plants is to be expected if the two colour factors responsible had segregated to yield equal numbers of T- and t-containing gametes. This is because at fertilization four combinations of gametes were possible: T males with T females, to give pure or *homozygous* talls; T males with t females to give *heterozygous* (hybrid) talls; t males with T females giving again heterozygous (hybrid) talls; finally t males with t females to give pure recessive dwarfs. Thus Mendel found that the externally visible characters, or *phenotypes* as they are now termed, of the F_2 appeared in the ratio of 3 tall to 1 dwarf, though their genetic constitution, or *genotype*, occurred in the ratio of 1 pure (RR) talls : 2 hybrid (Rr) talls : 1 pure (rr) dwarfs. Hybrid plants containing both factors for stature (Rr) are now described as heterozygous while those carrying the double dose of either the dominant or recessive factor are said to be homozygous for that particular factor or gene. Thus, in the F_2 generation of this pea breeding experiment, the three possible genotypes will tend to occur approximately in the ratio of 1 homozygous tall : 2 heterozygous dwarfs : 1 homozygous dwarf.

It should be apparent that it is possible for plants, or animals, to possess identical genotypes but, owing to environmentally produced variations, to have markedly different phenotypes. Conversely, plants with the same phenotype may have different genotypes, as happens with heterozygous and homozygous individuals possessing the same dominant allelomorph. Moreover, it should be borne in mind that the genotype not only determines the way in which the form, shape or colour of each particular part of an organism can express itself under certain environmental conditions; it also determines its entire physiological and biochemical make-up, so that its ability to tolerate a certain range of environmental conditions, or to manufacture particular enzymes, food reserves or ergastic materials, depends on its genetic constitution.

Mendel corroborated his hypothesis of segregation by selfing the purple flowers of the F_2 generation amongst themselves. In these experiments only one-third of the flowers, that is the homozygous purples, produced only purple flowering offspring. The remaining two-thirds, obviously the heterozygotes, produced purple to whites, as would be expected on the basis of the segregation of the colour factors at gamete formation, in the ratio of 3 : 1.

Pure (homozygous) purple and purple (heterozygous) hybrids may also be distinguished from one another by *back crossing* with a pure recessive (homozygous) dwarf plant. If the dominant homozygous plants are crossed with pure recessives, all the plants of the resulting generation will carry the factors Tt and be heterozygous purples. If, however, the purple flowered plants are heterozygous (Tt) then back crossing with dwarfs will yield progeny half of which will be tall heterozygotes and the other half pure recessive dwarfs.

With certain factors, the heterozygous condition of the genotype of the progeny resulting from breeding experiments such as those described above is apparent in the phenotype of the offspring. In the hybrids between different coloured flowers, one colour may be *imperfectly dominant* over the other, so that the resulting phenotype is of a colour more or less intermediate between the parents and so can be readily distinguished from them. Moreover, when these hybrids are bred amongst themselves the resulting F_2 generation consists of plants of three visibly distinct types: the two original, pure colours, and the hybrids of intermediate colour. The phenotypic ratio is then 1 : 2 : 1 – the same as that of the genotype.

Mendel not only investigated the inheritance of one pair of visibly different factors or allelomorphs, but he also experimented with garden peas possessing, at the same time, two or more sets of contrasting characters. For example, he studied crosses between strains of peas with smooth, yellow coloured seed coats and others with wrinkled, green coats, in the knowledge, gained from other experiments, that yellow was dominant over green and smooth over wrinkled. The phenotypes of the F_1 generation were yellow smooth seeds, since these were both dominant characters, though of course the genotypes would be heterozygous in respect of both factors (GgWw). When the plants from these F_1 seeds flowered they would produce, in equal numbers, gametes carrying the factors yellow or green, and simultaneously, wrinkled or smooth. Since each gamete would have to carry one factor for seed colour and one for shape, there would clearly be four possible combinations of these, GW, Gw, gW, and gw, and they would be produced in equal numbers. Since pollen having any one of these factor combinations would be equally liable to fertilize an egg cell with any combination, the phenotype of the F_2 generation would obviously be determined by a random combination of the four segregating factors. The seeds of the F_2 in Mendel's *dihybrid* in fact showed all four possible combinations of phenotype, but because of the dominance of yellow over green, and smooth over wrinkled, these appeared in numbers which, when analysed, were in the ratio of 9 yellow smooth : 3 yellow wrinkled : 3 green smooth : 1 green wrinkled. That is, only one-sixteenth of the total number of plants produced in the F_2 generation carried both recessive factors.

These experiments investigating *multiple factor inheritance* demonstrated to Mendel that there was an *independent assortment* of genetic traits between pure breeding lines when two or more pairs of contrasting characters are present. Accordingly, Mendel formulated his second basic principle of inheritance, the 'Law of Independent Assortment'.

Heredity and Environment

Although it is common usage to refer to characters which are inherited as being passed from one generation to the next, it is important to recognize that it is not the *visible properties* of the organism that are inherited. Instead it is the ability to produce certain distinctive properties or characters, or to develop in a particular way, provided that environmental conditions are suitable. Although some characters, for example many flower colours, are not appreciably influenced by external conditions, a large number, such as stature or the weight of seed produced, may be governed either by genetic constitution or environment. For example, pea seeds with an inherent property for tallness will never grow into tall plants, and so will be unable to exhibit this particular hereditary attribute, unless they are provided with certain minimum requirements of soil, water, temperature and light. Any worthwhile analysis of any of the inherited attributes or their variation in an organism must therefore take into account both genetical and environmental factors.

Even in a fairly well controlled environment it is often difficult to assess whether observed variability is due to genetical or environmental differences. When large numbers of a plant population are measured or weighed, in respect of some particular character, and these measurements are arranged in ascending order of magnitude, it will often be found that there is a considerable difference between the largest and the smallest, the heaviest and the lightest measurements. When these measurements are classified into separate groups, each differing by a constant amount, the groups containing the smallest number of measurements will be the two extremes. The group containing the greatest number, on the other hand, will be found to correspond very closely to the *arithmetical mean* of all the measurements. This most frequent measurement, the *mode*, can be shown on a graph by plotting along the ordinates the number of measurements in each group against the actual measurements in the abscissae. When these curves are symmetrical about the mode, as they commonly are, the character being investigated is then said to show a *normal distribution*. In such normal distributions there are equal numbers of the individuals being measured above and below the most common value, the mode, so that the median value, the mean and the mode are identical.

When the measurement of variation results in a normal distribution it is usually assumed that the variation is due in the main to environment and not to differences in genetic constitution. In point of fact, probably most normal distributions are due to both heredity and environment. Thus the variation which such curves show, even in experiments under well controlled environmental conditions, is the expression of slight environmental variations acting on a population carrying slight differences in genetic constitution. If a large number of measurements of a particular character cannot be arranged in a normal distribution, the suspicion is justified that the organisms which have been measured have not been taken from one genetically homogeneous population, especially if a *bimodal* or two peaked curve is produced.

The genetical homogeneity of a population can be confirmed by *selection experiments*. In these the largest individuals are selected and always crossed together and the process is repeated with the smallest. After such selection and crossing has been repeated for several generations, markedly different results will be obtained depending on the original genetic constitution of the population. If the original material was in fact homogeneous, or genetically *pure*, for the character being investigated, the offspring of the large and small individuals which were paired will not differ from each other in their *average* size, nor in the range of variation their progeny exhibit. Moreover, they will not differ from their ancestors in this respect when grown under similar environmental conditions. The variations observed must clearly be due to environmental differences.

If the population subjected to a selection experiment is not genetically pure for the character in question, or is a *wild population*, it is often possible, in only a few generations, to select from it *strains* which differ significantly in the attribute being measured. Moreover, the magnitude of the difference can often be gradually increased if selection is continued through several generations. In this way, two populations containing different or contrasting factors (genes) for a particular character, such as size, or yield, can be separated. Selection for desirable factors is widely practised in plant breeding and probably has been carried out, though unconsciously, since the birth of agriculture in prehistoric times. For example, early maturing seeds, and seeds from the most fertile plants with the highest yield, would in the main be taken (selected) and sown for the next year's crop. If these qualities had a genetic basis, as indeed they have, they would be transmitted through the seed to subsequent generations.

The Cytological Basis of Mendelian Inheritance

Mendel's carefully devised experiments, and his critically reasoned results, were fully accepted when early in the present century it became clear that his postulations about the segregation and independent assortment of genetic factors were perfectly consistent with the known facts about chromosome behaviour at meiosis during the formation of sex cells.

As a result of meiosis each gamete contains one haploid, or basic, complement of chromosomes. When gametes unite at fertilization the resulting diploid zygote contains two sets of genetic factors, one derived from each parent. This means that any given *allelic pair* of genes must be located in a homologous pair of chromosomes; and thus Mendel's first law of segregation depends on the *disjunction* of homologous chromosomes at meiosis. Likewise, if it is assumed that two gene pairs responsible for different characters lie in different chromosome pairs, it will be apparent that Mendel's second law is in fact an expression of the random assortment of chromosome pairs during meiosis (fig. 163).

Much of the direct evidence for the correlation between chromosome behaviour and Mendel's principles was derived from imaginatively planned breeding experiments carried out by an American, T. H. Morgan, and his collaborators, with a small fruit fly, *Drosophila melanogaster*. The advantages of this insect for cytogenetic research include its rapid rate of reproduction, enabling successive generations to be reared in a few weeks, and the possession of only four pairs of chromosomes. Many of the inherited character differences which Morgan studied in these flies behaved in complete accord with Mendel's principles. Others, however, did not show independent assortment but seemed to be passed from parent to offspring as though held or *linked* together. Soon it became obvious that since all plants and animals have large numbers of inherited factors or genes but relatively few chromosome pairs (4 in *Drosophila*, 7 in *Pisum*, 10 in maize, 23 in man), each chromosome must of necessity have associated with it many genes. It therefore became necessary to qualify Mendel's law of independent assortment, for the genes physically bound to one chromosome clearly would not segregate freely from one another: thus the random assortment of chromosomes would not determine how they would combine. They would in fact tend to be shared out in meiosis as a linked group. This means that if the contrasting characters responsible for the yellow smooth, and green wrinkled appearance of peas were located in the same chromosome instead of in different chromosomes only two kinds of gametes, instead of four, would be produced by the F_1 generation. The resulting F_2 generation would show only the two parental combinations, yellow smooth and green wrinkled. In other words, the two factors contributed together in the original cross, that is by each grandparent, would still be linked together.

The number of groups of linked genes, or *linkage groups*, will obviously depend on the number of chromosome pairs present in the organism being studied. In *Drosophila* there are four linkage groups, in *Pisum* seven, for this animal and plant possess four and seven chromosome pairs respectively. By a remarkably fortunate accident, Mendel chose for his breeding experiments seven independent character pairs associated with genes now known to be located in one of each of the seven chromosome pairs of the garden pea. It seems certain that without this good fortune the results of Mendel's experiments would have been much more complex; and clearly, without any knowledge of chromosomes he could not have produced any simple and acceptable interpretation for them. It is probable that the history of genetics would have been very different.

Despite the fact that they are located on the same chromosome, linked genes commonly show varying degrees of independent assortment. This too is explicable in terms of the behaviour of the chromosomes at meiosis and in fact occurs when there is an exchange of chromatid segments with the formation of chiasmata at diplotene (see p. 249). Another of T. H. Morgan's valuable contributions to cytogenetics relates to such *incomplete linkage* – complete linkage is a rare phenomenon – resulting from crossing over. This was his suggestion that the frequency of the apparent independent assortment, or *recombination*, of two linked genes is directly dependent on the linear distance separating them. In other words, the chance of a cross-over between segments occurring between two widely separated genes in a bivalent would be much greater than the chance of a cross-over between two genes lying close to one another. The frequency with which recombinations occur are now used as a means of measuring the distances separating genes, and by the analysis of *linkage relations* it has been possible to construct, for quite a number of organisms, detailed *chromosome maps* showing the relative positions of each known gene. It must be pointed out in this connection that when the frequency of the recombination of linked genes approaches 50%, it becomes impossible to separate the results from those occurring on the basis of random chromosome assortment.

Mutations

When organisms which are pure, or homozygous, for one or more characters are bred together, these particular characters usually appear in each successive generation. The genes responsible for the expression of these characters must therefore have arisen from pre-existing genes. This implies that in the course of cell division, both mitotic and meiotic, genes, and in turn whole chromosomes, produce exact copies of themselves from the materials present in the cell. Heredity may thus be said to depend on the exactitude of gene reproduction or *replication* (Chapter 26).

Genetics, however, is concerned not only with the inheritance of similarities but also with the occurrence of differences between related organisms. Indeed Mendelism, and the elucidation of the mechanism of heredity, depend on the results of crosses between plants possessing different genes (allelomorphs) at a particular chromosome locus which express themselves as unmistakable phenotypic differences, at least when present in the homozygous condition. It is now recognized that allelomorphs can exist in more than two states and that each gives rise to an inherited difference which may be very obvious, or quite insignificant, in its phenotypic expression. From the fact that genes exist in these different states it must be inferred that occasionally there is an error in the process of gene copying with the result that the copy differs from the original. The changed copy must then reproduce itself in its altered form. Any such change in the hereditary material of an organism is called a *mutation*. This term is used with reference not only to changes in the genetic constitution of the organism itself, but also to the altered phenotype resulting from the genetic change.

Mutations are abrupt events; when they occur they express themselves suddenly and not as a gradual change in phenotype. Moreover, they may be dominant, or recessive, to the normal state, and they may also revert to the original condition just as suddenly as they arose. They commonly arise in the reproductive organs during gamete formation, but they can occur in any body cell (*somatic mutation*) of an organism at any time during its development. Somatic mutations, however, unless they arise in cells ultimately concerned in gamete formation, that is in the *germ line*, cannot be inherited by future generations, except, of course, when they occur in parts which reproduce vegetatively. The frequency with which mutations occur varies very greatly and even in a given organism some mutations occur much more commonly than others. For example, the frequency of mutation per 1,000,000 gametes in the case of seven different characters in maize has been found to vary between 0 and 492. The frequency can, however, be greatly increased by irradiation with X-rays and gamma rays and by certain chemicals, such as mustard gas.

So far reference has been made only to the mutation of single genes, that is to *gene mutations*. Whole assemblages of genes, that is chromosomes, or parts of chromosomes, may undergo alterations which give rise to profound phenotypic changes. These *chromosomal mutations* include *deletions*, the loss of part of a chromosome, which if large enough is usually lethal to the individual inheriting it; *duplications*, where similar pieces of a chromosome occur in two places in the chromosome so that one or more genes are represented twice; *translocations*, in which there is an exchange of parts of a chromosome from a member of one pair to that of another (this must not be confused with crossing over between chromatids of homologous chromosomes during meiosis); *inversions*, involving the breakage of a chromosome in two places followed by a rejoining of the broken ends in such a way that the order of genes along the chromosome is reversed in this region. Studies of the effects produced by translocations and inversions, in which only the relative positions of groups of genes are altered, *position effects*, have led to the important realization that 'a chromosome is not just a container for genes, but a harmonious system of interacting genes'.

Other chromosomal mutations involve whole chromosomes or sets of chromosomes. These may be either additions or losses causing a numerical increase or decrease in the total number of chromosomes present in the nuclei of the organism. Losses of whole chromosomes are usually detrimental and zygotes resulting from the union of one or both gametes suffering from such a deficiency may fail to develop, or develop so abnormally that the resulting organism's chances of survival in competition with normal organisms are minimal.

Polyploidy

The most important chromosomal mutations are those in which whole complements of chromosomes are reduplicated. To distinguish them from the normal diploid state, an organism possessing more than one pair of each chromosome of its complement is termed a *polyploid*. Mutations of this sort occur quite commonly in plants, but are very rare in animals. Various categories of polyploids are recognized, depending on the number of extra chromosome complements present, so that in *triploids* each chromosome is represented three times; in *tetraploids* four times; in *hexaploids* six times and so on.

Polyploids usually arise by the failure of a division during gamete formation, so that the resulting sex cells contain the diploid instead of the haploid chromosome number. When diploid gametes unite at fertilization with a normal haploid, a triploid results. If diploid sperm fertilizes a diploid egg the offspring will be tetraploid. The physiological upsets in reproduction and the inevitable consequences of abnormal pairing of chromosomes during zygotene of meiosis, tend to make many polyploids, and especially those with uneven numbers such as triploids (3n) and pentaploids (5n), less fertile than their diploid relatives. Indeed, triploids are almost completely sterile. As a result of this reduced fertility such plants seldom survive if they reproduce by sexual means only. Thus most polyploids of this category are found in plants which can perpetuate themselves, or can be perpetuated, as many cultivated flowers and fruits are, by vegetative means.

Depending on the way in which they originate, two major classes of polyploids are recognized. The first, *autopolyploids* (AAAA), are commonly formed by some mechanical interference or injury to a plant which leads to the occurrence of a double set of its normal chromosome complement. If, for example, the shoot of a diploid tomato plant whose cells have nuclei with 24 chromosomes is cut back and then new shoots are allowed to grow from the cut surface, some of these new shoots will be found to be larger and more vigorous than normal. Cytological examination will show these cells to be tetraploid, with nuclei containing 48 chromosomes. If these tetraploid shoots are permitted to flower and fruit, the flowers will be much larger than in diploid plants and the resulting tomato fruits will be more or less seedless.

An *autotetraploid* condition can be induced in plants by treating dividing cells, such as stem apices, with *colchicine*. This substance, an *alkaloid* extracted from the corms of the autumn crocus (*Colchicum autumnale*) prevents the proper formation and functioning of the spindle at the metaphase of mitosis. In colchicine-treated cells, the daughter chromosomes, instead of moving along the spindle to the poles, fail to separate, with the result that a double set of chromosomes is formed. Cells subsequently derived from colchicine-treated cells will also be autotetraploid, as will be the resulting shoots they produce.

The second class of polyploids are *allopolyploids* (AABB). These result from the duplication of two chromosome complements derived from two different species which have been crossed. In this they differ significantly from autopolyploids, which contain multiples of only the basic set of chromosomes from a single parent. Autopolyploids may not differ very markedly, except possibly in size, from the parent species, whereas allopolyploids are in effect new species. A striking example of allopolyploidy is in the cross between cabbage (*Brassica oleracea*) and radish (*Raphanus sativus*). Both plants have a haploid set of 9 chromosomes so that the diploid hybrid possesses 18 chromosomes. Since, however, the two sets of chromosomes in the hybrid are not homologous, they fail to pair during zygotene of meiosis; consequently, these plants are extremely infertile. If, however, there is a doubling of the diploid hybrid chromosome complement, similar to that described for the tomato, zygotene pairing then is effected in the resulting allotetraploid ($2n=36$) and, since meiotic behaviour can now be normal, this Raphano-brassica hybrid is quite fertile. It has been established that allopolyploidy plays an important part in species formation in nature.

CHAPTER 26

THE NUCLEIC ACIDS AND HEREDITY

The central problem of growth, even of a single cell, is to find out how new material is formed and added to this cell so that it develops substantially in the image of the cell from which it was derived. All living matter consists of a great diversity of chemical substances including not only water and salts incorporated unchanged from the external environment, but also many substances which are the result of complex intracellular chemical transformations. In the manufacture of carbohydrates and fats, specific enzymes, or groups of enzymes, promote each of the complex chemical reactions leading to their formation (see Chapter 17). Unless stored away as food, most of these comparatively simple organic substances become involved soon, or even immediately after their formation, in some other enzyme-promoted reactions whereby they become part of the structure, or are involved in the metabolic machinery of the cell. Indeed it has already been emphasized that enzymes are at the centre of all biological activity (p. 201).

Enzymes are complex protein molecules, each constructed of specific amino-acid sequences and performing, with a remarkable precision of action, just one particular kind of molecular assembly. Although certain enzymes perform almost identical functions in different organisms, their specific composition differs from one species to another. How then are enzymes formed? Must it be assumed that enzymes require enzymes to make enzymes – so that there is an infinite series of them? Such an explanation is clearly unfeasible and illogical. It therefore becomes necessary to ascribe the specification of the amino-acid sequence essential for the formation of a new enzyme molecule to the intervention of some different, non-proteinaceous substance whose powers of *specification* are independent of the enzyme. Indeed it has become necessary to postulate the existence of a substance with a copying or *self-replicating* cycle which can transmit the exact specifications of structure to new molecules of its own kind. The simplest way in which such a substance could specify molecular sequences of amino-acids is by acting as a template for the formation of another. That is, the surface of the template substance acts as a mould, imposing a complementary, or mirror image, pattern on the substance being formed. A depression in the template would correspond with a protrusion in the substance being formed, or alternatively, there would be a correspondence of electrical charges.

The problems involved in self-replication, and their analysis, although still the concern of geneticists, has become during the past fifty years as much the province of biochemists as of biologists, since the ultimate solution of its problems must be at the molecular level. Indeed in this flourishing field of enquiry there has been a remarkably fruitful collaboration among the disciplines of chemistry, physics and biology. This collaboration began, however, long before any conscious attempt was made to unravel this fundamental and ingrained property of all living matter, or before this central problem of life was posed. Almost a hundred years ago purely chemical studies of the nucleus were carried out by the Swiss biochemist Miescher. This work was initiated as a result of Miescher's own realization of the universal occurrence of the nucleus and of its extreme importance as a constituent of all living cells. In his first series of investigations he isolated 'wholly pure nuclei' from pus cells which, in the days before antiseptics, he obtained in almost unlimited quantities from discarded surgical bandages. From these nuclei he prepared a substance which he named 'nuclein'. Amongst its several remarkable properties the most startling was that it was a stronger acid than any other known biological substance, and its very high phosphorus content. Indeed, so revolutionary and unacceptable were Miescher's findings that their publication was delayed for some ten years. In 1871, the year of their publication, Miescher found a less objectionable source of 'nuclein' in the isolated sperm heads taken from the ripe testes of salmon. This he collected from the fish as they made their spring spawning migration from the sea up to the headwaters of the Rhine. From the salmon sperm material he isolated not only his strongly acid 'nuclein', but also a highly nitrogenous substance which was combined with it and which he named 'protamin'.

The work of Miescher and of those who further investigated the chemical structure of *nucleic acid*, as his 'nuclein' was later called, showed that the substance was constructed from three sorts of chemical building blocks. The first, which gives nucleic acid its strongly acid properties is *phosphate*; the second a 5-carbon or pentose sugar called *deoxyribose*; the third a group of four bases, two being *purines* and two *pyrimidines*, each of which contains nitrogen. The purines are called *adenine* and *guanine*; the pyrimidines *thymine* and *cytosine*. It is from the sugar of this obviously complex molecule that its name *deoxyribose nucleic acid* (DNA for short) has been derived (fig. 211).

Organic chemists and biochemists have gradually pieced together information

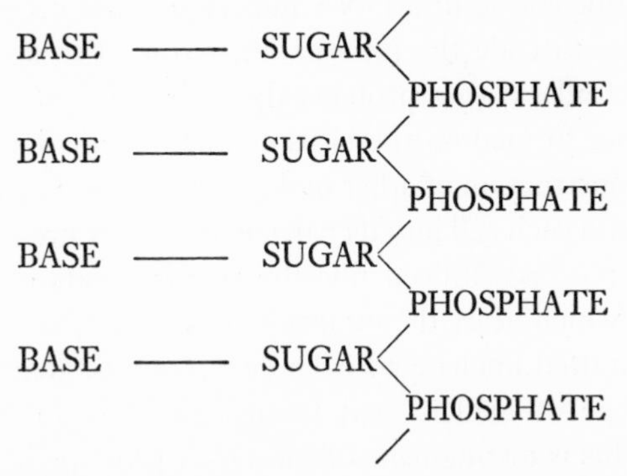

Figure 211 *Chemical formula for a single chain of DNA* (*after Watson and Crick*).

showing how the three building blocks contained in the DNA molecule fit together. As indicated in fig. 211 the deoxyribose sugar molecules are linked together by the phosphate, while to each sugar molecule is attached one of the purine or pyrimidine bases. Each group consisting of sugar-phosphate-base is termed a *nucleotide*, and the DNA molecule is a *polynucleotide chain*, which like all polymers is characterized by having a particular chemical unit repeatedly linked. Studies of the physical properties of the DNA molecule have indicated that this polynucleotide chain is not straight, but seems to form a spiral or helix round a central axis. Moreover, it seems that not one, but probably two such helices make up the molecule.

From this chemical and physical evidence, Watson and Crick proposed in 1952 that the molecule is a double structure consisting of two DNA chains, whose sugar-phosphate backbones form the double helix round a common axis. Each helix is thought to be linked together by pairs of purine and pyrimidine bases through weakly linked H-bonds. Moreover, it is not possible for just any purine-pyrimidine pair to link the two helices together: only the purine adenine (A) can pair with the pyrimidine thymine (T), and the purine guanine (G) with the pyrimidine cytosine (C). The A-T, G-C base pairs can, however, follow each other in any sequence along the DNA double chain (fig. 212).

This model of the DNA molecule provides all the requirements for a self-replicating substance. Its originators suggested that the molecules could split longitudinally by a breakage of the H-bonds, to form the two complementary halves. Both halves of the split DNA molecules act independently as a template and it is suggested that in each cell there is available a supply of the sugar, phosphate, and base building blocks necessary to form new DNA. These substances then assemble themselves into the four possible categories of nucleotides. From time to time the base of one of these nucleotides will attach itself by an H-bond to the appropriate base of the template DNA chain. By this means a new chain, complementary to the template, is formed and a new double helical is once again completed (fig. 213).

Studies using refined microchemical methods have proved that DNA occurs in the chromosomes of the nuclei of all plants and animals. Also, although there are only four different kinds of nucleotide in a DNA molecule it has recently been demonstrated that it is possible to code the information required to specify the different amino-acid sequences of all existing proteins through different sequences of these nucleotides. The enzymes formed on the basis of this information are then thought to be concerned in the construction of other molecules, including additional enzymes, which are required to build each cell into its particular and yet predetermined pattern. The DNA of the chromosomes indeed fills the requirements of a self-replicating system, carrying a code which bears the information necessary for enzyme formation and which can be transmitted unchanged from generation to generation.

There is another type of nucleic acid found especially in the nucleolus and cytoplasm of all cells. This is distinguished from DNA principally by the fact that it contains a different pentose sugar, *ribose*, as one of its three principal building blocks.

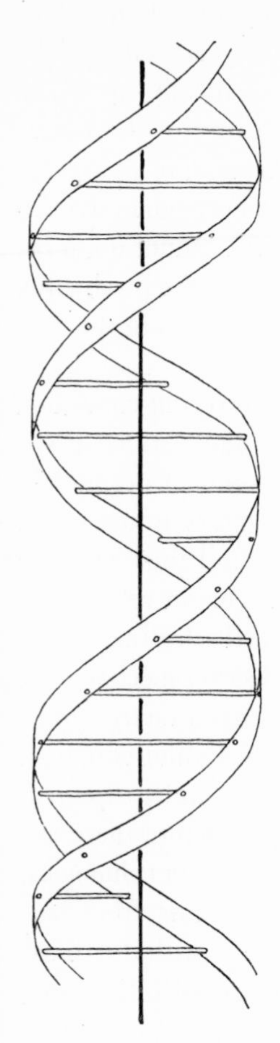

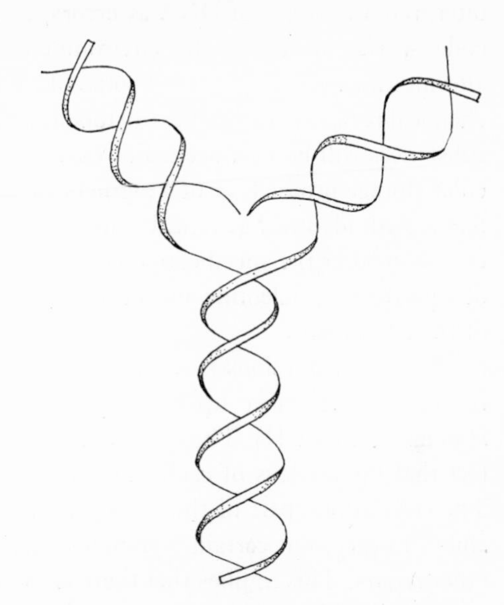

Figure 213 (*above*) *A diagrammatic representation of the replication scheme for DNA proposed by Watson and Crick, in which unwinding and replication proceed together* (*after Delbruck and Stent*).

Figure 212 (*left*) *Diagram of a section of a DNA molecule. The two ribbons symbolize the sugar-phosphate backbones of the two chains, and the horizontal rods the pairs of bases holding the backbones together* (*after Watson and Crick*).

Hence it is called *ribosenucleic acid*, or RNA. The great achievement of this thriving field of biological-biochemical research, however, has been the assemblage of conclusive evidence pointing to the fact that the substance directly associated with the storage and copying of hereditary information in the cell is the DNA of the chromosomal strands. But DNA itself does not directly specify the amino-acid sequences of each enzyme; its code is conveyed from the nucleus to the cytoplasm by RNA, which, as stated above, is most abundant in the nucleolus and the cytoplasm. Again by some sort of template mechanism it is believed that the RNA of the nucleolus receives sets of instructions coded on the DNA. These instructions, now in RNA form, are then passed over to the microsomes, sometimes called *ribosomes*, in the cytoplasm which are known to be active sites of protein synthesis. Support for this relationship between RNA and protein synthesis comes from the fact that cells in which protein synthesis is very active have a high RNA content.

Variations which are known to be the result of gene mutations can obviously be interpreted in terms of DNA as errors, or aberrations, in the copying of the DNA code. Variations caused by environmental differences presumably are effected by altering the individual rates of some of the large number of enzymatically controlled chemical reactions within the organism; consequently, different quantities of different substances will be produced. For example, the amount of lignification, or of a particular storage product, or of a pigment produced, may vary greatly between individual plants with identical genetical constitutions. What the environment cannot do, however, is to alter the specification coded on the chromosomal DNA for the production of a particular nucleotide and in turn, the relevant amino acid sequences in the cells of the organism.

As a plant develops from the embryo within the seed to its flowering condition, the cells which make up its ever increasing bulk differentiate into various tissue systems (see Part II). These cells pursue different paths of development despite the fact that the nucleus of each cell is endowed with identical hereditary information. The cells in one part of the plant may come to contain enzymes and thus have the ability to carry out certain metabolic activities which are not possible in cells in another region. This implies that there is some mechanism in each cell selecting certain genes so that they either operate or do not, and that the final selection mechanisms, like other characters, must be inherited and so presumably they are exactly copied during the growth and reproduction of each cell. The problem of cell differentiation, however, still remains one of the most complex yet most fascinating to be explored, but much ground will have to be covered at the biochemical level before there can be any significant correlation between chemical events in cells and the morphological changes which occur as they differentiate. Even so, it is now emerging from biochemical studies that genes are not merely structural units concerned with the transmission of hereditary information. They are units of function concerned with setting in motion the synthetic activities of the cell which eventually result in the phenomena of growth and differentiation.

CHAPTER 27

VIRUSES

Although the term 'virus', which in latin means a poison, and from which the adjective 'virulent' is derived, has a medical usage dating from the eighteenth century, the study of viruses and the diseases caused by them made no significant advance until 1892. In that year Ivanovski investigated diseased tobacco plants whose leaves were mottled and wrinkled and whose growth was stunted. He showed that this diseased condition could be transmitted to healthy plants simply by rubbing their leaves with the juice extracted from affected plants. Moreover, he found that this so-called *tobacco mosaic disease* could infect healthy plants even after it had passed through a filter capable of retaining particles of bacterial size, that is about 1 μ long. The full significance of this discovery was not immediately appreciated and it was still assumed that the disease was caused by a very small bacterium. Some six years later, however, after carrying out experiments with the bacteriologically sterile filtrates of sap from mosaiced plants which were still infective, Beyerinck realized that an entity quite different from a bacterium must have been responsible for the disease. This he characterized as a 'contagium vivum fluidum' – a contagious living fluid. Later, many other plant and animal diseases were shown to be caused by agents which could pass through a bacterial-retaining filter, hence their name 'filterable viruses'.

The consistent failure of workers in this field to reveal the cause of any virus disease, either by the microscopic examination of infective agents, or by cultural methods, seemed to confirm the early views that viruses were non-corpuscular. On the other hand, it was clear that whatever viruses were, they possessed two important properties which indicated that they were organisms. These were firstly, their ability to reproduce, and secondly, their ability to produce variants with new disease-producing properties. However, it was not fully appreciated for a considerable time that viruses multiply and vary only within the living cells of other organisms.

In the 1930's, biochemists made great advances in the study of proteins and enzymes, and the techniques they employed were applied to the study of viruses. In 1935 tobacco mosaic virus was isolated as a liquid crystalline protein. Some short time later, further study revealed that the virus contained only two substances: protein and nucleic acid (see Chapter 26). This most important discovery revealed that viruses have a strikingly simple chemical structure and so stand in marked contrast to the complexity of substances known to be contained even in the cell of a bacterium.

The crystallization of viruses and the subsequent study of the crystals with X-rays allowed direct and precise measurements of the size of virus particles to be made.

Moreover, their crystallization indicated that there was a remarkable uniformity of size and fixity of structure, a feature also contrasting strongly with the great variability of structure and arrangement of the components within a living cell. The most recent knowledge about the size and shape of viruses is derived from electron-microscope studies. It has been found that the tobacco mosaic virus (fig. 215) consists of straight rods about 300 mμ long and 12 mμ in diameter, and that potato virus X are flexible rods some 500 mμ long by 12 mμ in diameter. The *turnip yellow mosaic*, in common with many other plant viruses, are approximately spherical, and mostly occur as particles of a uniform and characteristic diameter, varying with different viruses from 20-28 mμ.

The nucleic acid of plant and of some animal viruses is ribosenucleic acid, RNA (see p. 317). Evidence based on certain experiments indicates that in each virus particle the nuclei acid forms a central core surrounded by an outer protein coat (fig. 214). By delicate procedures, it is possible to separate tobacco mosaic virus particles into their constituent protein and nucleic acid; the nucleic acid can then be tested by digesting with the enzyme *ribonuclease*, the only enzyme which can hydrolyse RNA. It can also be demonstrated that the nucleic acid can by itself initiate infection, though the 'level of infectivity' is greatly reduced, probably because the absence of the protein renders the nucleic acid unstable. This fact is of considerable genetical significance; so too is the discovery that it is possible not only to recombine the separated protein and nucleic acid to form rods of almost identical appearance, which are as infective as the intact virus, but also to produce infective rods from the protein

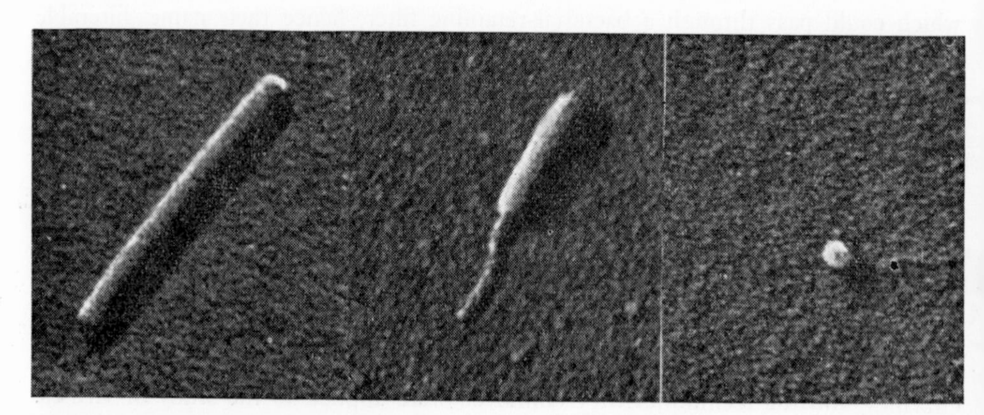

Figure 214 *Electronmicrographs of*
(*left*) *Normal particle of tobacco mosaic virus.*
(*centre*) *Partially degraded particle from a preparation treated with a detergent, showing threads containing nucleic acid projecting from the ends of the rod where the protein has been dissolved away*, *and*
(*right*) *A small piece of virus protein seen end on and showing a hole in the centre of the protein coat.* (*Photographs by Dr R. G. Hart.*)

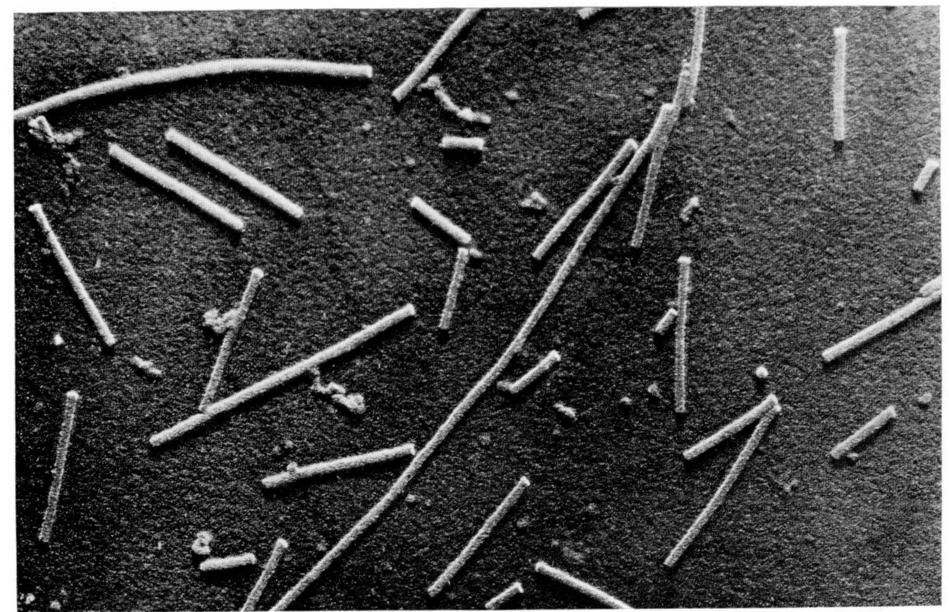

Figure 215 *The rod-shaped particles of Tobacco Mosaic Virus* × 33,000. (*Photograph by courtesy Rothampstead Experimental Station.*)

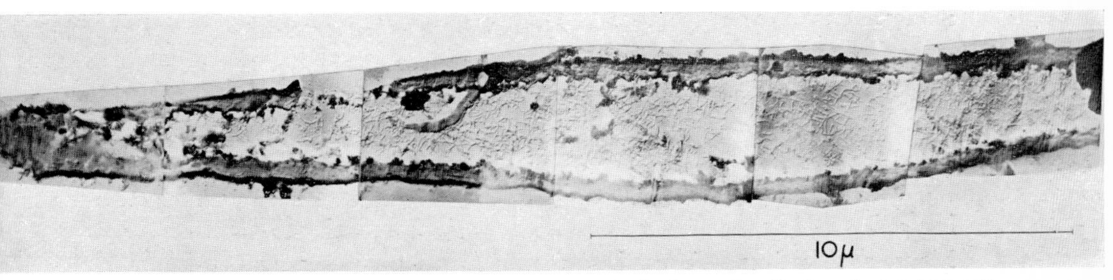

Figure 216 *Electronmicrograph of l.s. of a hair cell of tobacco leaf infected with T.M.V. Note the rod-shaped particles of which there are estimated to be more than* 10,000,000 *in the cell.* (*Photograph by Rothampstead Experimental Station.*)

Figure 217 *Rembrandt Parrot Tulips*
The striping on the petals is due to virus infection. (*Water colour drawing by H. Heustenburg* (1667-1726), *Tyler's museum, Haarlem.*)

of one strain and the nucleic acid of another. These newly constituted rods when introduced into a plant are identical in their infectivity and in the symptoms they produce with the strain from which the nucleic acid was contributed. It must be deduced therefore that the nucleic acid of the virus is the fraction of the particle carrying, in addition to its other inherited characteristics, the genetic information which determines the composition of the virus protein subsequently formed when it reproduces.

Because of their obvious simplicity of structure, viruses do not quite fit into the category of 'organisms' – nor can they be termed 'molecules'. Indeed the structures most closely resembling viruses are to be found amongst the cytoplasmic nucleoproteins of the normal living cell. Many such constituents resemble viruses chemically for they contain the same amino-acids, purines and pyrimidines, and genetically, since they replicate themselves only within the living cell. Indeed it has been suggested that viruses originated from cytoplasmic particles endowed with genetic continuity but which have become beyond the control of the cell.

It has been stressed elsewhere (Chapter 16) that all living cells receive raw materials from outside, and that each has the special ability to turn these into more complex molecules. These syntheses, which are controlled by the nucleus, involve complex series of mechanisms which utilize external sources of raw materials and energy for the maintenance of the life of the cell and the formation of new cells. In each cell nucleus, the genes located on the chromosomes, which consist largely of nucleic acid (DNA) and protein, direct the patterns of growth, development, and biochemical activity that must be followed as new cells are produced. When a virus enters a cell it seems to disorganize the metabolic activities controlled by the cell's nucleus; virus and host metabolism then combine in such a way that the genetic message imprinted on the virus nucleoprotein directs the course of further metabolism – that is towards the manufacture of new virus particles. The virus, however, is always dependent on the host for its food supply and on the host's synthetic mechanisms. It is for this reason that viruses can multiply only within living cells. These properties are summarized in Luria's definition of viruses – 'submicroscopic entities capable of being introduced into specific living cells and of reproducing only inside such cells' (fig. 216).

Virus Diseases of Plants

In addition to the 'classical' tobacco mosaic disease caused by a virus there are many other known plant virus diseases of very great economic importance. As the common symptom of most plant virus diseases is a marked reduction in the size and cropping power of the plant, intensive research has been undertaken in their study and control, especially of vegetatively propagated plants of economic importance, such as potatoes, strawberries, raspberries, and hops. Apart from their effect on cropping, virus diseases are in many cases accompanied by other symptoms, such as the striping or spotting, wrinkling and curling of the leaves, and a chlorosis (see p. 181) of the green parts of the plant. Leaf shape may be drastically altered, and in

Figure 218 *Potato leaf infected with potato virus Y (photograph by courtesy, Rothampstead Experimental Station).*

some plants unusual outgrowths may be produced from the leaf surface. The striping of petals is another frequent symptom, though in the case of 'broken' or Rembrandt tulips (fig. 217), this is considered to be aesthetically pleasing and tulips so infected have been preserved and used as propagating stock for some 400 years. Shoots and roots may also be variously affected by virus infection, though perhaps the most striking are *cankers* and the proliferation of lateral branches as 'witches' brooms'.

Several agents may be responsible for the spread of plant virus diseases: amongst the most important are insects, especially sucking insects, such as aphids and leaf hoppers. Some virus diseases may, however, be transmitted by contact, as when a diseased plant rubs against a healthy one. Virus diseases of horticultural plants may be spread by grafting, pruning, and even the cutting of flowers. Viruses are not carried by seed, though units of vegetative propagation, such as bulbs, corms, rhizomes, and tubers are frequent carriers. Great care is now taken, at least in the United Kingdom, to eliminate virus infection in potato tubers (fig. 218). To this end the 'seed' tubers are grown at some distance from the main crop in the north and west of the country. Here the climate is much less favourable than in the south and east for the survival of the aphids that spread the most important of the potato viruses. Most English farmers now buy certified seed potatoes from Scotland or Ireland, the crops of which are carefully examined and any diseased plants removed before the virus can possibly be spread to their healthy neighbours. This practice maintains the health of stocks, though at an estimated cost of about £5,000,000 per year. This is because new, certified 'seed' tubers must be planted each year and these have, of course, to be transported for considerable distances from the 'clean' areas where they are grown.

CHAPTER 28

EVOLUTION

For thousands of years man in his curiosity has speculated on the origins of the natural features around him. Ancient mythology abounds with legends concerning the birth of lakes and rivers, mountains and valleys, and of how the world became populated by plants and animals, including man himself. The origins of plants and animals, until the middle of the nineteenth century were diversely conceived by two opposed schools of thought. The first, which accepted the Biblical account of special creation in 'Genesis', believed that species were individually created and unchanging except for slight deviations which occurred from time to time, but these always reverted to their original form. The second accepted the concept that species could change gradually into new species: they could evolve. In its biological connotation the word *evolution* implies the origins of plants and animals by a process of development from earlier forms, as distinct from 'special creation'.

The concept of evolution gained increasing acceptance in the latter part of the eighteenth century. It was probably the French physician Lamark who made the most considerable contribution in support of evolution: not only did he submit evidence that evolutionary change occurred, but he also suggested factors which might produce such change. This was based largely on his observations that organs, such as various muscles in human beings, tend to become larger and better developed with use, while unused organs tend to become smaller. He assumed that such modifications, acquired by use and disuse during the life time of an organism, may be inherited, at least to some degree, by its offspring. In this way he accounted for the remarkably delicate, yet often elaborate structure of many of the organs of both plants and animals, which appeared to be so well suited to fulfil some particular function necessary for *survival*. These he believed to have gradually arisen by modification, and subsequent inheritance, during the course of generations. By this means organisms would in time become perfectly suited, or *adapted to their environment*. Moreover, once this adaptation was achieved, Lamark argued that the organism would then remain constant until conditions changed. Clearly, according to this theory of evolution, *the inheritance of acquired characters* implied that the environment was the moulder of the organism.

Although Lamark's crude hypothesis was later found to be untenable, nevertheless he did contribute the very important concept that evolution was a gradual process. More important however, was the fact that his ideas led Charles Darwin to the realization that a most valuable contribution in the study of evolution might be made by investigating plants and animals under *domestication*. The result was the *Origin of Species*, published in 1859 and still the most important biological work ever written.

In this, Darwin provided a huge array of evidence to demonstrate irresistibly that species were not immutable and that since they could change into different types, evolution must be accepted. Darwin's greatest contribution to biological thought, the kernel of the *Origin*, was the hypothesis that *natural selection* is the main force directing and controlling evolution. This theory is unquestionably the most outstanding generalization in the history of biology, and it has been suggested that it ranks with the great generalizations of the physical sciences, such as Newton's theory of gravity.

Darwin based his theory on three observable natural facts; firstly, that there is always an over-production of offspring by organisms so that there tends to be a geometrical increase in numbers; secondly, that despite this tendency, the numbers of any given species tend to remain fairly constant; and thirdly, that all organisms show appreciable variation. From the first two of these three observations, Darwin deduced that there must occur in nature a *struggle for existence*. From the third observation and this first deduction he further deduced that since individuals of a species are not all alike, some of the variation which occurs in a population will confer an advantage on its possessors in the struggle for survival, while other variations will be unfavourable. Thus, he reasoned that a high proportion of individuals carrying the advantageous variations will *on the average* survive, while those with unfavourable variations will tend to be eliminated or will not reproduce themselves. That is, natural selection will operate in favour of the *survival of the fittest*. Moreover, Darwin postulated that since some variations at least are inherited, the characters responsible for this differential survival will be passed on from generation to generation. Natural selection will thus be a constant force, acting to improve and maintain the adjustment of all plants and animals to their environment and mode of existence.

Alfred Russell Wallace, independently and more or less at the same time as Darwin, also reached the conclusion that natural selection was the operative force in evolution. Indeed this idea was first presented to the world in 1858 as a joint communication to the Linnean Society of London. Unquestionably, priority for the concept must go to Darwin, who had worked on this immense problem for twenty years and amassed a vast amount of evidence in its support. Wallace indeed generously referred to the shares of Darwin and himself, in respect of their contributions to the theory of natural selection, in the proportions of 'twenty years to one week'! Wallace's views were intuitive and by no means so fully developed as Darwin's, though the basic theory was the same. It is therefore to Darwin that the credit must go for the first full proof of evolution, and for the demonstration that it could be accounted for by a natural law.

The seeds of evolutionary thought were sown in Darwin's mind when, as naturalist on H.M.S. *Beagle*, he visited many Atlantic and Pacific islands, the east and west coasts of South America, as well as New Zealand and Australia. The first fruits of this voyage were for Darwin largely of geological significance and related to the formation of coral reefs. From the standpoint of evolution, however, his most important observations were on the geographical distribution of fossils in the east of South America and of the fauna of the Galapagos Islands. He became convinced that such distribution could not be explained by special creation but required an evolutionary theory. Thus Darwin states at the beginning of the *Origin of Species*, 'When on board H.M.S. Beagle, I was much struck with certain facts in the distribution of the organic beings inhabiting South America and in the geological relations of the present to past inhabitants of that continent. These facts . . . seemed to throw some light on the origin of species – that mystery of mysteries, as it has been called by one of our greatest philosophers.' In the *Origin*, the first fact to which Darwin draws attention is that in nature animals and plants vary, so that no two specimens are ever exactly alike, and that often the differences are very considerable. Moreover, he recognized that 'these individual differences are of the highest importance for us, for they are often inherited . . . and they thus afford materials for natural selection to act on and accumulate, in the same manner as man accumulates in any given direction individual differences in his domesticated productions.' On this latter topic Darwin himself had accumulated an enormous body of facts which he used to demonstrate the remarkable capacity for variation inherent in plants and animals.

Species

Although the title of this important work was the *Origin of Species*, Darwin nowhere defines the term 'species' and indeed, lays no special emphasis on species except in so far as he was concerned in finding out whether some fundamental distinction could be made between *species*, which according to current belief, were created as such when life began, and *varieties*, which developed in relation to local or temporary conditions. In fact he wished to know whether the thought could be entertained that varieties were species in the making, which would imply that species themselves were changing entities. Again it was his experiences on the *Beagle* that made him doubt the immutability of species, for he states that 'many years ago, when comparing, and seeing others compare, the birds from the closely neighbouring islands of the Galapagos Archipelago, one with another, and with those from the American mainland, I was struck how entirely vague and arbitrary is the distinction between species and varieties'. In this connection he made two points: first, that the organisms on isolated islands, while obviously related to those on the nearest mainland, differ from them in varying degrees; and second, that in the unusual and very remarkable family of birds, the Groundfinches, which are more or less confined to the Galapagos, there seemed to be no sharp distinction between the numerous so-called species – all were connected by gradations and intermediates. Thus Darwin concludes that 'no clear line of demarcation has yet been drawn between species and sub-species . . . or again between sub-species and varieties or between lesser varieties and individual differences. These differences blend into each other by an insensible series; and a series impresses the mind with the idea of an actual passage. From these remarks it will be seen that I look at the term species as one arbitrarily given. . . .'

Even with present knowledge the concept of species is remarkably difficult to define. It is more than just a group of similar plants and animals which, because they possess certain distinctive characters in common, taxonomists have (in most cases!) agreed to distinguish by means of a Latin name. *Species are populations, or groups of populations, inhabiting a geographical area which accords with the idea of a common origin for the whole population. The members of the population interbreed, or are potentially capable of interbreeding, with each other, while populations belonging to different species usually do not interbreed in the wild. If they do hybridize, their fertility is reduced.* From the evolutionary point of view, the infrequency of hybridization is important, for it implies that there is little *genetic exchange* between species, so that they are committed to separate evolutionary paths. If there was successful hybridization, most groups of species would consist of *hybrid swarms* which it would be impossible to separate or classify.

Isolation

The origin of new species thus depends largely on the effective *isolation* of part of the population. Isolation can be of several kinds. In *geographical isolation*, groups of a population become separated from one another by natural barriers and, since the groups are unable to interbreed, they might evolve along different, or divergent, lines. Isolation may be *ecological*, with different races of a population occupying different habitats, their tolerance to a particular *ecological niche* depending on a simple genetic difference.

Depending on the length of time of their isolation, various stages in the formation of new species may be found. Thus below the level of species there are *sub-species*, sometimes called *geographical races*. These are populations whose members possess characters separating them from other populations, though they are able to hybridize successfully when they meet in the wild. Once effectively isolated, however, gene differences may accumulate which are not disadvantageous within the group, but which lead to infertility between members of the two groups. Once this has been attained there will be no mixing between the groups even though there has been a breakdown of the geographical or ecological barriers originally isolating them. Clearly, in the formation of species some factor external to the organism may be necessary to initiate the isolation, but once achieved they become genetically isolated by gene and chromosomal alterations (i.e. by mutations) so that interbreeding becomes impossible.

Large Scale Evolution

Darwin however, was concerned not only with the variability, inconstancy, and the arbitrary nature of species – that is with the problems of 'small scale evolution'; he was also interested in much larger evolutionary trends and wondered how, for example, without accepting evolution, it was possible to account for the remarkable fact that animals, so widely different in adult form as are mammals, birds and reptiles, resemble each other so closely as embryos. He was also interested in the significance of rudimentary or vestigial organs, pointing out that they were meaningless and that their origins presented insuperable difficulties in terms of special creation. Their existence, however, is immediately intelligible once it is accepted that plants and animals have evolved through a series of stages before attaining their present condition. Organs adapted to one set of environmental conditions may thus persist even when a new and markedly different set of conditions has rendered them useless. Darwin illustrates this with the following example: '. . . in certain islands not tenanted by a single mammal, some of the endemic plants have beautifully hooked seeds; yet few relations are more manifest than that hooks serve for the transport of seeds in the wool or fur of quadripeds. But a hooked seed might be carried to an island by other means; and the plant then becoming modified would form an endemic species, still retaining its hooks, which would form a useless appendage like the shrivelled wings under the soldered wing covers of many insular beetles.' The significant fact stressed by Darwin about rudimentary organs is their uselessness; that is, they are rudimentary in function. Summarizing his views about the use and disuse of organs, Darwin draws the very important conclusion that 'the chief part of the organization of every living creature is due to inheritance; and consequently, though each being assuredly is well fitted for its place in nature, many structures have now no very close and direct relation to present habits of life'.

Palaeontology and Evolution

Another very important line of evidence in favour of evolution as distinct from special creation has gradually emerged from the *palaeontological record* or the study of *fossils*. Darwin made valuable contributions in this connection and showed that the character of fossils change gradually with time so that 'the fauna of each geological period undoubtedly is intermediate in character between preceding and succeeding faunas'. Since Darwin's time much more detailed evidence has come to light indicating that throughout geological time, which is measured in millions of years, there has been a remarkable succession of living forms indicative of a steady, gradual change – an evolutionary progression has been at work. The now classic example from the fossil record, unknown to Darwin, is the gradual evolution of the horse over a period of forty to fifty million years from small, four-toed animals with primitive teeth, to large one-toed animals with complex grinding molars of the modern horse. Over this vast period of time the trend has been towards greater size, rapid running, and a herbivorous diet. Palaeontology thus makes it possible to comprehend the results of evolutionary change over immensely long periods. In the geological record, the events of past ages are perfectly telescoped and it is now one of the most satisfying and strongest pieces of evidence of the evolutionists. Unfortunately, the palaeontological evidence is not equally satisfactory for all organisms, so that most has been derived from the fossils of vertebrates, with their bony skeletons, and from the shells of molluscs. Unfortunately, plants being much softer, occur as fossils much less frequently (fig. 220).

Darwin gained other evidence for evolution from the geographical distribution of plants and animals, and he states in this connection 'the first great fact which strikes us is that neither the similarity nor dissimilarity of the inhabitants of various regions can be wholly accounted for by climatal or other physical differences'. He cites the example of tracts of land in different continents with very similar climates which have very different floras and faunas. He also stressed that geographical barriers, such as mountains, deserts, or even rivers, are obstacles to the free migration of species and that barriers influence the floras and fauna they divide, in direct proportion to their size.

Natural Selection and the Survival of the Fittest

These various lines of evidence led Darwin to the unavoidable conclusion that evolution, or *descent with modification*, took place. But to assert that evolution was a fact was one thing, to account for it was another. Even in the early stages of his investigations Darwin realized that the changes brought about by the domestication of plants and animals would probably hold the answer to this most important part of the problem, since the changes wrought in this way were much more rapid than any which occur in nature. After searching enquiries, which included discussion with breeders and gardeners, he soon realized that *selection* was the essence 'of man's success in making useful races of animals and plants'.

Just how selection operated under natural conditions remained a mystery to Darwin for some time. The first clue came as a result of comparing and contrasting the characters of domestic races with those of wild races, for Darwin found usefulness the factor common to both. Although it was easy to see how through deliberate selection a breeder could produce useful characters, there could clearly be no such conscious selection by any animal, let alone plant, of any of its own characters. As stated in his Autobiography, a fortunate chance provided a valuable clue to this part of the problem. 'In October 1838, that is fifteen months after I had begun my systematic enquiry, I happened to read for amusement, Malthus on *Population*, and being well prepared to appreciate the struggle for existence which everywhere goes on from long-continued observation of the habits of animals and plants, it at once struck me that under these circumstances favourable variations would tend to be preserved and unfavourable ones to be destroyed. The result of this would be the formation of new species.' This work by Malthus, the political economist, referred to by Darwin was an *Essay on the Principle of Population as it affects the Future Improvement of Society*, published in 1798. It was a theoretical study on the growth of human populations, its main argument being that if all the offspring produced were to survive they would increase at an enormous rate: this they do not do, but remain on the average, constant.

The Malthus essay led Darwin to the realization that the struggle for existence must depend on the fact that all organisms produce more offspring than can survive and again reproduce their kind, so that there is bound to be competition for the *biological privilege of survival.* Darwin states that there is 'no exception to the rule that every organic being naturally increases at so high a rate that if not destroyed, the earth would soon be covered by the progeny of a single pair'.... 'Linneaus has calculated that if an annual plant produced only two seeds . . . and their seedlings next year produced two, and so on, then in twenty years there would be one million plants,' Darwin gives some examples in which limitations on increases in numbers do not operate; introduced plants for instance become abundant and spread throughout vast areas in a remarkably short time.

Checks however, are imposed on the increase of most natural populations of plants and animals at all stages of their development from seed, or egg, to adult, especially by the depredations of other organisms. Limits are also imposed by the amount of food available to any species. Climatic factors, particularly extremes of cold and drought exert periodic checks on population increase, mainly by reducing food supply with the result that competition for available food is intensified. Environmental conditions are always harsh for any species, but they become more so as the size of the population increases. It is, however, usually very difficult to discover the precise way in which the struggle for existence operates because of the complexity of the interrelations between different species.

There has been much misinterpretation in biological and particularly in political spheres about what Darwin implied by the phrase 'struggle for existence'. He certainly had no intention of limiting its meaning to fights or combats between organisms, in which the strongest, or fittest, would win and thus survive. He laid stress not so much on the survival of the individual, but rather on its capacity to reproduce its kind and leave progeny.

Evolution and Genetics

Although many people objected to Darwin's ideas on religious grounds, there were others who, while not doubting the fact of evolution, questioned the validity of natural selection as an operative force. Darwin's theory was only a working hypothesis and what later scientists wanted, was a tested theory based on factual and if possible, experimental evidence. Thus anti-Darwinists were especially critical of the absence of some concrete demonstration of the reality and intensity of the process of selection in the wild, as opposed to artificial selection, for which there was plenty of sound evidence. Criticism was also directed against the amount of raw material which selection had to work on; that is on the nature and amount of variability shown by organisms.

Darwin did not know how, or to what extent, variations could be inherited, for he wrote that 'the laws governing inheritance are for the most part unknown'. He believed that heredity was *blending* and not *particulate*, as Mendel was to show later. Darwin realized and recorded in consequence of this, that any new variants, unless they chanced to mate with similar variant characters, would be constantly diminished and eventually submerged. To maintain any reasonable amount of variability there would have to be a vast increase in what is now accepted as a normal mutation rate. Darwin's explanation for this weakness in his theory was that changes in the 'conditions of life' produced considerable increases in variability which were required for the operation of artificial or natural selection. But contrary to this explanation was the insurmountable difficulty that the variability of cultivated plants was greatest in those countries where they had been in cultivation for the longest time.

Once it was accepted that all inheritance was particulate, it became clear how variance with a genetic basis is conserved; so the most serious objection to Darwin's views was removed. Later it was realized that the conservation of variance was aided by the effects of dominance, since most mutant genes are recessive. This means that even deleterious recessives will not be selected against unless in the very rare event of their appearance in a homozygous condition.

The removal of these objections is not the only contribution of Mendelism in support of natural selection. Of the utmost importance is the phenomenon of recombination, which Mendel demonstrated in his experiments in pea crosses differing in two characters. He found in the F_2 that the two original types not only appeared together but also that these characters appeared to separate and recombine to produce two new types (Chapter 25). These plants are thus provided with an additional and very considerable source of genetic variation. In the long run of course, evolution must depend on the appearance of quite new gene types, that is on mutations (see p. 310) and consequent heterozygosity. Recombination also provides the 'biological rationale' for sex; without sex any mutation is confined to the line in which it originated, as, for example, in asexually reproducing species. With sex, new mutations can be combined with other mutations originating in other individuals. Particulate inheritance and sexual reproduction together, therefore, provide at least some of the variety in organisms necessary for the occurrence of rapid evolution.

Despite the discovery of particulate inheritance, early geneticists cast doubt on Darwin's belief that it was small variations that provided the raw material on which natural selection worked. Some pointed out, for example, that new varieties seem to arise suddenly by mutation and they suggested that new species arose in a similar way. Indeed, for a time considerable importance was attached to observations by the Dutch botanist De Vries, who noted sudden and striking changes in *Oenothera lamarkiana*, the evening primrose. From these, De Vries concluded that evolution proceeded by large, inherited 'jumps', so that new species arose at one stroke. Later, investigations revealed however, that these changes could be explained by the fact that *Oenothera* is exceptional in having a large number of translocations in its chromosomes (see p. 311). When self-fertilized, various forms of *Oenothera* tend to breed true, except for some 2% of the offspring which are quite unlike the parents. These are the *mutant species* which were the basis of the De Vries *mutation theory*. More recent studies of *Oenothera* have indicated that his observations were the result of the large scale recombination of existing genetic material. One of his 'new' species owed its origin to the production of a polyploid. Moreover, it soon became increasingly clear that large mutations are often monstrosities, unfitted to survive in nature and unable to reproduce themselves, even under artificial conditions.

Evolution and Polyploidy

The rejection of the hypothesis that species arise by single, major mutations made Darwin's concept of evolution by small changes once again acceptable. There is, however, one well recognized exception to this rule. It is known that new species can be formed abruptly by the crossing of two other species, followed by chromosome doubling, that is by allopolyploidy (see p. 313). The first example was when an 'artificial' species of *Primula*, *P. kewensis* (n=18) was produced by a doubling of the chromosome number in a sterile hybrid between *P. verticillata* (n=9) and *P. floribunda* (n=9) (fig. 219).

Primula kewensis probably owes its survival to human aid, but the cord, or rice grass, *Spartina townsendii*, is a new species which arose and has survived, it might be said, despite human intervention. An American species of *Spartina*, *S. alterniflora*, whose seeds were accidently carried to Britain in ships' cargoes, established itself on the south coast of England. It hybridized with the local European species, *S. maritima*, and from the hybrid a fully fertile allopolyploid arose, which is apparently hardier than either of the parent species and better adapted to tidal mud-flats, which it has rapidly colonized. The new species, *S. townsendii*, has rapidly spread along the sea coasts and in some places has become a positive nuisance because it entraps silt and is encroaching on beaches in certain coastal holiday resorts. Polyploidy in various ways has unquestionably played a role of considerable significance in the evolution of both wild and cultivated plants.

Neo-Darwinism

Attempts have been made to revive the Lamarkian doctrine of the inheritance of acquired characters in favour of natural selection, but none of the experimental evidence purporting to support it has ever been confirmed. Moreover, mathematical analysis shows, in vindication of the theory of natural selection, that a new variation giving its possessors even 0·1% of biological advantage over those without it, would spread quite rapidly through a population.

Although the power and influence of natural selection may occasionally be temporarily relaxed, so that certain species over-multiply, this relaxation of *selection pressure* allows the increase of abnormalities which would not survive under normal conditions. Eventually some environmental change, or the very size of the population, gradually exerts its selective influence towards the eventual reversion of the population to its normal size. Indeed it is now accepted that natural selection is a universal influence, operating in two apparently contradictory directions – encouraging or discouraging change. Not only does selection lead to the specialization of plants and animals and their adaptation to a particular mode of existence, but once a certain point is reached this omnipresent force then acts to stabilize and maintain the perfected type.

One of the remarkable features of the Darwinian concept of natural selection as the guiding force of evolution is that recent work has shown that only on a few points

Figure 219 Primula kewensis (*centre*), *an artificial species formed by the doubling of the chromosome number in a sterile hybrid resulting from the crossing of* P. verticillata (*right*) *and* P. floribunda (*left*). (*Photos by courtesy Royal Botanic Garden, Edinburgh.*)

has Darwin since been shown to have been in error. He was mistaken in his belief in blending inheritance, and in his acceptance of the idea that acquired characters can, as postulated by Lamark, play some part in evolution; his ideas about the nature of species, too, are not in accord with modern concepts. Nevertheless, present day evolutionary theory, or *Neo-Darwinism* as it has been termed, is simply the development of Darwin's theory as set down in the *Origin of Species*. Advance, in the main, has not been through the replacement of Darwin's misconceptions but as a result of our wider knowledge of many aspects of biology, especially in the fields of cytology and genetics.

PART VI

THE PLANT KINGDOM – A SURVEY

CHAPTER 29

THE ORIGINS AND DIVERSITY OF PLANT LIFE

It has been established that organisms are mutable, and that mutations acted on by natural selection provided the raw materials for evolution (see Chapters 25 and 26). Although it was indicated in surveying the mechanism of evolution that in general increasingly complex and highly adapted organisms have evolved from simpler ancestors, so far little consideration has been given to these 'lower' forms of plant life.

Life itself has not always existed on the earth. Indeed, it is believed that conditions on this planet, which it is estimated came into existence some four and a half thousand million years ago by the accretion of clouds of dust and gas particles surrounding the sun, has for much more than half its history been quite unsuitable for life. Thus life must have come into existence within the period of the earth's own evolution. The stages leading to the origin of life, that is to the formation of the first self-reproducing mass of protein, can only be conjectured. It has been suggested, however, that *carbides*, known to have occurred in the hot surface rocks, reacted with the superheated water vapour of the earth's early atmosphere to produce simple *hydrocarbons*, such as *methane* or *acetylene*. Later, more complex hydrocarbons, all of which could be classed as *primary organic substances*, would be formed. Ammonia is also believed to have existed in fairly high concentrations in the atmosphere during this era.

The earth's dense envelope of water vapour was probably split into hydrogen and hydroxyl ions by intense ionizing radiations from the sun. These ions are then thought to have entered into combination with the previously formed hydrocarbons to produce with the hydrocarbons, alcohols, aldehydes, ketones and simple organic acids and with the ammonia they would combine to produce, in particular, amines and amides. Thus, as the earth began to cool, its still quite hot oceans would contain a number of fairly elaborate carbon- and nitrogen-containing compounds, though as yet no living matter. Latent in the chemical structure of these substances there was, however, the capacity for further organic evolution, which ultimately led to the evolution of life itself.

Life undoubtedly began with the formation of carbon-containing substances of increasing complexity and molecular weight, some of which would ultimately attain colloidal dimensions. Now the all important feature of colloids is their capacity to adsorb substances from their environment and incorporate them as gels (see p. 153). This *power of addition* is the essence of growth in all living organisms and it would seem that by such additions many widely different types of large and complex molecules must have been formed. However, by no means all the structurally differentiated groups of colloids produced in this random fashion would survive. Even in this pre-life era a type of natural selection would operate in favour of those colloidal substances which tended to incorporate new materials most rapidly. Eventually out of one of these increasingly complex organic substances the very first, though very simple, self-reproducing systems must have been born. At this important moment in the earth's history about two thousand million years ago, the gap between the non-living and living was bridged and life began its remarkable, and still unfinished, evolutionary journey.

These first living organisms would of course be completely unlike any living organism existing at the present time, for the environment of the primaeval oceans in which they arose has radically altered. This change is in no small measure due to the influence of life itself. It is also certain that these original forms of life could not survive in existing environmental conditions, just as it is doubtful whether any present day organism could survive the primaeval environment in which life began. For this reason it is certain that life could not originate on the earth as it is today.

At a certain stage in the earth's history it seems probable that the intense ionizing radiations from the sun played an important part in the formation of the complex molecules which eventually assumed the attributes of life. Later, as environmental conditions on the earth changed and the dense enveloping cloud of water vapour dispersed, certain organisms must have developed a mechanism whereby they could utilize some of the sun's radiant energy; hence the first photosynthetic system was evolved. In the course of evolution a variety of such systems have been produced with different types and combinations of photosynthetic pigments adapted to the earth's continually changing environmental conditions. This is evidenced by the different categories of bacteria and algae existing today with their diversity of photosynthetic pigments (see Chapters 30 and 31).

Some marine algae, especially the red and brown algae, have attained considerable complexity and quite a high degree of specialization as shown by the present day kelps (*Laminaria* spp.) and wracks (*Fucus* spp.). There is, however, general agreement that it was neither the red nor the brown algae, but the much less specialized green algae which were the early ancestors of the highest forms of plant life, the flowering plants. This assumption is largely based on the fact that they both possess the same photosynthetic pigments and general metabolism. Many simple green algae survive in fresh and salt waters today, and there is evidence from fossils of Precambrian age that somewhat similar plants existed over a thousand million years ago.

Until the geological era known as the Cambrian (see Chart, fig. 220), about five hundred million years ago, plant life existed only in the oceans, which were probably much less salty than they are today. During this period, however, the land began to be colonized by certain algal-like plants. The origins and probable appearance of these first landward migrants have interested botanists for many years, but since the relevant fossil evidence is so meagre, conclusions about them must be largely conjectural. If these algal-like plants were to invade the land successfully they would almost certainly have to undergo such structural and physiological changes as would enable them to take in water and essential mineral nutrients from the muds over which they first grow and to control water loss whilst allowing gaseous exchange. As plants became increasingly well adapted to survival outside their original element, other forms even better fitted to survive the rigours of terrestrial life, gradually evolved. Even so, several of the primitive characters which could be traced back to their algal ancestry persisted. In sexual reproduction for instance the male gametes require the presence of free water in order to swim towards and eventually fertilize the female gamete or egg. This primitive character can still be observed in present day liverworts, mosses and ferns, plants which are the contemporary representatives of a very long sequence of evolutionary changes. It was only at a comparatively late stage in the evolution of the land flora, probably about two hundred million years ago, towards the end of the Palaeozoic era, with the complete development of the seed habit that emancipation from water at the time of fertilization was achieved.

Major Forms of Life and the Age of Geological Periods

ERA	*PERIOD*	*FORMS OF LIFE*	*AGE IN YEARS*
CAINOZOIC	QUATERNARY	AGE OF MAN	1,500,000
	TERTIARY	*ANGIOSPERMS* *and mammals dominant*	30,000,000
MESOZOIC	CRETACEOUS JURASSIC TRIASSIC	*appearance of angiosperms* *GYMNOSPERMS* *and reptiles dominant*	180,000,000
PALAEOZOIC	CARBONIFEROUS		225,000,000
	DEVONIAN SILURIAN ORDOVICIAN	*some gymnosperms* *PTERIDOPHYTES* *and fish dominant*	370,000,000
	CAMBRIAN	FIRST LAND PLANTS *ALGAE dominant*	500,000,000
ARCHAEOZOIC	PRE-CAMBRIAN	FIRST LIVING ORGANISMS	2,500,000,000
FORMATION OF THE EARTH			4,500,000,000

Figure 220 *Time scale of evolution*

CHAPTER 30

CLASSIFICATION AND NOMENCLATURE

The science of the classification of living things, termed *taxonomy* and meaning the rendering of order, has its origins in the fourth century B.C., when Theophrastus, a pupil of Aristotle, wrote his *Enquiry into Plants*, and classified plants as herbs, shrubs and trees. It was not until the eighteenth century, however, that a really significant stride was made in this important branch of biological science with the publication in 1737 of *Genera Plantarum* by the Swedish botanist Carl Linnaeus. He was concerned mainly with flowering plants, and used their reproductive parts as the criteria of his classification; hence it became known as the Sexual System of Classification and was based principally on the numbers and arrangement of the stamens and carpels of the flower. Since single characters of plants rarely indicate a real, or natural, affinity this was an *artificial system* of classification. It must be recognized, however, that Linnaeus did not regard his system as final but merely as the preliminary to a *natural system* in which the true relationships between plants would be shown. Such a system, based on the general similarities of all parts of the plant and not exclusively on one character, the sex organs, was in fact outlined in his *Philosophia Botanica* of 1751.

Darwin's writings on evolution, published in 1859, gave currency to the concept that different organisms may be related to one another by descent. This heralded a new era of classification based on *phylogeny*, or the racial history of living organisms. From the comparative study of living plants ranging from the simplest pond scums to the most highly specialized of flowering plants, aided by the still fragmentary knowledge of plants of past geological ages as revealed by the fossil record, botanists have attempted to construct a genealogical tree of the entire plant kingdom. In its compilation an attempt has been made to show the probably affinities of all the many and diverse groups of plants which exist now, or existed in past eras, so that they form a graded series, exemplifying successive stages in the evolutionary progression. The resulting evolutionary classification based on relationship by descent has been described as a *vertical* classification in contrast to the *horizontal* pre-Darwinian classifications which tended to consider organisms without thought to their past history.

Nomenclature

An important and essential part of any plant classification is the naming of its ultimate units, the species. From at least the fourteenth century at the latest, Latin was the language used by all men of science: thus it was inevitable that all plants were given Latin names. It was found quite impossible, however, to find a different name for each species, so that two plants which appeared to have similar though not identical characters were given the same first name, to which was added a second name to distinguish one from the other. When the resemblance between the plants was even closer a third name was usually added, while in certain cases a fourth name was found to be necessary. Thus the meadow buttercup became *Ranunculus pratensis erectus acris*.

Of greater and more lasting importance than his systems of plant classification was Linnaeus' introduction of a *Binomial System* of naming plants. According to this the official name of each plant species was restricted to two Latin words, no matter in what country it was first found or in what language it was first described. This use of a universal language of nomenclature helps to avoid ambiguity of meaning, for local or vernacular plant names often differ radically from district to district, even in a small country such as Great Britain. It conveys, moreover, the same information about the species in question to botanists throughout the world.

This now internationally accepted method of naming plants cannot be applied arbitrarily and a precise set of rules must be followed. In fact, so that 'the nomenclature of the past might be put into order and to provide for that of the future', the International Botanical Congress meeting in Vienna in 1905 formulated a series of rules for the naming of all plants. New names are now accepted only if these rules are followed. According to this code of nomenclature every plant must belong to a *species*, every species to a *genus*, every genus to a *tribe*, every tribe to a *family*, every family to an *order*, every order to a *class*, every class to a *division*, and each division to the plant kingdom. In naming species under the Binomial System, the first name, the *generic name*, indicates the genus to which the species belongs, while the second, the *specific name*, distinguishes the species of plant from others of the same genus. Generic names are always written with an initial capital letter and it is now recognized practice to use a small, or lower case, letter for all specific epithets,

The International Rules also lay down that after the specific name of each plant, the author of the name must be given. Thus modern nomenclature of the meadow buttercup is *Ranunculus acris* Linnaeus, though Linnaeus is conventionally abbreviated to L. When ecological, cytological, genetical, or purely taxonomic research indicates that the specific name of a plant should be changed, the name of the original author is given in brackets after the plant's specific name, followed by that of the author responsible for the change in name. For example, *Ranunculus lutarius* (Révell) Bouvet, the mud crowfoot, and *Nuphur lutea* (L.) Sm., the yellow water lily.

Despite the existence of these International Rules the possibility still exists that different authors have given different names to the same species. To minimize possible confusion, it is now accepted that anyone referring to British flowering plants should use the specific names given in the *Flora of the British Isles* by Clapham, Tutin and Warburg. Similarly, the 'check-lists' of species which have been prepared for several lower groups of plants should be used as a basis for their nomenclature.

Present Day Systems of Plant Classification

Linnaeus, in his Sexual System of Classification, recognized twenty-three groups of flowering plants and in a twenty-fourth group, the Cryptogamia, he placed all plants appearing to be without visible organs of reproduction. By the latter part of the nineteenth century, the Cryptogamia of Linnaeus had come to include three major divisions of simple plants.

The most primitive of the Cryptogamia were called the Thallophyta, a Division embracing the seaweeds and pond scums (Algae) and the moulds and mushrooms (Fungi); secondly, there were the Bryophyta, comprising the liverworts and mosses; thirdly, the Pteridophyta, with the ferns and their allies – the simplest of the plants possessing vascular systems. The remainder of the Plant Kingdom, that is the cone-bearing and flowering plants, because their organs of reproduction were evident and not hidden, were termed the Phanerogamia.

A NINETEENTH-CENTURY CLASSIFICATION OF THE PLANT KINGDOM
(after Eichler 1886)

CRYPTOGAMAE (includes plants with no visible organs of reproduction)
- Division THALLOPHYTA
  - Class Algae (seaweeds and pond scums)
  - Class Fungi (moulds, mushrooms and toadstools)
- Division BRYOPHYTA (liverworts and mosses)
- Division PTERIDOPHYTA (ferns and fern allies)

PHANEROGAMAE (includes plants with visible organs of reproduction)
- Division SPERMATOPHYTA (seed-producing plants)
  - Class Gymnospermae (cone-bearing plants)
  - Class Angiospermae (flowering plants)

The separation of plants into cryptogams and phanerogams is no longer retained in modern systems of classification, though the terms themselves are still quite useful. Neither can the Division Thallophyta, within the Cryptogamia, be retained, for apart from the lack of evidence of any close relationship between Algae and Fungi, the Algae themselves constitute such a diverse assemblage of simple plants that this Class cannot be maintained even as one Division. Indeed, it is still accepted that although the Plant Kingdom can be divided into two Sub-kingdoms, these are based on the presence or absence of a true nucleus. Plants without a true nucleus constitute the Sub-kingdom Procaryota, which includes two Divisions, the Bacteria, and the Cyanophyta or blue-green algae. All other plants possess a true nucleus and are grouped within the Sub-kingdom Eucaryota. This Sub-kingdom contains ten separate Divisions, six of which were included within the nineteenth century Class Algae. These algal Divisions are Rhodophyta, Chrysophyta, Phaeophyta, Chlorophyta, Euglenophyta, and Pyrrophyta. The old Class Fungi now becomes a separate Division Eumycophyta.

The Bryophyta, in contrast to the Thallophyta, constitutes a natural, and therefore still acceptable Division; hence it is retained in modern systems of classification.

Not all botanists, however, agree about the status of the Pteridophyta. Some suggest that as vascular plants they should be grouped with the seed plants, the Spermatophyta, into one Division Tracheophyta. This proposal, which emphasizes the universal occurrence of tracheary tissues as the essential character of the vasular system of all these plants, is however by no means generally accepted. Indeed, on balance, it seems better to retain the Pteridophyta and to split this Division into three Subdivisions: the Filicopsida, the ferns; the Sphenopsida, the horsetails; the Lycopsida, the club-mosses. The Division Spermatophyta, or seed plants, is also retained and also its two major Classes, Gymnospermae and Angiospermae. This more acceptable and rational classification of the Plant Kingdom is as follows:

SUB-KINGDOM PROCARYOTA (plants with a 'nuclear apparatus' but no 'true' nucleus)
- Division BACTERIA
- Division CYANOPHYTA – blue-green algae

SUB-KINGDOM EUCARYOTA (plants with a 'true' nucleus)
- Division RHODOPHYTA – red algae
- Division CHRYSOPHYTA – golden-yellow algae
- Division PHAEOPHYTA – brown algae
- Division CHLOROPHYTA – grass-green algae
- Division EUGLENOPHYTA – euglenoids
- Division PYRROPHYTA – dinoflagellates
- Division EUMYCOPHYTA – fungi
- Division BRYOPHYTA
  - Class Hepaticeae – liverworts
  - Class Musci – mosses
  - Class Anthocerotae – horned liverworts
- Division PTERIDOPHYTA
  - *Sub-division Filicopsida* – ferns
  - *Sub-division Sphenopsida* – horsetails
  - *Sub-division Lycopsida* – club-mosses
- Division SPERMATOPHYTA – seed plants
  - Class Gymnospermae – conifers
  - Class Angiospermae – flowering plants

CHAPTER 31

BACTERIA

The Bacteria, a large and diverse group of micro-organisms, are mostly unicellular and widely distributed in the air and in fresh and salt waters. They are also abundant in the soil and amongst dead and decaying organic matter, and many occur in and on the bodies of living plants and animals.

Although first described by Van Leuwenhoek in 1683, the critical study of these organisms only began in the nineteenth century. Early investigators believed them to have affinities with the fungi because in the main they are colourless and without photosynthetic pigments. Hence Naegeli in 1857 proposed naming them the Schizomycetes, meaning 'fission fungi'. The name Bacteria, proposed in 1872 is, however, preferable since it is now abundantly clear that bacteria and fungi bear no close relationship.

The systematic position of bacteria has been the subject of much controversy, but it is now generally agreed that together with the blue-green algae, with which they have several features in common, they constitute a very distinctive group of plants. They are considered to be plants, principally because they possess cell walls and so are unable to ingest solid food particles as do animals. Like plants, they take in water and dissolved substances through their intact cell walls. They differ, however, so radically in many other features from other plants that some have suggested that the bacteria constitute a distinct kingdom of the living world.

A widely held, though quite erroneous conception of the role of bacteria in nature is that they are disease-producing organisms, particularly harmful to man. In fact only a comparatively few bacterial species are *pathogenic*. Most are not only harmless, but are essential for the existence and well-being of other organisms. Thus soil fertility depends entirely on the activities of bacteria; some break down and mineralize organic matter, while others are concerned with the fixation of atmospheric nitrogen (see p. 184). Similarly, the recycling of nutrients in the lakes and oceans of the world depends to a large extent on bacterial activity.

Since the majority of bacteria lack chlorophyll they are unable to carry out photosynthesis, consequently their nutrition, in contrast to the *autotrophic*, self-feeding, nutrition of green plants, is *heterotrophic*. They depend on an external supply of organic material for their energy requirements. Amongst these are the relatively non-exacting bacterial *saprophytes* which, through enzyme activity, break down dead organic matter in the soil.

A few bacteria do possess chlorophyll and some carotinoid pigments, and thus being able to carry out photosynthesis, are autotrophic (see p. 205). Their chlorophyll

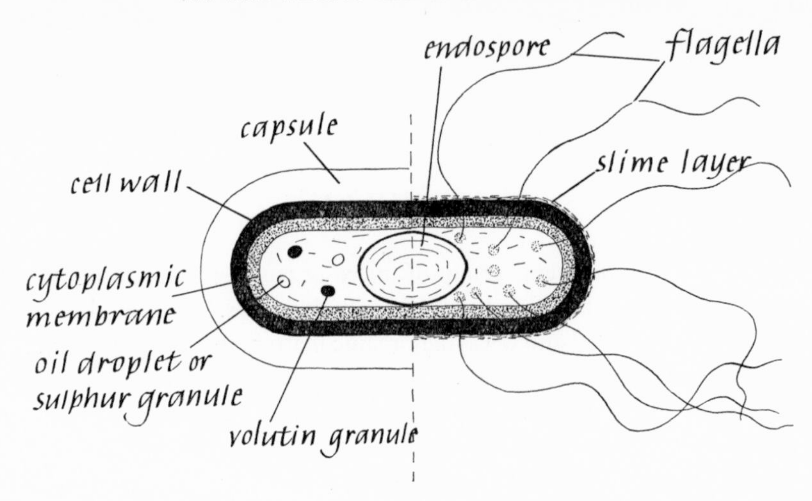

Figure 221 *Composite diagram showing the typical anatomical structures common to many bacteria;* (*left*) *a capsulated, non-flagellated bacillus;* (*right*) *a flagellated, non-capsulate bacillus* (*after Hawker, Linton, Folkes and Carlile*).

differs only slightly in its composition from that of higher plants. Other autotrophic bacteria do not possess chlorophyll and yet are able to synthesize carbohydrates from carbon dioxide and water. In the absence of chlorophyll they clearly cannot obtain energy for such synthesis from sunlight. They derive it instead from the oxidation of various substances. Nitrifying bacteria oxidize ammonia and nitrates, sulphur bacteria oxidize sulphuretted hydrogen, and the iron bacteria ferrous iron; such bacteria are described as *chemosynthetic*. Indeed, the metabolism of bacteria as a group is much more varied and flexible than that of higher organisms, which tend to be fairly rigidly fixed in their chemical potentialities. It has been suggested that this is because the bacteria and blue-green algae evolved during an early stage in the earth's history, when environmental conditions were very different from those existing today. This resulted in the development of organisms adapted to the greatest variety of situations in which life could possibly be sustained.

Structure of the Bacterial Cell (fig. 221)

Bacteria range in size from 0·5–50μ in length, though the majority are only from 1–2μ long and about 0·5μ in diameter. Thus they can only be studied adequately with the highest magnifications – $\frac{1}{12}$ oil immersion objective – of the light microscope. Much of our recent knowledge of their internal structure has been revealed through the electron microscope.

The cell walls of bacteria are rigid structures, of complex chemical composition, consisting of proteins, polysaccharides and sometimes lipids, and in many species *diaminopimelic acid*, which is also a constituent of the walls of blue green algae. The chemical composition of the bacterial wall is a species characteristic, and on the reaction of the wall to particular treatment, bacteria are distinguished either as *gram-positive* or *gram-negative*. The walls of gram-negative bacteria have a higher lipid content and greater variety of amino-acids than those of gram-positive bacteria.

Within each cell there is a living protoplast consisting of a *nuclear apparatus* and cytoplasm. The nuclear apparatus, a poorly defined spherical or ovoid body, is quite unlike the nucleus of higher plants and animals. It becomes elongated or dumb-bell shaped in dividing cells, but there is nothing comparable to a mitosis, although some investigators have reported the appearance of chromosome-like bodies. The genetic material of the nuclear body is, however, unquestionably DNA (see Chapter 26).

The cytoplasm, which is usually non-vacuolated and does not show any of the streaming associated with higher plant cells, is characterized by the presence of *volutin* or *metachromatic* granules. In the few bacteria which possess chlorophyll, *bacteriochlorophyll*, the pigment is not aggregated into chloroplasts as in higher plants. The chlorophyll when examined under the light microscope appears to be distributed throughout the cytoplasm, but recent electron microscope studies indicate the presence of *chromatophores*, which have a lamellar structure and in which the chlorophyll is contained.

Many bacteria produce an extracellular material of a slimy or gelatinous nature. This may take the form of a *capsule*, a sharply defined, adherent covering layer round each cell, or in motile forms (see below) it may constitute a less well defined *slime layer* which may part freely from the cells. Capsules and slime are believed to be morphologically and biochemically distinct.

Motility in bacteria is generally associated with the presence of organs of locomotion known as *flagella*, of which there may be one or several to each cell. Sometimes these arise closely grouped together as bunches. Each flagellum is a long sinuous filament about 12 mμ in diameter, that is, similar in thickness to a single protein molecule. They are attached to one end of the protoplast and aligned away from the direction of motion. The flagella propel the organism by rhythmic spiral or corkscrew movements. Because of their small diameter, flagella can be seen with the light microscope only after the use of special staining techniques which cause the flagella to become much thicker.

Under certain environmental conditions, as for example following the exhaustion of nutrients essential for continued vegetative growth, highly resistant *endospores* are produced within the cells of a considerable number of bacterial species. Endospores are resistant to dessication, high temperatures, and other unfavourable environmental conditions. On the return of favourable conditions, these spores may germinate, each giving rise to a new vegetative cell.

Three major morphological bacterial types are recognized: the *coccal*, *bacillary*, and *spirillar* forms. Most of the *cocci* are spherical though a few are kidney-shaped. Their cells may divide regularly or irregularly, in one, two, or three planes, and may separate or remain attached to one another, thus giving rise to cell arrangements which may be important in identification. Some divide, for example, in one plane to

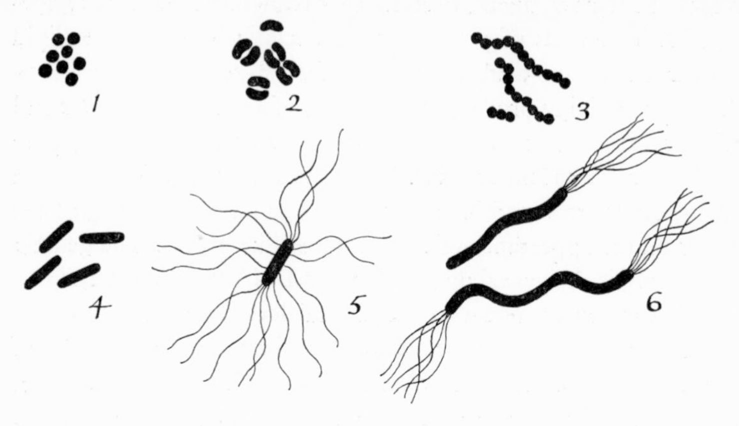

Figure 222 *The morphology of some typical bacteria.* 1 *Coccoid.* 2 *Diplococcus.* 3 *Chain of* Streptococcus. 4 *Rod.* 5 *Flagellate rod.* 6 *Flagellate spirillar.*

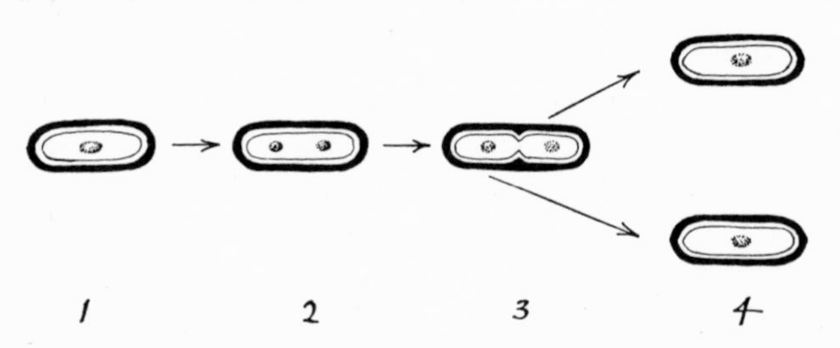

Figure 223 *Diagram showing binary fission in a bacillus.*

produce pairs of cells, *diplococci*; others form quite long chains. Regular divisions in two planes at right angles to one another result in *tetrads*, while irregular divisions in two or three planes give grape-like, or *botryoidal*, cell clusters (fig. 222).

The *bacilli* are bacteria whose cells are straight or slightly curved cylinders and, like the cocci, these may occur singly or remain attached to one another in chains.

As their name implies, the *spirillar* forms are spirally curved rods, and the cells of the type-genus *Spirillum* are long and cork-screw shaped up to 50μ long.

Reproduction and Growth

Bacteria normally, but not invariably, reproduce by the transverse *binary division* (division into two parts) of each cell into two daughter cells. The first stage of this process involves the equal division of the nuclear body, and the subsequent separation of the protoplasts by a transverse cell membrane. Ingrowth of the cell wall then occurs, and the final separation of the daughter cells is effected by a splitting of the cross wall across the middle. Under conditions of optimum growth, with divisions

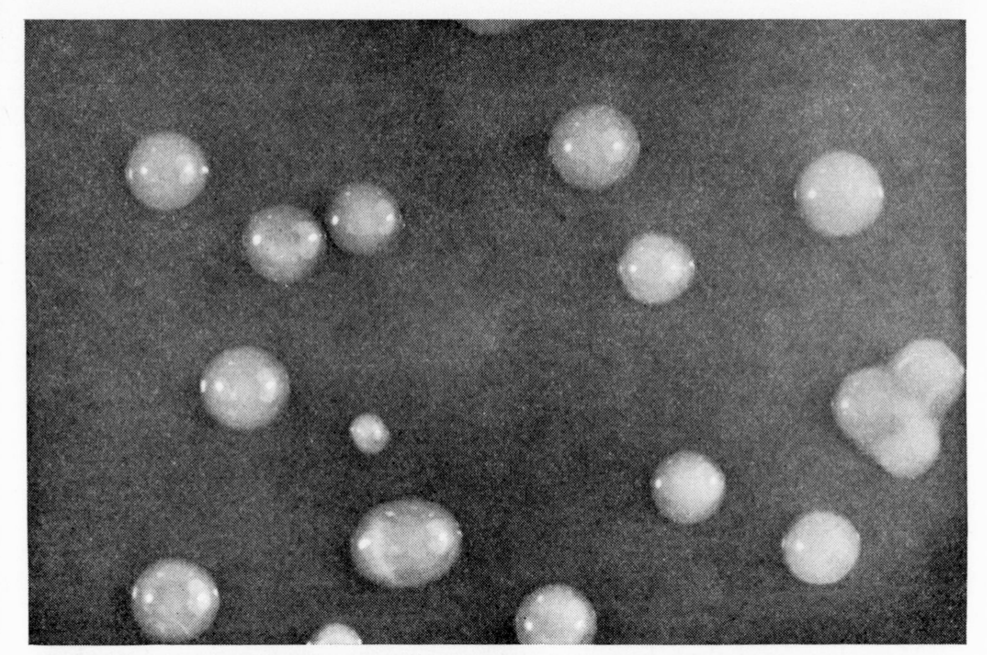

Figure 224 *Colonies of crown gall bacterium* (Agrobacterium tumefaciens) *on a glucose-yeastrel-chalk medium. The glistening appearance is characteristic.* (Figures 224-227 *by courtesy of Scientific Services, Dept. of Agriculture and Fisheries for Scotland.*)

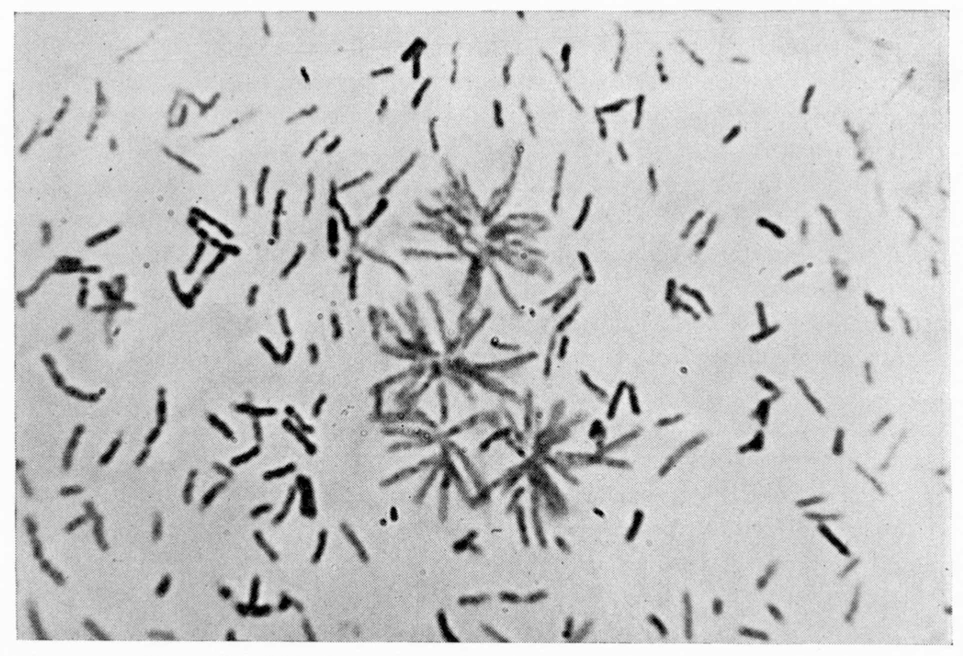

Figure 225 *Star cells of* Agrobacterium tumefaciens *on a culture of carrot broth. The bacteria appear to be taking part in some fusion process.*

occurring every hour, some 17 million cells can be produced from a single cell each day (fig. 223).

In the laboratory, bacteria are grown on solid media containing agar-agar and specially enriched nutrient solutions. After innoculation on to such media, they grow to form colonies, which quickly become visible to the naked eye. The appearance of a colony is constant for a given species and therefore valuable for purposes of identification. Most important in this connection is the appearance of the colony in vertical section: its colour, surface appearance, the nature of the colony margin, and often its odour (fig. 224); also whether it grows under aerobic or anaerobic conditions.

A sexual process has been found to occur in certain small gram-negative bacteria: two cells fuse over a small area, in which there is *sexual conjugation* (cf. p. 370), and nuclear material passes between. Although occurring rarely in nature, some laboratory mutants show a considerable degree of syngamy between compatible strains. The study of certain aspects of sexual reproduction in bacteria has contributed to the unravelling of some of the fundamental problems of genetics (fig. 225).

Bacterial Plant Diseases

Many diseases of plants have been attributed conclusively to bacteria. One of the most widespread, occurring year after year in various countries throughout the world, is caused by *Pectobacterium carotoferum* (also known as *Erwinia atroseptica*). This rod-shaped, facultative, gram-negative anaerobe, will attack a very considerable number of cultivated plants. Of these, the most important economically is the potato in which it causes *blackleg* and *tuber soft rot*. In this disease, the base of the stem becomes a striking dark brown or black colour, and instead of spreading outwards, the branches and leaves tend to grow upwards, giving the plants a compressed appearance. Also the leaves tend to turn yellow and may become curled and contorted (fig. 226). Only rarely do tubers of any size develop on infected plants, because their very necessary supply of translocated food substances is severely restricted by the disease in the aerial parts. Probably a different strain of the same bacterium causes soft rot of the tubers. These soon become transformed into soft, decaying, pulpy masses, held together only by their corky epidermis (fig. 228).

Another common *plant pathogen* is *Agrobacterium tumefaciens* whose occurrence is characterized by the formation of remarkable growths and excrescences of the diseased parts. Because these occur at the crown, or collar, of the roots of the affected plants (frequently fruit trees, but also roses and sugar beet), they are termed *crown galls*. The host cells are not destroyed by the bacteria but are stimulated into uncontrolled and irregular cell division. *A. tumefaciens* is a typical *wound parasite*, and can induce the formation of galls and tumours only through wounds (fig. 227).

Figure 226 *Potato blackleg; natural infection in the field. Note the wilting and collapse of the stems.*

Figure 227 *Crown gall on tomato (artificial infection).*

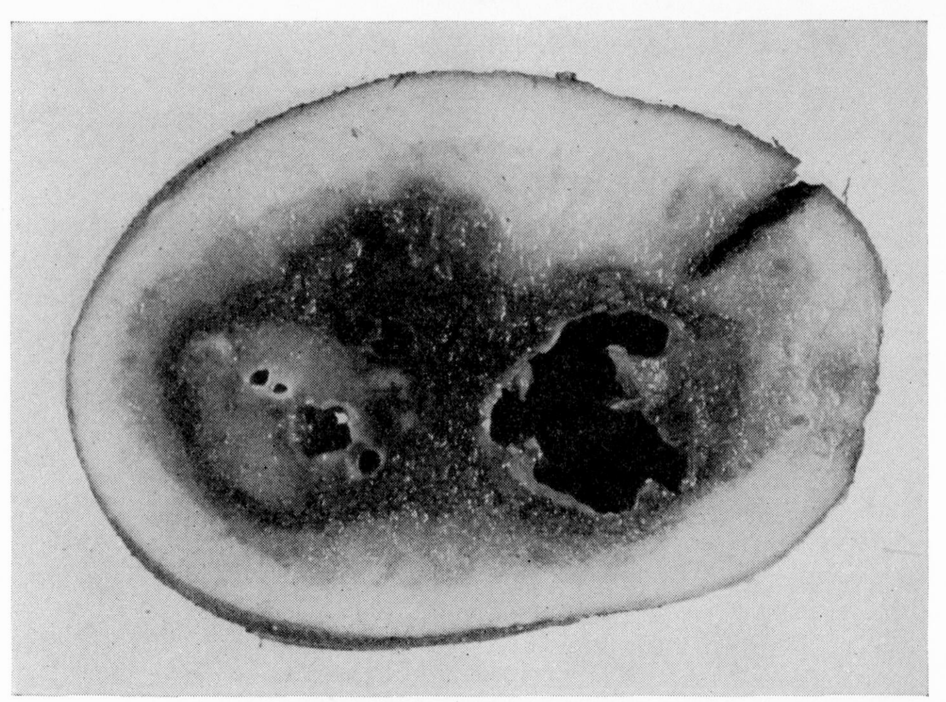

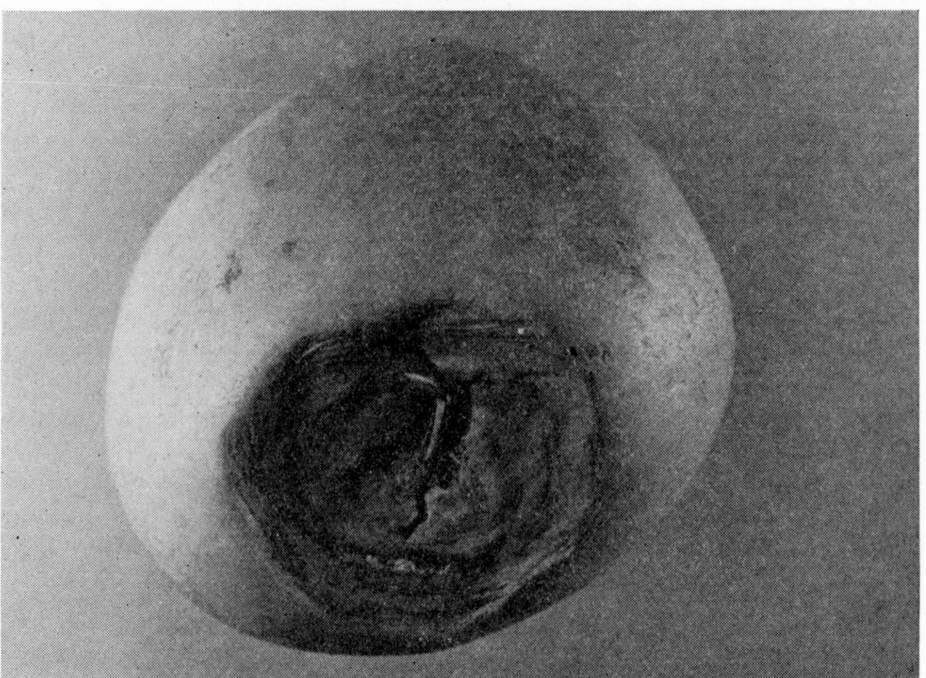

Figure 228 (*top*) *Potato tuber soft rot caused by various pectolytic bacteria.* (*bottom*) *Potato blackleg, tuber infection by way of a stolon.*

CHAPTER 32

DIVISIONS CYANOPHYTA, RHODOPHYTA, CHLOROPHYTA, CHRYSOPHYTA AND PHAEOPHYTA (ALGAE)

Alga is a Latin word meaning a seaweed, and although botanists still use it when referring to these primitive marine plants, and to pond scums and similar slimy growths on rocks and stones in lakes and streams, the term has now little taxonomic value. Indeed, these widely occurring plants are of such great diversity that it is generally agreed amongst *phycologists*, the botanists who make a special study of these plants, that they constitute at least seven separate divisions of the Plant Kingdom. Their only common features are that they are non-vascular, photosynthetic plants with unicellular organs of reproduction. This last character, in particular, distinguishes them from the less primitive Bryophyta (see Chapter 33).

Those who have collected seaweeds (marine algae) from a sea shore will doubtless know that at least three categories of these plants can be distinguished on the basis of colour. Some are bright green, some a dark or dusky brown, and others red. The chlorophyll pigments which give the leaves and other organs of flowering plants their green colour, and the associated carotins and xanthophylls, are also present in most algae. In the brown and red algae, however, they are masked by other pigments. The masking pigment in the brown algae (Division Phaeophyta) is *fucoxanthin* and in the red algae (Division Rhodophyta), *phycoerythrin*. Although the algae are broadly classified on the basis of their pigmentation, associated with this character there are fundamental differences in metabolism and consequently in the nature of their food reserves. For example, in the green algae (Division Chlorophyta) the principal food reserve is starch, in the Phaeophyta it is the alcohol *mannitol* and a complex polysaccharide, *laminarin*, while in the golden yellow algae (Division Chrysophyta), which are all microscopic forms, the food reserve is oil. There are also fundamental differences in the structure of the reproductive bodies (asexual spores and gametes) in each Division.

Apart from these differences on which the various algal Divisions of the Plant Kingdom are based, the algae, considered as a whole, exhibit an enormous diversity of form and structure, ranging from unicellular plants of only a few microns in diameter to multicellular forms which may be almost tree-like, several metres in length, and at the same time displaying a considerable degree of differentiation in their internal tissues. Even within each Division there is a wide diversity of form.

Most algae are aquatic plants, growing permanently submerged, either in freshwaters or in the sea. The commonest algae in lakes and in the sea are the free-floating microscopic forms, some of which are unicellular and others associated together to form colonies of various types. This *phytoplankton community* in the oceans comprises a bulk of living plant material vastly greater than all the terrestrial vegetation of the world (see Chapter 17, p. 207): indeed it constitutes the pasturage of the sea. In streams and rivers and the littoral regions of ponds and lakes, other algal communities, *benthos*, occur on stones, twigs, and on higher aquatic plants. Seaweeds are also *benthic* algae and they are nearly always attached to rocks. Algae of the benthos often become detached from their substratum and float freely on the surface of the water, as for example the green, slimy tangles of filamentous green algae which appear at certain times of the year on ponds or small lakes. Vast areas of the Sargasso Sea ('sargassum' is the Spanish for seaweed) become carpeted with the brown alga *Sargassum*. Not all algae, however, are aquatic; some occur in relatively dry situations, such as rocks, tree trunks, and drying mud. Many unicellular or simple filamentous species live in soil, and some of these play an important role in soil economy, especially in the tropics (see p. 352).

Although there is still some diversity of opinion concerning algal classification, the following algal Divisions of the Plant Kingdom are now generally recognized:

Procaryota (see p. 342)
- Division CYANOPHYTA – the blue-green algae

Eucaryota
- Division RHODOPHYTA – the red algae
- Division CHRYSOPHYTA – the golden-yellow algae
- Division PHAEOPHYTA – the brown algae
- Division CHLOROPHYTA – the grass-green algae
- Division EUGLENOPHYTA – the euglenoids
- Division PYRROPHYTA – the dinoflagellates

The diagnostic characters of some of these Divisions will be outlined in the following pages, and of the Chlorophyta, Chrysophyta, and Phaeophyta, detailed descriptions of the structure and life histories of representative genera will be given.

DIVISION CYANOPHYTA

The most striking feature of the blue-green algae, or Cyanophyta, is that their cells are fundamentally different from those of other plants, being much simpler in their organization. They possess, however, many points of similarity with certain bacterial cells (see Chapter 30), particularly in that there is no true nucleus; hence they are grouped with the bacteria in the Sub-kingdom Procaryota. Electron microscope investigations have shown that instead of a nucleus there is a *nucleoplasm* composed of a mass of fine fibrils, which in some species are dispersed throughout the cell, and in others concentrated in reticular structures of various shapes in its central region. DNA has been identified in the nucleoplasm of many blue-green algal cells. Arranged round the periphery of the cells are photosynthetic lamellae and although these too can only be seen with the electron microscope, it is clear from examination of cells with the light microscope that the photosynthetic pigments occur in an outer *chromatoplasm*. The photosynthetic pigments are a blue *phycocyanin*, chlorophyll, and carotinoids; under certain environmental conditions there is also an abundant production of the red pigment, phycoerythrin. The cell wall differs from that of other plants in that it consists of two concentric parts: a thin inner layer, which is more or less confluent with the protoplast, and an outer, much tougher gelatinous or mucilaginous *cell sheath*.

Sexual reproduction is unknown amongst the Cyanophyta and the vehicles of asexual reproduction, when present, are always non-motile spores.

A considerable diversity of form is encountered within the Division Cyanophyta. This ranges from single cells, through small regular or irregular colonies of a few cells (*Merismopedia* and *Chroococcus*), to large irregular colonies as in the genus *Microcystis*. There are also filamentous genera such as *Oscillatoria*, which consists of broad, closely adhering, cylindrical cells. *Anabaena* is a genus whose filaments resemble strings of beads, the individual cells being spherical or barrel-shaped. In addition to these vegetative cells, which constitute the greater part of each *Anabaena* filament, *spores* and *heterocysts* also occur. The spores are considerably enlarged cells, with thickened resistant walls, and contain abundant food reserves. They serve to tide the alga over periods of unfavourable environmental conditions. Heterocysts are empty-looking cells, often slightly broader than the rest of the filament, with transparent protoplasts and thickened walls. Their function is still something of a biological enigma (fig. 229).

The great majority of species of the Cyanophyta occur only in freshwaters; frequently they are so abundant in the phytoplankton of lakes that they discolour the surface waters. Such *water blooms* also occur in the sea. Indeed, the Red Sea is said to have gained its name from the colour imparted to it from time to time by blooms of the *Oscillatoria*-like blue-green alga, *Trichodesmium erythraeum*, whose filaments have a reddish tinge.

In recent years it has been demonstrated that certain species of blue-green algae are able, like certain bacteria, to fix atmospheric nitrogen (see Chapter 15, p. 184), and further that the nitrogen fixing systems of these algae is physiologically similar to those found in other nitrogen fixing organisms. These algae are thus the most completely autotrophic organisms known, since they are able to synthesize their most complex biochemical requirements from carbon dioxide, water, free nitrogen and mineral salts. Because of this, blue-green algae can flourish in situations where nitrogen fixing bacteria cannot grow because of a lack of carbohydrates, for example on bare rock faces. They are, therefore, important pioneer colonizers (see Chapter 21, p. 238). As with bacteria, the nitrogen fixed by blue-green algae is eventually set free in the form of nitrogenous substances which can be utilized by other plants unable to fix it for themselves.

In certain tropical countries nitrogen fixing blue-green algae play an important role in maintaining soil fertility. During the rice growing season in India, for example, species of Cyanophyta that have been shown by experiment to be able to fix atmospheric nitrogen are present in great numbers. In such ricefields, crops have been grown year after year without the addition of manure to the soil. There is considerable evidence to indicate that the blue green algae are largely responsible for maintaining the level of soil fertility, the part played by bacteria being negligible.

DIVISION RHODOPHYTA

The Rhodophyta, or red algae, have certain features in common with the Cyanophyta, though this does not indicate any relationship. One of the points of similarity is that both lack motile asexual spores and together are the only algal divisions to do so. Also, both contain, in addition to chlorophyll, the red pigment phycoerythrin and the blue, phycocyanin. In most Rhodophyta, phycoerythrin is present in such considerable amounts that it masks all other pigments. The pigments, unlike those of the Cyanophyta, are contained in *chromatophores*, which in the simplest members are single star-shaped (*stellate*) organelles; in others there may be several lobed chromatophores lying against the cell wall and thus *parietal* in position; the more advanced members have many chromatophores in each cell and these are small and disc-like. The cells contain true nuclei, usually one per cell, which divide by mitosis. Certain species, however, possess some large multinuclear cells, each with between 3000 and 4000 nuclei. The cell walls are well defined and composed of cellulose and pectic substances. Most cells contain a central vacuole bounded by a peripheral layer of cytoplasm. The food reserves are usually stored in the form of a starch like carbohydrate, *floridean* starch, small grains of which occur in the cytoplasm; there may also be some soluble sugar.

Sexual reproduction is unique amongst the algae in that non-motile male gametes, *spermatia*, are transported passively to, and lodge against the female sex organs, the *carpogonia*, within which they effect fertilization.

The vast majority of red algae are exclusively marine in their distribution, being attached to rocks or other seaweeds. These *epiphytic* forms are sometimes restricted to a particular species and there are some Rhodophyta that are partly, or completely, parasitic. The partial parasites show a considerable reduction in the amount of photosynthetic pigments; the true parasites are colourless and seem to obtain all their food from their hosts.

The Rhodophyta show a very considerable diversity of form. Two genera are unicellular; others have cells united end to end forming simple or branched filaments; the majority, however, are plants of considerable size with a fairly complex cellular organization. Some of these, such as *Delesseria*, are leaf-like; others such as *Plumaria* and *Ptilota* are moss- or fern-like in appearance (fig. 230). *Porphyra*, which is common on rocks at high water mark, has a thin membranous *thallus* attached to the substratum by a cushion-shaped holdfast.

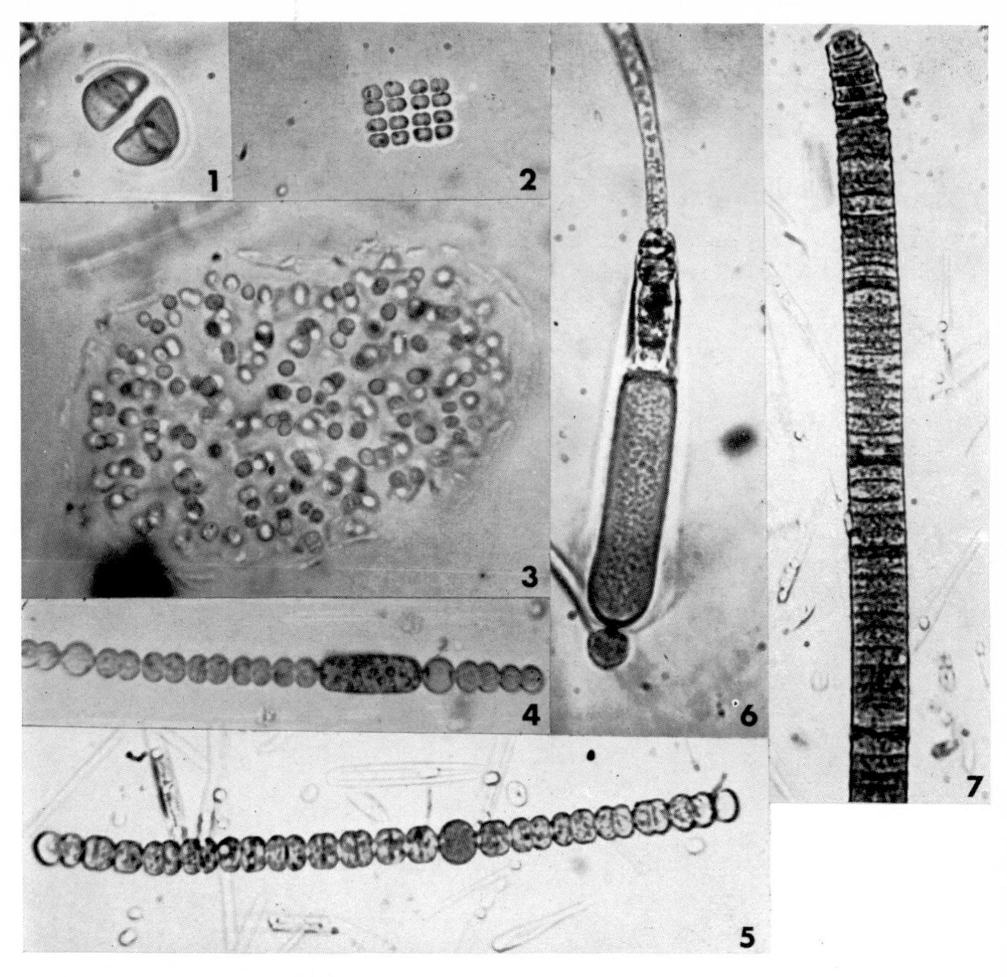

Figure 229 *Photomicrographs of representative types from the Division Cyanophyta.*

1 Chroococus turgidus.

2 Merismopedia *sp.*

3 Aphanocapsa pulchra.

4 Anabaena catenula *with spore adjacent to a heterocyst.*

5 Anabaena catenula *with heterocyst and gas vacuoles (pseudovacuoles) in its cells.*

6 Gloeotrichia *sp. with tapering trichome, basal heterocyst and large adjacent spore.*

7 Oscillatoria *sp.*

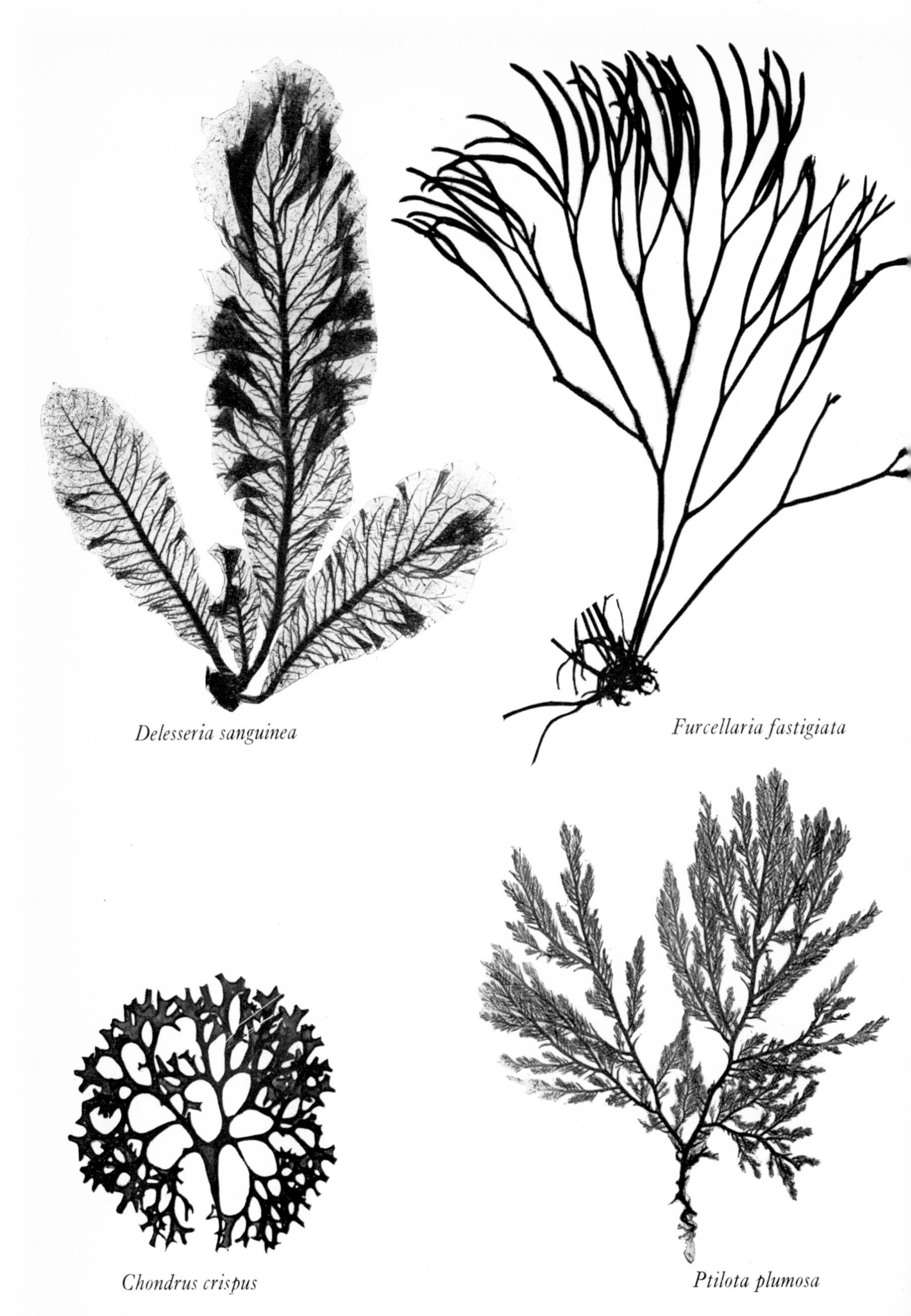

Figure 230 *Some representative red algae* (Rhodophyta) (*reproduced from Johnstone and Croall, 'Nature printed British Seaweeds'*).

DIVISION CHLOROPHYTA

The Chlorophyta, or green algae, are characterized by having the same photosynthetic pigments as other green plants and these pigments are present in the same proportions (see p. 216). Starch accumulates in their cells as a product of photosynthesis. Many members of the Chlorophyta, especially the freshwater forms, are unicellular and thus of microscopic size (e.g. *Chlamydomonas*, and *Chlorella*); many of the marine species are multicellular and quite large (e.g. *Enteromorpha* and *Ulva*). Reproduction may be asexual or sexual, and the reproductive cells are commonly motile. Typically these motile cells arise from the anterior end of the cell and possess two, or four flagella of equal length. Sexual gametes, which may be of equal or unequal size, are always produced within unicellular sex organs.

Two classes of the Chlorophyta are recognized:

1. Chlorophyceae, which embraces both unicellular and multicellular forms with freely exposed, unicellular sex organs;
2. Charophyceae (the stoneworts), which are multicellular, macroscopic freshwater plants, possessing unicellular sexual organs borne within multicellular, sterile envelopes.

Descriptions of the structure and reproduction of some representative members of the Chlorophyceae, of which there are some 6000 known species, are given in the following pages.

Class Chlorophyceae

Chlamydomonas (figs. 231 and 232)

A commonly occurring unicellular alga, in both fresh water and salt water, is *Chlamydomonas*. These microscopic plants are for much of their life motile, a characteristic normally associated with animals. However, since their nutrition is autotrophic they are unquestionably members of the Plant Kingdom, and because their photosynthetic pigments are similar to those of other green, starch-producing plants, they are placed in the Division Chlorophyta.

According to the species, of which several hundreds have now been described, the individual plants may be spherical, oval, or pear-shaped, ranging in size from 30 μ to 100 μ in diameter. A few are naked, but the majority are bounded by a thin wall, said to be of hemicellulose rather than true cellulose, thickened at the anterior end to from a colourless *papilla*. As in all living cells, each *Chlamydomonas* cell contains a nucleus and cytoplasm, and also a prominent chloroplast. The chloroplast is commonly in the form of a deep cup with a thickened base, in which is embedded the *pyrenoid*, a conspicuous proteinaceous body associated with starch production. Indeed, a sheath of starch grains may surround the pyrenoid. The less conspicuous nucleus is suspended by strands of cytoplasm within the cup formed by the chloroplast. On the edge of the chloroplast, towards the anterior end of the cell, there

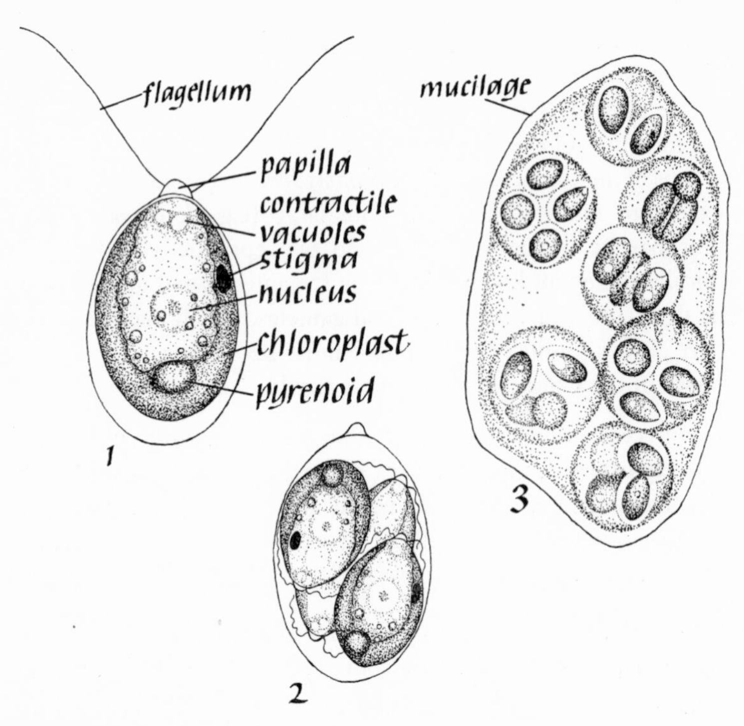

Figure 231 Chlamydomonas
1 *Vegetative cell of* C. klinobasis.
2 *Zoospore formation in* C. klinobasis (*after Skuja*).
3 *Palmella stage in* Chlamydomonas braunii (*after Goroschankin*).

is a small though very obvious lens-shaped structure, the *stigma* or *eye-spot.* This organ, which is deep red in colour, is concerned with the reception of light (fig. 231.1).

In a limited region of clear cytoplasm just beneath the colourless papilla of the anterior end, a pair of small, highly refractive structures can be discerned in some of the larger species, if optical conditions are good. When observed closely for a period, they can be seen to enlarge, collapse, and then reform. Consequently the function of these *contractile vacuoles* is believed to be the elimination of waste materials from the cell.

Also at the anterior end of each cell, and lying in a plane at right angles to the two contractile vacuoles, are two fine flagella. The flagella, which are equal in length, are cytoplasmic in origin. They pass through fine canals in the cell wall to reach the exterior, where by backwardly directed strokes they propel the cell. Under this impetus the cell moves forward with some rapidity, rotating about its longitudinal axis as it moves.

Reproduction in *Chlamydomonas* is either vegetative, that is asexual, or by sexual means. The first stage in both types of reproduction is marked by the immobilization of the cells on the withdrawal of the flagella, and by the contraction of the contents of the cell away from the cell wall. The cell contents then undergo several successive divisions. In asexual reproduction there may be only one or two divisions, thus producing from the contents of the original cell 2, 4, or 8 protoplasts. These protoplasts, which are still contained within the parent cell wall, develop their own cell walls and two flagella, and they move in this state for some time within the parent wall. Eventually the parent wall is ruptured, and these motile daughter cells, or *zoospores*, are liberated, to enlarge ultimately to the size of the parent cell. Under conditions of optimum growth and with the entire process of division occurring only once every twenty-four hours, more than 2,000,000 *Chlamydomonas* individuals can be produced from one cell within a week (fig. 231.2).

When grown in culture in the laboratory, dividing individuals often fail to produce motile zoospores and the contents of the divisions remain within the parent cell, which then secretes mucilage. The enclosed daughter cells eventually separate and enlarge. Each such cell may in turn divide; this leads to the formation of large but irregular gelatinous masses of non-motile groups of cells. When conditions are once favourable to normal growth, the constituent cells of this *palmelloid-stage* of *Chlamydomonas* develop cilia and escape from the enveloping mucilage as zoospores, so that new motile individuals are again produced. In some genera closely related to *Chlamydomonas*, this *palmelloid habit* is permanent (fig. 231.3).

When there is a depletion of nutrients in the environment, more numerous divisions of the cell contents often become apparent, with the result that 16, 32, or 64 motile cells are produced within a parent cell. These *gametes*, like zoospores, possess two flagella, but they are much smaller and they are without a cell wall. When liberated from the parent cell they swim actively for a time, but eventually two of them, usually originating from different parent cells and sometimes differing in size, first become entangled by their flagella, then gradually come into more intimate contact by their anterior ends. There follows a gradual fusion of the two protoplasts and nuclei, so a diploid *zygote* is formed. The zygote is motile as long as the four flagella persist, but soon these are withdrawn, and the whole becomes surrounded by a thick wall, and it enters on a period of rest. This spherical, resistant body, which can survive considerable dessication, becomes reddish in colour on account of the accumulation of oil in its cytoplasm (fig. 232).

When environmental conditions become favourable for the germination of the zygote its colour reverts to green and, at the same time, the cell contents undergo meiotic division. When the four zoospores thus produced are liberated, they grow into adult haploid plants, which can, under favourable conditions, reproduce asexually to give rise in a short time to a very large *Chlamydomonas* population.

Gonium, Eudorima and Volvox (fig. 233)

Some *Chlamydomonas*-like cells occur, not singly, but grouped together in

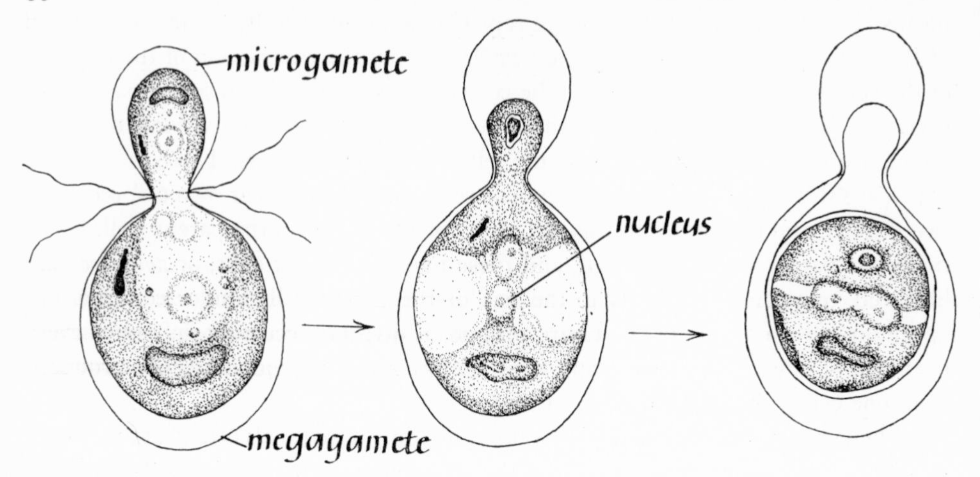

Figure 232 *Stages in the sexual reproduction of an anisogamous* Chlamydomonas *sp.*

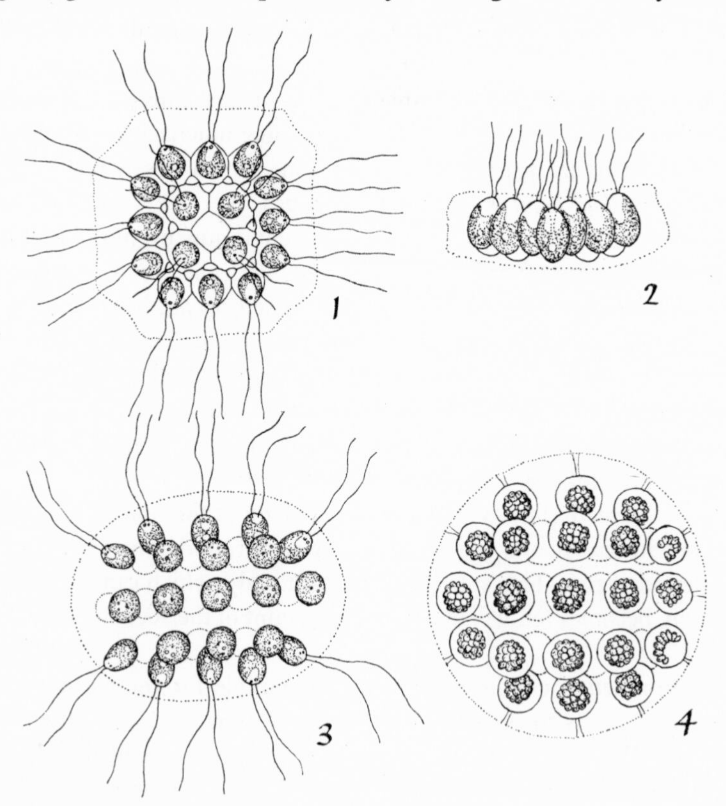

Figure 233 1 Gonium pectorale, *surface view of colony.*
2 G. pectorale, *side view of colony.*
3 Eudorina elegans.
4 E. elegans *showing formation of daughter colonies.*

mucilage, forming regular, motile colonies of constant and characteristic shape. For example, colonies of *Gonium* are flat plates, one cell thick, consisting of 4 or 16 *Chlamydomonas*-like cells embedded in mucilage. *Eudorina* is a colony of 32 cells spaced equidistantly round the periphery of a spherical mass of mucilage. The much more complex colonies of *Volvox* are also spherical, but composed of several thousand cells set in a hollow ball of mucilage about the size of a pin-head. In some *Volvox* species the individual cells are joined to one another by fairly conspicuous protoplasmic connections.

When *Gonium* and *Eudorina* reproduce, all the constituent cells form daughter colonies in much the same way as *Chlamydomonas*. In *Volvox*, however, a few cells of each colony, which are conspicuously larger than the rest, lack flagella. These cells alone divide to form *daughter colonies*. The new colonies are liberated into the hollow interior of the parent colony: here they gradually enlarge until eventually the parent colony ruptures and they are set free. In *Volvox* there is a *division of labour*: in this multicellular organism only certain cells reproduce, while all the others are purely vegetative.

Chlorella (fig. 234)

It has been shown (p. 357) that asexual reproduction in the unicellular alga *Chlamydomonas* and its relatives is usually preceded by the withdrawal of the flagella so that the cells lose their motility. It has been suggested that during the course of evolution, in quite a number of the Chlorophyceae, this motionless period has become increasingly prolonged at the expense of the period of motility; in one important group, the order Chlorococales, all motility has been lost. A common and widely distributed genus of this order is *Chlorella*, some ten species of which have been described from a variety of habitats. These habitats include not only lakes and ponds and the oceans of the world, but also very small bodies of water. In fact the green tinge which often develops in glass vessels, such as flasks or jars, left exposed to the atmosphere is invariably due to *Chlorella*. Species of this alga are also common in media rich in organic matter, such as sewage waters. They also occur in soil and in the cells or tissues of a number of invertebrate animals, such as the protozoa *Paramecium*, *Ophrydium*, and *Stentor*, the coelenterate *Hydra viridis*, and sponges – the alga then being termed *zoochlorella*.

The spherical or broadly ellipsoidal cells of *Chlorella*, which exist singly, are from 2–12 μ in diameter, depending on the species. Each cell has much the same internal structure as a cell of *Chlamydomonas*, though the stigma, contractile vacuoles, and flagella of the latter are lacking. The cell wall is thin and smooth and the single chloroplast is a cup-shaped structure, parietal in position. In some species (*Chlorella vulgaris*) a pyrenoid is lacking; in others (*C. pyrenoidosa*) a pyrenoid is present.

Reproduction of *Chlorella* is entirely asexual and by means of non-motile *autospores*. From 2 to 16 of these are produced within the parent cell, which later ruptures

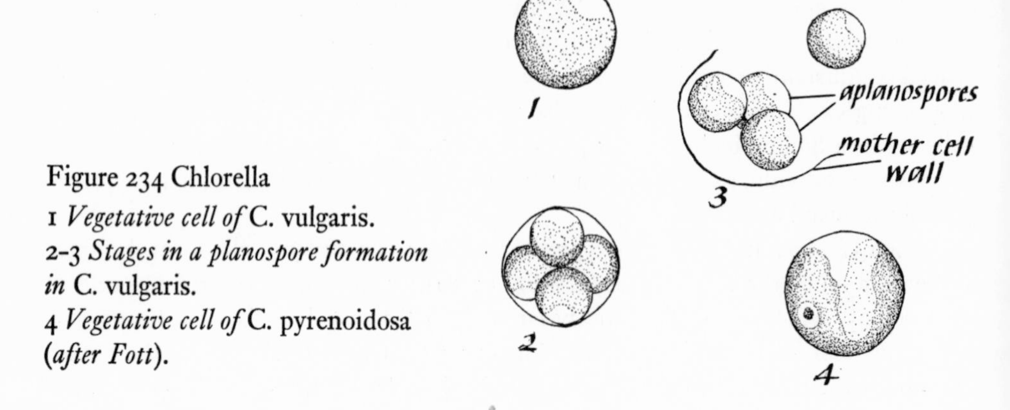

Figure 234 Chlorella
1 *Vegetative cell of* C. vulgaris.
2–3 *Stages in a planospore formation in* C. vulgaris.
4 *Vegetative cell of* C. pyrenoidosa (*after Fott*).

so that they are liberated. Each autospore then enlarges to become a mature *Chlorella* cell. Under ideal conditions the rate of reproduction of the alga can be extremely rapid and this and other characteristics have led to its frequent use in physiological studies of plant growth, respiration, and especially photosynthesis. In recent years considerable research has been undertaken in America and Japan on the mass culture of *Chlorella* as a source of food. Also in America its use as a biological source of oxygen, and as a possible food in space exploration, is being actively explored.

Ulothrix (fig. 235)

Not all simple green algae are motile; many members of the Chlorophyta are sessile and thus more conventionally plant-like. They consist, in essence, of long rows, or *filaments*, of non-motile cells, all identical in structure and function, and attached to some substratum by a basal cell. Species of *Ulothrix* are common in flowing water or on the wave-lashed rocks round lake margins.

In *Ulothrix*, each filament is attached to the substratum by a modified basal cell, but all the other cells, which vary somewhat in width, possess a characteristic band-like chloroplast, which forms an incomplete cylinder just within the cell wall. Usually each chloroplast contains several pyrenoids and, as in *Chlamydomonas*, the single nucleus of each cell is suspended in the middle of the cell by fine strands of cytoplasm. When the cells divide transversely, the filament increases in length, but multiplication of the filaments is by the formation of zoospores, which are sometimes produced by all but the basal cells.

When zoospore production begins the vegetative cells become a deeper green in colour and their contents begin to round up. Eventually each cell becomes visibly subdivided into from 2 to 32 parts, the number being constant along the length of a given filament. Generally, the zoospores so formed are of two kinds: the larger, the *macrozoospores*, of which up to 8 are formed per cell, each possess four flagella; the smaller, *microzoospores*, of which 16 or 32 can be formed, may possess four, or some-

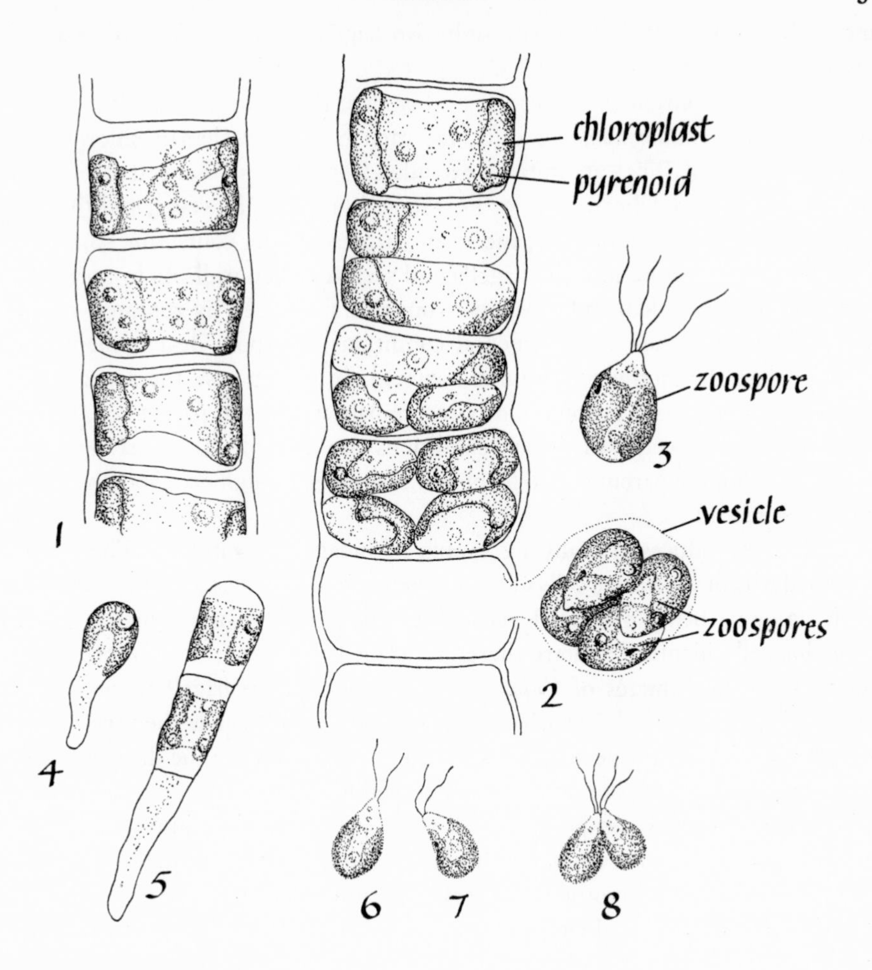

Figure 235 Ulothrix zonata

1 *Vegetative filament.*

2 *Formation of zoospores from vegetative cells.*

3 *Quadriflagellate zoospore.*

4–5 *Stages in the formation of a new filament from zoospore.*

6–8 *Stages in sexual reproduction.*

times only two flagella. Those with only two flagella may function either as micro-zoospores or as gametes.

The *Ulothrix* zoospores, in respects other than the possession of flagella, closely resemble motile *Chlamydomonas* cells, for each has a cup-shaped chloroplast and prominent eye-spot. They are initially extruded from their mother cell through a pore in the cell wall into a delicate vesicle. This soon disappears, however, and these naked motile cells swim away vigorously, and so are dispersed. After contacting some suitable substratum the zoospore loses its flagella and secretes a cell wall. As in normal vegetative growth, a new filament develops from this single cell by repeated transverse divisions. Under certain environmental conditions, zoospore development may be arrested before the motile condition is assumed. In such a case the separate protoplasts, which might have become zoospores, remain within the parent cell, round off, and each secretes a cell wall. When conditions are suitable, these *akinetes* usually germinate within the parent cell to form new filaments, though occasionally zoospores are formed instead.

Ulothrix reproduces sexually by means of biflagellate gametes. These gametes are formed within vegetative cells of the filaments, in much the same way as zoospores, usually 32 or 64 being produced per cell. On their release, the gametes, which are morphologically identical and are therefore termed *isogametes*, fuse to form a diploid zygote, as do the gametes of *Chlamydomonas*. The quadri flagellate zygotes retain their motility for a period, but when they withdraw their flagella they secrete a thick wall and enter into a rest period as resistant zygospores. When the diploid zygospore germinates, the first division is meiotic; succeeding divisions, therefore, give rise to haploid *aplanospores* or zoospores, which subsequently develop into normal haploid vegetative filaments. Thus *Ulothrix*, although a simple, non-motile, attached filament, reproduces by means of motile zoospores and gametes, a process which, by its close resemblance, suggests a phylogenetic relationship between *Ulothrix* and *Chlamydomonas*.

Ulva (fig. 236)

Ulva lactuca, the sea lettuce, often grows in profusion in rocks situated between tide zones, especially in areas where there is some pollution from sewage. The sea lettuce, which consists of a membranous expanded *thallus*, two cells in thickness, is attached to the rocks by a rhizoidal *holdfast*. The cells of the thallus are all alike, and in cross section appear isodiametric; they are vertically elongate to the thallus surface. Each cell contains a single large cup-shaped chloroplast with a single pyrenoid. The rhizoids of the holdfast originate within the lower regions of the thallus and the cells from which they arise send out long colourless outgrowths that grow downwards between the two layers. Eventually these outgrowths emerge and become closely associated to form the pseudoparenchymatous holdfast, a perennial organ which produces new plants each growing season.

The life cycle of *Ulva* is of special interest in that there is an alternation of genera-

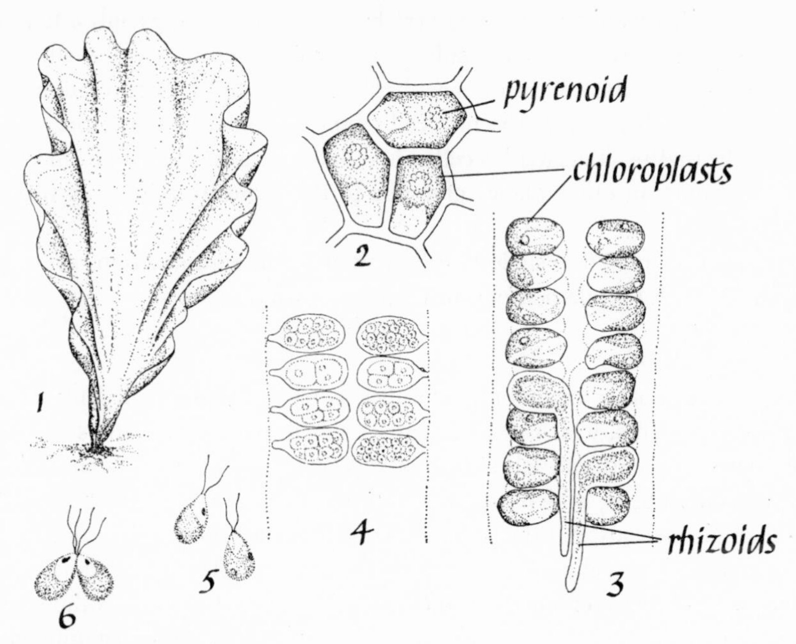

Figure 236 Ulva lactuca
1 *Small attached plant.*
2 *Cells of thallus in surface view.*
3 *T.s. of thallus near base showing rhizoid formation.*
4 *Gametangia with biflagellate gametes forming from vegetative cells.*
5-6 *Stages in the fusion of gametes.*

tions. These generations are morphologically similar though cytologically dissimilar, the sporophytic phase being diploid while the gametophytic is haploid. The biflagellate gametes (32 or 64) produced by the gametophyte arise on the cell margins by a series of mitotic divisions and are eventually liberated through a protrusion that develops on the *gametangium*, as each of these cells is now called. Most species of *Ulva*, including *U. lactuca*, are isogamous, though some are anisogamous: all, however, would seem to be heterothallic; consequently only gametes derived from different thalli fuse with one another.

The zygote is quadriflagellate and after swimming for a time settles down, withdraws the four flagella, and secretes a cell wall. Germination usually follows within twenty-four hours, the result being a *diploid* filamentous germling, which, by successive divisions in two planes, gives rise to a two-layered diploid thallus, morphologically indistinguishable from the haploid. As with gamete production, cells towards the thallus margin function as *sporangia*. The first division of these cells is meiotic; subsequent mitotic divisions produce 32 or 64 quadriflagellate, haploid zoospores. The naked zoospores, which are then liberated through a pore in the sporangium wall, are only motile for a very brief period – perhaps only a few minutes – before coming to rest on some substratum and secreting a cell wall. The first division of this, the first cell of the new haploid (gametophyte) generation, is transverse the lower cell becomes the first cell of the rhizoidal holdfast; the upper, the first cell of the thallus. This thallus cell at first divides transversely to form a filament, but later divisions in other planes give rise to the typically foliaceous two-layered thallus.

Many features of *Ulva*, such as cell structure and reproduction, suggest fairly close affinities with the filamentous alga *Ulothrix* (see p. 360).

Oedogonium (fig. 237).

Oedogonium, another common green alga, is also an unbranched filament. Like *Ulothrix*, the filaments, which usually grow attached to the leaves and stems of other aquatic plants in ponds and lakes, have a specialized basal cell forming a holdfast. All the vegetative cells, which are two to three times longer than they are broad, possess a single nucleus and one large chloroplast in the form of a cylindrical network lying within the cellulose cell wall. Each *reticulate* chloroplast contains a considerable number of pyrenoids with their associated starch grains. Although all the cells of each filament (except the basal cell) are capable of division, in a number of the more common species, divisions are most frequent in cells towards the upper end. Cell division in *Oedogonium* is unique in the Plant Kingdom in that the lower daughter cell is contained by the old cell wall and cut off from the upper cell by a new septum which forms after the division of the nucleus. The upper cell is formed by the extension of a ring of cellulose which develops round the upper end of the original cell. Thus the lower daughter cell is surrounded largely by old cell wall, the upper by newly-formed cell wall. The small upper portion of the old wall and the original septum, however, appear on the upper cell as a 'cap'. Since one particular cell often undergoes several successive divisions and on each occasion a new cap is formed, a series of these striations, or *cap cells*, accumulate at the end of the cell. This is a diagnostic feature of the genus *Oedogonium*.

Oedogonium reproduces asexually by means of zoospores formed within vegetative cells, but unlike *Ulothrix*, only one zoospore is produced in any one cell. Zoospore production begins with the rounding up of the protoplast and, as its development proceeds, a characteristic crown of flagella becomes apparent round a colourless papilla or *beak*. Each zoospore has also a photo-sensitive eye-spot. The zoospore, which has no cell wall, is liberated through a break near one end of the wall of the *zoosporangium*, as the zoospore producing cell is now termed. The zoospore swims away from the zoosporangium, rotating as it does so. Motility is retained for only a short time, usually less than an hour; the zoospore then comes to rest, withdraws its flagella, secretes a new cell wall, and by successive divisions a new filament is formed (figs. 237 and 238).

The sexual reproduction of *Oedogonium* is peculiar in that the male and female

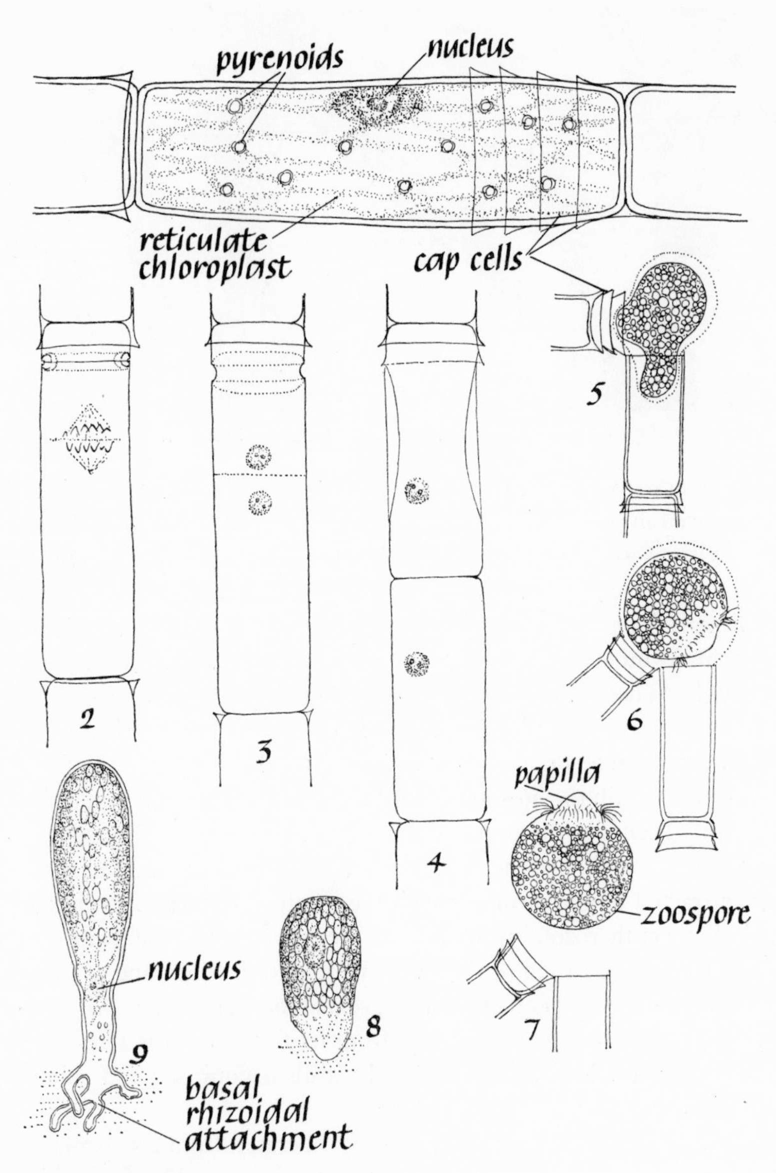

Figure 237 Oedogonium

1 *Vegetative cell showing reticulate chloroplast and cap cells.*

2–4 *Stages in cell division showing formation of cap cells.*

5–7 *Liberation of a zoospore.*

8 *Attachment of zoospore to substratum by posterior end.*

9 *Early stage in the development of a new plant.*

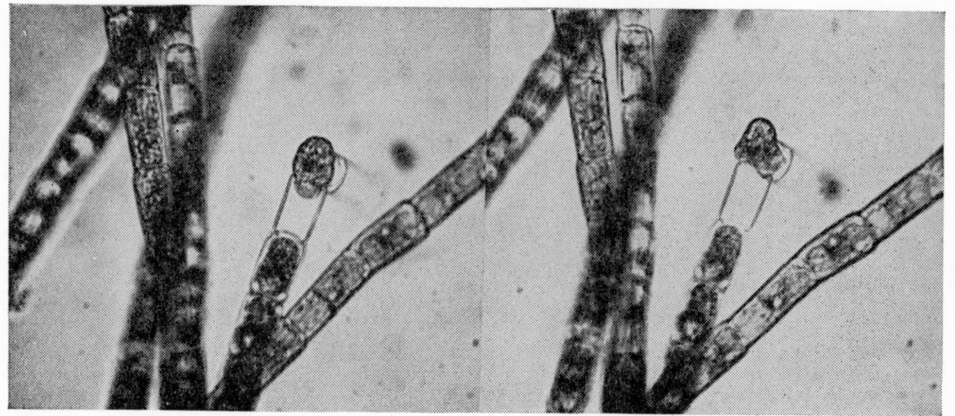

Figure 238 *Two stages in the liberation of a zoospore in* Oedogonium *sp.*

gametes are markedly different in appearance. The male gametes, *antherozoids*, are usually produced in pairs, in short disc-shaped cells which are formed in rows by the repeated divisions of a vegetative cell. These cells are termed *antheridia*. Each antherozoid resembles a small zoospore, having a colourless beak surrounded by a crown of flagella. The antherozoids, which are released from the antheridia through a transverse slit, swim actively towards one of the enlarged cells of a female filament, an *oogonium*. Each oogonium contains a single female gamete, or *ovum*. The oogonia, which originate from cap cells, are much broader when mature than the vegetative cells. The ovum, which is non-motile, is formed by the rounding up of the cell contents. It remains within the oogonium until the oogonium ruptures on maturity. This rupture usually occurs at the upper end of the oogonium and adjacent to a *receptive spot* on the ovum, which, like the beak of a zoospore, is colourless. The motile antherozoids are attracted to and swim through the resulting aperture. Eventually the anterior end of one antherozoid penetrates the receptive spot of the ovum, and fertilization is effected on the fusion of the two gamete nuclei. Since one of the gametes is much larger than the other, and non-motile, sexual reproduction in *Oedogonium* is said to be *oogamous*, and the zygote resulting from its fertilization is termed an *oospore*. This zygote soon develops a thick cell wall; it also acquires a red colour through accumulating oil as a food reserve (fig. 239).

The resistant diploid oospore is eventually liberated from its oogonium, though there is often a delay between liberation and germination. The first division of the germinating oospore is meiotic, and four haploid zoospores are produced. These, when liberated, settle down and develop into new filaments.

Although some species of *Oedogonium* are monoecious, others are dioecious. In other species reduced filaments called *dwarf males* produce the male gametes. These filaments, which grow on or near the oogonia of the female filaments, consist only of a basal attachment cell supporting a tier of antheridial cells, each of which, as in other forms, produces two male antherozoids.

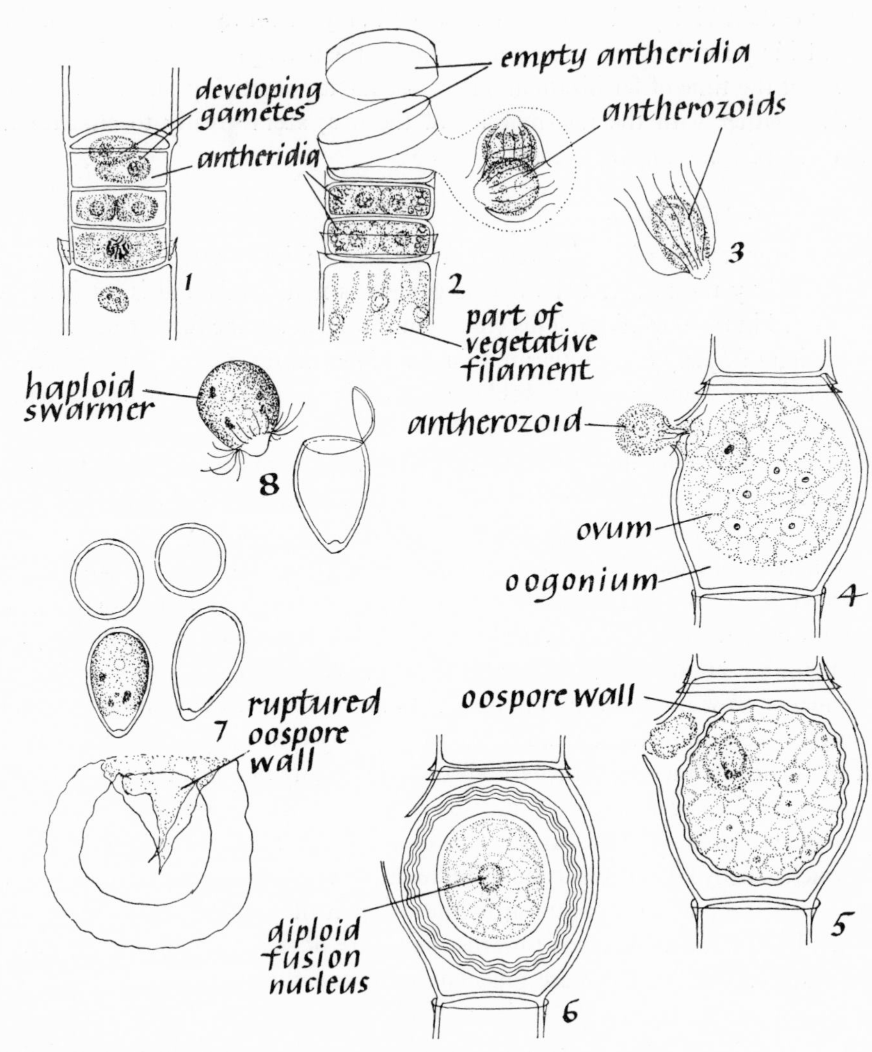

Figure 239 Oedogonium

1 *Antheridia and developing antherozoids.*

2 *Liberation of antherozoids.*

3 *Single antherozoid.*

4-6 *Stages in the fertilization of ovum and formation of a resistant oospore.*

7-8 *Germination of oospore and the formation of haploid swarmers (after Mainx).*

The oogamous mode of reproduction of *Oedogonium*, being advanced, would seem to confer certain biological advantages. In the bulky ovum there is a store of food material laid up for the succeeding generation, so the male gametes need only supply a nucleus at the time of fertilization. The consequent potentiality for increased production, together with the non-motility of the ova, seem greatly to enhance the chances of fertilization being effected.

Spirogyra (figs. 240 to 242).

Apart from the marked difference in the size of its gametes, *Oedogonium* is characterized by the fact that the female gamete is non-motile and is retained and fertilized within the oogonium. This condition is carried a stage further in the sexual reproduction of *Spirogyra*, another unbranched filamentous member of the Chlorophyta, for though there is no noticeable difference in the size of the male and female gametes, neither is liberated during the process.

Spirogyra, of which some five hundred species have been described, often appears as an abundant green mat on the surface of small ponds and lakes in summer (fig. 240). It derives its name from its conspicuous and very characteristic chloroplast. In some species there is only one chloroplast per cell but in others there may be several: they always take the form of slender ribbons of irregular outline wound, generally, in a lax spiral round the outer portion of the protoplast. Conspicuous along the length of each chloroplast are numerous pyrenoids (figs. 240 and 241).

Filaments grow in length by mitotic divisions and the subsequent elongation of the daughter cells so formed. Unlike *Oedogonium*, any cell is capable of division and when the filaments increase in length all the cells in any one filament appear to be approximately the same size; so it must be assumed that they are at the same stage in their growth cycle. Indeed, all the cells of a filament tend to divide together, an event which usually takes place at about midnight. Unlike cell division in higher plants, the new cell wall, which appears after the division of the nucleus, is a ring-like growth, which gradually extends towards the centre of the cell, with the result that the chloroplast and cytoplasm are pinched and eventually separate into two equal parts.

No motile stages have ever been observed in *Spirogyra* or any genera related to it, and vegetative reproduction is by the fragmentation of the filaments. When *Spirogyra* grows in masses, in small ponds during the summer, the filaments perform gliding

---

Figure 241 Spirogyra

1 *A single cell with two intertwined chloroplasts.*

2 *An oblique diagrammatic view of a* Spirogyra cell.

3 *Cell division showing the ring-like inward growth of the new cell wall separating the two daughter nuclei* (*after Strasburger*).

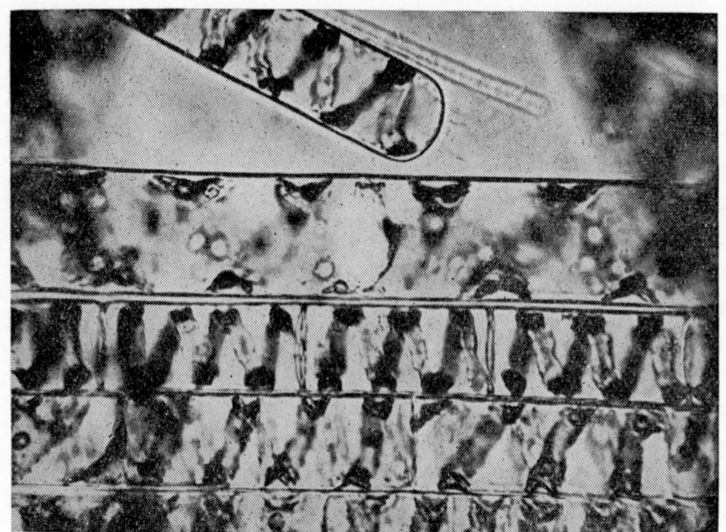

Figure 240 *Filaments of a* Spirogyra *with a single chloroplast.*

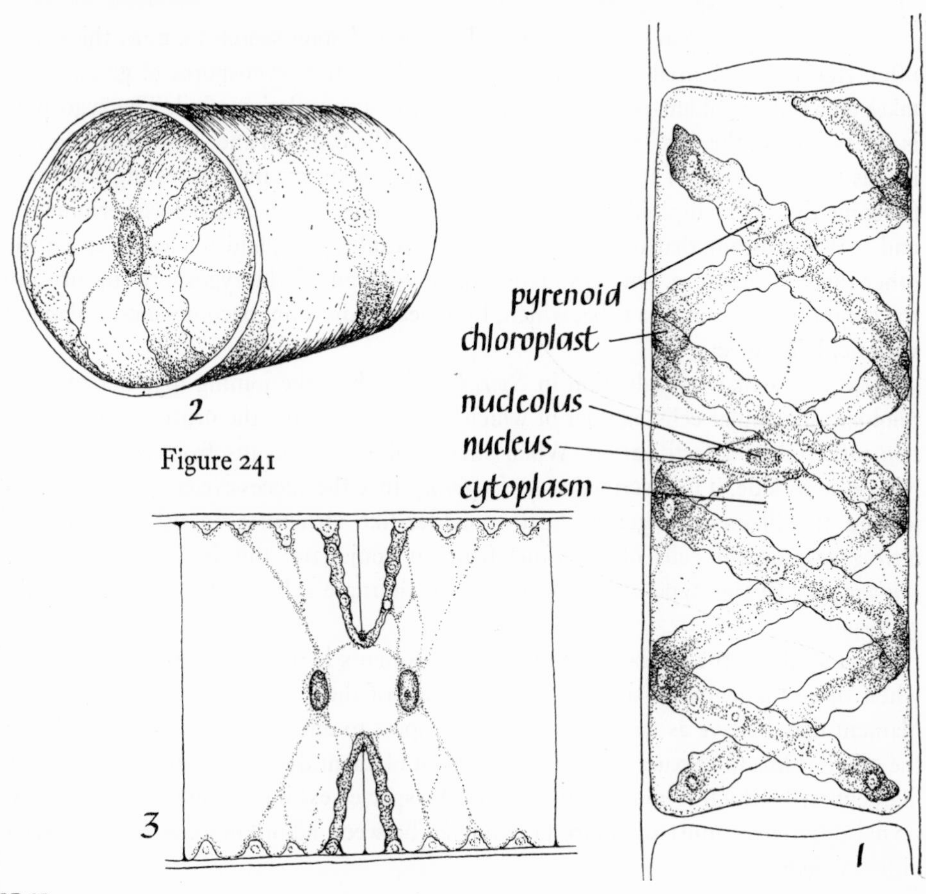

Figure 241

movement – this can be demonstrated by placing *Spirogyra* in an illuminated jar – and come to lie side by side in contact with one another (fig. 240). Small protuberances, or *papillae*, then grow out from the cells in adjacent filaments, an event which marks the onset of sexual reproduction. As the papillae increase in size, the filaments are gradually forced apart and their opposing ends become flattened by mutual pressure. Ultimately the opposing walls break down over this area of contact, with the result that a continuous canal, the *conjugation tube*, forms to connect the cavities of the two cells of the different filaments. In sexual reproduction as in cell growth, all the cells of the adjoining filaments tend to be at a similar stage in the process (fig. 242).

During the formation of the conjugation tubes, the contents of the cells of one of the filaments contract from their walls, so the spiral form of the chloroplasts becomes less obvious. The contents of these contracting cells are the male gametes; the female gametes, in the opposite filament, contract at a later stage and to a lesser degree, and the form of their chloroplasts is still discernable. As sexual reproduction proceeds, the cell contents of the 'male' filaments are gradually discharged through the conjugation canals into the cells of the 'female' filament. Here the two gametes coalesce and their nuclei fuse.

The resulting zygote assumes an oval shape and soon secretes a new, thick, and often richly ornamented wall. This *zygospore*, like other zygospores of green algae, takes on a red or golden-yellow colour, due to the accumulation of oil. The zygospore is released from the female cell by the rupture of the cell wall and, being fairly heavy, it falls to the bottom of the pond or lake, where it may remain in a resting condition for some time. The diploid zygospore nucleus divides meiotically before germination and it is significant that only one of the four resulting haploid nuclei survives; the other three disorganize. On germination the outer walls of the zygospore rupture and the contents grow out as a tube, which, by repeated division, becomes a new filament with haploid nuclei.

Because sexual reproduction in *Spirogyra* involves the joining together of morphologically similar cells, neither of which is free swimming, the process is a *conjugation* rather than a fertilization. When such conjugation results from two filaments lying side by side, it is described as *scalariform*, since the successive conjugation tubes joining the filaments together form a ladder-like structure. In other species of *Spirogyra* adjacent cells of the same filament conjugate: this is known as *lateral conjugation*. In this type of conjugation only alternate cells of the filament contain zygospores.

The study of the sexuality of *Spirogyra* filaments is of considerable interest, for when three filaments lie side by side over part of their length, the cells of a given filament may behave as male gametes with respect to one filament, but as females to the other. Thus the sexual behaviour of a given filament depends on the nature of the filament with which it comes into contact. In species exhibiting lateral conjugation, sexual differences must therefore be stronger between adjoining cells than between different filaments.

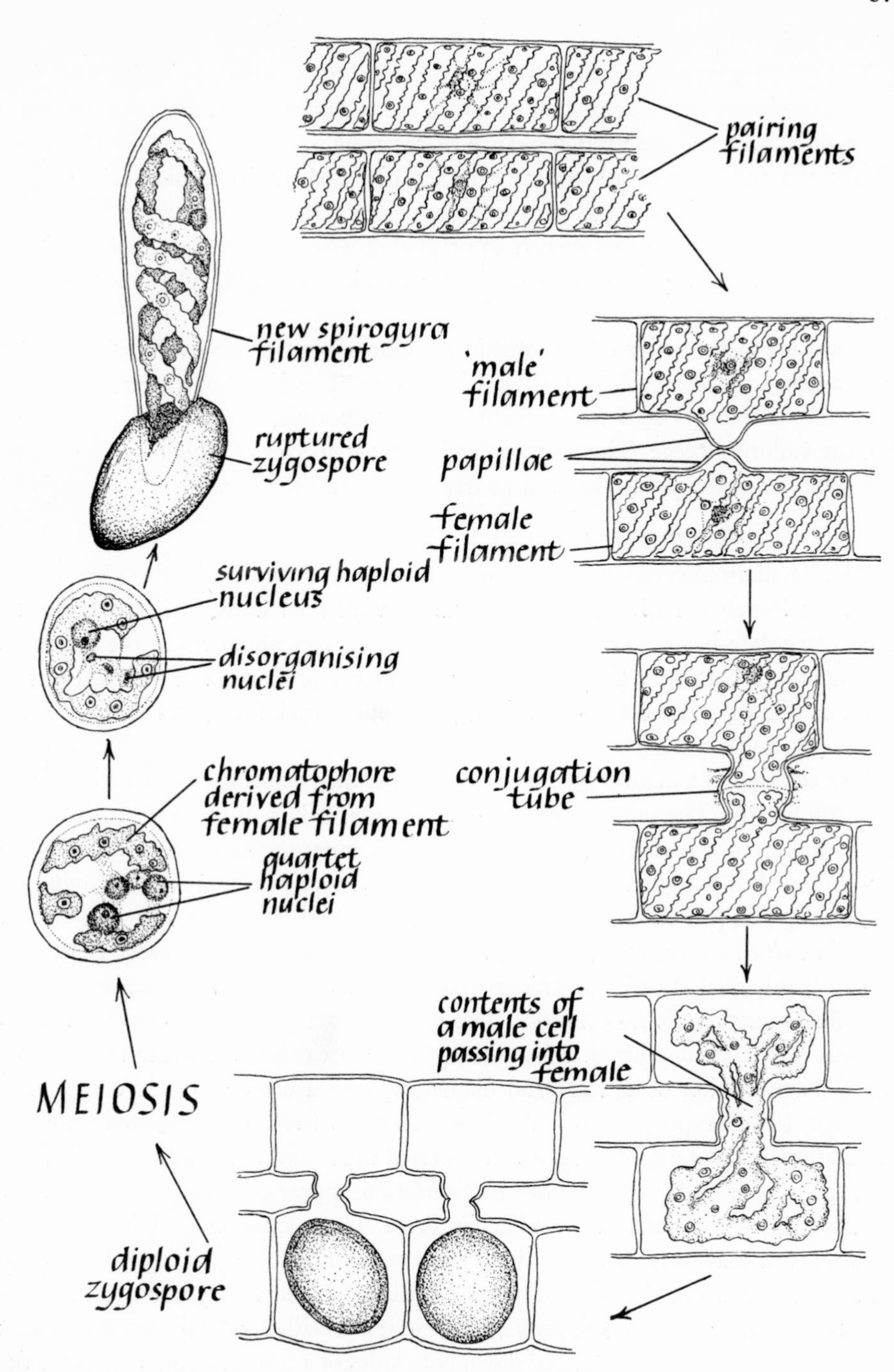

Figure 242 *Stages in the sexual reproduction of* Spirogyra.

DIVISION CHRYSOPHYTA

The Chrysophyta, which are all microscopic algae, are either unicellular, or form colonies or filaments. Their pigments, which are yellowish-green to golden-brown in colour on account of the preponderance of carotinoids, are localized in chromatophores; the products of photosynthesis are oils and an insoluble carbohydrate, *leucosin*. Many members of the Chrysophyta possess cell walls composed of two overlapping halves, which are frequently impregnated with silica. When motile cells are present they usually possess two dissimilar flagella, one whip-like and the other pinnate.

There are three major classes within the Chrysophyta: Class 1 Xanthophyceae, Class 2 Chrysophyceae, Class 3 Bacillariophyceae. The Xanthophyceae, which includes the commonly occurring filamentous alga *Vaucheria*, were at one time grouped with the Chlorophyceae. The Chrysophyceae, most species of which are motile, are very common in the phytoplankton of freshwaters and the oceans.

Class Bacillariophyceae (figs. 243 to 247).

The Bacillariophyceae, or Diatomaceae (diatoms), a very distinctive class of unicellular or loosely colonial algae, have cells with silicified walls, fitting one into the other, like a date-box or pill-box. Diatoms are often very abundant in the sea and in freshwaters; in both they frequently comprise a large proportion of the total phytoplankton. They are also common in soils, on dripping rock faces, and amongst damp mosses (fig. 243).

The cell wall of a diatom *frustule*, as each individual cell is called, is a structure of some complexity. The outer of the two overlapping halves of the wall, because it is usually uppermost, is termed the *epitheca*, and the inner the *hypotheca*. Each consists of a more or less flattened valve (the top of the date- or pill-box) and the *connecting band* or *cingulum* (the side of the box) at right angles to it. Frustules may thus be seen either in *valve view* or, when the cingulum is uppermost, in *girdle view*. Both walls of the frustule consist of an organic matrix composed mainly of pectin, or a pectin-like substance: there is no cellulose. The matrix provides the framework on which siliceous material is deposited. When diatom valves are examined under a microscope with a magnification of at least 100 diameters, they are seen to bear conspicuous markings; this is especially so if the living contents have been removed either by incineration, or by digestion in hot concentrated nitric and hydrochloric acid. These markings, which under even higher magnification appear as small dots, are in fact thin spots or perforations in the siliceous sheet. They occur with such remarkable regularity and constancy that they are of great taxonomic value (fig. 244). In the pill-box or *centric* diatoms the arrangement of markings is radially symmetrical about a central point; in the date-box or *pennate diatoms* it is usually bilaterally symmetrical, a longitudinal pattern being arranged down both sides of a central strip. Very often the central strip may be perforated by a complex, longitudinal V-shaped slot, the *raphe*, as, for example, in the diatom *Pinnularia*. In valve view this slot appears in *Pinnularia*

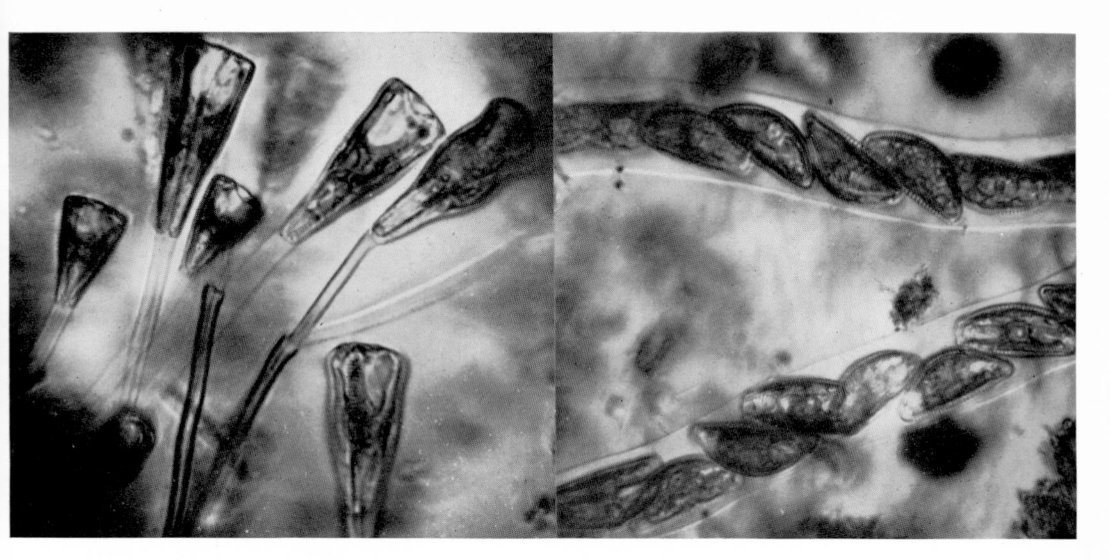

Figure 243 *Two freshwater diatoms.*
(*left*) *The stalked diatom* Gomphonema constrictum.
(*right*) Cymbella prostrata, *a diatom which forms mucilaginous tubes.*

Figure 244 *Cleaned frustules of some freshwater diatoms.*
(*top*) Cymbella cistula *var.* maculata.
(*centre*) Pinnularia viridis *var.* fallax.
(*bottom*) Navicula oblonga *var.* subcapitata.

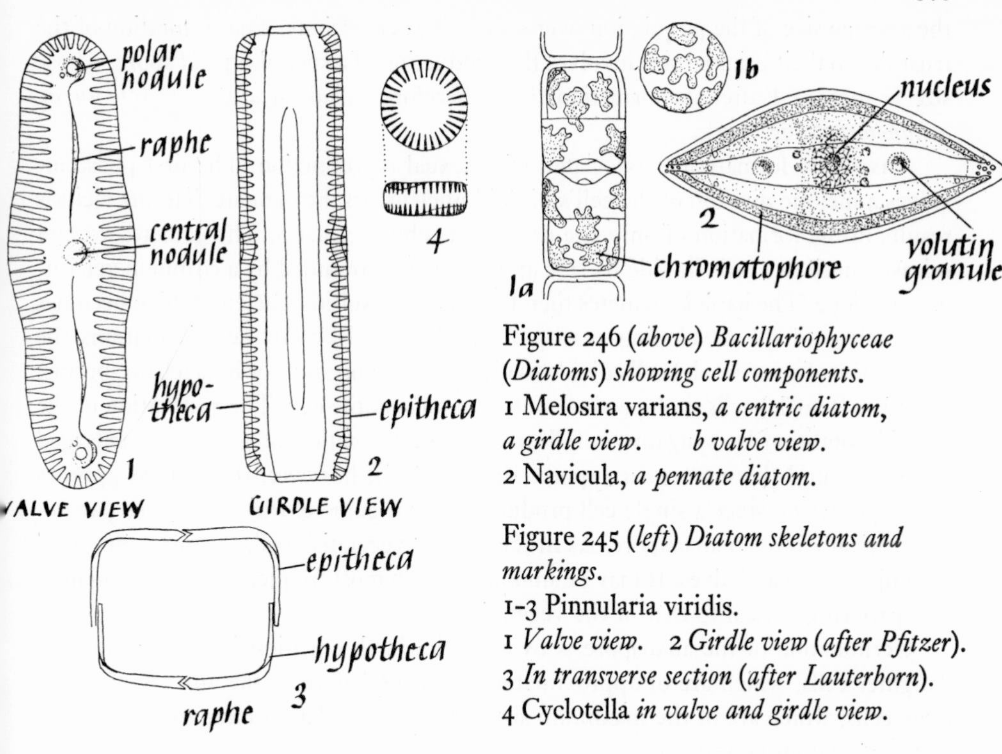

Figure 246 (*above*) *Bacillariophyceae (Diatoms) showing cell components.*
1 Melosira varians, *a centric diatom, a girdle view. b valve view.*
2 Navicula, *a pennate diatom.*

Figure 245 (*left*) *Diatom skeletons and markings.*
1-3 Pinnularia viridis.
1 *Valve view.* 2 *Girdle view* (*after Pfitzer*).
3 *In transverse section* (*after Lauterborn*).
4 Cyclotella *in valve and girdle view.*

as a sigmoid line extending from a thickening of the wall at one end, a *polar nodule*, to a somewhat similar *central nodule*, and thence to the other polar nodule (fig. 245).

The cells of *centric diatoms* usually contain many discoid, or irregularly shaped, chromatophores. The cells of the pennate diatoms, including *Pinnularia*, contain two laminate chromatophores, which extend longitudinally along opposite sides of the cell (fig. 246).

Pennate diatoms, such as *Pinnularia*, are often motile. It is still uncertain, however, how motility is achieved. The most probable explanation is that there is a flow of cytoplasm along the outside of the raphe from one polar nodule to the other, while a stream flows in the opposite direction along the inside of the raphe. There is, therefore, a continuous circulation of cytoplasm, similar in effect to the caterpillar track on a tank or tractor. The numerous pennate diatoms which thrive on the bottom and marginal muds of lakes, ponds, and rivers can in time of drought, which they are able to withstand for considerable periods, move into the deeper, wetter layers of mud as the surface dries out. Motile pennate diatoms are also quite common in the soil.

The nuclei of most diatoms are probably diploid. Asexual reproduction is by longitudinal binary fission: each of the two resulting daughter cells retains one of the two halves of the original cell wall, but they develop a new frustule which fits inside the old (see fig. 247). One of these daughter cells will therefore be the size of the parent and the other slightly smaller; consequently there is a gradual reduction in the average size of the population over successive generations. The restoration of the frustules to their original size involves the production of a special type of spore, whose size is increased after its formation; it is therefore called an *auxospore* (cf. *auxin*, *auxanometer*) (fig. 247).

Auxospore formation is associated with sexual reproduction. The first phase involves a meiotic division of the cell's diploid nucleus. In the pennate diatoms meiosis results in the formation of only one or two amoeboid gametes. The gametes are not released until two cells lie side by side and become surrounded by a common gelatinous envelope. The haploid gametes then fuse, so the resulting nucleus, which becomes the nucleus of the developing auxospore, is diploid. In many centric diatoms the protoplasts of some (male) cells divide to give 4, 8, or more uni- or biflagellate sperms; the other (female) cells each produce only one non-motile egg. The restoration of the diploid condition by syngamy is followed by the formation of a new and enlarged cell wall round the mature auxospore. In *Pinnularia*, however, the process appears to be *apogamous*, since a single cell produces a single gamete, which develops parthenogenetically into an auxospore. As in the normal vegetative cell, the auxospore wall is composed of two halves. It may be smooth, though most frequently it is ornamented in a pattern identical to that of the vegetative cells.

Germination of the auxospore is by a longitudinal, equational division into two daughter cells, which are of approximately the same length as the auxospore: these large cells, which are of the maximum size for the particular species, are the parents of a new diatom population.

DIVISION PHAEOPHYTA

The vast majority of the plants included in this Division are the macroscopic seaweeds which form the dominant element in the littoral flora of arctic and temperate seas. Only three microscopic freshwater genera, containing a few species, have so far been described.

The photosynthetic pigments of the Phaeophyta occur in chromatophores, of which there are usually several in each cell. The pigments are masked by fucoxanthin, the substance which gives these algae their typically brown colour. The products of photosynthesis are carbohydrates stored in a dissolved state. Of these substances the most common are a dextrin-like polysaccharide *laminarin* and an alcohol *mannitol*.

The Phaeophyta are classified on the basis of their life cycles and accordingly can be placed in one of the following three classes:

Class 1. Isogeneratae, includes plants which show an alteration of two morphologically similar, though cytologically dissimilar, generations.

Class 2. Heterogeneratae, includes plants which exhibit an alternation of morphologically dissimilar generations. Of these the diploid sporophyte is macroscopic; the haploid gametophyte is microscopic and usually consists of only a short branched filament.

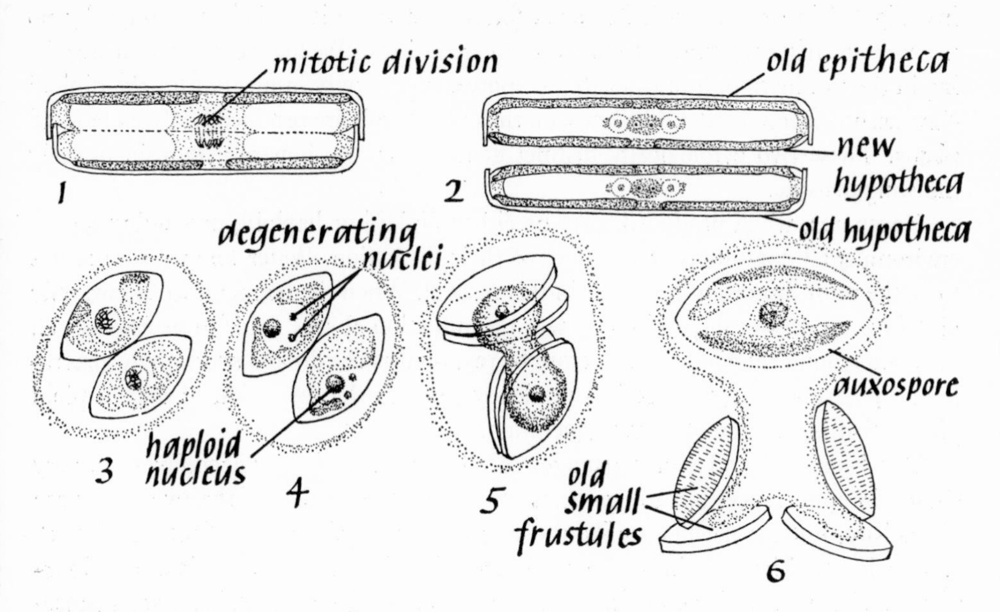

Figure 247 *Reproduction in diatoms.*
1–2 *Stages in cell division in* Navicula oblonga (*after Lauterborn*).
3–6 *Stages in sexual reproduction and auxospore formation in* Cocconeis placentula (*after Geitler*).

Class 3. Cyclosporae, includes plants with only a large diploid generation, the haploid male and female gametophytes being reduced to a few cells formed within the sporophyte.

Class Isogeneratae

Ectocarpus (fig. 248)

Ectocarpus is a common brown alga usually found attached to larger seaweeds, such as *Fucus* and *Laminaria*, and appearing to the naked eye as brown tufted outgrowths on their thalli. These tufts, which are the erect portions of the alga, arise from a basal system of prostrate branches, which in some species penetrate the host seaweed to which they are attached. Indeed, quite a number of the forty known British species of this genus are said to exhibit mild parasitism and are restricted in their occurrence to one particular host.

The erect portion of the alga is composed of branched filaments, made up of rows of cylindrical or barrel-shaped cells which become smaller and acutely pointed at the extremities of the branches. Each cell of every filament contains a single nucleus and a few irregular, band-shaped, or small plate-like brown *chromatophores* (fig. 248).

The life histories of some species of *Ectocarpus*, especially *E. siliculosus*, have been investigated in detail, and it has been found that there is a distinct, though by no means regularly occurring, alternation of generations. Asexual reproduction, resulting in the production of biflagellate zoospores, occurs only in plants with the diploid chromosome complement. Gametes, on the other hand, are produced only by haploid plants. These two cytologically distinct generations are, however, morphologically indistinguishable.

Zoospores, when produced, may be either diploid or haploid, depending on the environmental conditions at the time of their formation. Water temperature seems to be the most important influence in this respect. When the temperature is low, only diploid zoospores occur, so in cold seas reproduction always tends to be asexual; all the plants found therein, may therefore be regarded as the diploid sporophyte generation. In warmer waters there is a tendency towards the formation of only haploid plants, that is, the gametophyte generation.

The zoospores and motile gametes of all members of the Phaeophyta are very similar in appearance, but the gametes tend to be the smaller of the two. They are biflagellate, but the flagella, unlike those of the Chlorophyta, are of unequal length and are inserted laterally in the body. When swimming one flagellum is directed forwards and the other backwards. Each zoospore and gamete contains a small, disc-shaped chromatophore and a quite prominent eye-spot (fig. 248.5).

Haploid zoospores are produced only in *unilocular sporangia*. Development begins with the enlargement of the small terminal cell of a very short lateral branch. Gradually this cell increases to several times its original size; simultaneously its chromatophores increase considerably in number. The initial meiotic division of the original cell nucleus is followed by successive mitotic divisions, which continue until there are 32 or 64 nuclei. These eventually become the nuclei of an equal number of pyriform zoospores, which are liberated as a mass through a small opening in the tip of the sporangium. The zoospores then separate from one another and swim away actively, ultimately settling down to form new haploid plants.

Diploid zoospores are produced within *plurilocular sporangia*, which differentiate from the terminal cell of a lateral branchlet. A succession of transverse divisions of this cell gives rise to a row of from six to twelve cells. These cells then divide vertically. Similar transverse and vertical divisions are repeated until several hundred small compartments are produced in some thirty to forty transverse rows. The protoplast of each compartment rounds up and becomes a diploid zoospore (fig. 248).

When plurilocular sporangia arise on haploid plants which have developed from haploid zoospores but contain haploid gametes, they are termed *gametangia*. The gametes, which fuse with one another after liberation, are morphologically similar: sexual reproduction in *Ectocarpus* is therefore isogamous. There is never a fusion of gametes produced by the same plant. The diploid zygote which results from this sexual fusion develops into a new sporophyte plant.

Haploid gametes may develop parthenogenetically into haploid plants. As the diploid generation may give rise to diploid zoospores which then produce new diploid plants, so there may be a reduplication of the haploid phase of the life cycle, without the intervention of the diploid generation.

The essential feature of the complex and very variable life cycle of *Ectocarpus* is the alternation of haploid and diploid generations, which are identical in vegetative structure, but differ in their nuclear constitution.

Class Heterogeneratae

Laminaria (fig. 249)

Differing very markedly in appearance from the small tufts of *Ectocarpus* are the massive seaweeds called the *kelps*. Some kelps are of very great size: *Macrocystis* and *Nereocystis* of the Pacific Ocean may reach lengths of up to 300 feet. The North Sea

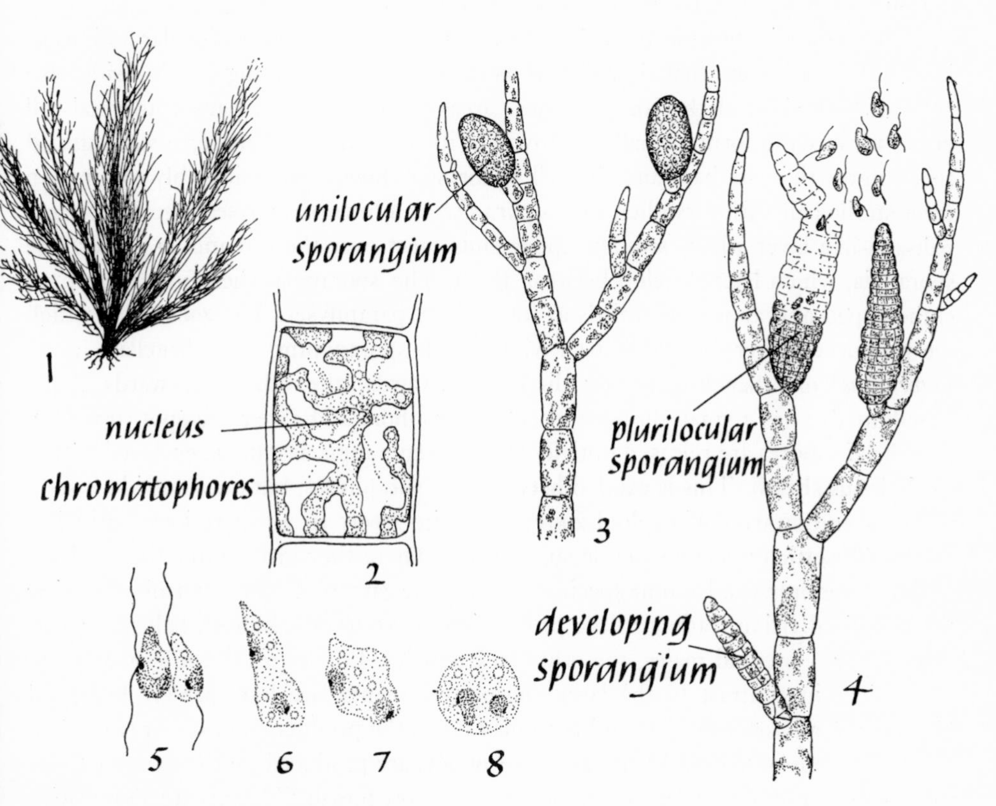

Figure 248 Ectocarpus siliculosus

1 *Whole plant.*

2 *Vegetative cell.*

3 *Filament bearing unilocular sporangia.*

4 *Filament bearing plurilocular sporangia.*

5-8 *Stages in sexual reproduction.*

and Atlantic kelps, the most common of which are various species of *Laminaria*, though larger than the other seaweeds with which they grow, are much smaller than these Giant Kelps, measuring only some 3 to 4 feet in length.

Like *Ectocarpus*, these members of the Phaeophyta exhibit an alternation of generations. In *Ectocarpus*, however, the sporophyte and gametophyte generations are morphologically identical; in *Laminaria* these two phases of the life cycle differ. The sporophyte generation, the seaweed itself, is differentiated into a finger-like holdfast attaching the plant firmly to the substratum, usually rocks. Arising from this base is a slender, flexible stalk, or *stipe*, supporting an expanded leaf-like blade, or *lamina*, which in most species is entire; in *Laminaria digitata*, however, the lamina is dissected. The lamina grows in length by meristematic activity of the cells at its base. It may become detached and cast ashore by winter storms at the end of each season, and new lamina may arise from the old stipes each spring.

The sporangia, produced on the sporophyte generation, are unilocular and occur in such vast numbers that they appear as dark patches extending over considerable areas of both sides of the lamina. These areas are termed *sori*. Each epidermal cell grows upwards to form a small outgrowth at its outer face; a transverse wall cuts off this outgrowth at its base and the cell so formed elongates considerably to form an erect sterile cell with a swollen cap, a *paraphysis*. These paraphyses together form a palisade-like layer whose swollen upper ends meet over the top and so protect the sporangia, which later develop between them. The sporangia when fully grown are club-shaped and about two-thirds as long as the paraphyses. The zoospores, which are produced either in 32's or 64's within each sporangium, are biflagellate, as in *Ectocarpus*, one flagellum being directed forwards, the other backwards. Each flagellum also has a small disc-shaped chromatophore and a red eye-spot (fig. 249).

The zoospores are released initially from the sporangia as a mass, enclosed within a gelatinous sheath. This is exuded between the paraphyses, but once outside it soon ruptures and swarms of haploid zoospores swim freely in all directions until they eventually settle on some suitable substratum. There they grow into either male or female gametophytes. In some species the sex of the gametophyte is determined during the meiotic division leading to the production of zoospores. Indeed, half the gametophytes are potential males, the other half females. Both sexes of the gametophyte generation, in contrast to the large sporophyte plants, are but sparsely branched filaments of microscopic size, and both may begin the production of sex organs when only a few cells in length. Even before sex organs are produced on the gametophytes the two sexes can be distinguished, for the cells of the female filaments are about twice as broad as those of the males. The male filaments produce clusters of one-celled antheridia at the ends of one- or two- celled lateral branches, and each protoplast develops into a single antherozoid with characteristic laterally inserted flagella. The oogonia of the female gametophytes are also one-celled, and as they develop each cell elongates upwards. The single, non-motile ovum, although extruded from the oogonium when mature, remains attached to the oogonial wall. The ovum when

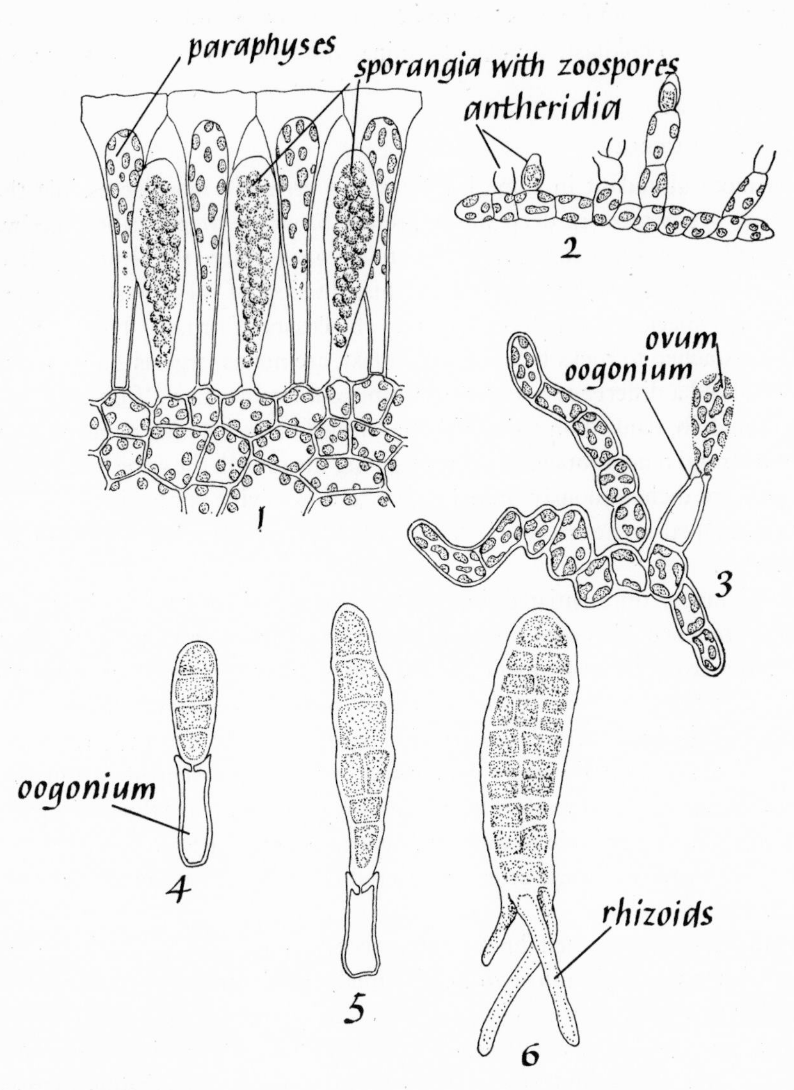

Figure 249 Laminaria

1 *T.s. through lamina of* L. saccharina *in sorus region showing sporangia and paraphyses.*

2 *Male gametophyte with antheridia.*

3 *Female gametophyte with oogonium and extruded ovum.*

4-6 *Stages in the formation of a germling* (2-6 *after Kylin*).

fertilized by an antherozoid becomes the diploid zygote and this develops by successive divisions into a sporophyte *germling*, which becomes attached to the substratum by rhizoids which grow out from its lowermost cells. As the germling develops it becomes differentiated into holdfast, stipe, and lamina, and so a new sporophyte is produced.

Class Cyclosporae

Fucus (figs. 250 to 252)

Even more abundant in some localities and certainly more accessible than the *Laminarias*, which grow in deep water, are the brown seaweeds called the 'wracks'. These usually grow on rocks in the upper tidal zones, where the algae are alternately exposed and submerged by tidal movements. Typical of these wracks is the genus *Fucus*, several species of which occur round the coasts of Britain. The plants, which are mostly attached to rocks by a small holdfast, are not as large as *Laminaria*; nor is there so marked a difference between the stipe and lamina. Each 'frond' consists of a thickened midrib, flanked on either side by 'wings' of tissue. The wings on the older parts of the frond tend to break away, thus giving the midrib the appearance of a stipe. The fronds are dichotomously branched, since they divide successively at their tips into pairs of equal branches. The whole thallus may attain a length of two or three feet (fig. 250).

The thallus is differentiated into three regions. A central *medulla region* of numerous branched filaments embedded in mucilage: these run mainly along the length of the frond. The filaments grade into smaller, polygonal parenchymatous cortical cells, which are possibly *storage regions*, though they contain some chromatophores. The principal *photosynthetic region* is in the outer limiting layers of small palisade cells; these contain many more small, brown, disc-shaped chromatophores than do the cortical cells beneath. The cells of this outer layer, like those of a meristem, are always potentially capable of division: hence they are collectively termed *meristoderm*. The outer walls of these cells are covered by a protective mucilaginous cuticle (fig. 251).

Growth in length of each branch is initiated by a large pyramidal *apical cell*, which divides periodically into two longitudinal, equal parts, thereby giving rise to the *dichotomous branching* so typical of every *Fucus* thallus. The various tissues of the thallus are produced by cutting off cells from the sides and base of the apical cell, and by the subsequent subdivisions of these cells. The thallus increases in thickness by divisions of the meristoderm cells, and by elongation of the cells in the layers below: thus the mass of interwoven hyphal filaments which constitute the cortical region is constantly accumulating. In *Fucus vesiculosus*, series of bladders develop on each side of the midrib; gas collects in these and buoys up the thallus when submerged in the sea.

There is no form of asexual reproduction in any *Fucus* species, though in some instances, vegetative propagation may occur by the fragmentation of portions of the thallus.

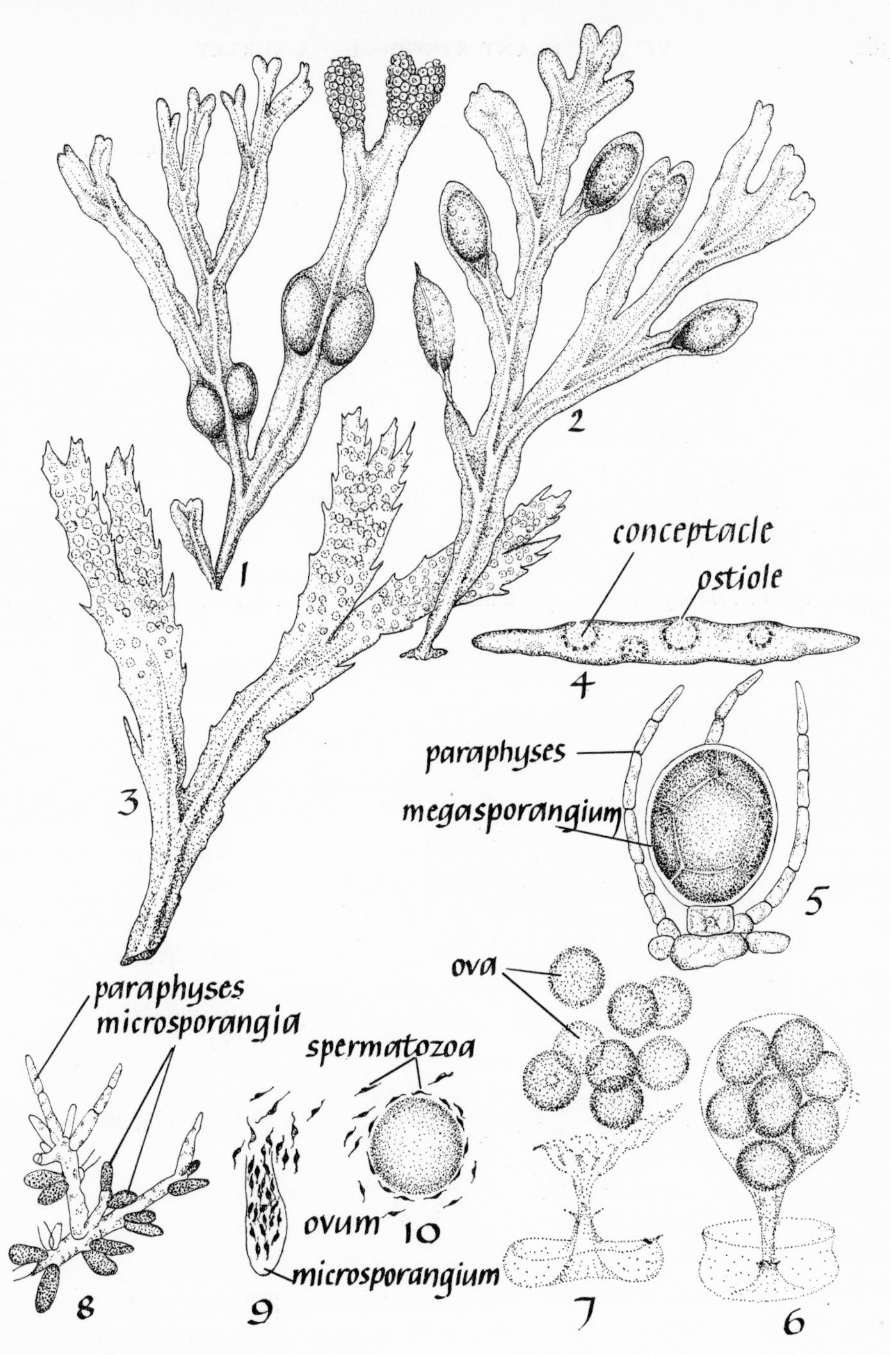

Figure 250 Fucus

1 Fucus vesiculosus. 2 F. spiralis. 3 F. serratus.

4 *T.s. through fertile region of thallus showing conceptacles.*

5 *Megasporangium of* Fucus vesiculosus. 6-7 *Stages in liberation of ova.*

8 *Microsporangium of* F. vesiculosus. 9 *Liberation of spermatozoa.*

10 *Spermatozoa swimming round ovum prior to its fertilization.* (5-9 *after Thuret.*)

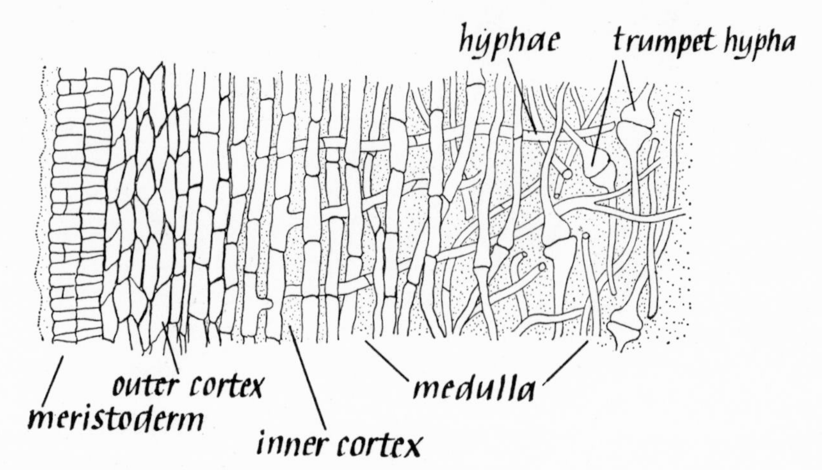

Figure 251 *T.s. through thallus of* Fucus vesiculosus *showing the main tissue regions.*

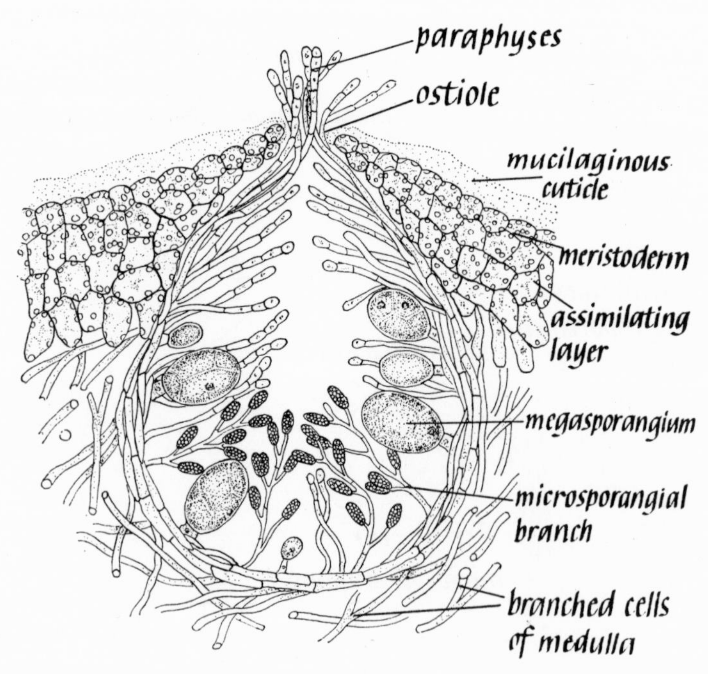

Figure 252 *T.s. through conceptacle of* Fucus spiralis *showing microsporangia and megasporangia.*

Sexual reproduction is oogamous, as in *Laminaria*, but more complex. The small motile antherozoids which fertilize the non-motile ova, are biflagellate, and, in other respects, quite typical of those produced by other members of the Phaeophyta. The organs of reproduction are formed within flask-shaped cavities sunken into the considerably swollen ends of the forked fronds. These cavities, or *conceptacles*, which are crowded together, open to the exterior by means of a small pore or *ostiole*. Each appears as a dot on the swollen end of the thallus. The reproductive organs arise from the walls of the conceptacles amongst sterile hairs (paraphyses), the ends of which protrude through the ostiole. The paraphyses are largely concerned with the secretion of mucilage. In *Fucus serratus* and *F. vesiculosus*, a particular plant gives rise to either all male, or all female gamete-producing conceptacles. In *F. spiralis* male and female gametes arise within the same conceptacle (fig. 252).

Before the cytological events involved in the reproduction of *Fucus* were fully investigated, the reproductive organs which develop in the conceptacles were thought to be antheridia and oogonia. It is now known that a meiosis occurs within these bodies, which must therefore be termed *sporangia*. These sporangia are comparable with the pollen sacs and ovules of flowering plants. The *Fucus* plant itself must therefore be regarded as the sporophyte generation. The spores it produces are of two sizes: those which eventually give rise to spermatozoids are *microsporangia*; the much larger ova arise from *megasporangia*.

Microsporangia are produced at the ends of small branched filaments which arise in considerable numbers from each male conceptacle wall. Each is ovoid in shape and initially possesses a single nucleus. The first division of this diploid nucleus is meiotic, so four haploid cells, the *microspores*, are produced. Each of these then undergoes four mitotic divisions, to give a group of sixteen haploid cells, which must be regarded as the gametophyte generation. This generation is thus even more reduced than in *Laminaria*. Since there are four of these sixteen-celled gametophytes, every microsporangium contains sixty-four haploid cells in all. Each of these cells eventually rounds up and develops as a biflagellate male gamete or *spermatozoid*.

Each megasporangium arises from the wall of the female conceptacle as a large single oval cell with dense contents, borne on a short *stalk cell*. The first division of the nucleus of the megasporangium initial is also meiotic and results in the production of four haploid megaspores. These megaspores divide immediately to form four binucleate gametophytes. Thus each megaspore now contains eight nuclei which round off, with a portion of cytoplasm, to become eight non-motile ova.

The outer tissues of the *Fucus* fronds, when uncovered at low tides, tend to dry out and contract, with the result that pressures are set up against the conceptacle walls. The mucilage within is squeezed out as droplets through the ostioles, and the contents of the micro- and megasporangia, if mature, are extruded with it. In both cases, although the outer sporangium wall bursts, the gametes when extruded are still enclosed within an envelope composed of the inner wall layer. In the sea, the gametes are soon liberated from these envelopes, and rapidly each non-motile egg becomes surrounded by hundreds of spermatozoa. One flagellum of each spermatozoid appears to attach itself to the egg, while the other unattached flagella engage in whipping movements, which cause the egg to rotate vigorously in the water. Eventually one of the spermatozoids penetrates the ovum and the nuclei fuse. At this point, despite the presence of all the other sperms round the ovum, its rotatory movement ceases abruptly, thus ending the brief and barely recognisable gametophytic phase in the life cycle of *Fucus*.

The zygote resulting from any fertilization begins to divide almost immediately after nuclear fusion has been accomplished. By continued cell divisions the young sporophyte, as it must now be termed, soon develops and at an early stage appears as a small club-shaped embryo with rhizoidal attachment cells at its base and a tuft of hairs arising from an apical depression. It is from the base of this depression that the initial, pyramidal, apical cell of the *Fucus* thallus is eventually formed. At an early stage in its development, the cylindrical embryo starts to flatten and exhibit the dichotomous branching so characteristic of these seaweeds.

CHAPTER 33

DIVISION EUMYCOPHYTA (FUNGI)

In the older classifications of the Plant Kingdom the Division Thallophyta included all non-vascular plants with unicellular organs of reproduction and was subdivided into two classes, the photosynthetic Algae and non-photosynthetic Fungi. Indeed the Fungi are thought by some authorities to have arisen from algal ancestors by the loss of their photosynthetic pigments. This view, however, is not accepted by all *mycologists* – the botanists who study these colourless plants. More recent classifications place the Fungi in a separate Division of the Plant Kingdom, the Eumycophyta, which ranks with the various algal Divisions, such as the Chlorophyta and Phaeophyta.

The Eumycophyta is a very large, diverse and economically important Division, containing more than 70,000 species. Its most widely known members are the mushrooms and toadstools, and the moulds that frequently grow on bread, jam, cheese, and other foodstuffs. Slightly less familiar to the non-botanist are the fungi which can cause great havoc as parasites of cereal and horticultural crops. Others live and grow in and on animals, including man. Any fungal disease of an animal is termed a *mycosis*.

Because they lack chlorophyll, fungi are unable to synthesize organic food from carbon dioxide and water in the presence of light as do green plants. Like animals, they are forced to depend on organic matter and so live either as *saprophytes* on dead organic materials, or as *parasites* on other living organisms. In contrast to the self-feeding or *autotrophic* nutrition of green plants, fungi are *heterotrophic*. They have, however, quite remarkable synthetic powers and when a suitable external supply of organic matter is available they can produce a variety of complex organic substances. Thus the majority of fungi, even though normally parasitic, if supplied with suitable conditions, can be grown artificially on synthetic media. Commonly the solid, jelly-like medium agar-agar, to which various organic and inorganic substances have been added, is used.

Although the simplest type of fungal thallus is unicellular, as in some aquatic *chytrids* which parasitize certain freshwater algae, the majority are typically filamentous. Such plant bodies are made up of delicate branched threads termed *hyphae* which together constitute the *mycelium*. In the more primitive fungi these hyphae are without cross walls or *septae*, though septae occur in the more advanced forms.

The chemical composition of the cell wall varies in different types of fungi, though in the majority it is composed principally of *chitin*, a substance chemically related, though not identical, to the chitin forming the exoskeleton of insects. In some fungi, cellulose is the main wall constituent. Most commonly excess food is stored in the hyphae as glycogen, but a number of fungi accumulate oil droplets. The alcohol mannitol is also found.

As with other groups of the Plant Kingdom, the classification of the Eumycophyta presents many difficulties. There is, however, fairly general agreement that all fungi can be placed in one of the following four classes:

1. *Phycomycetes*, in which the mycelium may be single-celled, or filamentous in which case the vegetative hyphae are without cross walls. Biflagellate zoospores are produced in the aquatic members of the group – hence their name phycomycete, meaning 'algal-like fungus'. All spores, whether motile or non-motile, are produced in sporangia.

2. *Ascomycetes*, in which usually four or eight sexual spores are produced in a sac or bladder, the *ascus*. The hyphae are septate and no motile spores are ever produced.

3. *Basidiomycetes*, in which the sexual spores are characteristically produced externally and usually in fours, on a structure termed a *basidium*.

4. *Fungi Imperfecti*, in which the sexual stages are completely unknown, so that it is impossible to place them with any certainty into any one of the above classes. The grouping of any fungus into this fourth class is clearly tentative until more is known about its life history. Indeed, the Fungi Imperfecti is a heterogeneous class containing components of the other three classes.

CLASS PHYCOMYCETES

These 'alga-like' fungi which constitute the smallest class, with little more than one thousand species, must not be thought of as a 'natural' grouping, but rather as a class whose members have reached a similar level of vegetative and reproductive complexity. Its members exhibit a considerable range of structure and reproductive behaviour, as the few commonly occurring types briefly referred to in the following pages show.

Many of the Phycomycetes exist as parasites of a variety of terrestrial and aquatic plants and animals. Thus the 'damping off' fungi, the 'white rusts' and the 'downy mildews', which all belong to this Class, are angiosperm parasites, and cause considerable destruction to a great many plants of economic importance. The potato famine, for example, which ravaged Ireland in 1845-46 was caused by the 'downy mildew', *Phytophthora infestans*. A related fungus, which occurs fairly commonly in greenhouses and nurseries, causing the 'damping off' of seedlings, is *Pythium debaryanum*.

Pythium (figs. 253 to 255).

The mycelium of *Pythium*, which consists of rather slender, non-septate hyphae, can live either saprophytically in the soil, or parasitically on the seedlings of a wide variety of plants of horticultural importance. As a parasite it attacks the seedlings at or just above the soil surface, its hyphae penetrating both between the cells as

Figure 253 *Mustard seedlings whose stems (left) have collapsed due to infection by the fungus* Pythium debaryanum.

intracellular hyphae, and into the cells as *intercellular hyphae*, drawing nourishment from them.

The ravages of the fungus are greatest in the cortical region: it kills so many of the cells whose turgor is important for the support of the stem, that the stem can no longer support the shoot, which then collapses (fig. 253).

As in most of the algae already studied, reproduction in *Pythium* is both sexual and asexual. In asexual reproduction some of the hyphae grow outwards and their ends swell to form a globose or oval terminal sporangium. Each sporangium is cut off from the hypha from which it was formed by a cross wall. The sporangium may remain attached to this hypha and thus germinate where it was formed, or it may become detached and carried away by wind or water. Under certain environmental condititions the sporangium may germinate simply by putting out a *germ tube* which, by its growth, becomes a hypha capable of infecting a new host plant. This germination behaviour occurs in a moist atmosphere; if the sporangium is inundated with water, however, mobile zoospores are formed. First, a very thin-walled, bladder-like *vesicle* is formed at the tip of a tube which emerges from the sporangium. The protoplast of the sporangium then passes into the vesicle by way of the tube, and, after a period of quiescence, divides up into a large number of biflagellate zoospores. The zoospores are kidney-shaped and swim by movements of the two flagella arising from the concave side of the body. Their movements, which first are apparent within the vesicle, become increasingly vigorous, until suddenly the thin vesicle wall bursts and the zoospores disperse in all directions in the soil-water film. After a period of swimming the zoospores come to rest and then encyst. Asexual reproduction takes place most commonly when the fungus is living in the soil as a saprophyte amongst the dead remains of a previously parasitized host. The encysted spores germinate by sending out a germ tube and, if new seedlings are present in the soil, these may soon become infected with the fungus (fig. 254).

In contrast to asexual reproduction, sexual reproduction in *Pythium* usually occurs within the tissues of the host plant. The tips of some hyphae swell considerably and a septum forms, cutting off a globose *oogonium* within which there is a dense multinucleate *oosphere* surrounded by a less dense layer, the *periplasm*. Other hyphal tips, which are often branches of the same hypha, swell to a lesser extent than those forming oogonia; these become the much smaller, elongate or club-shaped *antheridia* with multicellular contents. These, too, are cut off by septa (fig. 255).

On coming into contact with the oogonium the antheridium sends out a *fertilization tube*, which penetrates the oogonial wall and the periplasm. During these developments only one functional nucleus remains in each *gametangium*, as the oogonia and antheridia are termed, the others having disintegrated. The surviving male nucleus passes through the fertilization tube into the oosphere, where it fuses with the remaining female nucleus to form a diploid zygote, now termed the *oospore*. The oospore develops a smooth, thick, resistant wall. After a period of rest, and when provided with suitable conditions, the oospore germinates. It sends out a germ tube which can reinfect and cause the 'damping off' of seedlings with which it comes into contact.

Albugo (figs. 256 to 259)

The 'white rusts' or blister diseases of plants of the wallflower family, Cruciferae, are caused by a fungus related to *Pythium*, *Albugo candida* (previously called *Cystopus candida*). The disease commonly affects cabbage crops.

The symptoms of the disease, which can often be found in gardens on the weed shepherd's purse, can be seen with the naked eye as white pustules on the stems and leaves, and as swellings of the surrounding tissues (fig. 256). These are places where asexual spores have been formed and are being liberated. The branched, generally non-septate mycelium of the fungus grows between the cells of the host, so that it is intercellular. The individual hyphae, however, produce at intervals numerous, very small, globose branches which penetrate the host cells and absorb food materials from them. After ramifying through the host tissues the hyphae form a dense mat immediately beneath the host epidermis from which grow erect clusters of short club-shaped hyphae (fig. 257). Apart from their characteristic shape and arrangement, these *sporangiophores* can be readily distinguished from vegetative hyphae by the fact that the upper portion is thin-walled, and the lower is considerably thickened.

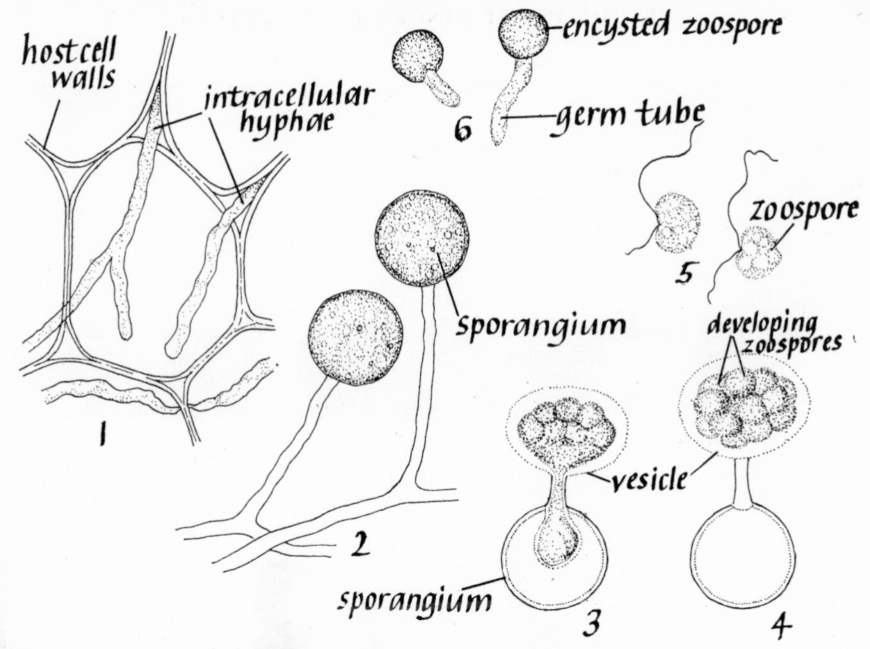

Figure 254 *Stages in the life cycle of* Pythium.
1 *Hyphae invading cortex of host plant.*
2 *Sporangia.*
3–6 *Germination of sporangium and zoospore formation.*

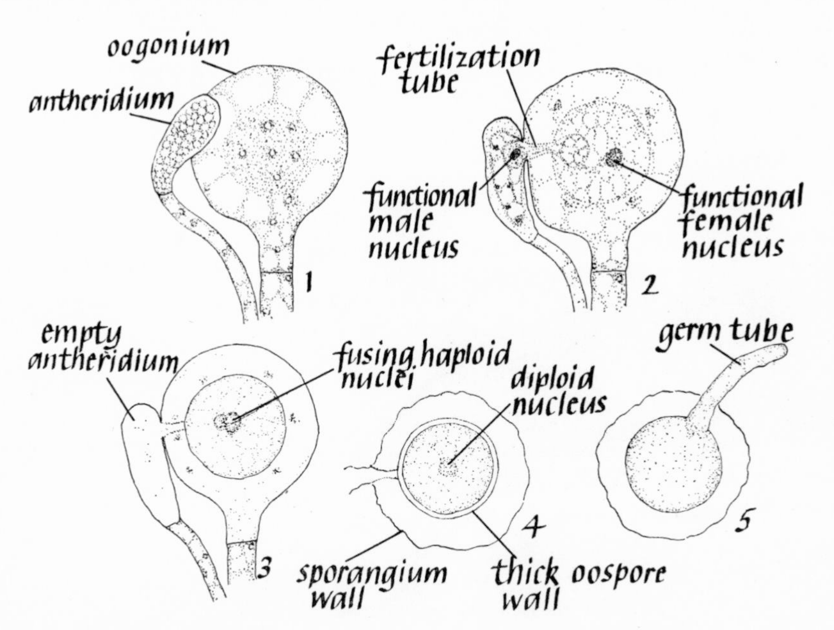

Figure 255 Pythium debaryanum – *stages in sexual reproduction and germination of oospore.*

Figure 256 *Plants of shepherd's purse*, Capsella bursa-pastoris, *infected by* Albugo candida. *The swollen white patches on the stems mark the sites of conidiosporangial eruptions.*

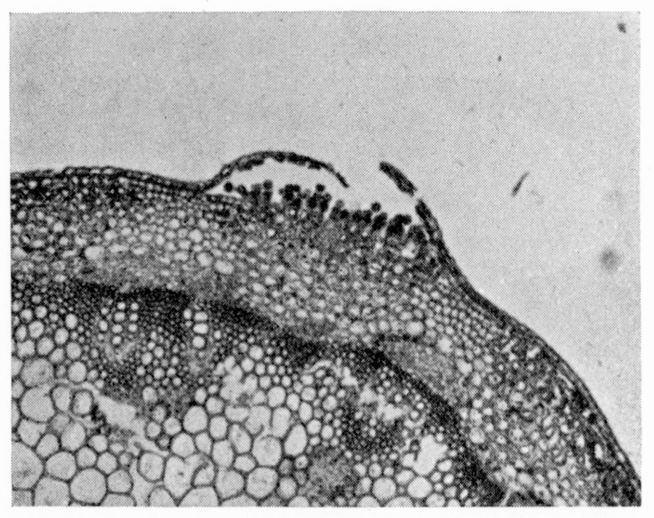

Figure 257 *T.s. stem of* Tragopogon pratensis *infected by* Albugo candida, *showing conidiosporangial eruption on surface. Note the ruptured epidermis.*

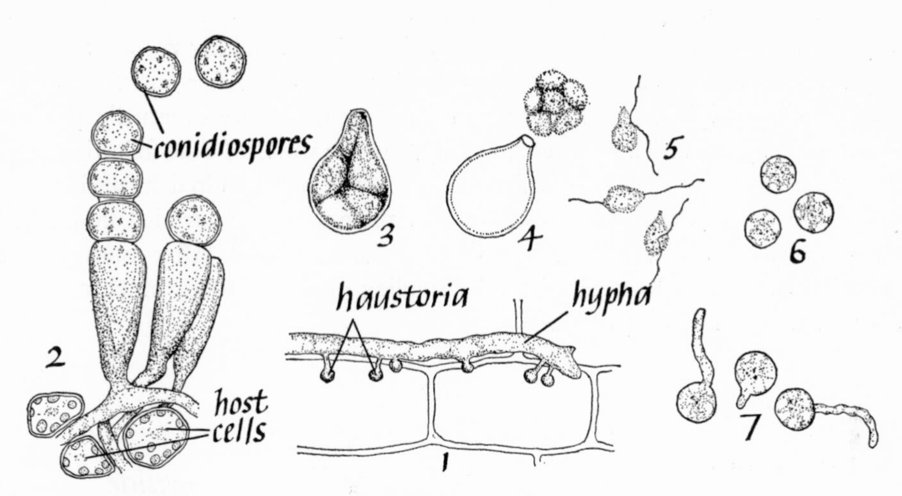

Figure 258 *Stages in the life cycle of* Albugo candida.
1 *Hypha with haustoria penetrating host cells.*
2 *Conidiospore production.*
3–5 *Zoospore production from conidiospores.*
6–7 *Germination of conidia in dry conditions.*

When the sporangiophores reach a certain stage in their development there is a slight enlargement of the upper end, which is cut off as a sporangium containing from five to eight nuclei. Soon, however, the region of the sporangiophore immediately beneath this sporangium enlarges, and a second sporangium is cut off. The process is then repeated again and again, very many times. As a result, the accumulating chain of sporangia, termed *conidiosporangia* or *conidiophores*, pushes out the underlying host epidermis and eventually causes it to burst. The white powdery blister-like patches mentioned above are, in fact, areas of these conidiosporangial eruptions. With the rupture of the host epidermis the *conidiospores* are blown away by wind. Of the vast numbers produced, very few germinate, but the protoplasts of those that are disseminated to damp conditions divide to produce numerous kidney-shaped biflagellate zoospores, somewhat similar to those of *Pythium*. The zoospores after swarming for some time encyst and then send out a germ tube that may grow through a stomata, thus infecting a new host. When environmental conditions are dry the conidiosporangia may germinate directly into hyphae and so spread the disease without the intervention of zoospores (fig. 258).

Sexual reproduction in *Albugo*, which occurs towards the end of the host's growing season, is similar in many ways to that in *Pythium*. Oogonia and antheridia are formed from hyphae which penetrate fairly deeply into the tissues of the stem or petiole of the host. The formation of these organs and their nuclear behaviour are similar to *Pythium*. When mature, the antheridium forms a slender fertilization tube that penetrates the oogonial wall and grows through the periplasm surrounding the oosphere nucleus, with which it eventually fuses. The resulting zygote, termed an oospore, soon secretes a thick, warty, three-layered wall. After an initial meiotic division of the diploid fusion nucleus, thirty-two nuclei are eventually produced within the oospore, which then rests, usually over the winter. In the following spring the oospore germinates with the formation of over one hundred biflagellate zoospores. On the rupture of the oospore wall these are first extruded into a thin-walled vesicle, which later bursts so that they are liberated. After swarming, the zoospores encyst and later germinate by sending out germ tubes which can infect new Cruciferous hosts (fig. 259).

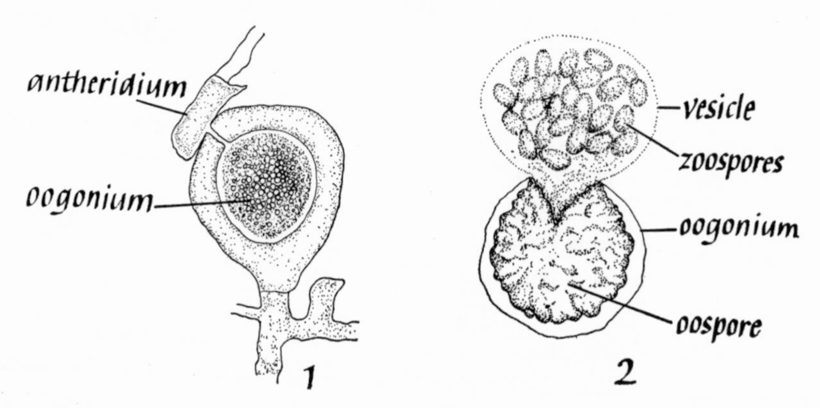

Figure 259 *Sexual reproduction in* Albugo candida.
1 *Sexual fusion.*
2 *Zoospore production from a mature oospore (after De Bary).*

Mucor and Rhizopus (figs. 260 to 261)

One group of Phycomycetes never give rise, as do *Pythium*, *Albugo*, and their relatives, to mobile cells; they are characterized by the production of zygospores instead of oospores. Zygospores, which have already been encountered in the algal genus *Spirogyra*, are resting spores, resulting from the complete fusion of two *gametangia*.

Mucor, a genus with many known species, serves as an example of the general life cycle of this group of fungi, commonly known as the *moulds*. Most *Mucor* species are saprophytes, living on dead organic matter, a number of them occurring in the soil. Some related forms are mild parasites and others are known to cause diseases (*mycoses*) of animals, including man.

The spores of *Mucor* and related genera, especially *Rhizopus*, are abundant in the atmosphere. Thus it is a fairly simple matter to obtain growths of these fungi by exposing moist bread to the air until it becomes 'mouldy'. Alternatively, petri dishes used for culturing fungi and bacteria and containing malt agar should be left open for a short time. After a few days the fine thread-like mycelium can be seen on these substrates. The mycelium of *Mucor* is composed of a mass of branched hyphae and on agar in a petri dish each will be seen to be more or less circular in outline. This is to be explained by the fact that each mycelium has originated from an aerial spore which on germinating has produced a system of branched hyphae whose tips have grown out more or less equally in all directions. Each hypha increases in length by apical growth and most of the hyphae tend to be without cross walls, at least in their earlier stages. Septa do, however, occur in the older parts and, as with *Pythium* and *Albugo*, cross walls are produced during the formation of reproductive structures.

After a few days of purely vegetative growth the organs of asexual reproduction of the fungus (sporangiophores) become visible. These consist of spherical sporangia arising from the ends of long, unbranched aerial hyphae. Various stages in the development of these structures can usually be seen in a *Mucor* culture. Initially, they appear simply as erect aerial hyphae which, however, elongate rapidly. After growth ceases the hyphae tips swell and there is an internal accumulation of protoplasmic materials. As the tip becomes larger and more obviously spherical, its many nuclei move towards the periphery of the sphere, leaving the central region less dense and somewhat vacuolated. Gradually a dome-shaped wall forms between these two regions and eventually forms the tip of the sporangiophore, the *columella*. The multinucleate region beyond and within the larger sphere constitutes the sporangium. In each sporangium the protoplasm becomes divided up into a considerable number of small, multinucleate segments, each of which ultimately rounds up, acquires a wall and so becomes a *sporangiospore*. During the period of these internal changes the sporangium wall becomes dark brown in colour and ornamented with minute, closely set, crystals of calcium oxalate, giving it an irregular outline (fig. 260.2).

When mature, the *Mucor* sporangium becomes converted into a *sporangial drop* as its wall dissolves, except for a small collar which remains round the base of the columella. At the same time water passes through the columella into the spore mass, which is embedded in mucilage. When exposed to the air the sporangial drop dries and the spores within become very firmly stuck to the columella. As yet no one has explained satisfactorily how the spores are eventually liberated and dispersed. There is no doubt that this happens, for they are always abundant in the atmosphere. The study of the germination of *Mucor* spores in culture has shown that this cannot take place immediately after spore-formation and indeed they can remain dormant for some considerable time. However, the spores are ripe and when conditions are suitable the spores swell considerably; after a few hours each puts out one or more germ tubes which grow rapidly and branch repeatedly so that a new mycelium is established.

Many species of *Mucor* have an additional means of asexual reproduction, which seems to occur especially under conditions unfavourable for the further growths of the mycelium. The contents of the hyphae become concentrated at points along their

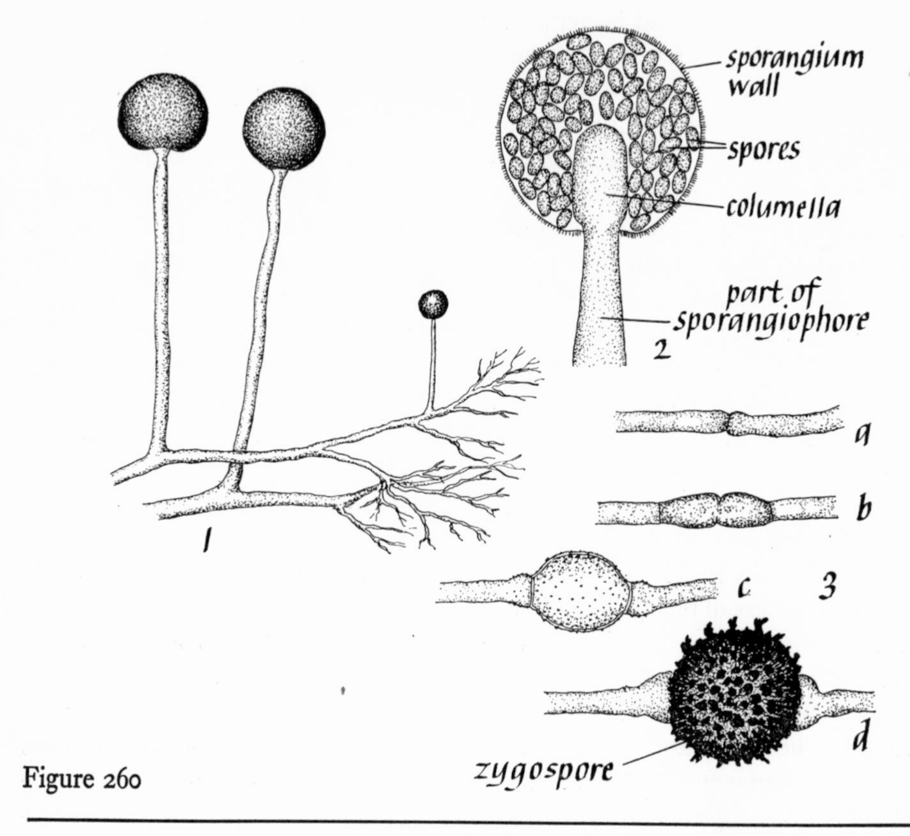

Figure 260

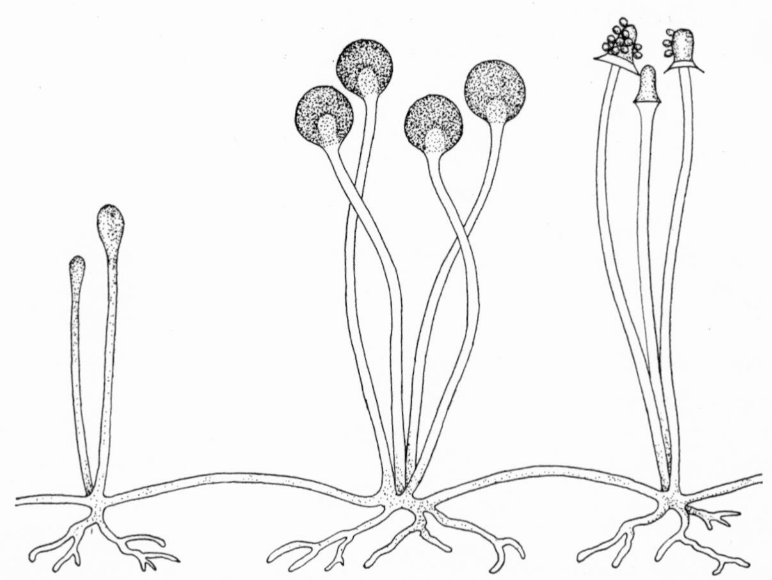

Figure 261

length so that the intervening regions appear to be empty. Round these visibly denser regions a thick wall is formed, the resultant structure being a *chlamydospore*. These are resistant to dessication, but will germinate and form a new mycelium when favourable growing conditions return. Chlamydospores occur particularly, it seems, in soil-inhabiting species of *Mucor*.

Sexual reproduction in *Mucor* has several features which recall conjugation in the green alga *Spirogyra*. Sometimes when two hyphae from different mycelia grow so that they come into contact, each begins to produce a small protuberance at the point of contact. These lateral outgrowths (*progametangia*), the tips of which become flattened by mutual pressure, enlarge and become delimited by a cross wall so that a multinucleate gametangium is formed. The part of the lateral outgrowth remaining outside each gametangium is the *suspensor*. After a time the double wall separating the gametangia dissolves from the central region outwards and the multinucleate contents intermingle, the individual nuclei probably becoming associated in pairs and eventually fusing. The resulting *fusion-cell* becomes a *zygospore* and develops a black, thick, resistant wall of very irregular outline, within which there accumulates oily food reserves (fig. 260.3).

Though termed a spore, the *Mucor* zygospore is not dispersed, but in most cases rests where it was formed. After a period of dormancy the zygospore wall ruptures and the germ tube which grows out from it immediately develops into an erect sporangiophore, which subsequently produces spores.

There are a few species of *Mucor* in which the mycelium derived from a single spore will by itself form zygospores, but in most species sexual reproduction takes place only between hyphae of different mycelial strains. These strains, which are morphologically indistinguishable, are referred to by mycologists as 'plus' and 'minus', and it is only when a 'plus' contacts a 'minus' that zygospores result. 'Plus' and 'plus', or 'minus' and 'minus' in contact, produce no sexual response. Species exhibiting this phenomenon are said to be *heterothallic*, while the few which appear to have only one strain of mycelium are termed *homothallic*.

Commoner than *Mucor* is the closely related genus *Rhizopus*. The black sporangia of *Rhizopus nigricans*, for example, are often more common on damp bread than *Mucor*, with which *Rhizopus* is frequently confused. In *Rhizopus* species, however,

---

Figure 260 *Stages in the life cycle of* Mucor.

1 *Part of mycelium producing sporangiophores.*

2 *Upper portion of sporangiophore showing columella and spores within sporangium.*

3 *a–d Stages in sexual reproduction.*

Figure 261 *Part of a mycelium of* Rhizopus nigricans *showing rhizoid-like hyphae and from left to right, stages in sporangiophore production and the liberation of spores (after G. M. Smith).*

the mycelium becomes differentiated into three types of hyphae: the branched rhizoidal hyphae, which penetrate the substratum, drawing nourishment from it; stout aerial hyphae termed *stolons*, which grow horizontally above the substratum, though, where they bend downward and touch it, tufts of the rhizoid-like hyphae form; vertically erect sporangiophores, which tend to be shorter and somewhat thicker than those of *Mucor* (fig. 261). Development of the sporangiophores follows much the same course as in *Mucor*, but when mature the *Rhizopus* sporangium wall splits into a number of fragments, so there is no formation of a sporangial drop. The centre of the columella collapses and the spores which dry on its surface are easily detached and dispersed by wind. *Rhizopus nigricans* is heterothallic, and although common as a saprophyte it can occur as a parasite causing 'soft rot' on apples and other fruit in storage.

CLASS ASCOMYCETES

A much larger but more natural group of fungi than the Phycomycetes are the Ascomycetes, all of whose members are characterized by their spore-producing unit, the *ascus*, which usually gives rise to eight *ascospores*. Although in some Ascomycetes the asci occur singly, in the majority they are grouped in elaborate fruiting bodies, or *sporophores*.

When present, the mycelium of all of these fungi is septate and the individual cells are either uni- or multinucleate. An interesting feature about the septae is that each is centrally perforated by a minute pore, through which the cytoplasm between adjoining cells is said to stream. Not only do hyphae branch profusely, there are also fusions, or *anastomoses*, between individual hyphae, so that the mycelium often becomes a complex network.

The asci are the products of sexual reproduction, but very many Ascomycetes also reproduce by asexual means and, indeed, in some genera this would seem to have become the principal means of reproduction. Many of the fungi placed in the Fungi Imperfecti are almost certainly Ascomycetes, in which sexual reproduction has been partially or completely suppressed. Asexual reproduction is by means of conidia, which show great variety of form. In many of the commonly occurring species chains of spores constrict off, usually from specialized, erect hyphae termed *conidiophores*.

Saccharomyces (fig. 262)

The simplest of the Ascomycetes are the Yeasts. These are probably primitive fungi, although some mycologists consider them to be degenerate. Mention has already been made of the special fermenting properties of these fungi from which they derive their generic name, *Saccharomyces*, meaning 'sugar fungus'. Yeasts are of great economic importance (the baking, brewing and wine industries being dependent on them), and much research has gone into the selection and breeding of strains of yeast which will carry out particular fermentations. In addition to their economic value, however, some species are plant and animal pathogens and a number are now known to be pathogenic to man causing serious and even lethal diseases.

The yeasts are fungi which are unicellular as a result of the complete suppression of mycelial development. When grown under certain conditions, however, some yeasts will develop as a mycelium. It has been suggested that the unicellular condition of yeast has developed as an adaptation to life in sugar-containing solutions. Bakers' yeast, *Saccharomyces cerevisiae*, can be made to multiply very rapidly in a sugar solution. This it does by the formation of small bud-like outgrowths from one or other of the ovoid cells. During its formation the cell nucleus divides and one of the resulting nuclei passes into the bud; the bud is then separated off from the parent cell by a wall. The daughter bud then enlarges rapidly, though may itself produce a bud before enlargement is complete and before separating from the parent. Under conditions of rapid growth the formation of new buds may be much more rapid than the maturation and separation of those already formed. As a result, short chain-like filaments arise with constrictions marking the points at which the cells will later separate. These may be branched or unbranched (fig. 262).

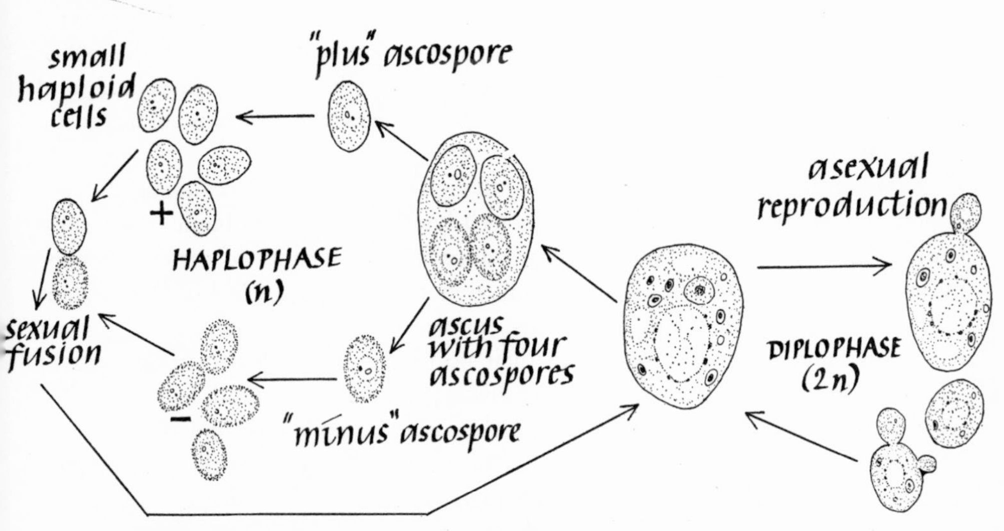

Figure 262 *Diagrammatic representation of the life cycle of* Saccharomyces (*adapted from Rose*).

In addition to this vegetative means of propagation, yeasts also produce ascospores, though this does not seem to happen very frequently under natural conditions. Such sexual reproduction can, however, be induced in yeasts grown on agar. If some of the actively growing cells are removed from the characteristic white colonies produced under these conditions and spread on to the surface of fresh, sterile agar in a petri dish containing only 0·5% sodium acetate, the ascus stages should develop. These arise from normal vegetative cells following the meiotic division of the nucleus. Each of the four resulting nuclei rounds off with some of the cytoplasm to become a haploid ascospore. The ascospores are liberated with the breakdown of the ascus wall.

Heterothallism has been demonstrated in many strains of *Saccharomyces*, each ascus forming two 'plus' and two 'minus' spores. By careful dissection and pipetting with a micromanipulator, these individual spores can be picked out and cultured separately. The result is a colony of slow-growing, haploid cells, smaller than those of the normal diploid yeasts. Should a 'plus' and 'minus' yeast come together, the cells, and later their nuclei, may fuse and the resulting diploid cell will then bud to give rise to the normal, larger, vigorously growing yeast. Thus there is an alternation of cytologically and morphologically distinct generations in the yeasts. The diploid generation is termed the *diplophase*, the alternate haploid state, the *haplophase*.

Eurotium (*Aspergillus*) *and Penicillium* (figs. 263 and 264)

Another group of Ascomycetes are those which, like the yeasts, reproduce largely by vegetative or asexual means, asci and ascospores being formed somewhat infrequently. Indeed, the asexual stage of the fungus *Eurotium* to be described below, was for a long time called *Aspergillus*; *Eurotium* referred to the sexual stage until it was realized that they belonged to one and the same plant. The latter name has been retained. The fungus is mostly a richly branched, septate mycelium, and the asexual spores are *conidia* produced on conidiophores whose form is characteristic of the various related genera.

Eurotium typifies fungi of this group, though a common and economically very important relative is *Penicillium*, now well-known for its antibiotic properties. Penicillium is also of gastronomic importance in the ripening of certain cheeses. Because of their prodigious spore production there are nearly always abundant *Eurotium* conidia in the atmosphere. This, coupled with their ability to utilize a great variety of food substances, results in their occurring as common contaminants of foodstuffs and of cultures of other organisms in mycological and bacteriological laboratories. The 'blue fur' which can quickly cover damp leather and clothes is invariably caused by *Eurotium*. Some species are animal and human pathogens, causing diseases of the lungs (*aspergillosis*, from the old name for the fungus *Aspergillus*) with symptoms closely resembling those of tuberculosis.

The mycelium of the fungus consists of much-branched, septate hyphae, the cells of which are multinucleate. While still growing and expanding vigorously the mycelium produces large numbers of conidiophores. These arise from single hyphal cells, which then may be termed *foot cells*. Each conidiophore is erect and unbranched, and its apex swells into a spherical head, the vesicle. This is a multinucleate structure, and from it there buds out a number of bottle-shaped projections. These are termed *phialides* and when mature they begin to form conidia, one below the other, in chains. The conidia are small, globose, and rough walled. Since conidiophores and conidia are produced in such abundance, the colour of the latter, frequently bluish-green, though sometimes black or even yellow, becomes the predominant colour of the *Eurotium* colony (fig. 263).

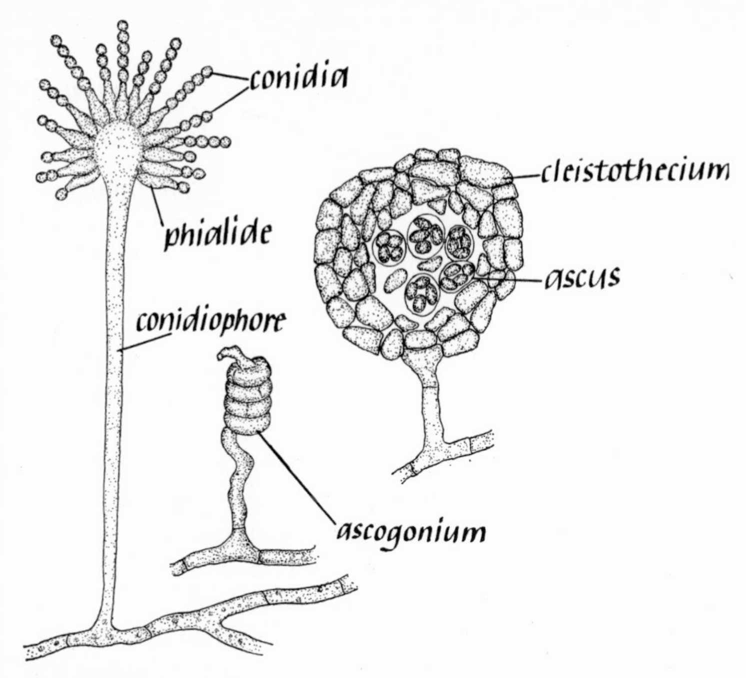

Figure 263 Aspergillus, showing Conidiophore, Ascogonium, and Cleistothecium with asci.

It is important to note that the conidial apparatus of *Penicillium* differs from that of *Eurotium* and consists of an upright, aerial conidiophore, which is septate and branches dichotomously, usually four or more times. The conidia are constricted off in chains from groups of small, almost parallel, terminal cells also named *phialides* (fig. 264).

When grown on rich, sugar-containing media in fairly high temperatures (25-30°C) some species of *Eurotium*, though by no means all, will give rise to asci. Many species would seem to have completely lost their ability to reproduce sexually. The female sex organ is an *ascogonium*, which develops by the coiling of a hypha to form a close spiral, whilst another hypha, the antheridium, coils over it. There is some doubt as to whether the antheridium is always functional, though sometimes there appears to be a fusion of these two sex organs. If functional, there is a pairing of nuclei in the ascogonium; if not, the ascogonium nuclei pair and fuse with each other. As these developments are taking place sterile hyphae grow up around the ascogonium and antheridium and become interwoven to form a pseudo-parenchymatous mass, the *cleistothecium*. While the latter is still developing as a globose *ascocarp*, generally soft

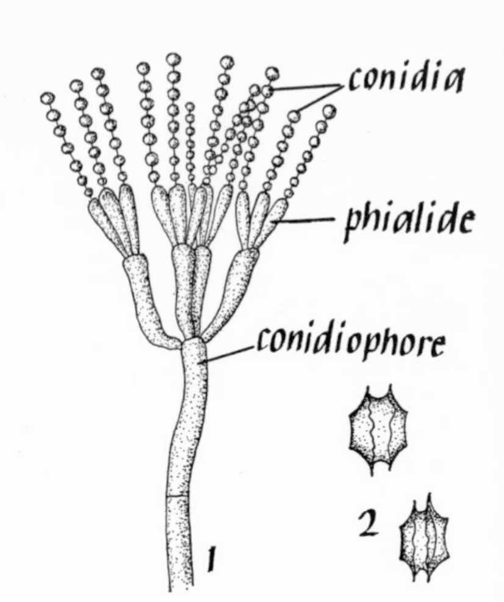

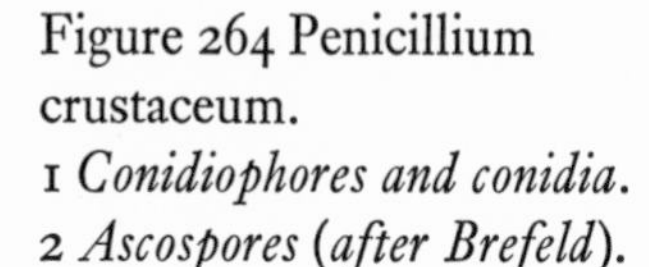
Figure 264 Penicillium crustaceum.
1 *Conidiophores and conidia.*
2 *Ascospores (after Brefeld).*

and yellow, the ascogonium inside divides into several sections, each of which may send out a branch which may become further branched. These are the *ascogonous hyphae* and at the end of each, a globose, ovoid or pear-shaped ascus is formed containing eight ascospores. Each ascus which develops within the mass of sterile tissue of the cleistothecium is derived from the binucleate cell immediately below the tip of the ascogonous hypha. The cell enlarges and the two nuclei within fuse. As it enlarges further to become the ascus, the diploid fusion nucleus divides meiotically to form eight ascospores, each basically shaped like a pulley wheel though sculptured in various ways on the outer surface in different species. Each ascospore on germination can produce a new *Eurotium* mycelium.

The ascocarp in *Eurotium* and related fungi, is a comparatively simple structure, typically without an opening, and the asci formed within it release their ascospores within the cleistothecium, as this closed ascocarp is termed (fig. 263).

Erysiphe (figs. 265 and 266)

Some, but by no means all authorities on the fungi, class as more advanced members of the Ascomycetes those fungi whose ascocarps are globose or flask-shaped structures with a definite wall of their own and which, except in the case of *Erysiphe* and its near relatives, open to the exterior by a pore or slit, the *ostiole*. These *perithecia*, as they are termed, may occur singly or in groups within a firm mass of fungal tissue, the *stroma*.

Typical of those forms in which perithecia are produced singly are the 'powdery mildews', which are obligate parasites of the leaves, and to some extent, other organs of many plants of agricultural and horticultural importance. The causal fungi belong to the genus *Erysiphe*, of which one of the most widespread species is *E. graminis*, which attacks barley, oats, wheat, and other cereals and grasses, causing a discoloration and a general weakening of the plants. In the main the fungus develops on the

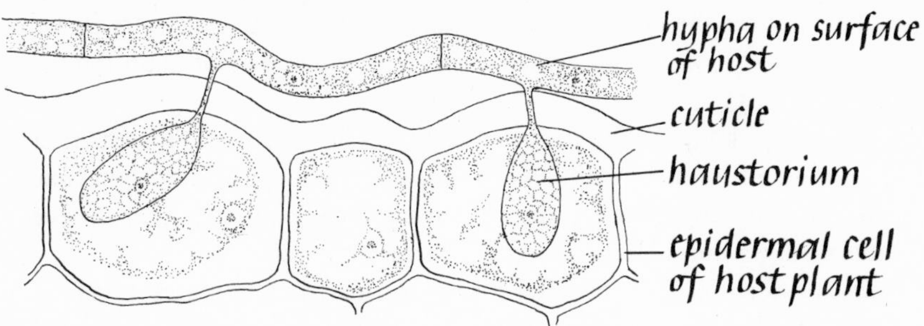

Figure 265 *Part of a hypha of an* Erysiphe *sp. showing haustoria penetrating the epidermal cells of a host plant.*

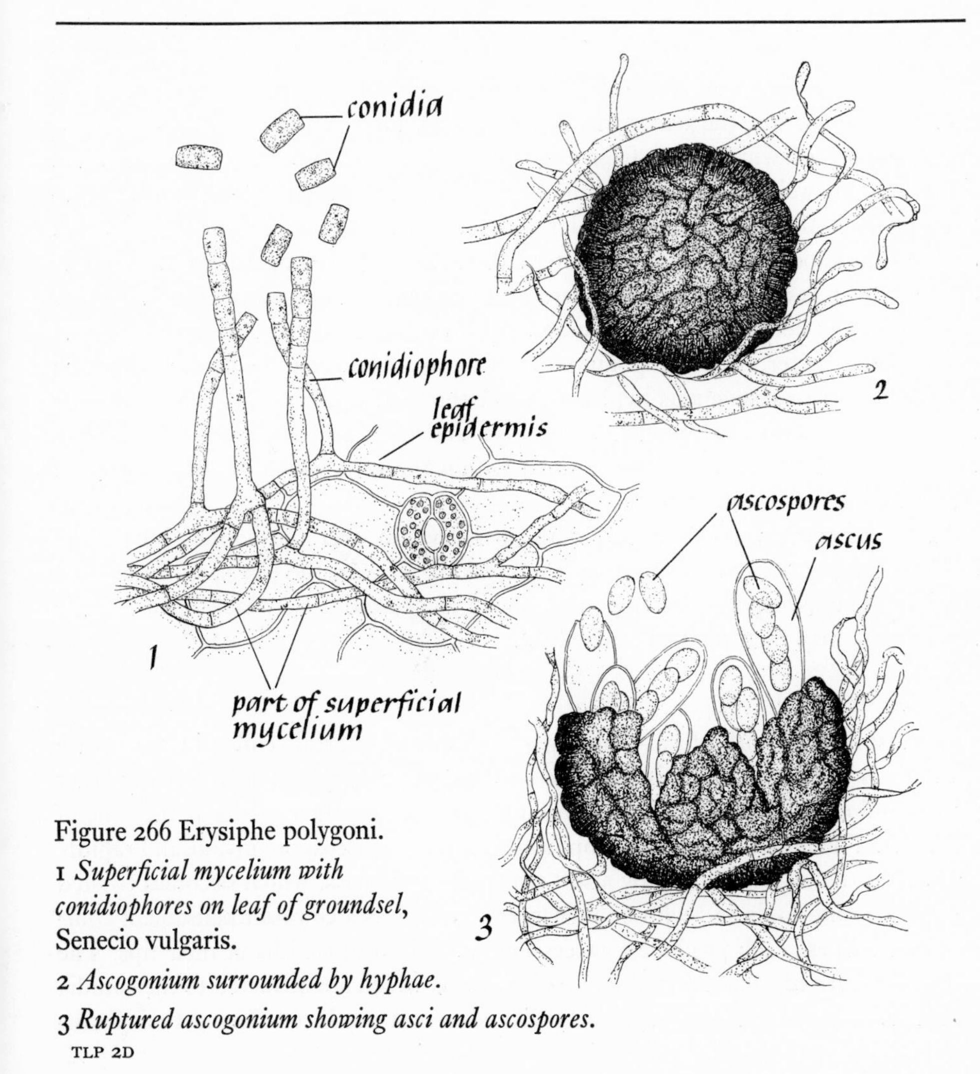

Figure 266 Erysiphe polygoni.

1 *Superficial mycelium with conidiophores on leaf of groundsel,* Senecio vulgaris.

2 *Ascogonium surrounded by hyphae.*

3 *Ruptured ascogonium showing asci and ascospores.*

upper surface of the leaves, the mycelium consisting of a network of colourless hyphae. These cover the epidermis of the infected parts and penetrate its cells here and there by means of *haustoria*, which once inside enlarge and obtain food from the protoplasts (fig. 265).

Only a few days after the fungus has infected its host, asexual reproduction begins with the production of large numbers of tall, erect hyphae, which soon function as conidiophores. They constrict conidia at their tips one below the other, so eventually long chains of these uninucleate spores are formed (fig. 266).

Conidial production may proceed for some time, but it ceases as the growing season of the host begins to come to an end, and there follows a phase of sexual reproduction. The sexual organs, ascogonia and antheridia, develop at the ends of hyphae which have grown together. The uninucleate ascogonium is the broader of the two. The smaller antheridial hypha divides to form a terminal antheridium and an inner stalk cell. A pore forms where the ascogonium and antheridium are in mutual contact and the antheridial protoplast migrates through the pore and the gamete nuclei fuse.

After fertilization, the sex organs become surrounded by compact layers of sterile hyphae, more of which arise from the cell immediately beneath the ascogonium. Eventually the walls of the perithecium, as this fruiting body is termed, is from six to ten cells thick, the outer layers of which lose their contents and become thick-walled. Some of the superficial cells of this outer layer develop into elongate appendages, the form of which is characteristic in different genera related to *Erysiphe*: thus some are pointed, others hooked, and others branched in various ways. Within the developing perithecium the fertilized ascogonium divides into a number of cells, each of which grows out into an acsogenous hypha of two or three cells in length. The penultimate cell of each possesses two nuclei, which fuse, and from a meiotic division followed by a mitosis, eight ascopores are formed within the cell, which swells to form an ovoid, sac-like *ascus* (fig. 266).

The asci remain enclosed within the perithecium over the winter, but in the following spring they are exposed by the breaking away of the top part of the perithecium. The ascospores are then shot out of the turgid asci, which open at their apices; they may then reinfect a new host.

Claviceps (fig. 267)

An Ascomycete with a flask-shaped perithecium and of great economic importance is *Claviceps purpurea*, which is parasitic on the ovaries of rye, as well as many other grasses and cereals. The host plants are infected through their pistils at the time of flowering. The hyphae which develop from an infecting ascospore invade and rapidly destroy the ovule, replacing it by a soft white mycelial mass, which becomes twisted and thrown into folds and whose outer layer develops as a compact palisade of conidiophores. These each produce a succession of small, oval conidia at their tips. The conidia are carried to uninfected flowers by insects which are attracted to the conidia on account of the sweet, sticky, nectar-like secretion produced during their form-

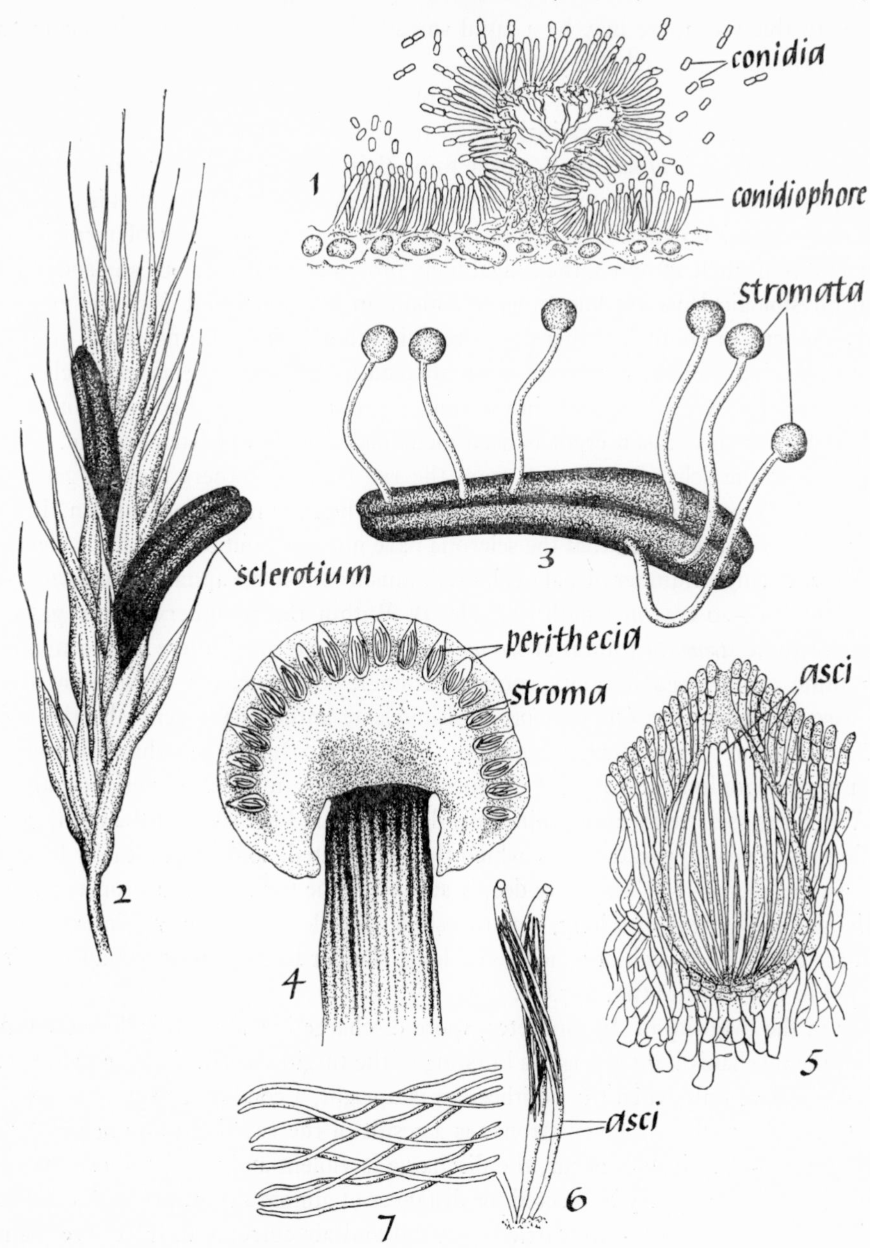

Figure 267 Claviceps purpurea

1 *Conidiophores and conidia production* (*after Tulsane*).
2 *Inflorescence of rye with sclerotia.* 3 *A sclerotium with stromata.*
4 *L.s. through a stroma showing perithecia.*
5 *L.s. through a perithecium showing asci* (*after Tulsane*).
6 *Asci.* 7 *Ascospores.*

ation. In this way there may be a rapid spread of the fungus from only one or two plants originally infected (fig. 267.1).

While the conidia are being produced by the mycelial mass, the whole begins to compact and harden and gradually it is transformed into a very tough, pseudo-parenchymatous *sclerotium*, pink-purple to black in colour. The sclerotium is similar in general shape to a rye grain (whose position it now occupies), though it is considerably longer and broader. The sclerotium of *Claviceps* is the *ergot* of medicine. If eaten even in small amounts, the fungal body produces a most serious and sometimes fatal physiological disease known as 'ergotism' in both man and domestic animals. This happens in countries where rye bread is eaten if flour has not been properly cleaned during milling. Cattle are often affected by grazing on grasses which carry the sclerotia. Powerful alkaloids in the fungus produce a marked constriction of the capillaries; for this reason ergot is used medicinally to control haemorrhage.

Some of the sclerotia may fall from the rye panicles; others may be gathered with the harvested grain and are thus dispersed when the next crop is sown. In the following spring, provided that the sclerotia have not dried out too much, they germinate, producing a number of pale-coloured, mushroom-like, capitate outgrowths, on stalks some 10-20 cms in length (fig. 267.3). Within the periphery of the globose heads of these *stromata* (plural of *stroma*), as they are termed, there arise a number of minute cavities. Each cavity contains a single multinucleate ascogonium from the base of which arise one or more multinucleate antheridia. Eventually the male nucleus migrates into the ascogonium. Several ascogonous hyphae then grow from the ascogonium, and asci are produced at their tips in the characteristic manner.

While the asci are forming, thin walls develop round the sides of the cavities enclosing the sexual apparatus from which they originated, so they eventually become flask-shaped perithecia. These are deeply sunken in the tissues of the stroma opening to the surface by way of a long, narrow ostiole. Sterile paraphyses are intermingled with the asci, within each of which eight, long, slender ascospores are produced lying parallel to one another (fig. 267.6).

As in the majority of Ascomycetes, spore discharge in *Claviceps* is dependent on water, the mechanism involving the bursting of the turgid asci. In *Claviceps*, however, this takes place only when the perithecium is upright, a condition experienced for a short time by each on a given stroma as a result of the twisting movements of the fertile head. When it does occur, the discharge is violent and the ascospores, which are long and septate, may be ejected for distances of almost a centimetre. Beyond the perithecia, the ascospores are carried by wind and air currents to infect rye plants and so initiate another life cycle.

Neurospora (fig. 268)

No summary of the Ascomycetes would be complete without some mention of the perithecia-forming genus *Neurospora*. This is not because of its economic or medical importance but because in recent years a great deal of evidence relating biochemical properties of different strains to their genetic constitution has accumulated. *N. sitophila* and *N. crassa*, fungi which frequently infect bakeries (hence their common name 'red bread mould'), have figured particularly in these genetical researches.

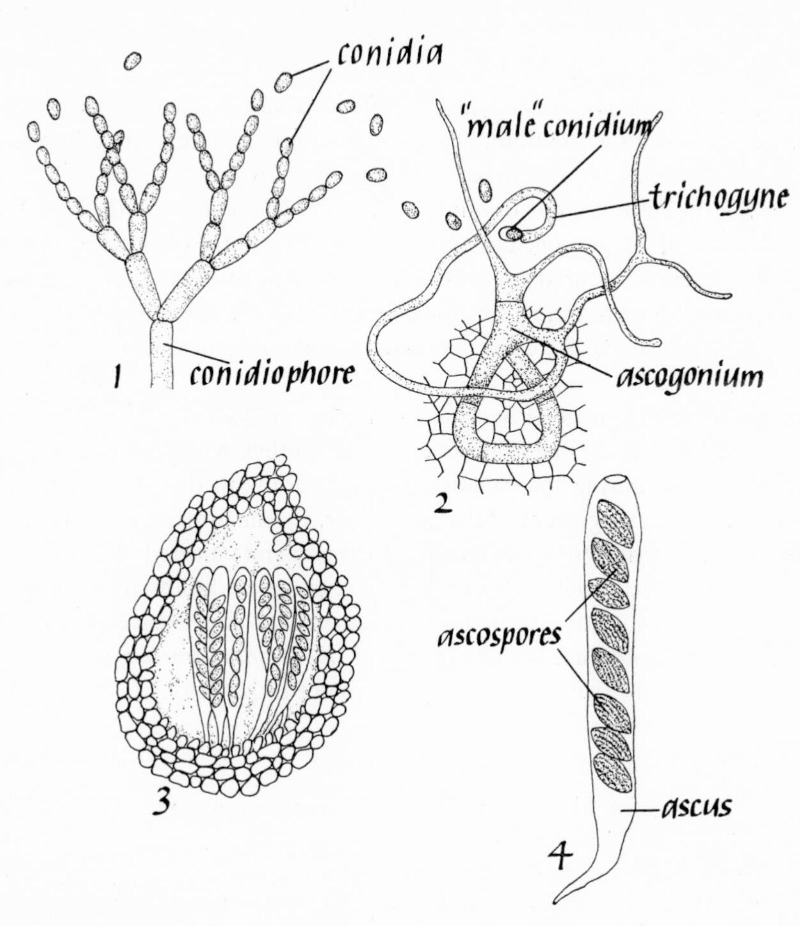

Figure 268 Neurospora
1 *Conidiophore producing conidia.*
2 *Sexual reproduction.*
3 *A perithecium with asci.*
4 *Ascus with ridged ascospores* (*after Alexopolous*).

The mycelium of *Neurospora* consists of numerous, septate, branched hyphae from which aerial hyphae (conidiophores) arise, producing enormous chain-like masses of pink conidia. By this asexual method of reproduction the fungus can propagate itself more or less indefinitely. Indeed, when it invades microbiological laboratories it is difficult to eradicate because of this prolific conidial production (fig. 268).

Neurospora sitophila is heterothallic: sexual reproduction and the subsequent production of perithecia require the mating of 'plus' and 'minus' strains. There appears, however, to have been a degeneration of the sexual organs, for a conidium may act as a 'male' cell and, on contacting an ascogonium of the opposite mating type, it will effect plasmogamy. The *ascogonium* consists of a stalk supporting an oogonial region of a few cells and a long, sometimes branched, septate, receptive region, the *trichogyne*. Except for the trichogyne, the whole is encased in a protective hyphal sheath. In addition to a conidium acting as a male cell, a vegetative hypha of the opposite mating type may also function in this way.

Following the fusion of one or other of these 'male' elements with the trichogyne of the ascogonium, the perithecium begins its development. At maturity a *Neurospora* perithecium is dark-coloured, pear-shaped, and slightly beaked. Numerous club-shaped asci develop within it, and within these, eight dark brown or black ascospores form, arranged one above the other and with characteristic nerve-like ridges on their walls.

The very great advantage of *Neurospora sitophila* in genetic studies is that not only are there four ascospores of one strain and four of the other in each ascus, but the order of events occurring during the meiotic divisions leading to their formation is faithfully set out in the arrangement of the ascospores. By micromanipulation the individual spores can be removed one by one from the asci and cultured separately. In this way each of the nuclei produced in a given meiosis can be followed through the life cycle of the resulting plants. Genetical studies on *Neurospora* have led to the establishment of a new and vital branch of biology, *biochemical genetics*, which has been of inestimable value to the furthering of the science of heredity.

CLASS BASIDIOMYCETES

The Basidiomycetes, like the Ascomycetes, comprise a natural group of the fungi whose most important distinguishing feature is the *basidium*. As with the ascus, this is a special type of sporangium, usually producing four spores externally. The large and conspicuous mushrooms, toadstools, and puffballs belong to this Class, though also included in it are two most important groups of plant parasites, the *rusts* and *smuts*. Two sub-classes of Basidiomycetes are usually recognized: the rusts, smuts, and related forms, with basidia transversely divided into four cells, are included in the Heterobasidiomycetes; the mushrooms and toadstools and their allies, with one-celled basidia constitute the Homobasidiomycetes.

Sub-class Heterobasidiomycetes

Puccinia (fig. 269)

One of the economically most important plant diseases, especially in North America, is *Puccinia graminis*, the stem rust of wheat. The fungus has a complex life

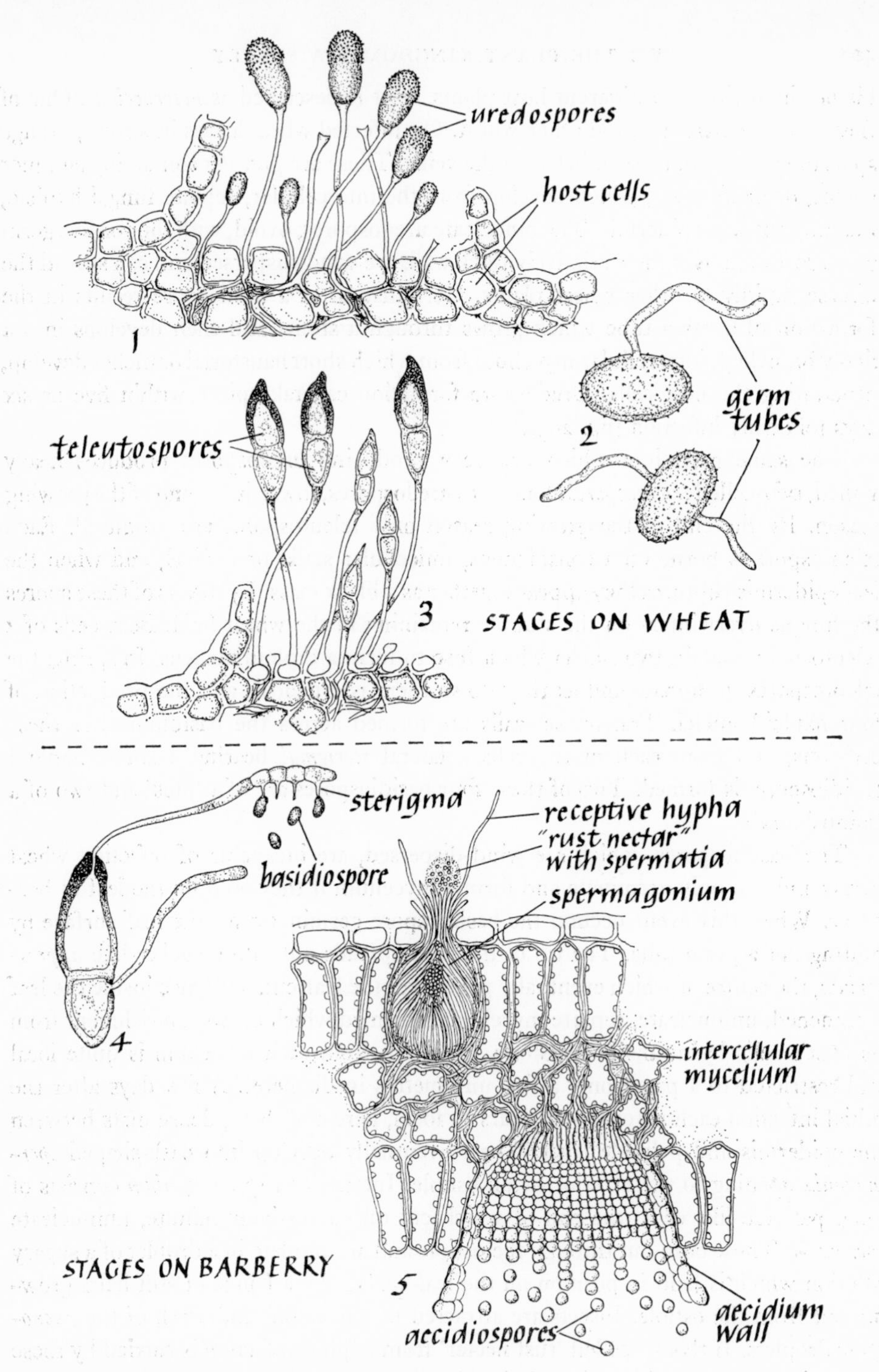

Figure 269 *Stages in the life cycle of* Puccinia graminis.
1 *Uredospore production.* 2 *Germination of uredospores.* 3 *Teleutospore production.*
4 *Germination of teleutospore and basidiospore production.*
5 *Formation of spermatia and aecidiospores.*

history involving two different host plants, so it is described as *heteroecious*. One of these hosts is barberry, the other wheat. On infected wheat leaves in spring, orange spots or streaks can be seen between the veins. These are *pustules* containing summer spores, or *uredospores*, which develop from the intercellular, septate fungal hyphae, bursting the leaf epidermis. The binucleate uredospores, ovoid, with four or five germ pores scattered over their relatively thick wall, are wind-dispersed and can spread the disease rapidly to other wheat plants. Germination of a uredospore results in the formation of a germ tube which grows through a stoma and then develops into a richly branched, intercellular mycelium from which short haustorial branches develop, penetrating the host cells. Uredospore formation can take place within five or six days following infection (fig. 269).

The same mycelium which has been producing uredospores produces heavy walled, two-celled *teleutospores* along with uredospores, towards the end of the growing season. By the end of the growing season only teleutospores are produced. Each teleutospore is borne on a conspicuous, unicellular stalk, or pedicel, and when the leaf epidermis ruptures they appear together as a black mass. By means of these spores the fungus overwinters on the stubble remaining in the wheat field. Both cells of a teleutospore contain two nuclei which fuse to form a diploid nucleus. In spring, the teleutospores germinate and as they do so there is a meiosis and the production of four haploid nuclei. Transverse walls are formed across the basidium after these divisions, and from each of the cells a lateral *sterigma*, bearing a single haploid basidiospore, is formed. Two of these four basidiospores are of a 'plus' and two of a 'minus' strain.

The basidiospores, which are wind-dispersed, are incapable of infecting wheat plants and can only germinate and form a mycelium if they land on the leaf of barberry. When this event occurs, the basidiospore germinates on the leaf surface by putting out a germ tube. The tip of the tube spreads out into a sucker-like *appressorium*, the centre of which eventually penetrates the leaf cuticle. Once inside the leaf a branched, uninucleate, septate mycelium is formed which draws nourishment from its host's cells by means of haustoria. Infection from each mycelium is quite local and restricted to a patch only a few millimetres in diameter. A few days after the initial infection each mycelium appears to form, here and there, dense mats between the epidermis and palisade layer. These eventually develop into flask-shaped *spermagonia* opening to the exterior by an ostiole. Internally a *spermagonium* consists of long, palisade-like cells, the end of which cut off successively minute, uninucleate *spermatia*. These ooze out through the ostiole and accumulate in a droplet of a sugary solution which is held in position on the leaf surface by a fringe of stiff hairs growing out from the ostiole. Insects are attracted by the colour and smell of the *pycnospore* droplets. If this so-called 'rust nectar' from a 'plus' infection is carried by these insect vistors and so mixes with a 'minus' one, there is evidence to suggest that some 'plus' pycnospores fuse with 'minus' flexuous hyphae. The resulting fusion leads to the production, a few days later, of a cup-shaped *aecidium* on the lower leaf surface.

The cells which form this aecidium are binucleate or *dikaryotic*, one nucleus of the *dikaryon* being a 'plus' and the other a 'minus' strain.

The wall of each *aecidial cup* consists of a specialized layer of cells, and the base is lined with a palisade layer of dikaryotic cells. Each erect palisade cell cuts off a chain of cells of two types: polyhedral *aecidiospores*, alternating with smaller, flattened, separating cells. The discharge of the aecidiospores is violent and explosive, and once free from the aecidium they are wind dispersed.

The aecidiospores although produced on the barberry cannot infect it; and if they are blown on to leaves of wheat they germinate by putting out one or more germ tubes, which enter the leaf by way of the stomata. Within the leaf a dikaryotic mycelium once more produces a local infection and the resultant intercellular mycelium in due course disseminates the fungus to neighbouring plants by uredospores. The complex life cycle is then complete. It should be noted that not all rusts have so complex a life cycle as *Puccinia graminis*. Some live on only one host and so are termed *autoecious*.

Sub-class Homobasidiomycetes

Agaricus (figs. 270 to 273)

Mushrooms and toadstools, the beginning and end of fungi to the man in the street, are in fact merely the short-lived fruiting bodies (*fructifications* or *sporophores*) derived from a usually unseen but widely dispersed subterranean mycelium, which in many cases is perennial. The basidia which are produced on these fructifications do not arise directly as germ tubes from spores, as in the lower Basidiomycetes, but are the terminal cells of an extensive mycelium.

Of the Homobasidiomycetes, the gill fungi (the field mushroom, *Agaricus campestris*, and the cultivated mushroom, *A. bisporus*) may be taken as well studied, and certainly easily obtainable types. They must not, however, be taken as typical in all respects of the group, for *Agaricus* species are quite atypical in their mycelial organization.

Sex organs have never been described for any member of the group, though there is the equivalent of a sexual process. When a basidiospore is liberated and germinates it does not give rise to a fructification-producing mycelium. Instead a uninucleate, primary mycelium, or *monokaryon*, develops. If this comes into contact with another primary mycelium of a different strain, fusions of cells of adjacent hyphae occur and nuclear migrations bring about the establishment of binucleate cells. In some forms (e.g. *Coprinus* species), the monokaryon hyphae produce chains of uninucleate cells resembling rust spermatia. These cells when liberated can fuse with hyphae of the opposite strain. This fusion of uninucleate cells and hyphae, or of two hyphae, are clearly suggestive of a sexual process. From these, a secondary, binucleate mycelium (a *dikaryon*) is formed. The cells of the dikaryon undergo a special and very unusual type of cell division, which leads to the formation of *clamp connections* and, more important, ensures that each cell of the mycelium contains two nuclei, one of each *mating type*. In essentials, a cell about to divide puts out a short outgrowth that bends

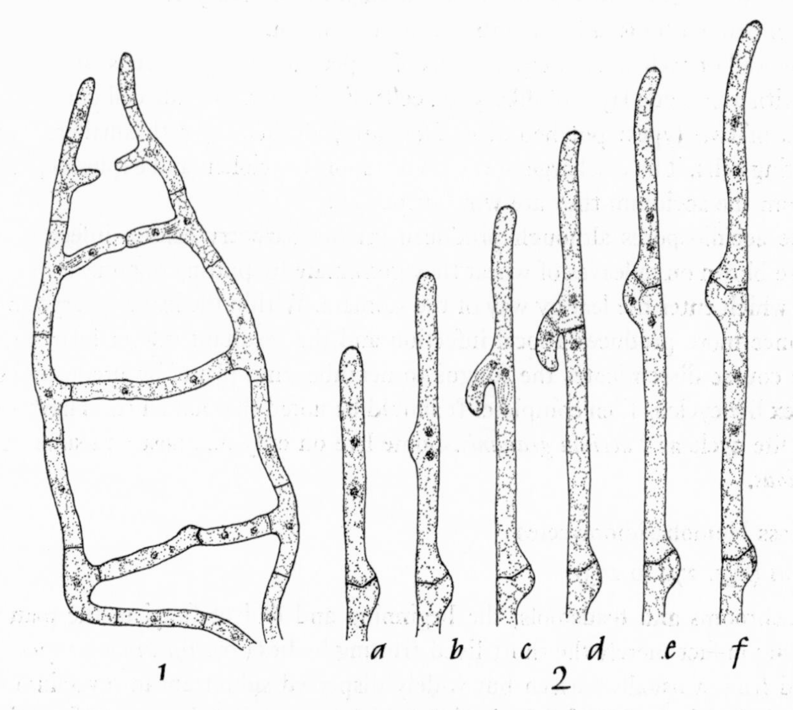

Figure 270 1 *Diagrammatic representation of the formation of diplophasic cells in a basidiomycete by the conjugation of haplophase mycelia.*
2 *Successive stages in the formation of a clamp connection.*

downwards towards the base of the cell. One of the two nuclei present migrates into this outgrowth, the *clamp*, while the other remains in the cell. In these positions the two nuclei divide simultaneously. The resulting daughter nuclei within the cell move some distance apart so that one lies above and the other below the outgrowth. Of the daughter nuclei formed in the outgrowth, one remains in it, the other moves back into the cell. At this stage one septum is formed cutting off the base of the outgrowth, and another across the cell in the middle of the clamp. At the same time the free end of the clamp becomes connected and opens into the cell and the daughter nucleus in the clamp now passes over the bridge so formed into the cell (fig. 270).

Fructifications or sporophores are produced only by secondary, binucleate mycelia. In *Agaricus*, this consists of a compact mass of interwoven hyphae. These develop from below-ground, rope-like portions of the mycelium, and appear first as solid ovoid masses of compacted interwoven hyphae. Gradually the upper portion becomes differentiated as a cap, or *pileus*, which is supported by the stalk, or *stipe*. Where the pileus joins the stipe, a transverse internal cavity forms as a ring round the base of the pileus. From the top of this cavity and radiating from the centre a large number

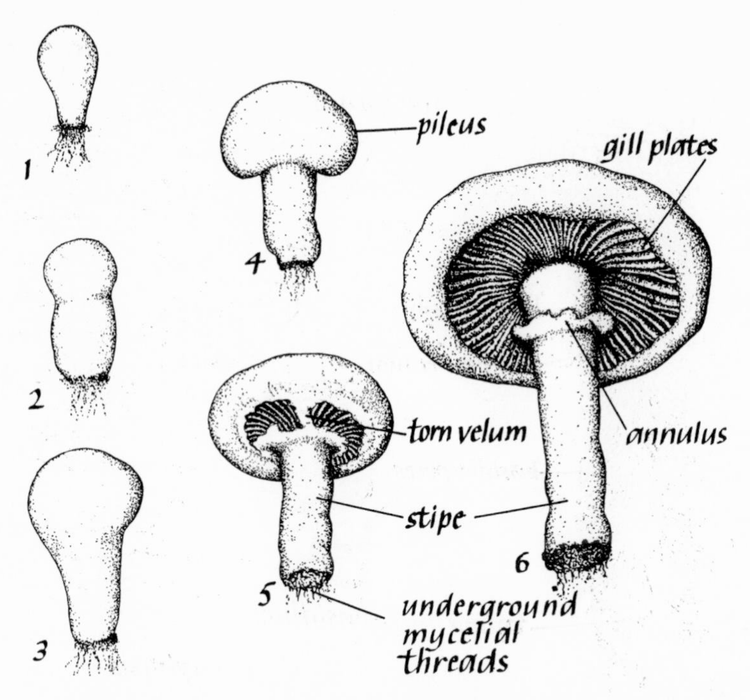

Figure 271 1-6 *Stages in the development of a sporophore of* Agaricus bisporus.

of lamellar structures, the *gills*, are formed, which project downwards into the cavity. It is on these gills that the spores are produced (fig. 271).

With the development of the gills the pileus increases considerably in diameter. Growth is very rapid indeed beyond this 'button stage', in which condition the edge of the pileus is joined to the stipe by a thin veil, or *velum*. This serves to protect the spore-bearing gills in the cavity within. The continued enlargement of the pileus ruptures the velum, remnants of which can be seen as a membranous ring, the *annulus*, round the stipe. If the undersurface of the fructification is now examined the gills (between 300 and 600 on a mature pileus of *A. campestris*) can be seen radiating from the centre.

If the pileus is examined in tangential section under the microscope, a mature gill can be seen to be composed of an internal region of loosely packed, elongate cells, the *trama*. From the trama, branches curve outwards towards both sides of the gill and divide to produce compact layers of iso-diametric *subhymenial* cells. The outermost layer of cells constitutes the *hymenum*, a palisade-like layer of club-shaped cells which are the *basidia* in various stages of development (fig. 272). A young basidium is binucleate but soon the two nuclei fuse to form a diploid nucleus, which then divides meiotically, producing four haploid nuclei; these tend to congregate towards the outer end of the basidium. Four equally spaced, small outgrowths, the *sterigmata*, then de-

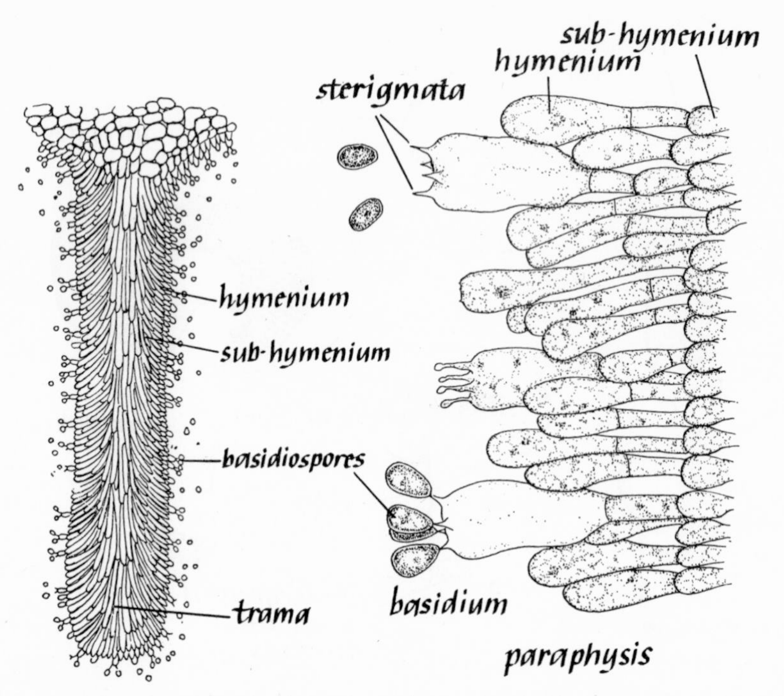

Figure 272 Agaricus campestris (*left*) *Tangential section of pileus in region of gill.* (*right*) *Detail of hymenium showing production of basidiospores from basidia.*

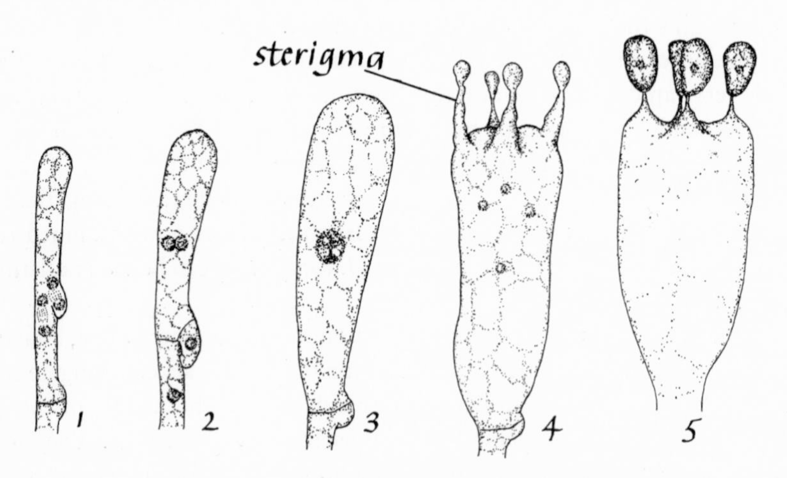

Figure 273 *Stages in the development of a basidium and basidiospores* (*after G. M. Smith*).

velop on this outer end and the tip of each expands to become a basidiospore. During this time a vacuole develops towards the base of the basidium, and its enlargement seems to force the protoplasm into the developing basidiospores (fig. 273). When nearly full size, each spore receives a nucleus by way of the narrow sterigma. In the cultivated mushroom each basidium bears only two basidiospores – hence its name *A. bisporus* – and each receives two haploid nuclei, one of each strain, from the basidium.

When mature the spores, which change from pink to purple, are violently discharged by a process which is believed to depend on the turgor of the basidium. In their ejection, however, they never approach the separating, adjoining gill. Once free of the hymenum, the spores fall down between the gills, and below the pileus they are dispersed by air currents. A ripe pileus is estimated to liberate some half a million spores a minute for two or three days – possibly totalling 10,000,000,000 spores in all. Each spore is potentially capable of giving rise to a new mycelium, though it must be presumed that only a minute fraction of those produced ever do so.

MYCORRHIZAE

Ectotrophic Mycorrhizae

Many fleshy Basidiomycetes are commonly found in woodlands, and certain species are found only in the neighbourhood of certain types of trees (fig. 274). The handsome, deep orange-coloured edible toadstool *Lactarius deliciosus*, for example, is common in pine and other coniferous woodlands. A few, such as the Honey Agaric, *Armillaria mellea* are parasites which invade and often kill trees. Their white gilled fructifications can often be found on dead tree stumps. If the bark of these trees is stripped away, the mycelium of the invading fungus can be seen as dark brown thongs or *rhizomorphs* which grow upwards from the soil (fig. 275). But few woodland Basidiomycetes are parasites; most are sapophytes whose mycelia can be observed amongst rotting leaf litter and wood fragments. From these the fungi take their nourishment and in so doing contribute to the degradation processes leading to the formation of soil humus.

If the leaf litter in a beechwood, for example, is disturbed, part of the tree's very extensively branched root systems will be found. The fine terminal branches of these root systems – the plant's chief organs of water and nutrient absorption – develop mainly in the upper layers of the soil. Closer examination should reveal, however, that the greater part of this *fibrous root system*, as it is called, terminate in rootlets shorter and thicker than ordinary rootlets and a creamy yellow to dark brown in colour (fig. 276).

A transverse section of such a root tip, of which each tree has millions, will show under the microscope that the normal anatomical features of the young root are surrounded by a continuous sheath of densely interwoven hyphae. These also penetrate inwards between the living cortical cells – though they do not penetrate them – to form a continuous intercellular network, the *Hartig net*. Such swollen roots have no root hairs and being partly fungus, and partly root, are termed *mycorrhizae*, meaning

Figure 274 *Sporophores of* Oudemansiella (Armillaria) mucida *growing from the trunk of a beech tree. The fungal mycelium is beneath the bark.*

Figure 275 *The honey agaric,* Armillaria mellea. *Part of the trunk of a tree of* Pinus sylvestris *killed by the fungus, after removal of the bark. The black, cord-like rhizomorphs travel from the soil up the trunk, growing through the living tissues between the bark and the wood, eventually destroying them and killing the tree. (Photo from 'Trees and Toadstools' by M. C. Rayner, reproduced by permission of Faber and Faber.)*

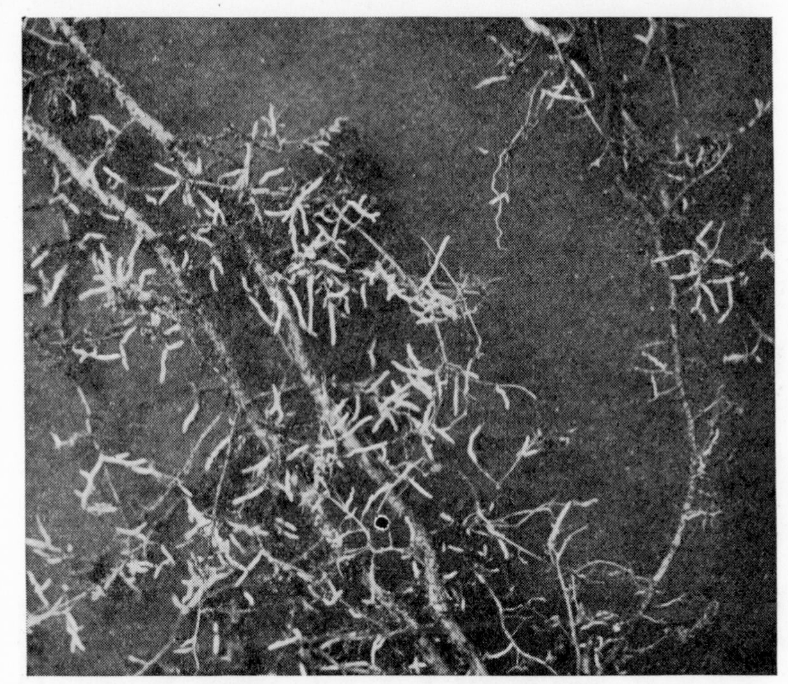

Figure 276 *White-tipped, swollen roots of* Tilia europea – *mycorrhizae. The white tips are sheaths of densely interwoven fungal hyphae.*

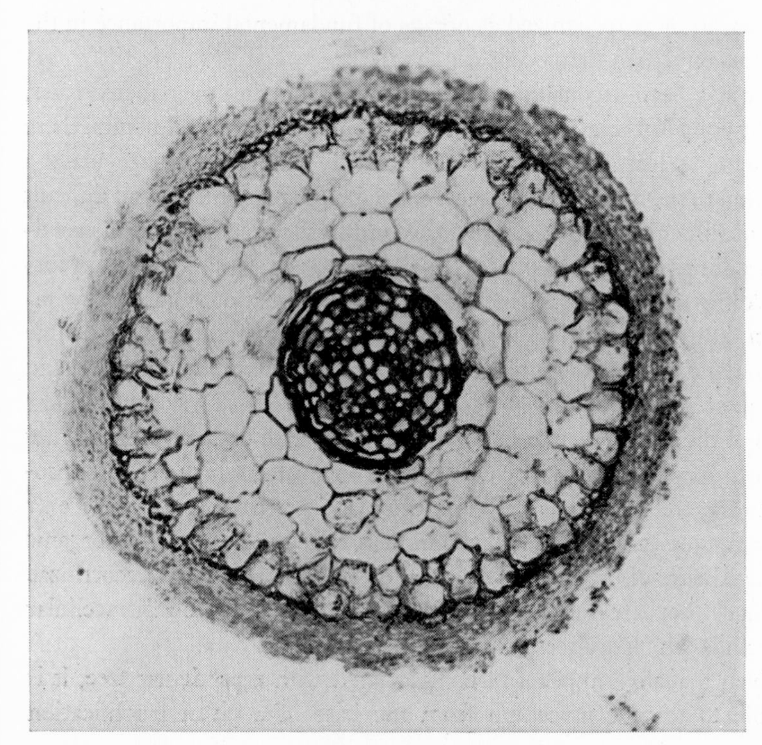

Figure 277 *T.s. of root of* Tilia europea *surrounded by a sheath of fungal hyphae, the Hartig net.*

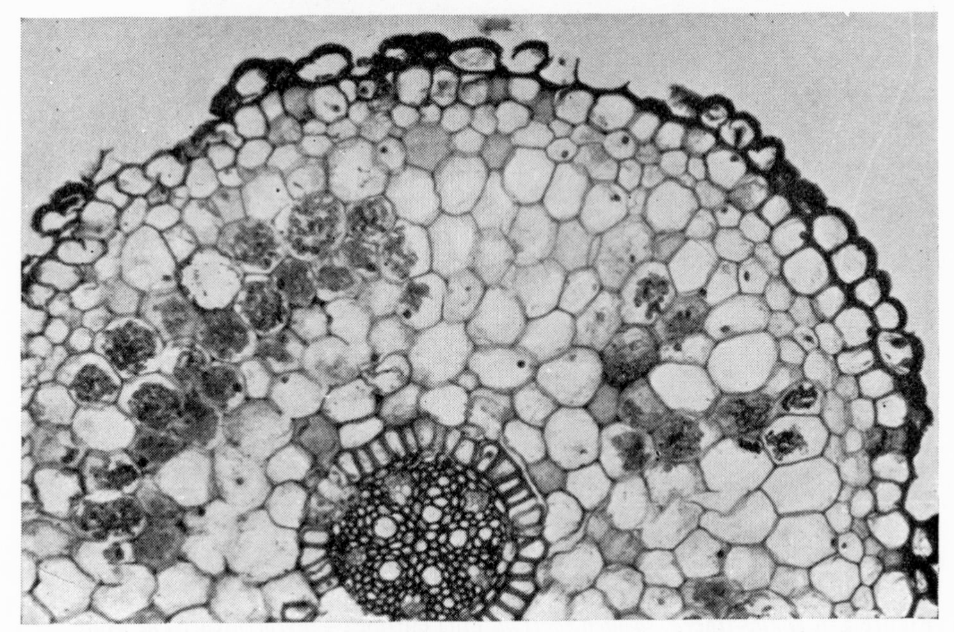

Figure 278 *Endotrophic mycorrhizae in the cortex of root of an orchid, a* Philesia *sp.*

'fungus roots'. They are now recognized as organs of fundamental importance in the nutrition of the trees on which they occur (fig. 277).

Although there has been a considerable controversy, ranging over many years, about the exact physiological relations of the partners of all mycorrhizal plants, there is general agreement, at least amongst forest botanists, that mycorrhizae make a valuable contribution to the well-being of trees. Indeed, it is frequently found difficult to raise seedlings of pine and spruce satisfactorily in forest nurseries on non-woodland soils. Such seedlings often have poorly developed root systems without mycorrhizae, and the seedling trees appear stunted. Mycorrhizal formation, followed by improved growth can, however, be brought about by introducing seedlings of the same species from a woodland nursery and growing them for a season in the non-woodland beds before the tree seeds are sown.

The mycelium of the fungal mantle is in direct contact with the soil, and recently it has been shown to be particularly efficient in absorbing salts, which are then probably passed on to the tree. There is, however, no evidence that the roots are ever parasitized by the fungus though the latter doubtless benefits by obtaining organic food from the living tissues of the tree roots. Indeed, because these tree mycorrhizae 'feed on the surface' they are termed *ectotrophic*, in contrast to the intracellular mycorrhizae of orchids which are termed *endotrophic* (fig. 278).

Although a given toadstool appears to be associated with a particular tree, it is virtually impossible to trace a mycelium from the base of a given fructification (sporophore) to the mycorrhizae of a particular tree and so have absolute proof of the association. Such proof can only be secured by exacting laboratory techniques in which tree seedlings are grown in *pure culture* (that is free from bacteria and any other contaminating micro-organisms) and then bringing these into contact with pure cultures of the fungus believed to be concerned in the mycorrhizal association. By such experiments it has now been demonstrated that the Scots Pine (*Pinus sylvestris* see p. 463) may be associated with a number of Basidiomycetes including species of *Boletus*, *Amanita*, *Cortonarius* and *Russula*. No successful mycorrhizal synthesis has so far been achieved in the case of the Beech.

Endotrophic Mycorrhizae

The roots of heather (*Calluna vulgaris*), which normally grow in the acid peaty soils of heaths and moors, usually contain mycorrhizae. The new heather roots produced each spring are infected with the fungal mycelium (usually a species of *Phoma*) which grows not only on the surface but also penetrates the cortical cells so that they are endotrophic. It has been suggested that this fungus can fix atmospheric nitrogen (see p. 185) which is then stored in nitrogenous compounds within the hyphae. The latter, however, are eventually digested by the cortical cells of the heather, which benefits especially from the resulting supply of nitrogenous materials. These materials are always deficient in the soils on which heather grows.

Many orchids also possess endotrophic mycorrhizae, the fungal hyphae forming tight coils inside the cortical cells of their roots and tubers. Since these too are eventually digested it is presumed that the orchid benefits from the products of this digestion. Endotrophic mycorrhizae are particularly important in the germination of orchid seeds. Here it seems that the fungus makes certain essential food materials available to the developing embryo within the orchid seed (fig. 278).

LICHENS

The partnership between two organisms, such as occurs in a mycorrhizal association, may be referred to as a case of *symbiosis*, which literally means *living with* or *together*. This term, coined in 1879 by the distinguished French botanist Anton de Bary, was intended to refer to all cases involving mutualistic relations between two or more different organisms such as the associations between *Chlorella* (*Zoochlorella*) and various protozoa and sponges (see p. 359); mychorrhizae; flowers with their highly specialized pollination mechanisms; also parasites and their hosts. De Bary in fact described the latter as 'the best known and most exquisite expression of symbiosis'.

Symbiosis in its modern usage has a much more restricted definition and the term now connotes not just the living together of two or more organisms, but the existence of reciprocal relations usually beneficial to both parties.

The symbiotic association which apparently most impressed De Bary were the plants called *lichens*. These may be described as *dual organisms* in which a fungus

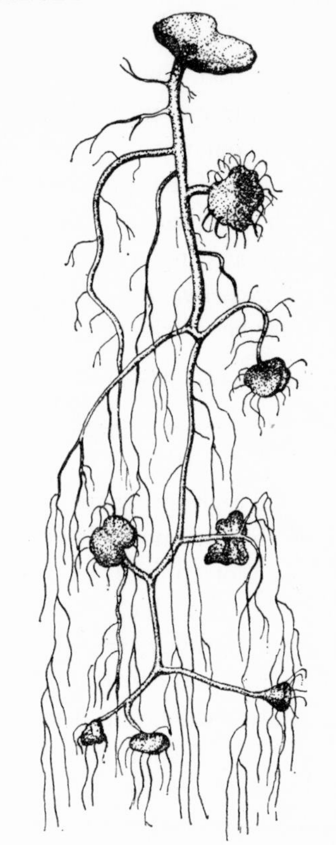

Figure 279 *Hanging tresses of the lichen* Usnea barbata (*after Wettstein*).

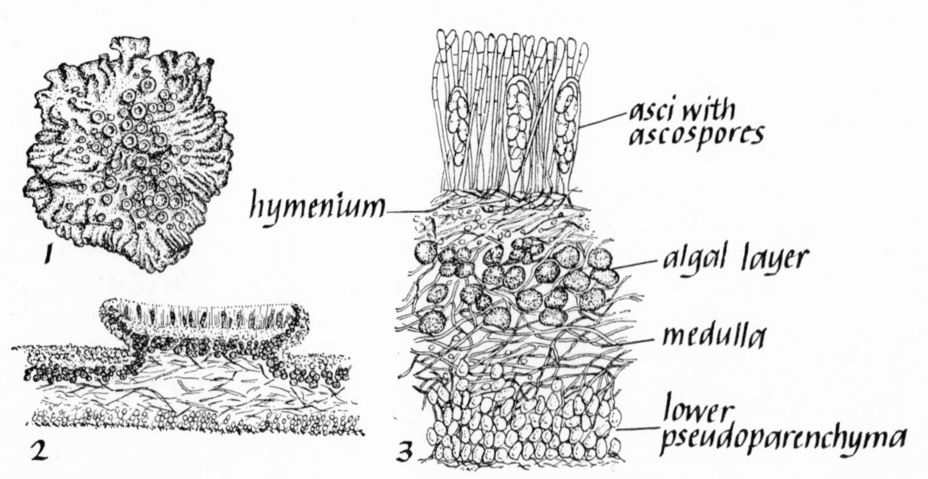

Figure 280 *Lichens*

1 *The foliose thallus of* Xanthoria parietina *with apothecia developing on its surface.*

2 *L.s. of thallus and apothecium to show main tissue regions.*

3 *L.s. through part of an apothecium.*

grows together with a simple alga to form a completely self supporting and mutually beneficial combination. Some 16,000 lichen species have been described and in the vast majority the fungus is an Ascomycete, while the algal partner is either a blue-green alga (Cyanophyta), or less commonly an unicellular green alga (Chlorophyta). Although the algal partner can exist by itself, the fungus alone cannot develop to maturity. Nevertheless, the two organisms would seem to derive mutual benefit from their association. The alga being photosynthetic produces carbohydrates which are utilized by the fungus, while the fungus absorbs and retains moisture which is beneficial to the alga.

Lichens grow in a variety of situations and are of especial ecological importance as pioneers in the colonization of bare rock surfaces. By their vital activities they tend to disintegrate the rock immediately beneath them, and when the lichen itself eventually dies, its remains, together with the disintegrated rock particles, form a primitive soil on which their first successors, usually mosses, can establish themselves.

Some lichens are leaf-like and resemble certain liverworts while others, described as *fruticose*, have cylindrical or ribbon-like bodies, usually grey in colour, which may grow erect like little shrubs (e.g. *Pettigera canina*); others such as *Usnea barbata* hang downwards in long tresses from the branches of trees (see fig. 279).

The body of a lichen is termed a thallus and in some the alga and fungus are uniformly distributed through it. In others, such as the orange-yellow *Xanthoria parietina* which can be found on stone walls, roofs, and on coastal rocks above high water mark, the flattened foliose thallus is internally differentiated into three zones. The upper and lower zones are of closely compacted *pseudoparenchyma* and between is a less compact *medullary zone* of branched hyphae. The algae in *Xanthoria* are the cells of the green alga *Pleurococcus* and these occur in a layer just above the medullary zone (fig. 280).

Increase in the size of each thallus is by very slow marginal growth, and the thalli may increase in numbers by fragmentation. Vegetative reproduction occurs in many lichens by means of minute, bud-like outgrowths (*soredia*), which occur as a powdery covering over the upper surface of the thallus. Each soredium consists of one, or at most a few algal cells enclosed by fungal hyphae. These are dispersed by wind and on reaching a suitable substratum each may germinate to produce a new lichen thallus.

Reproduction is also effected by the production of ascospores formed in asci, which arise in sessile, cup-shaped *apothecia* very much like those produced by a Discomycete. Other species may produce asci in *perithecia*. A new lichen thallus will develop from these ascospores only if they germinate in the neighbourhood of the appropriate algal cells.

CHAPTER 34

DIVISION BRYOPHYTA

The Bryophyta constitute a small but very natural Division of the Plant Kingdom. All are diminutive plants, either leafy or *foliose* in form, or consisting of a dorsiventrally flattened thallus without leaf-like appendages, growing over the surface of the ground and therefore described as *prostrate* in habit. The majority of these comparatively simple plants grow in rather moist situations, consequently there is little development of water absorbing tissues. Some of the more advanced forms possess a simple central conducting system in the stem. This, however, is never differentiated into xylem and phloem as in higher plants.

In all bryophytes the presence of free water is essential for the process of sexual reproduction because their biflagellate male gametes must swim to effect the fertilization of the non-motile female egg. These female gametes are always produced singly and fertilized within the base of a multicellular, flask-shaped structure, the *archegonium*. In the archegonium, the female gamete is protected both before fertilization and during much of the period when the resulting zygote is developing. The male and female reproductive organs are borne on the plants themselves, which therefore, constitute the gametophyte generation. The diploid zygote is the first cell of the sporophyte generation; although morphologically distinct, and eventually producing large numbers of haploid spores, it remains attached to the gametophyte throughout its life. In some bryophytes it is wholly dependent on it for its nutrition, in others only partially so. This alternation of morphologically distinct haploid and diploid generations is an outstanding feature of the life histories of all bryophytes.

The Bryophyta are without question a group of very great antiquity, although because of their delicate nature there is unfortunately very little fossil evidence of them. It is generally agreed that certain forms resembling bryophytes were amongst the earliest terrestrial plants and that their progenitors were probably algae belonging to the Chlorophyta. There is clearly a very considerable gap between the most advanced of the algae living today and the simplest bryophyte. There is an equally large gap between the Bryophyta and the more advanced, fern-like plants. Indeed the Bryophyta occupy an isolated position in the Plant Kingdom. It is suggested that they represent one of nature's early, though not very successful, experiments in the direction of the evolution of terrestrial plants. In contrast to higher and more successful land plants, however, the gametophyte generation is always the dominant phase of their life history and, having a more limited ecological range, is in the vast majority of cases less independent of the environment than in flowering plants. In this respect the Bryophyta stand in an intermediate position between the

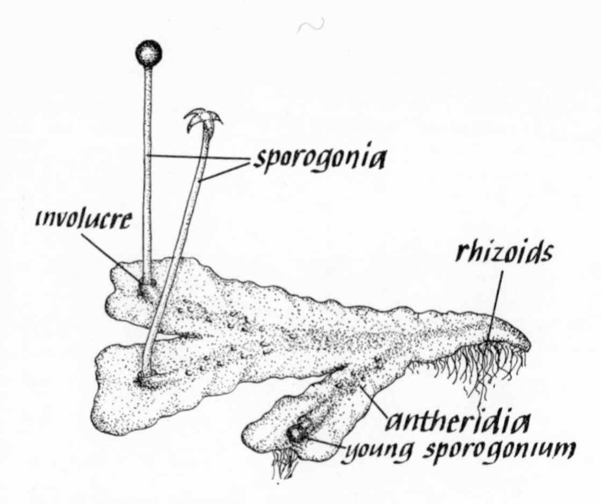

Figure 281 *Thallus of* Pellia *showing stages in the development of sporogonia.*

algae and the higher terrestrial plants, in which the sporophyte is without exception the dominant phase of the life cycle.

It is now customary to arrange the Bryophyta into three classes (see p. 342); the Hepaticae; the Musci; and the Anthocerotae, a small class of special significance in the form of the sporophyte. Of these families the most primitive is considered to be the Hepaticae. The simplest hepatics consist of flattened, dichotomously branched thalli with little internal differentiation of their tissues; a few are, however, leafy or *foliose* in form. The Musci are typically small, upright or procumbent, leafy plants, usually massed together as cushions or tussocks. Many mosses can survive in much drier situations than liverworts, as for example on treetrunks, walls, rocks, and even on house roofs. Indeed many mosses have a great capacity for resisting drought and can withstand considerable dessication from which they can recover very rapidly.

Class Hepaticae (Liverworts)
Pellia and Marchantia (figs. 281 to 292)

One of the simplest of liverworts is *Pellia*. Its gametophyte consists of a flattened, dichotomously branched thallus, only a few inches in length. The central part of the thallus is thickened, so that when examined from the upper surface, the plants appear to have quite a distinct midrib. When removed from the very damp soil or mud on which this liverwort usually grows, and examined on the ventral surface, a mass of densely interwoven hairs, to which pieces of soil or mud adhere, will be seen along the central line (fig. 281). These hairs are unicellular *rhizoids* whose function is anchorage and absorption. A transverse section of the thallus examined under the microscope shows little differentiation of the cells composing it. All are similar in shape and all contain numerous discoid chloroplasts (see fig. 286).

Marchantia (fig. 282), which superficially resembles *Pellia*, has a more complex

Figure 282 *Well-developed plant of* Marchantia *showing abundant production of gemmae cups.*

thallus with some internal differentiation, the upper region being photosynthetic. In transverse section this region can be seen to be divided into numerous chambers, covered by a single layer of epidermal cells. Each chamber communicates to the exterior by a multicellular, barrel-shaped pore. Though reminiscent of the stomata of flowering plants, these pores, visible with the naked eye as small dots on the surface of the thallus, have no regulatory powers as do stomatal guard cells (fig. 283). The photosynthetic cells arise from the base of each chamber as closely grouped, short filaments, and each cell contains numerous, disc-shaped chloroplasts. The region beneath the photosynthetic zone is one of storage. On the lower surface of the thallus there is, as in *Pellia*, a central strand of rhizoids, but protected in this case by a double row of multicellular scales.

In *Pellia* growth is initiated by new cells being cut off from a single apical cell located in the base of a small depression at the tip of each dichotomous branch of the thallus. In *Marchantia* there is a transverse row of apical cells within a similar small depression.

Vegetative reproduction in all liverworts with dichotomously branched thalli is by the progressive death of the older parts. As this dying back process eventually reaches a dichotomy, the two surviving branches become two separate liverwort plants. In *Marchantia*, special vegetative or asexual reproductive bodies, termed *gemmae*, are produced in *cupules* on the upper surfaces of the thallus (fig. 284). The cupules arise behind the growing point and the cells lining the floor of each cupule

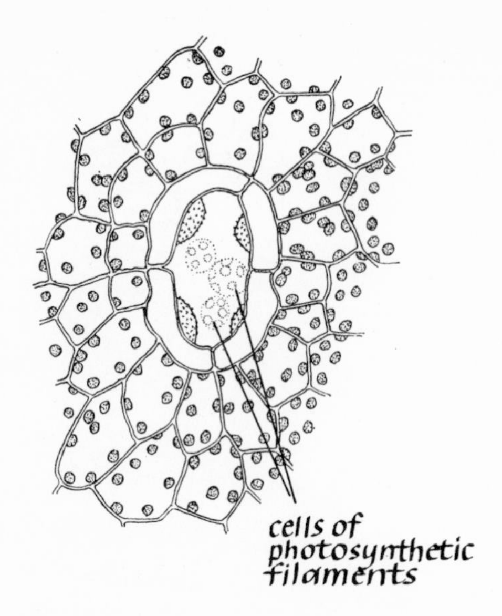

Figure 283 *Detail of the epidermis of* Marchantia *thallus in region of an air pore.*

are all potential gemmae. The latter, when mature, are disc-shaped structures, several cells thick in the mid region and with a cleft on each lateral margin in each of which there is a growing point. The gemmae are first severed from their stalks and then forced out of their cupules by mucilage extruded from cells in the cupule base. On falling on to the soil, the gemmae first develop rhizoids from certain colourless cells of the thicker central area. At a later stage the cells of the growing point begin to divide in the same manner as those in the growing points of mature thalli. In fact growth and dichotomy of the two growing points of each gemma takes place in opposite directions (fig. 285).

Although one of the significant advances of the bryophytes over the algae is their fairly successful adaptation to a terrestrial existence, the other great advance is in the development of multicellular sex organs. Indeed, the underlying structure of the sex organs is remarkably similar, not only in all liverworts and mosses, but also in many of the more advanced groups of plants (see Chapter 34).

In *Pellia*, the male sex organs, *antheridia*, are produced over the region of the so-called mid-rib of the thallus, where they are visible as small dark spots. Transverse sections show that the antheridia are spherical organs each arising on a short stalk from the base of an *antheridial chamber* which is produced by the upward growth of gametophyte tissue around the developing antheridium. The chambers open to the exterior by narrow pores, and the single antheridium within each, develops from a single superficial cell of the thallus. By a series of divisions there arises from this cell the stalk consisting of but a few squat cells. It supports a compact mass of colourless *sperm mother cells* which are enclosed by a wall composed of a single layer of cells.

Figure 284 *Detail of thallus surface of* Marchantia polymorpha *showing gemmae cups containing gemmae, and the surface of the thallus. The limits of the individual air chambers and their pores can be clearly seen.*

Figure 285 *A gemma removed from a gemmae cup of* Marchantia polymorpha.

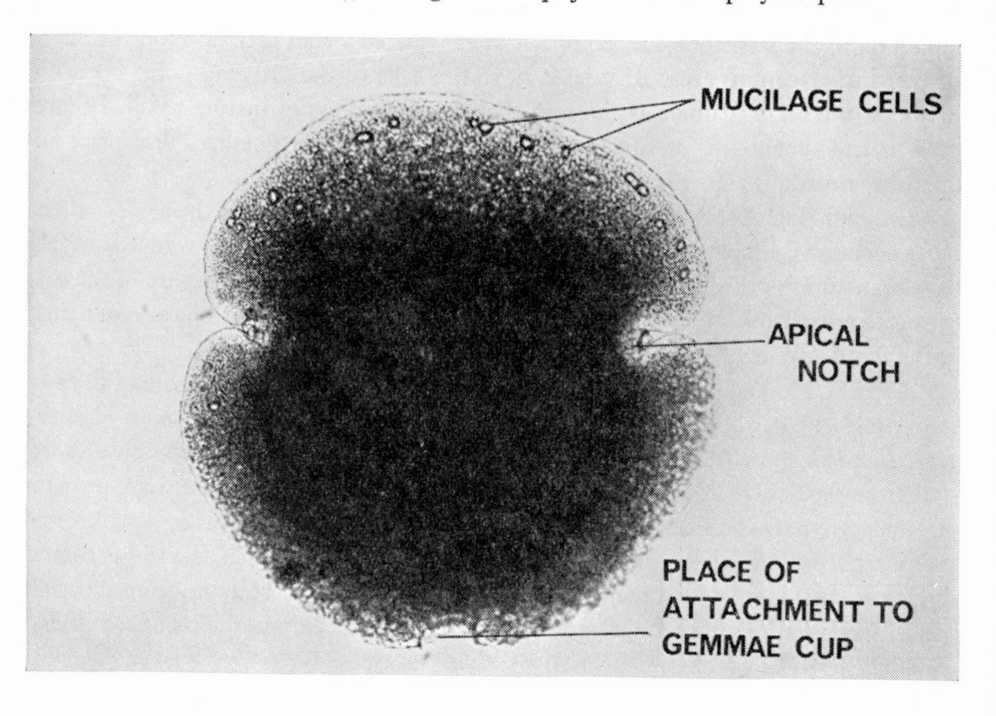

Each mother cell metamorphoses into a single *antherozoid*, which in *Pellia* is the largest of all the bryophytes. Each antherozoid consists of an elongated, spirally coiled body with two long flagella inserted at separate points in the anterior end (fig. 286).

In *Pellia* the female sex organs (archegonia) develop just behind the growing point of the thallus, after the antheridia have been formed. These develop in groups beneath which the thallus becomes considerably thicker. Behind them a flap of tissue, the protective *involucre*, grows upwards and then arches over the archegonia so that they come to lie in a small pocket. As in the formation of the antheridia, each archegonium arises from successive divisions of a single superficial cell of the thallus. When fully formed, each archegonium is a multicellular, flask-shaped structure consisting of a swollen base, the *venter*, with a wall, one or two cells thick. The venter contains a single spherical egg, and just above the egg a much smaller *ventral canal cell*. Arising from the venter is a narrow, cylindrical, hollow neck, consisting of four or five rows of cells. The neck is closed by four *cap cells* and within the neck there is a series of *neck canal cells* (fig. 287).

It is only when a film of water covers the *Pellia* thallus that the antherozoids are liberated and fertilization is effected. In the presence of water the mature antheridia rupture and the antherozoids, still within the sperm mother cells, are extruded 'en mass' on to the thallus surface. On contact with the covering film of water, the sperm mother cells separate and spread over the thallus. A proportion of them, purely by chance, reach the archegonial region and the antherozoids are then liberated from their mother cells. At this stage the antherozoids are *chemotactically* attracted (see p. 53) to the archegonial necks. These exude some proteinaceous substance, and the antherozoids swim the final stage of their journey towards them. The water covering the thallus also causes the opening of the archegonial cap cells, an event initiated by the swelling of mucilage derived from the degeneration of the neck and ventral canal cells. On entering the open neck of an archegonium, the antherozoid penetrates the mucilage filling the neck and passes with a wriggling movement down to the venter where it fertilizes the egg.

The diploid zygote, the initial cell of the sporophyte generation, or *sporogonium*, develops within the venter of the archegonium which gradually enlarges and so forms an enveloping, protective sheath, the *calyptra*, round the zygote. In its development, the zygote divides first transversely. The upper cell of this division gives rise, by a series of other divisions, to the spore-containing *capsule* or *theca*; the lower cell produces sterile tissues, the *foot* and *seta*, which are concerned respectively with the feeding and support of the capsule. The foot is a cone-shaped organ, which as it increases in size penetrates the tissues of the thallus, and from which it absorbs food materials. Until the sporogenous tissues of the capsule are almost mature and ready to be dispersed, the seta remains very short. The capsule, when mature, is a spherical body consisting of an external layer, two or more cells thick, surrounding a mass of *spore mother cells*. Some of these cells divide meiotically, each forming four ovoid, haploid spores. Others elongate, and gradually their walls develop very characteristic

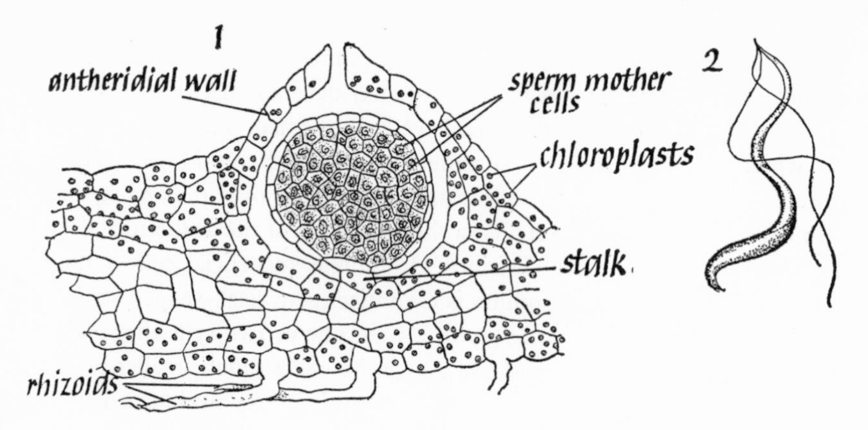

Figure 286 Pellia epiphylla
1 *T.s. through thallus showing antheridial chamber.*
2 *Single antherozoid.*

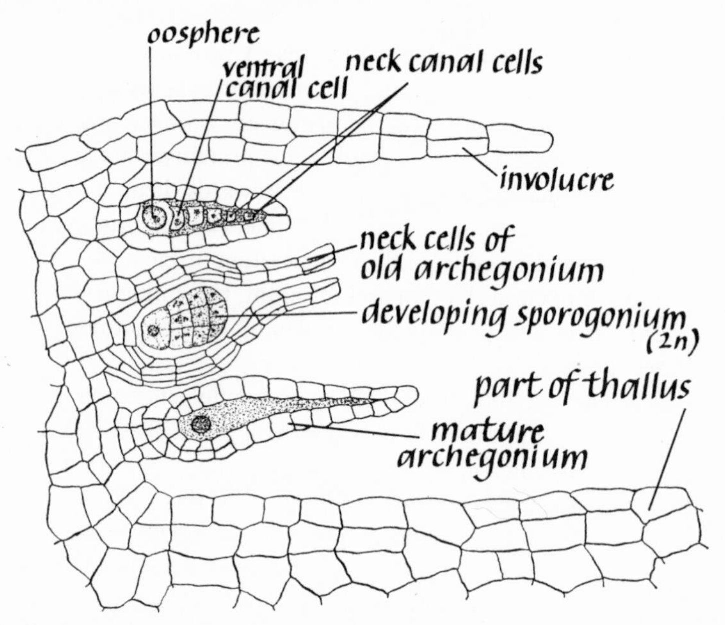

Figure 287 *L.s. of thallus tip of* Pellia *showing stages in the development of the archegonia and an embryo sporogonium.*

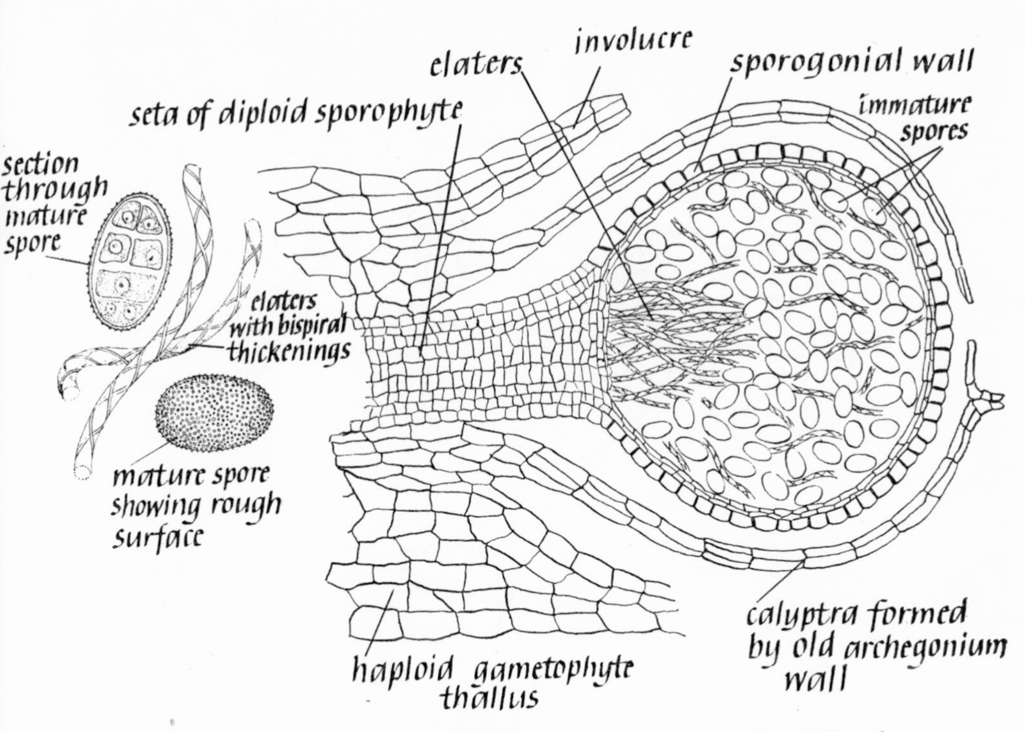

Figure 288 *L.s. through thallus tip of* Pellia *showing young sporogonium before the seta has elongated. Spores and elaters are shown on the left.*

spiral thickenings. These *elaters* are interspersed between the spores, though a large number of them are grouped together as a tuft arising from the capsule base (fig. 288).

When the capsule is fully mature, the seta elongates very rapidly, rupturing the calyptra and thus carrying the capsule several inches above the prostrate thallus. In this aerial position, the capsule dehisces by the splitting of its wall into four equal valves which fold down against the seta. The elaters, which are hygroscopic, exhibit quite violent twisting movements as they dry out. This activity loosens the spore mass and assists in its discharge and dispersal (fig. 281).

If on release the haploid spores fall on to some suitable substratum, they germinate, giving rise to a filament, on which an apical cell eventually develops. By the successive division of this cell, the thallus of a new gametophyte generation is formed and so the life cycle of *Pellia* is completed.

Although the structure of the male and female sexual organs, and of the sporogonium, is essentially the same in *Marchantia* and *Pellia*, there are two important differences. Firstly, in *Marchantia* antheridia and archegonia are produced on separate thalli, thus the plants are dioecious; secondly, they are borne above the thallus on stalked, upright branches – the *antheridiophores* and *archegoniophores*,

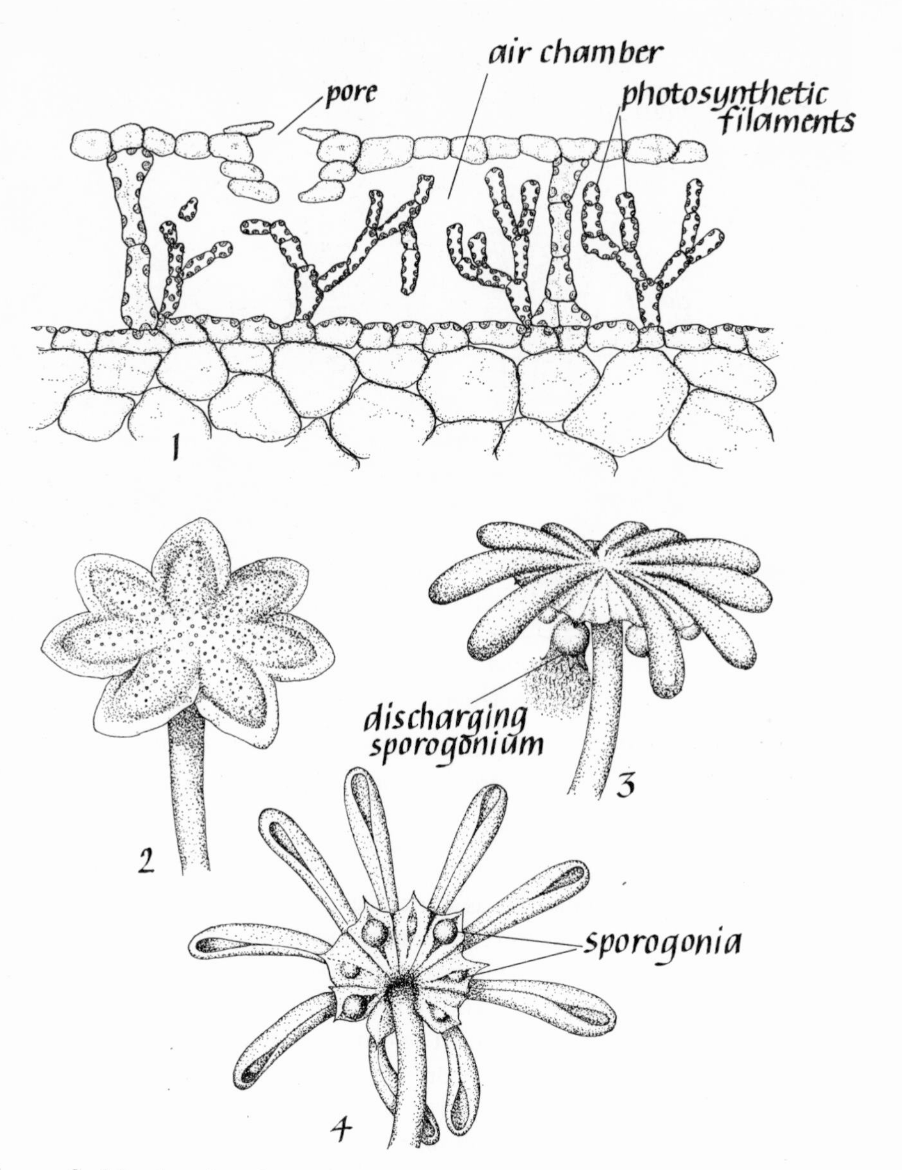

Figure 289 Marchantia polymorpha

1 *T.s. of upper region of thallus showing photosynthetic zone.*
2 *Antheridiophore showing antheridial pores on the surface.*
3 *Side view of archegoniophore with a discharging sporogonium.*
4 *Under surface of archegoniophore with developing sporogonia.*

Figure 290 *The liverwort* Marchantia polymorpha *bearing mature archegoniophores. The bright yellow spheres beneath the archegoniophore in the foreground are sporogonia which are liberating their spores. Note the rhizoids on the under-surface of the thalli on the left.*

respectively. These structures are modified, prostrate branches of the thallus (fig. 289).

Each antheridiophore consists of a stalk, bearing a small, slightly lobed, umbrella-like disc. Embedded in this disc and opening to the exterior are a series of antheridial chambers. The oldest and most mature occur towards the centre of the disc, the youngest and least developed, to the outside. In longitudinal section, the upper surface of the cap of the archegoniophore is seen to be differentiated into an upper photosynthetic region, while beneath are reduced, rhizoid-like structures, protected by scales similar to those found on the lower surface of the prostrate portion of the thallus (figs. 290 and 291).

In the early stages of its development the archegoniophore is an eight-lobed disc, borne on a very short stalk. There is an acropetalous formation of a series of archegonia down the centre of the upper surface of each of these lobes. The archegonia, which are very similar to those of *Pellia*, consist of a venter with a large egg and a neck closed by neck canal cells. Fertilization of the archegonium takes place when the stalk of the archegoniophore is still very short, the disc being only slightly above the level of the rest of the thallus.

The antherozoids are exuded out on to the surface of the antheridiophore when the latter is covered with a film of water. It has been suggested that these male gametes are transferred to the archegonial discs by means of rain-drop splashes. If a rain-drop makes a direct hit on a ripe antheridial disc, some of the water splashed off may land on an archegonial disc, should one be within range. This disc too, will be covered with a film of water and on reaching it, the swimming efforts of the antherozoids are thought to be sufficient to carry them to the now open archegonial necks, towards which they exhibit a chemotactic response.

Once a fertilization has been effected, the stalk of the archegoniophore elongates considerably, and at the same time there is a conspicuous upward expansion of the tissues forming the central area of the disc. This causes the margins of the disc to curve downwards and become inverted, so that the archegonia eventually come to lie with their necks pointing down towards the thallus. Lobes of tissue develop between each of the eight rows of archegonia. Because these look somewhat like petals, they are termed the *pseudoperianth*. As in the case of *Pellia*, fertilization stimulates division of the cells of the venter to form a protective calyptra, which envelops the developing sporophyte until maturity. The sporophyte, which develops from the diploid zygote, consists when almost mature, as in *Pellia*, of a wedge-shaped foot, which absorbs food from the adjoining gametophyte tissues in which it is embedded, and a short seta, supporting a spherical capsule. The seta, surrounded by a wall one cell thick, contains a mass of spore cells between which spirally thickened elaters are interspersed. The spore mother cells divide meiotically giving many haploid spores (fig. 292).

Late in the development of the sporophyte the seta increases in length somewhat suddenly as a result of the elongation of its approximately isodiametric cells. This increase in length ruptures the calyptra and the capsule is pushed beyond the lobes of the pseudoperianth. The spores are liberated by an irregular dehiscence of

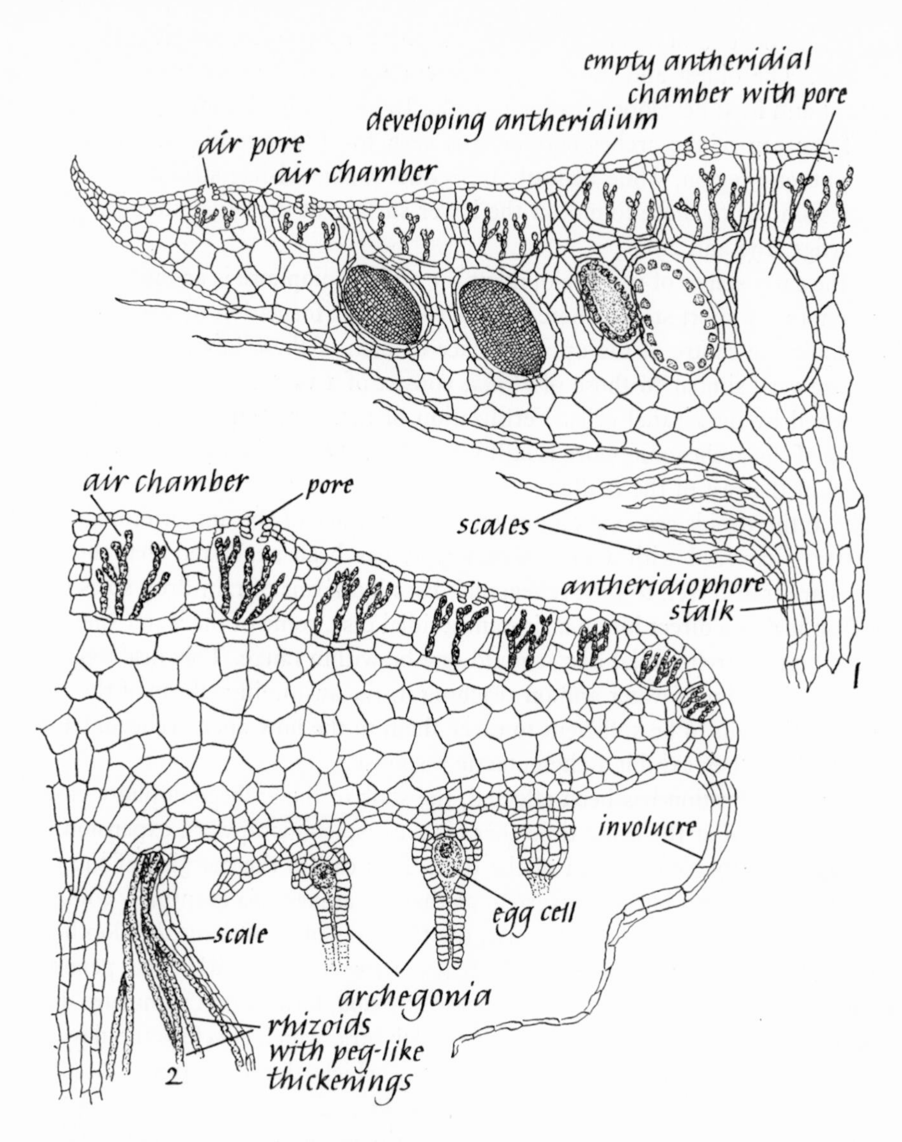

Figure 291 (*above*) *L.s. of antheridiophore and* (*below*) *L.s. of archegoniophore of* Marchantia polymorpha.

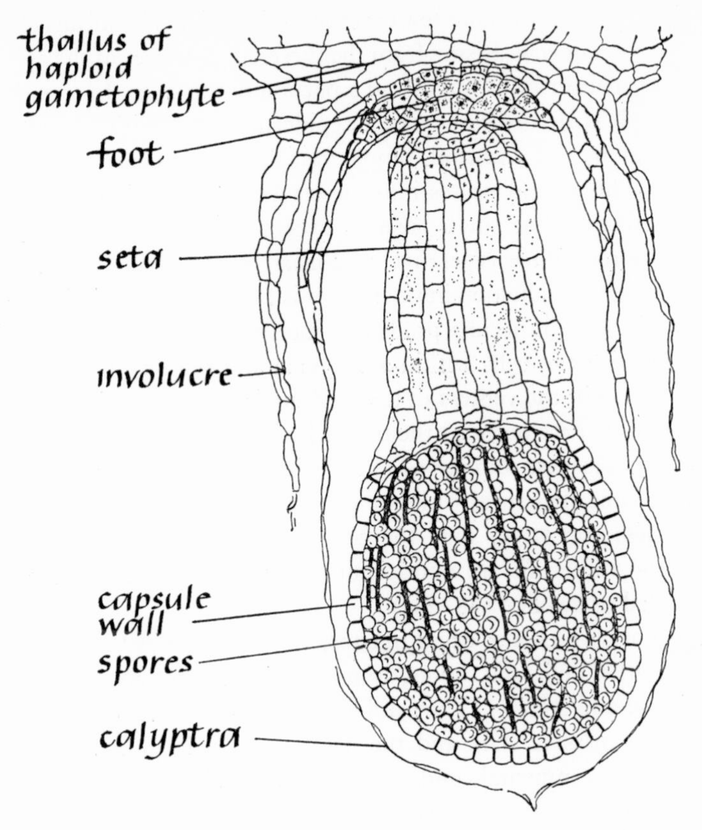

Figure 292 *L.s. through a sporogonium of* Marchantia.

the capsule and their dispersal is assisted by the hygroscopic movements of the elaters. The spores increase considerably in size when they germinate, and eventually form a filamentous *protonema*. The cell at the apex of this filament begins to function as an apical cell. Resulting from the activity of this cell, which eventually forms a transverse row of apical initials, a new *Marchantia* gametophyte generation develops.

Class Musci (Mosses)

Funaria (figs. 293 to 299)

Moss plants, like liverworts, represent the gametophyte generation of the life cycle. The mosses are, however, more complex in their form and structure than the liverworts. Indeed, in some respects they resemble the higher plants in that they have a definite stem, with three or more rows of alternate, sessile leaves, and in those forms which grow erect, there are root-like structures, rhizoids, which anchor the plants to the substratum. Moss rhizoids differ from those of liverworts in that they are multicellular, branched structures, with characteristically diagonal cross walls.

Growth of the plants, with but few exceptions, is initiated by means of a pyramidal apical cell. The rows of cells arising from the three cutting faces of the apical cell each develops into a vertical row of leaves and a portion of the stem. In transverse section the stem is a simple structure with an outer epidermal layer, without stomata, bounding a cortical region, and a central, simple vascular strand consisting of thin-walled elongated cells. This strand passes into the leaves as their mid-rib. The leaves too are simple structures, being single layered, except in this mid-rib region (fig. 293).

A few mosses reproduce vegetatively by means of gemmae though this is rather exceptional. Sexual reproduction in the mosses is fundamentally similar to that of the liverworts, that is with antheridia producing motile, biflagellate antherozoids. These swim to and fertilize egg cells within archegonia and the resulting zygotes develop into sporogonia within the venters of the archegonia. The antheridia are produced in *antheridial cups* which are borne at the tips of leafy shoots. The cups are formed by a circle of protective leaves, sometimes reddish in colour. The antheridia themselves are stalked, elongated structures with a single layered wall. The upper few cells of the wall are colourless and larger than the cells below, and thus form a conspicuous cap. Between the antheridia are multicellular, hair-like paraphyses, the end cells of which are pointed or swollen (fig. 294).

The archegonia, which also occur in cups, may be borne on the same plants as the antheridia, but either on lateral shoots, as in *Funaria*, or at the apex of different plants, as in *Polytrichum* and *Mnium*. They differ from those of liverworts in that each is borne on a fairly massive stalk and the neck tends to be much longer. Although adapted to drier environmental conditions, fertilization in the mosses depends on the presence of free water in the antheridial and archegonial cups (fig. 295).

Dehiscence of the mature antheridia does not occur until water is present, which they then absorb in considerable amounts. This causes internal pressures to develop which rupture the apical cap and so release the antherozoids; these are then forced out as a mucilaginous mass. Only later, when this mass comes into contact with the water in the cup, are the individual antherozoids finally liberated.

As each archegonium matures, the apex of the neck bursts open and the neck canal cells disorganize; at this stage it is ready to receive an antherozoid. There is some uncertainty as to how the antherozoids are transferred from the antheridial to the archegonial cups but, as in *Marchantia*, it seems probable that rain splashes are important. In certain mosses it seems probable that small insects, which feed on the sweet mucilaginous substances secreted from the reproductive organs, are also agents of transfer. Once within the archegonial cup, the antherozoids swim towards the archegonial neck by chemotactic attraction (fig. 296).

Fertilization occurs when an antherozoid passes down the long archegonial neck and fuses with the egg enclosed within the venter. Although a number of archegonia may be fertilized at more or less the same time, only one eventually develops into the diploid sporophyte. As in the liverworts, the sporophyte depends to a considerable extent on the gametophyte for the raw materials necessary for its development. To this end the basal part of the developing sporophyte grows downwards into the gametophytic tissues as a conical or dagger-like prolongation, the foot. The terminal region enlarges considerably to become the spore-containing capsule, which in most mosses is much more complex than in the liverworts. The foot and capsule are joined by a slender stalk, which elongates considerably, but until this happens the whole sporophyte remains within the gradually enlarging archegonial venter, now termed the calyptra. This calyptra, however, ruptures round its base when the seta eventually elongates and the upper portion is carried upwards on top of the capsule which it covers like a cap.

The form of the capsule varies greatly in different mosses. At least in the early stages of their development capsules are partially independent of the gametophytes which supports them for they are photosynthetic. All show a very much higher degree of differentiation than those of liverworts. The capsule of the common moss *Funaria* is however, fairly representative of such structures. When fully grown the capsule is pear-shaped and hangs down from the seta which supports it. The narrower basal region or neck, termed the *apophysis*, is a sterile, photosynthetic region producing no spores. Numerous stomata occur on this region, with guard cells which coalesce to form a single, ring-shaped unit (fig. 293.2).

Above the apophysis, the capsule gradually broadens out into the spore-producing region which, in longitudinal section, shows a high degree of internal differentiation. The outer wall, composed of several layers of cells, is bounded externally by an epidermis. Within this layer there is a wide, cylindrical system of extensively ramifying air spaces traversed by filaments, or *trabeculae*, of chloroplast-containing photosynthetic cells. A barrel-shaped spore sac forms a layer within this region though it is bounded by internal and external layers of sterile tissues. The centre of this region of the capsule is occupied by a *columella* of colourless parenchymatous cells. The important feature to note about the moss capsule is that although essentially a spore producing structure, dependent on the gametophyte for water and dissolved minerals, it nevertheless shows a significant advance over the sporophyte of liverworts: it is photosynthetic and so not entirely dependent on the gametophyte (fig. 298).

The apex of the *Funaria* capsule is closed by a conical lid or *operculum*, which is attached to the rim of the capsule by a ring of swollen epidermal cells, the *annulus*. Beneath the operculum a series of cells form a distinctive cone, which is in fact a double ring of sixteen *peristome teeth* possessing characteristic bars of transverse thickening. As the capsule drys out, it changes in colour from green to reddish-brown and becomes deeply furrowed externally. Eventually the operculum is shed with some violence, but the haploid spores inside the capsule are still held there by the closely fitting peristome teeth. As the capsule dries out, however, these teeth bend upwards and outwards, though any increase in humidity brings about their rapid closure. It seems that the movements of the peristome teeth are largely responsible for the dispersal of the spore mass. This mass tends to become crowded into the region immediately under the peristome, as a result of the contraction of the lower part of the capsule. Twisting movements of the hygroscopic seta may further assist in shaking out and dispersal of the spores (fig. 299).

The spores germinate readily under moist conditions and develop into filamentous protonema, which resemble the filaments of certain green algae. This resemblance is, however, only superficial and must not be taken as evidence for an algal ancestry of the bryophytes. The protonema become attached to the substratum by rhizoids, while lateral branches give rise to 'buds' in each of which a pyramidal apical cell soon becomes established. From this cell a new moss plant develops. The protonema die once the gametophytes produced from it have become established.

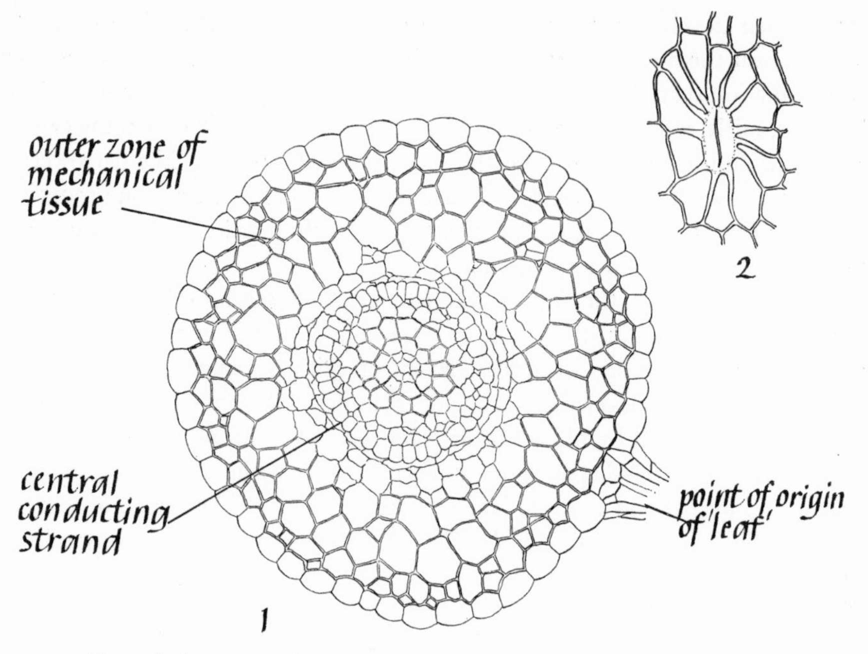

Figure 293 Funaria hygrometrica

1 *T.s. stem showing central conducting strand.*

2 *Detail of stoma.*

Figure 294 *L.s. of apex of male plant of* Funaria *showing antheridial cup with antheridia.*

Figure 295 *Archegonial cups (female 'flowers') of* Polytrichum. (*Photo by Dr J. D. Dodds.*)

Figure 296 *L.s. of apex of female plant of* Funaria *showing archegonial cup with archegonia.*

Figure 297 *Capsules of the moss* Funaria.

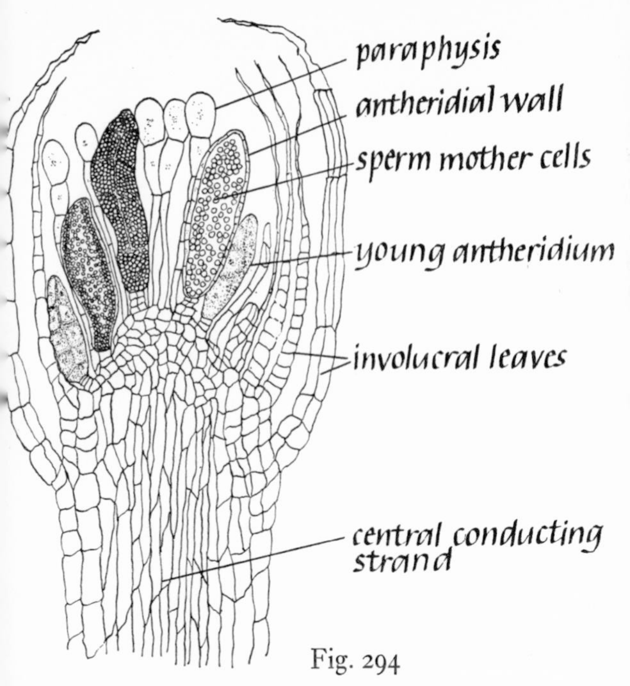

Fig. 294

Fig. 295

Fig. 297

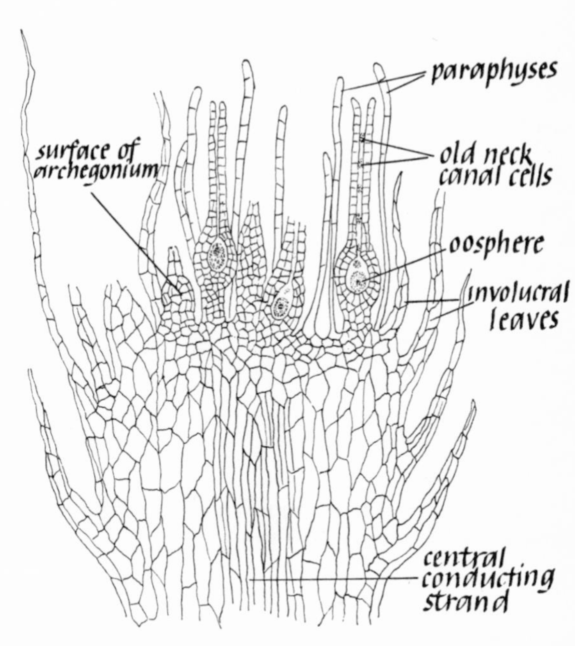

Fig. 296

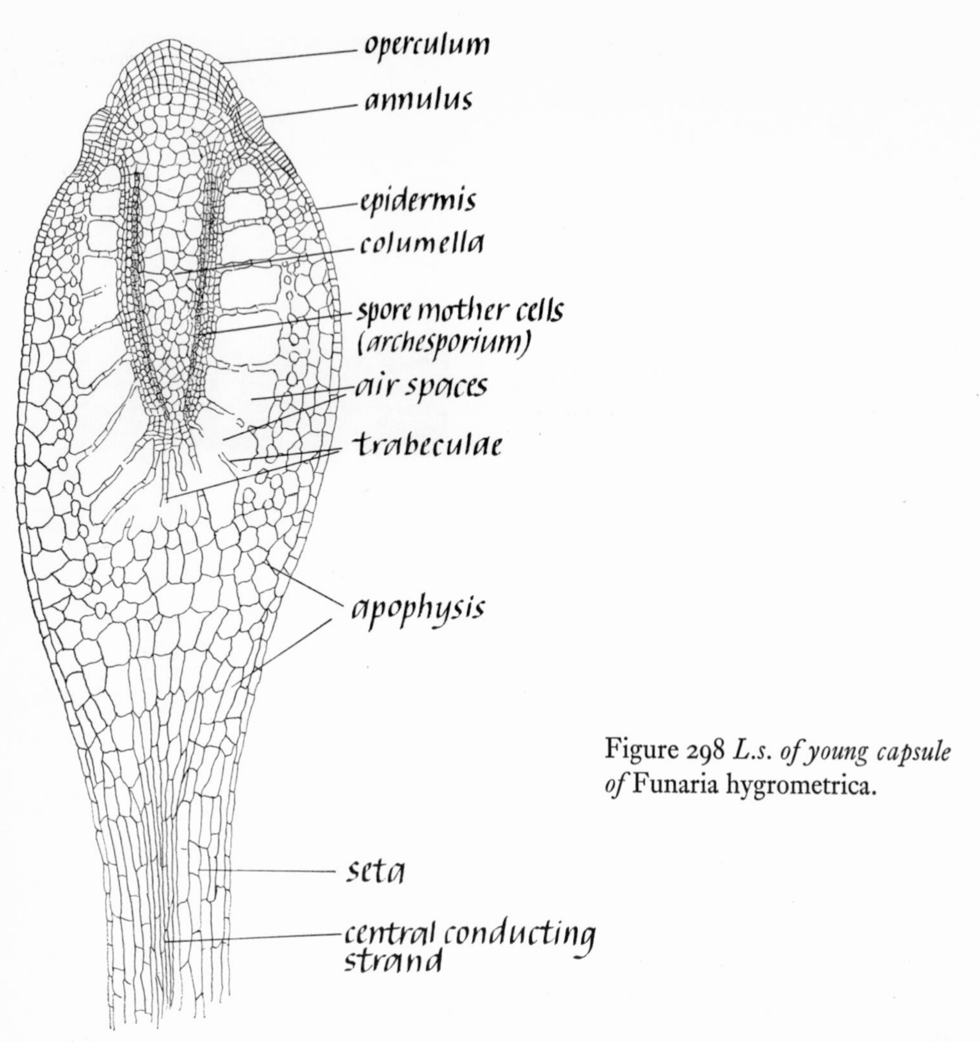

Figure 298 *L.s. of young capsule of* Funaria hygrometrica.

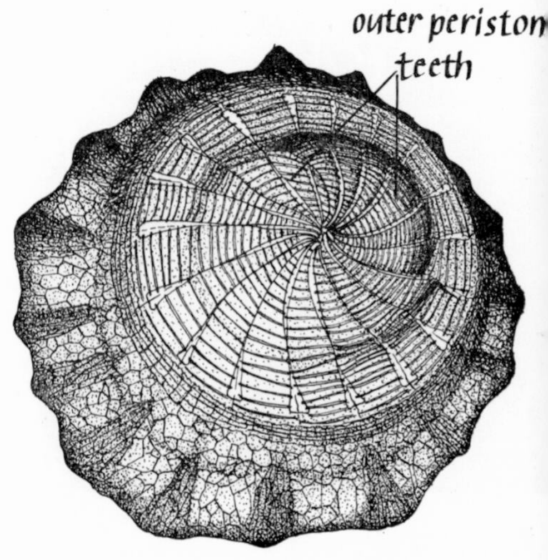

Figure 299 *Detached peristome of capsule of* Funaria hygrometrica.

CHAPTER 35

DIVISION PTERIDOPHYTA

In the evolution of the land flora from aquatic, algal-like ancestors, three distinct evolutionary levels appear to have been attained. The Bryophyta did not achieve any significant differentiation of a vascular system, and, being only partially adapted to terrestrial conditions, neither the free-living gametophyte generation nor the sporophyte dependent on it, reached any considerable size.

At a higher level, the sporophyte gained its independence from the gametophyte and achieved a vascular system differentiated into xylem and phloem. Being better adapted to the rigours of life on land the sporophytes attained considerably greater dimensions. They were still, however, unable to free themselves completely from the aquatic environment, their gametophytes requiring the presence of free water for sexual reproduction. This second evolutionary level, which corresponds to the *vascular cryptogams*, constitutes the Division Pteridophyta.

The third evolutionary level corresponds to those vascular plants which produce ovules and seeds – the Division Spermatophyta. Their very reduced gametophyte generation is never released from the sporangium. In this way the sexual organs are very well protected; the plants, therefore, do not require the presence of free water at the time of their sexual reproduction. The final link with their remote algal ancestry is thereby severed (p. 338).

The Pteridophyta thus stand in an intermediate Division between the Bryophyta and Spermatophyta. They are distinguished from the Bryophyta in that the sporophyte at an early stage in its development becomes independent of the gametophyte; they differ from the Spermatophyta in that neither the spores nor the gametophytes which develop from them are ever liberated from the sporangium in which they are formed. As with Bryophyta, however, the life history involves a clearly defined alternation of generations, but the sporophyte is always the dominant phase. When mature it has an internal conducting system consisting of xylem and phloem. Generally, the sporophyte is differentiated externally into true roots – not just rhizoids – stem, and leaves, and the sporangia are borne on the leaves (*sporophylls*) or at the tips of special branches.

Of the plants possessing these general pteridophyte characters, the ferns, horsetails, and club-mosses are each sufficiently distinct categories to warrant their being placed in separate Sub-Divisions. Thus the ferns comprise the Sub-Division Filicopsida, the horsetails the Sphenopsida, and the club-mosses the Lycopsida.

Some botanists have proposed that all vascular plants, that is the two Divisions Pteridophyta and Spermatophyta, be grouped together into a Division called the

Trachaeophyta. This system of classification, which may be encountered especially in fairly recent American botanical literature, emphasizes the universal occurrence of tracheary tissues as the essential character of the vascular system of the sporophyte. This classification is, however, by no means universally accepted.

SUB-DIVISION FILICOPSIDA (FERNS)

The Filicopsida is the largest and most diverse group of pteridophytes. Its members are characterized by the possession of large (macrophyllous) leaves, which are spirally arranged and associated with leaf gaps in the vascular cylinder of the stem. The sporangia are usually produced in large numbers and grouped together in clusters termed *sori*, borne on the margins or lower surfaces of the leaves.

Some 10,000 species of ferns from a wide range of habitats throughout the world have been described. They are very numerous and diverse in tropical rain forests, where many species occur as *epiphytes* on trees. Many Australasian ferns are themselves tree-like. Even deserts and mountains support ferns, and the common bracken, *Pteridium aquilinum*, is cosmopolitan in its distribution. In addition to the varied and highly successful present-day ferns, plants belonging unmistakably to this group are quite numerous as fossils. These extend back to about the middle of the Devonian period, some three hundred million years ago (fig. 220).

A quite typical example of a fern is the Male or Shield Fern, *Dryopteris felix-mas*, a plant commonly found in rather damp and shady places. It is of fairly robust appearance, with leaves of from two to three feet long, forming a terminal crown which arises from a subterranean stem, that is, a rhizome. The fern plants themselves represent the diploid sporophyte generation in the life cycle, but, as with liverworts and mosses, these are the products of sexual reproduction, which takes place within a quite separate haploid gemetophyte termed the *prothallus* (fig. 300).

The fern gametophyte is small, dorsi-ventrally flattened and heart-shaped, resembling somewhat the gametophyte of a thallose liverworts. Like the liverwort gametophyte, it grows by repeated divisions of an apical cell, which occupies the 'notch' of the heart. The lobes of the gametophyte thallus are a single cell thick but the central region is several cells deep. Colourless rhizoids develop on the underside of the central region and attach it to the substratum. On this underside, and thus protected from dessication, the antheridia arise between the rhizoids, while the archegonia, which tend to develop at a later stage, occur behind the apical notch.

The sex organs of the fern are much smaller than those of the Bryophyta: the wall of the antheridium consists of only a basal cell and three wall cells, the middle one of which is a cap cell. They enclose sporogenous tissue, which gives rise in each antheridium to thirty-two antherozoids. Each antherozoid is rather like a small, spirally coiled spring with a tuft of numerous long flagella at its anterior end.

The archegonia are sunken deeply into the tissues of the prothallus; only the neck cells, which are curved back towards the antheridial area, protrude. At the time of fertilization the neck and ventral canal cells disintegrate, as in the Bryophyta, the

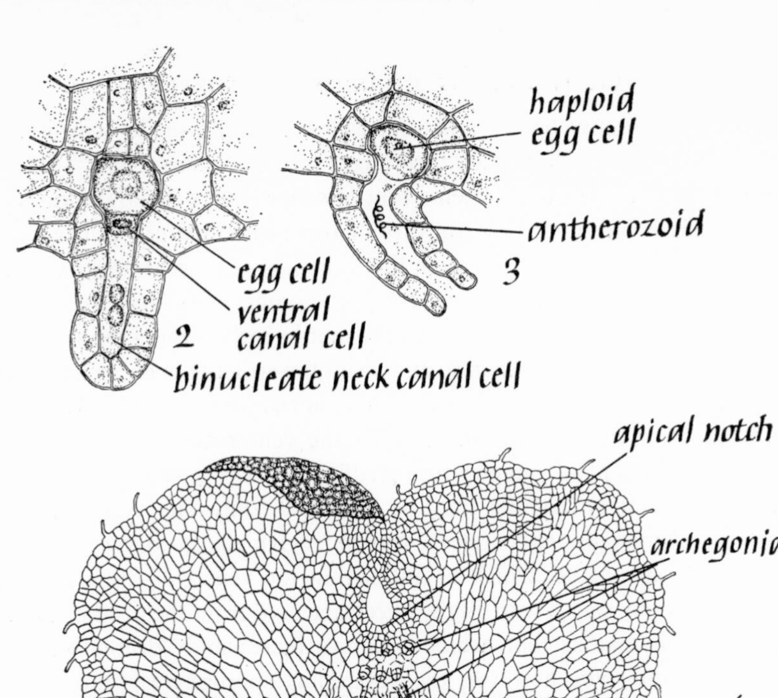

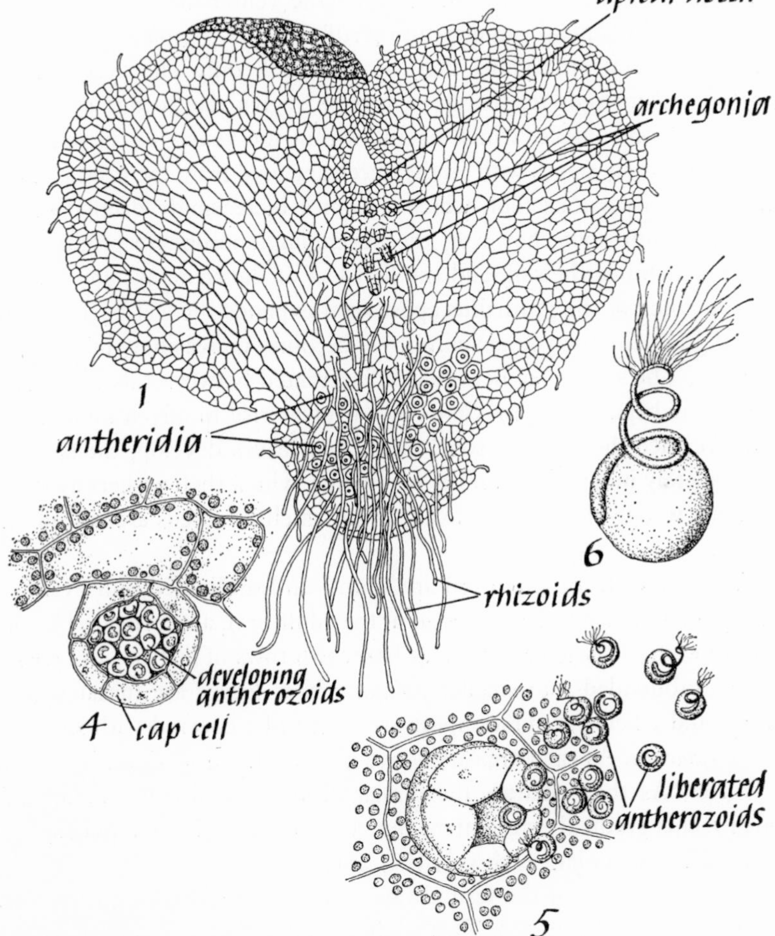

Figure 300 *The male or shield fern* (Dryopteris felix-mas).

1 *Ventral surface of prothallus showing rhizoids, antheridia and archegonia.*

2 *Mature archegonium.*

3 *Archegonium with antherozoid in neck canal prior to fertilization.*

4 *L.s. of antheridium with developing antherozoids.*

5 *Antheridium in vertical view showing escape of antherozoids.*

6 *A single antherozoid.*

neck of the archegonium opens, and mucilage containing malic acid, is extruded. The malic acid acts as a chemotactic stimulant to the antherozoids.

Fertilization can occur only when a film of water covers the lower surface of the prothallus. This brings about the rupture of the antheridial cap cell, while the remaining ring of wall cells swell so much that the mass of sperm mother cells inside is extruded onto the prothallial surface. Here, in contact with the film of water, the wall of each mother cell breaks down, so the motile antherozoids are set free. These gametes show a chemotactic response and swim towards the open archegonial necks, which they eventually enter. After straightening out somewhat, they move downwards with an undulating movement. On reaching the venter one gamete penetrates the egg; when the two haploid gametes fuse fertilization is completed.

Although several archegonia may be fertilized, only one zygote continues to develop; each gametophyte, therefore, can only give rise to one sporophyte. The development of the zygote, which begins within the venter of the archegonium, is sustained in the early stages with all the necessary food from the prothallial tissues by way of a parenchymatous foot, which becomes increasingly deeply lodged within these tissues. Quite soon, however, the developing sporophyte produces a primary root which penetrates the soil, and the first leaf of the shoot system grows upwards through the notch of the prothallus apex. As it expands the leaf begins to photosynthesize and gradually the young sporophyte becomes increasingly independent of the gametophyte. The stem apex becomes differentiated between this first leaf and foot, and as the leaf begins to grow vigorously it gives rise to adventitious roots, which eventually replace the primary root. As further leaves develop, the sporophyte becomes completely independent of the prothallus, which then withers away. The stem grows from a wedge-shaped apical cell, from which new cells are cut off on the two inner faces.

The first leaves to be produced are simple and undivided, but eventually compound, bipinnate foliage leaves, typical of the adult fern, are formed. The main stalk, or *rachis*, of each of these newer leaves bears two rows of leaflets, the *pinnae*, which are further subdivided into smaller *pinnules*. New leaves are initiated beneath the stem apex, and when they first appear are seen to be covered with small, brownish scales, the *ramenta*. As each appears above ground, the upper end is helically coiled like a crozier. As they enlarge, the pinnae, which are also incurved, unfold, and the coiled rachis gradually straightens out. Up to twenty large bipinnate leaves may be produced by each plant each year (fig. 301).

The perennial stem of the fern always remains underground, so it is, in fact, a rhizome (see Chapter 4, p. 64). This is always short and stocky and, as it ages, becomes thickly covered with the bases of the leaves formed in previous years. The rhizome contains a complex vascular system. If the rhizome is macerated and the soft parenchymatous ground tissue is dissected away, there remains a cylindrical network with numerous small broken strands arising from the larger strands of the main framework of the net. The small strands are leaf traces, while the large holes

Figure 301 *Young frond of* Dryopteris felix-mas *showing its coiled pinnae.*

in the net are the leaf gaps (see fig. 302). A transverse section of a rhizome therefore shows a broken ring of vascular strands with sections of smaller leaf traces to the outside, all embedded in the parenchymatous ground tissue. Each vascular strand, or *meristele*, consists of a central core of xylem surrounded by a ring of phloem. The phloem, in turn, is surrounded by a pericycle and endodermis. The xylem is composed of pitted or scalariform tracheids, but there are no vessels; the phloem comprises sieve tubes with sieve plates on their side walls, but there are no companion cells (figs. 303a and 303b).

Internally the leaves are similar in their anatomy to those of higher plants: an upper palisade and lower spongy mesophyll communicate to the outside by numerous stomata on their lower surfaces. On the lower surface of the leaves of older plants sporangia develop in clusters, each termed a *sorus*. The sori lie over the veins, or at the vein endings of the pinnules; usually seven or eight occur on each. As the sori develop they appear in early summer as pale green, kidney-shaped plates, the *indusia*, protecting the sporangia forming beneath them. When the sporangia are mature, the indusium shrivels, and the sori are then revealed as small, dark spheres, clustered round a central axis. A transverse section of a sorus on a fruiting pinnule best illustrates its structure. Since each sorus lies over a vein, the vein can be seen in the section immediately above the sorus; intimately associated with it is a cushion-like receptacle from which are borne the numerous stalked sporangia. From the centre

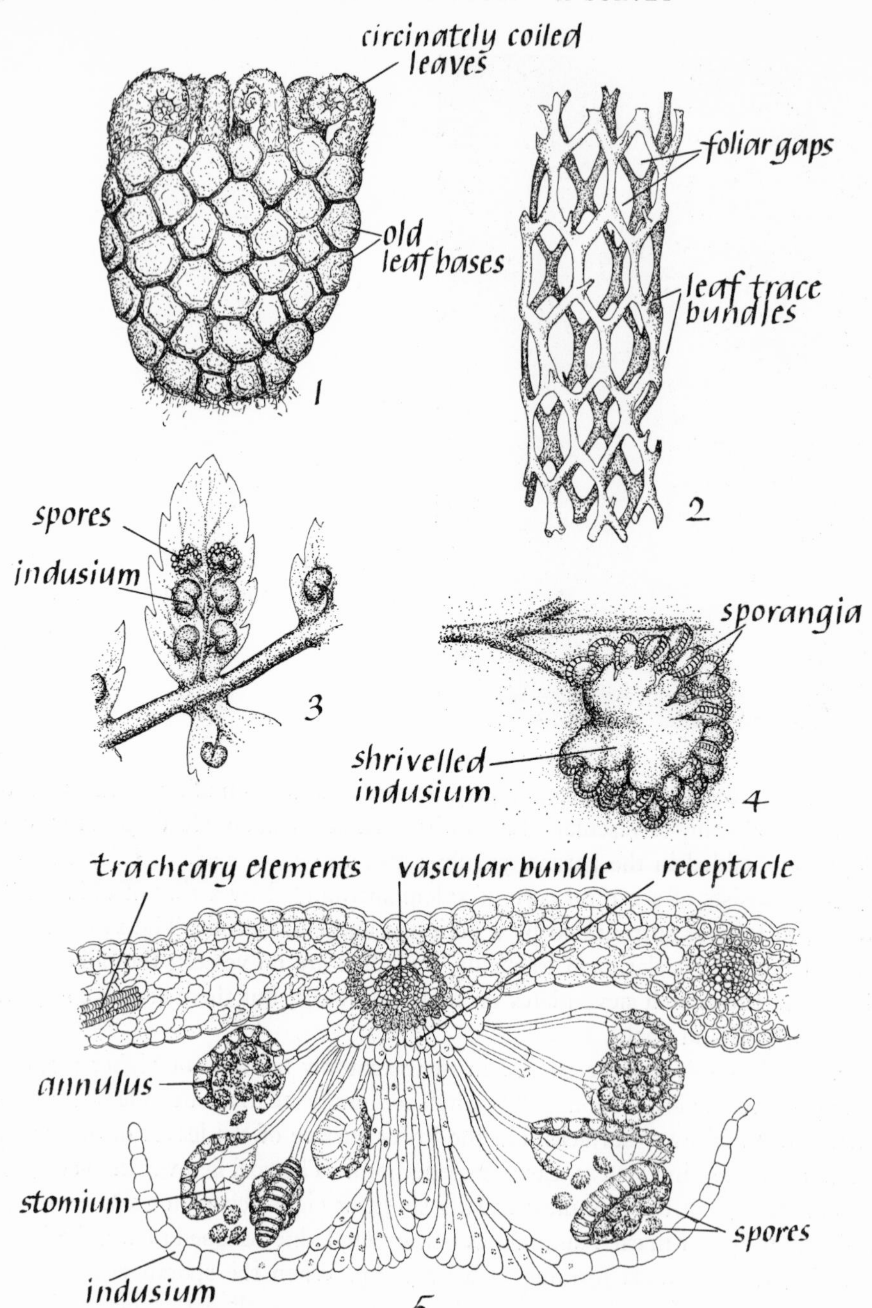

Figure 302 Dryopteris felix-mas

1 *A rhizome.* 2 *Vascular system dissected from a macerated rhizome.*

3 *Under-surface of pinna showing sori.*

4 *Detail of mature sorus with almost ripe sporangia.* 5 *T.s. frond across a sorus.*

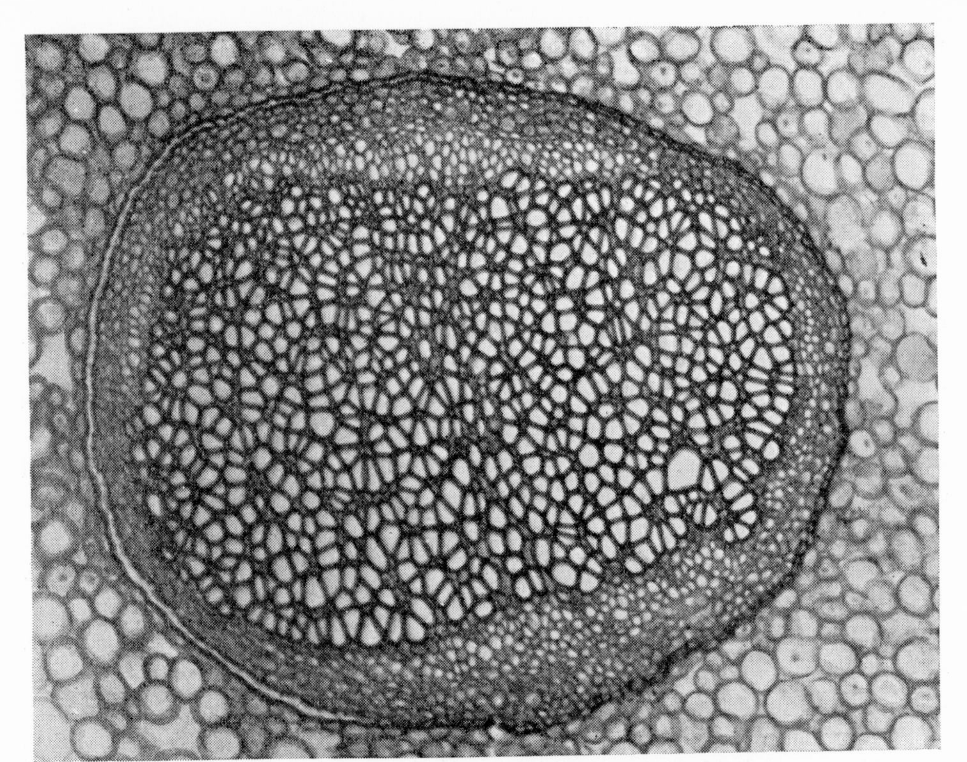

Figure 303a *A meristele from the t.s. of rhizome of* Dryopteris felix-mas.

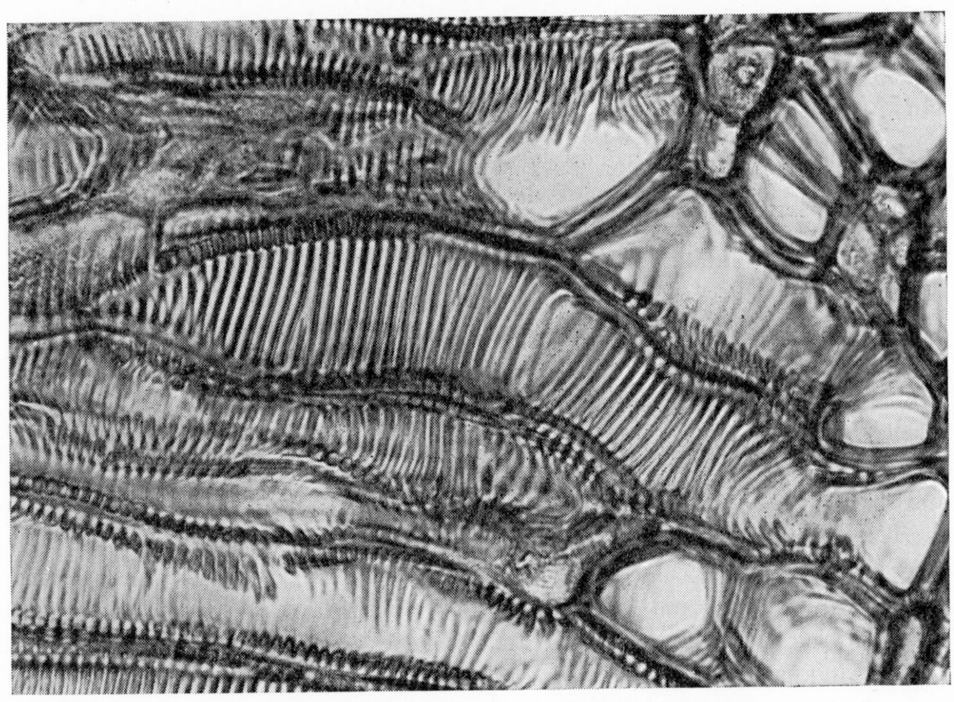

Figure 303b *L.s. of tracheids of* Dryopteris *in a leaf trace arising from a meristele.*

of the receptacle arises the stalk of the umbrella-shaped indusium, the edges of which curve inwards, thus protecting the sporangia (see fig. 302.5).

Each sporangium grows from a single superficial cell and, when fully developed, consists of a slender stalk, bearing at its end a flattened, biconvex, oval spore case, the capsule (fig. 305). Its wall is one cell thick and lined by a nutritive layer of tapetal cells surrounding a central mass of 12 spore mother cells. Each of these cells eventually divides meiotically producing in all 48 haploid spores. While these developments in the sporogenous tissue occur, considerable changes take place, especially in the single line of cells forming the narrow margin of the lens-like capsule. From the stalk on one side, and extending half-way down the opposite edge, these cells become considerably thickened on their inner tangential and radial walls, and together form the *annulus*, an organ of dehiscence. The remainder of these marginal cells and the other wall cells on both the convex faces of the capsule remain thin-walled. The thin-walled marginal cells constitute the *stomium* and, as the capsule matures and dries out, the annulus tends to straighten, for its cells lose water. As a result the stomium becomes subjected to an increasing tension. Eventually it ruptures and the spores within the capsule are violently scattered as the annulus straightens out. This catapult-like method of spore release, aided by wind, ensures their effective dispersal over a fairly wide area round the plant.

As they fall on some suitable substratum the spores germinate to give rise to short filaments of chloroplast-containing cells, similar in many respects to moss protonema (see fig. 304). The typically heart-shaped prothallus develops by repeated divisions of the wedge-shaped apical cell which is formed at the end of the filament, so completing the life cycle of the fern.

SUB-DIVISION SPHENOPSIDA (HORSETAILS)

The Genus *Equisetum*, the horsetails, are the only living representatives of a large and diverse group of pteridophytes which attained an almost world-wide distribution during the Carboniferous era some two hundred million years ago. During the period of the great coal-forming forests, the Pteridophyta were abundantly represented by the giant tree-like *Calamites* and the slender, climbing or prostrate *Sphenophyllum*. Of the present-day horsetails, the largest European species, *Equisetum telmatia*, may grow to a height of seven or eight feet, though its stem is only about an inch in diameter (see fig. 306). The majority of the twenty-five known species are, however, small herbaceous plants. The genus as a whole is widely distributed from the tropics to arctic regions, and the various species occur in a range of habitats from lake margins to very dry areas.

The principal characteristic of all the plants, both living and extinct, included in the Sphenopsida is the conspicuous subdivision of the ribbed stems of the dominant sporophyte generation into distinct nodes and internodes. At each node there is a whorl of small, wedge-shaped leaves, while branches arise in the axils of these leaves, thus also forming whorls at the nodes. In *Equisetum* the leaves are fused to form a small,

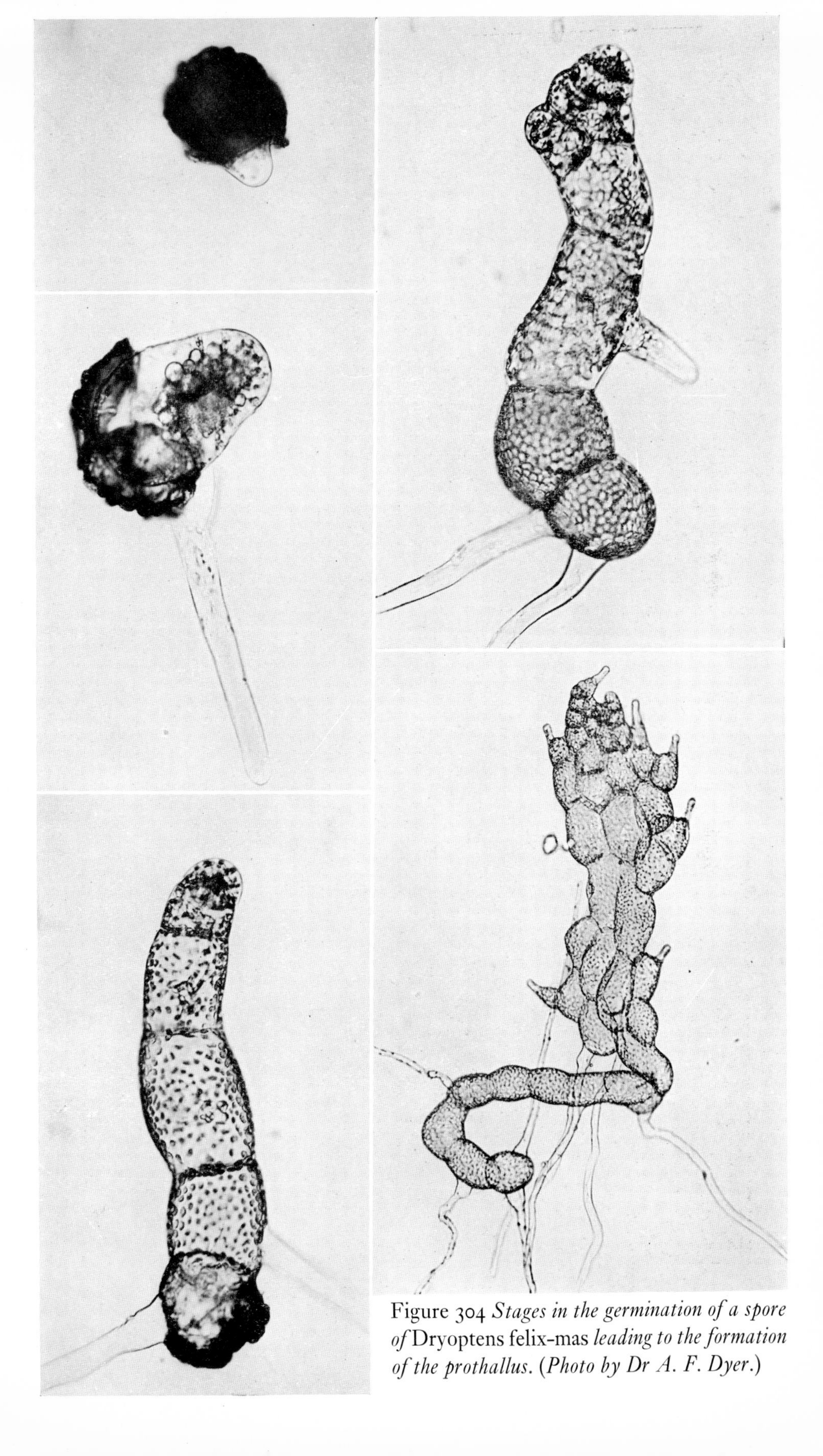

Figure 304 *Stages in the germination of a spore of* Dryoptens felix-mas *leading to the formation of the prothallus.* (*Photo by Dr A. F. Dyer.*)

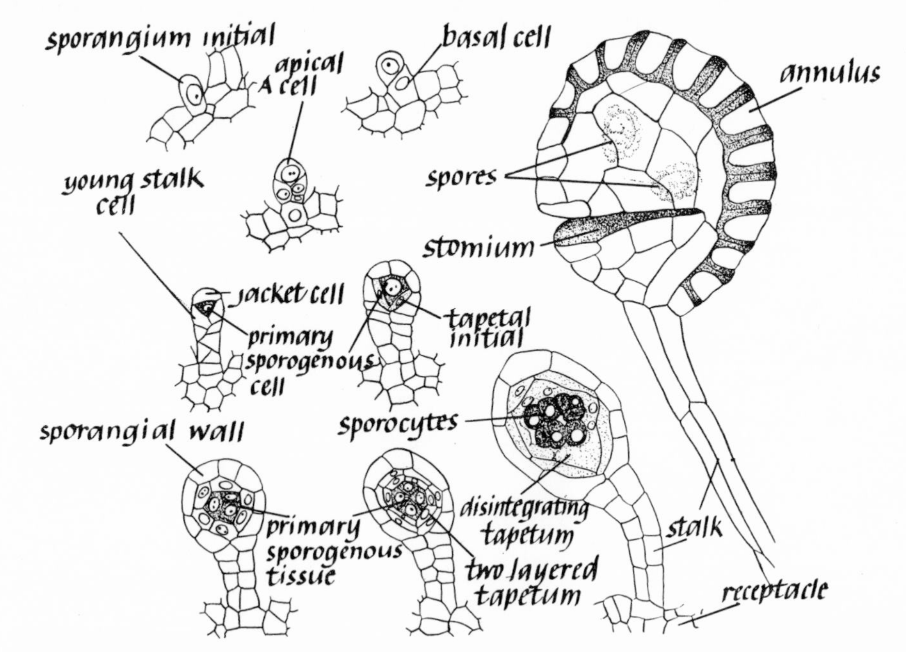

Figure 305 *Stages in the development of a fern sporangium* (*after Foster and Gifford*).

Figure 306 *Young plants of* Equisetum telmatia.

Figure 307 *Detail of the stem of* Equisetum telmatia *showing whorls of small, wedge-shaped leaves lying against the stem, and the whorls of branches.*

toothed sheath; the axillary branches break through the base of this sheath as they develop (see fig. 307).

In some species of *Equisetum*, such as the common field horsetail (*E. arvense*), the upright aerial stems, which develop annually from a horizontally growing underground rhizome, are of two kinds. One type are short-lived, unbranched, and, being without chlorophyll, are a yellowish brown colour and bear a cone-like structure, the *strobilus*, at the stem apex (see fig. 308). These fertile stems produce spores from the cones between May and June, then they begin to die back. The other stems are green with whorls of slender lateral branches; these persist throughout the growing season, usually dying back with the first autumn frosts. In some species, such as the large *E. telmatia*, only branched stems are formed and these produce cones at their apices. In *E. limosum*, a widespread aquatic species, the long, slender, green stems are always unbranched.

The stem of *Equisetum* consists of epidermis, cortex, endodermis, and a vascular cylinder in the centre of which is a pith. In older stems this pith degenerates leaving an empty space. In addition to this large central cavity, which is interrupted at each node by a thin diaphragm of tissue, the stems generally have two rings of longitudinal cavities. The larger of these, the *vallecular canals*, occur in the cortex. Each, as their name implies, is associated with one of the longitudinal grooves or valleys which are so characteristic a feature of the external morphology of the stem. The much smaller *carinal canals*, named after the Latin *carina* meaning a keel, are located deeper in the stem and are adjacent to the primary xylem of each vascular bundle. As their name indicates, they lie on a radius with one of the stem ridges, thus alternating with the vallecular canals (fig. 309).

The vascular bundles form a continuous ring of tissue in the nodal regions of the stem, but in the regions between the nodes they are distinct and so spaced that one lies beneath each of the stem ridges. Since there is no secondary thickening in *Equisetum*, each bundle consists of primary xylem and phloem (fig. 309).

The cortex is composed of a variety of cell types, its tissues being concerned with support, photosynthesis and storage. The supporting tissues are collenchyma and sclerenchyma, the latter usually forming columns just within each stem ridge. Much of the remaining outer tissue of the cortex consists of thin-walled parenchyma containing numerous chloroplasts. This *chlorenchyma* is the main photosynthetic tissue of the plant. Within the chlorenchyma there is colourless parenchyma, primarily concerned with storage.

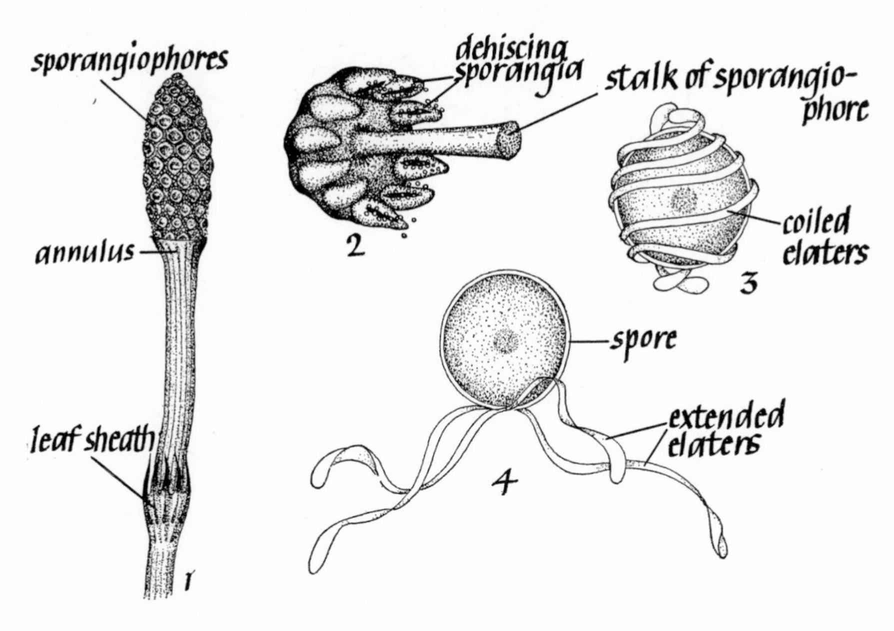

Figure 308 Equisetum arvense

1 *Strobilus of* Equisetum arvense.

2 *Detail of detached sporangiophore showing dehiscing sporangia (after Dodel-Port).*

3-4 *Spores with elaters.*

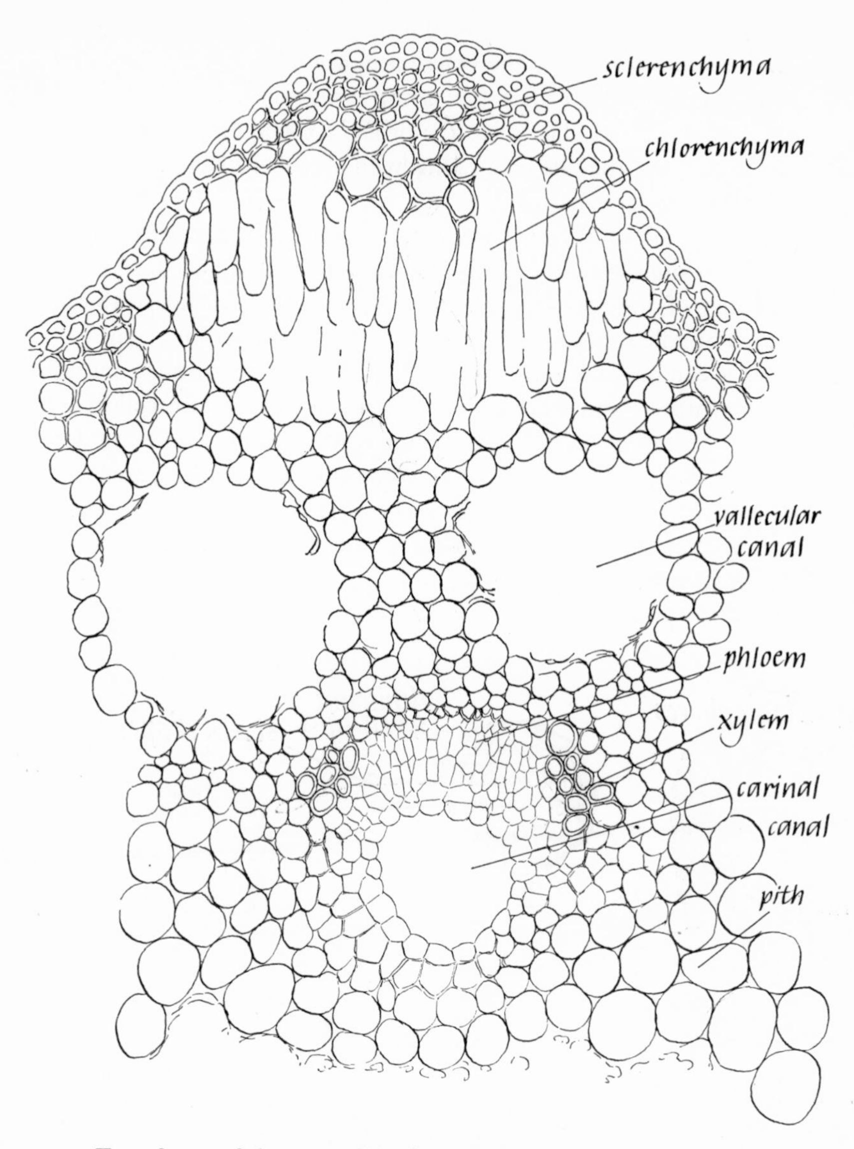

Figure 309 *T.s. of part of the stem of* Equisetum arvense.

The epidermal cells in most species have highly silicified external walls, which make the stem rough to the touch; this is the reason for *Equisetum* plants being called 'scouring rushes'.

The reproductive structures of the sporophyte are the terminal cones or ***strobili.*** Each consists of an axis, the continuation of the stem axis, bearing successive whorls of sporophylls or, as they are sometimes termed, sporangiophores. Each sporophyll consists of a hexagonal disc attached at right angles to the cone axis by a short stalk. The discs of adjacent sporophylls fit closely together, thus enclosing and protecting a ring of from 5 to 10 sporangia, which are directed inwards from each disc and thus encircle its stalk. When the sporangia are mature the sporophylls separate from one another by the elongation of the strobilus axis. The haploid spores then escape through a longitudinal cleft formed down the inner wall of each sporangium (see (figs. 308 and 310).

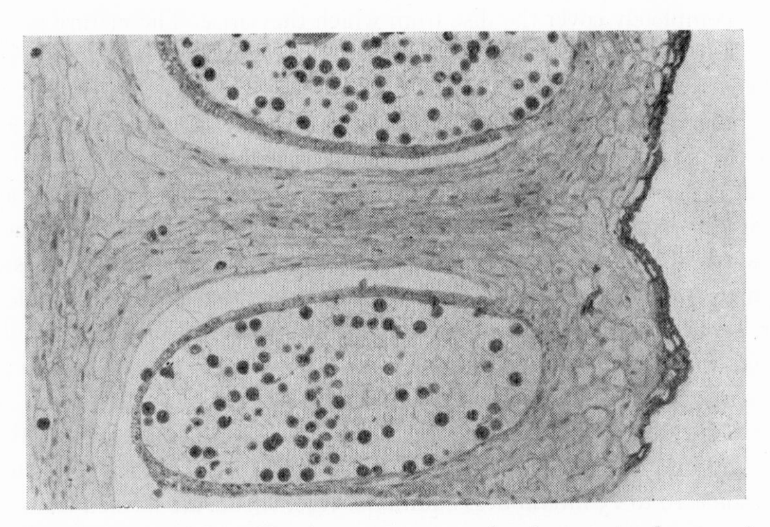

Figure 310 *L.s. strobilus of* Equisetum arvense *showing a pair of sporangia.*

The spores of *Equisetum* are more elaborate than those of the ferns. As the spores mature they secrete a wall consisting of four concentric layers, the outermost of which is laid down in four spiral strips. These strips are called elaters since, like the elaters of liverworts, they help to expel the spores from the sporangium. As the spores dry, the elaters partly peel away from the wall beneath, remaining attached to it only at one common point. Once liberated from the capsule the elaters may also help in the wind dispersal of the spores (fig. 308).

In *Equisetum arvense*, although the difference is not immediately apparent, the spores are of two types: smaller green spores and larger brownish ones. If, however, large numbers of spores are measured and the results of the measurements plotted on a graph, this size difference becomes very obvious, for the resulting curve is *bimodal* with one peak in the region of 34μ, the other at about 43μ. This production of spores of two types is termed *heterospory*, in contrast to the *homosporous* condition of most ferns. *Equisetum arvense* is not, however, truly *heterosporous*: although the smaller spores produce only small prothalli on which only antheridia are formed, the larger spores give rise to both antheridia and archegonia. When growth conditions are favourable more archegonia are produced. Thus *Equisetum arvense* can be said to show an intermediate stage in the development of heterospory, a condition which is fully developed in more advanced forms. Many species of *Equisetum* produce only hermaphrodite prothalli.

The gametophytes, which are usually only a centimetre or so in diameter, consist of a colourless basal cushion of tissue attached to the substratum by rhizoids (see fig. 311). Standing upright from this basal portion are numerous small, flattened, irregularly-branched lobes, which are green and photosynthetic. These green lobes eventually completely cover the disc from which they arise. The mature sex organs, antheridia and archegonia similar in structure to those of the ferns, lie on the prothallus between the lobes.

As in other archegoniate plants, fertilization can only be effected when a film of water covers the prothallus. The naked, spirally-twisted antherozoids have numerous flagellae at the anterior end and escape from the antheridium through an aperture formed by the disintegration of the cap cell. The antherozoids are chemotactic and swim towards the open archegonial necks. Frequently many antherozoids reach a given venter, but only one penetrates the egg. Unlike the majority of pteridophytes, however, several sporophytes may develop on the same prothallus.

The embryo sporophyte, developing from the diploid zygote, differentiates into foot, primary root, and stem quite early in its development. Growth of both root and shoot is from a wedge-shaped apical cell. Cells lateral to the apical cell of the shoot apex develop into the first leaf sheath of the young stem. This primary shoot only develops some 10 to 15 internodes; additional erect shoots are formed from buds on the primary shoot.

SUB-DIVISION LYCOPSIDA (CLUB MOSSES)

The tendency towards a separation of the sexes of the gametophyte generation is developed to a high degree in the Lycopsida, a well-defined group of pteridophytes whose living members, like the Sphenopsida, are small, but whose ancient members were tree-like. The Lycopsida were, indeed, one of the most conspicuous components of the Carboniferous forests. The living members, which belong to the genera *Lycopodium* (fig. 312) and *Selaginella*, are prostrate, moss-like plants, though there is a small aquatic genus *Isoetes*, the plants of which have erect, tapering leaves; hence they are commonly known as Quillworts.

Selaginella, which is represented in the British flora by only one species, *S. spinosa*, will be described as an example of the Lycopsida. For examination in the laboratory

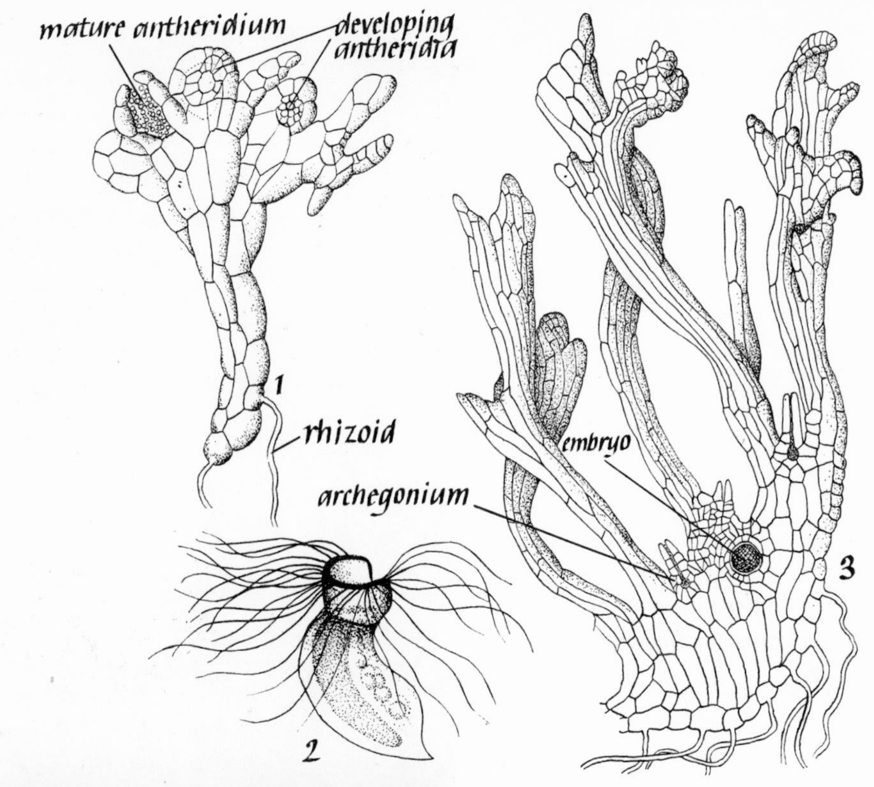

Figure 311 Equisetum arvense
1 *Male gametophyte with antheridia (after Hofmeister).*
2 *Antherozoid (after Belajeff).*
3 *Female gametophyte with archegonium and developing embryo (after Hofmeister).*

Figure 312 *Strobili of* Lycopodium selago. (*Photograph by Dr J. D. Dodds.*)

Figure 313 *Under surface of plant of* Selaginella krausiana *showing rhizophores.*

the species *S. krausiana* can usually be obtained quite easily, for it grows abundantly in greenhouses. The plants – the sporophyte generation – are small, creeping, and moss-like, with a slender, branched stem thickly covered with sessile leaves. The leaves occur as two rows of larger ventral leaves and two of small dorsal leaves. Some branches are leafless and when in contact with the soil these give rise to adventitious roots (fig. 313).

In transverse section, the stem of *S. krausiana* is traversed by two *steles*, each of which when fully formed consists of a central mass of xylem ensheathed by a single or double layer of parenchyma cells. Outside this is a single layer of sieve tubes, which in turn are surrounded by pericyclic and endodermal layers also one cell thick. Between the steles and the cortex there is a conspicuous air space bridged by *trabeculae*. These greatly elongated endodermal cells retain their characteristic Casparian strips (fig. 314).

The leaves at the tips of some of the stems are all of the same size and densely crowded together, thus making a compact cone. The leaves forming the cones are arranged in four longitudinal rows: each bears a sporangium on its upper surface;

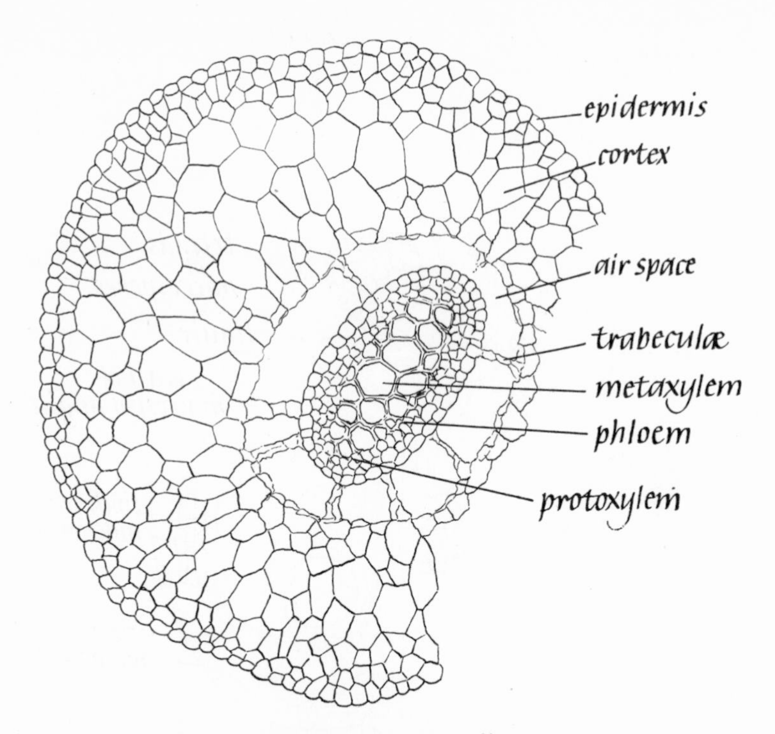

Figure 314 *T.s. of rhizophore of* Selaginella martensii.

Figure 315 *Fertile shoots of* Selaginella biformis. *The larger megasporangia can be seen in the lower parts of the strobili.*

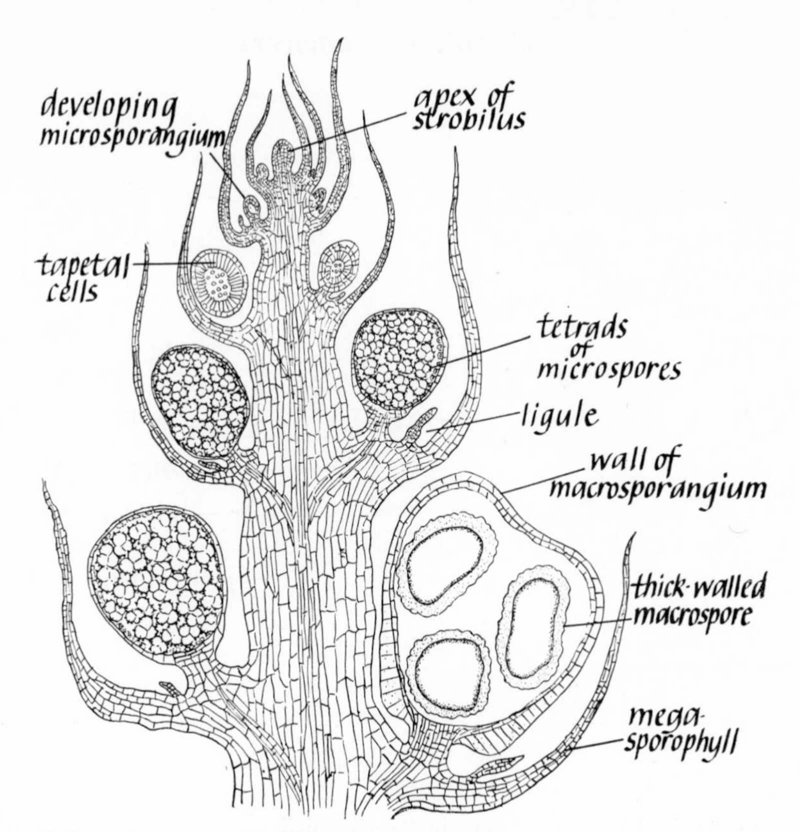

Figure 316 *L.s. of strobilus of* Selaginella krausiana.

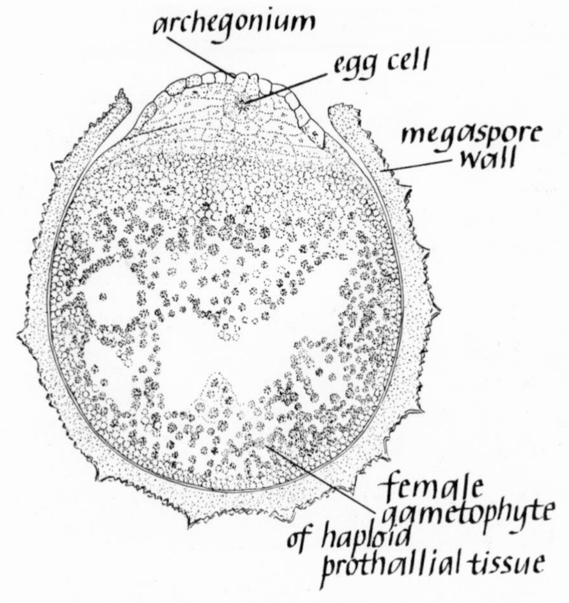

Figure 317 *L.s. megaspore of* Selaginella martensii.

they are, therefore, sporophylls. The lower sporophylls bear large sporangia, which when mature contain only four very large spores, *megaspores.* The sporangia on the sporophylls of the uppermost part of the cone, which are much smaller, contain a large number of *microspores* (fig. 315 and 316).

The megaspores, which contain a considerable store of food when mature, begin their development as gametophytes while still in the *megasporangium.* The original haploid megaspore nucleus divides repeatedly to form a mass of parenchymatous tissue; this becomes differentiated into a large-celled storage region within and a small-celled region against the triradiate ridge formed by the contact of the four megaspores of the tetrad. These are the tissues of the female gametophyte. Eventually the spore coat ruptures along the ridges and colourless lobes of the small-celled tissue protrude through the resulting cleft. After the megaspores have been shed from their sporangia, archegonia begin to develop in this protruding region. These female sex organs are similar to those of the ferns and horsetails though more deeply sunk into the tissues of the reduced prothallus, consequently only a few neck cells protrude (fig. 317).

The development of the microspores into male gametophytes begins before they are liberated from the *microsporangium.* The first division of each microspore results in the formation of a small prothallial cell and a larger antheridial initial. The small cell represents the extremely reduced male prothallus. The antheridial initial becomes subdivided in several planes to form jacket cells, which represent the wall of a single antheridium enclosing a group of sperm mother cells. During these developments the microspores are shed from the microsporangium and, after further division, the spore mother cells give rise to 128 or 256 haploid biflagellate antherozoids (fig. 318). These are liberated on the disintegration of the antheridial wall and the rupture of the old spore wall. These antherozoids require the presence of free water to swim successfully and thus reach the archegonial neck, the cells of which spread apart when ready to receive the male gametes. In some species, however, fertilization may occur when the female prothallus is still within the megasporangium, but in the majority fertilization is effected after the prothallus has fallen to the ground, though still partially enclosed within the megaspore wall.

Fertilization brings about the establishment of a new diploid generation, and the resulting embryo develops within the venter of the archegonium and is dependent on the food materials stored in the female prothallus.

The first division of the zygote is transverse, the inner cell of the division giving rise by a series of many further divisions to the embryo proper, while the upper or outer cell forms the *suspensor.* The enlargement of the cells of the suspensor cause the developing embryo to be pushed further and further down into the food-rich cells in the centre of the prothallus. The embryo itself becomes differentiated at an early stage into a root and shoot apex. Between the root and apex the foot becomes apparent on the opposite side of the embryo from the suspensor. The foot (fig. 319) remains in close contact with and draws food from the cells of the prothallus until the young sporophyte has developed leaves and becomes an independent plant (fig. 319).

Selaginella exhibits a truly heterosporous condition which results in the production of distinct, though very reduced, male and female prothalli. Thus the male prothallus consists of but one cell associated with the antheridium, and the female prothallus is largely a colourless mass of cells containing a store of food material laid down entirely by the leafy sporophyte of the previous generation. Moreover, it is this food which supports the development of the initial stages of the subsequent sporophyte generation. Some species of *Selaginella* produce only one megaspore, which is not shed from the megasporangium – a protection similar to that which seed bearing plants afford to the developing embryo.

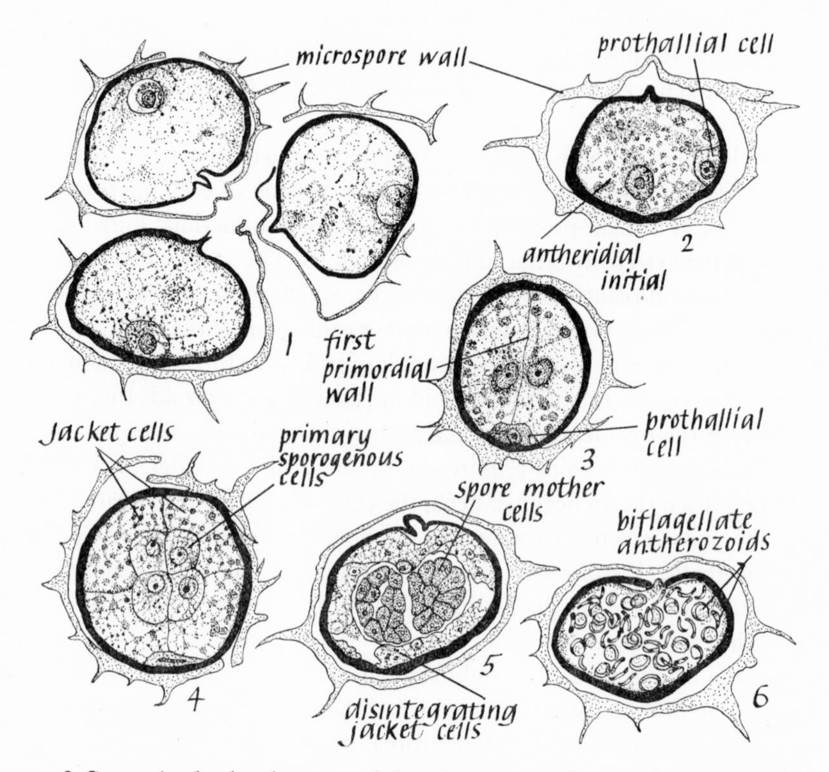

Figure 318 *Stages in the development of the microgametophyte and antherozoid formation in* Selaginella krausiana (*after Slagg*).

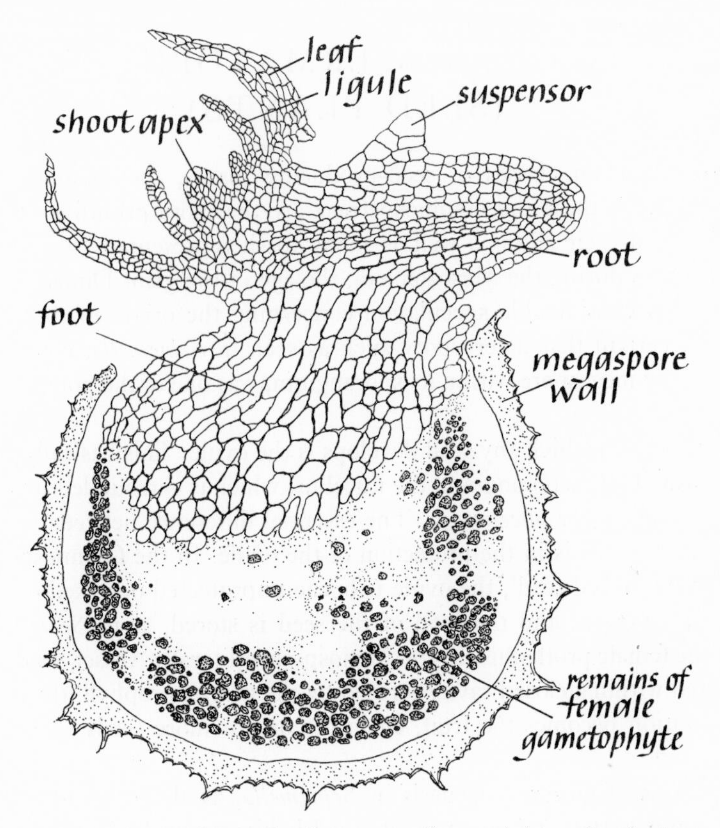

Figure 319 *L.s. megaspore of* Selaginella martensii *containing a developing sporophyte embryo.*

CHAPTER 36

DIVISION SPERMATOPHYTA (SEED PLANTS)

There are two main classes of seed-producing plants, the Gymnospermae and Angiospermae. Of these the Gymnospermae are the more primitive. They include the conifers and their allies as well as many fossil representatives which were the dominant plants during the Mesozoic era, the age of the giant Dinosaurs. Although there has been considerable speculation concerning the origin of the *seed habit*, it seems fairly certain that heterospory such as seen in *Selaginella*, coupled with the retention of the megaspore within its sporangium, was one of the potent factors in its evolution.

The organ from which any seed develops is the ovule. This basically consists of a centrally located megasporangium, the nucellus, which is surrounded by one or more protective envelopes or *integuments*. The essential difference between the two major groups of seed plants is in the protection of the ovule. In the Gymnosperms, which means literally 'naked seed', the ovule is borne unprotected or naked on the surface of the *megasporophyll*, and the food of the seed is stored, as in *Selaginella*, in the tissues of the female prothallus. In the Angiosperms (literally 'vessel, seed') the ovules are protected within a closed cavity formed by the megasporophyll, the ovary, which after fertilization becomes the fruit, enclosing one or more seeds (see Chapters 23 and 24).

The process of megasporogenesis in *Selaginella*, as already noted, is a possible approach towards the attainment of the seed habit, especially in those cases where the development of the female gametophyte and embryo may occur within the sporangial cavity. However, the megasporangium of *Selaginella* lacks an integument, and in this respect, and in the absence of any vascular system, it differs markedly from even the simplest of Gymnosperm ovule. Furthermore, growth of the female gametophyte and embryo in *Selaginella* is entirely at the expense of food previously stored in the megaspore itself, whereas the gametophyte and embryo of a seed depend for their nutrition on the food material supplied to them by the closely adjacent tissues of the ovule.

CLASS GYMNOSPERMAE

Sub-Class Cycadophytae

The most primitive of the living seed plants are the cycads. These are stout-stemmed plants which may attain heights of fifty to sixty feet, with a crown of large fern-like or palm-like leaves. All the species, of which about sixty have been described

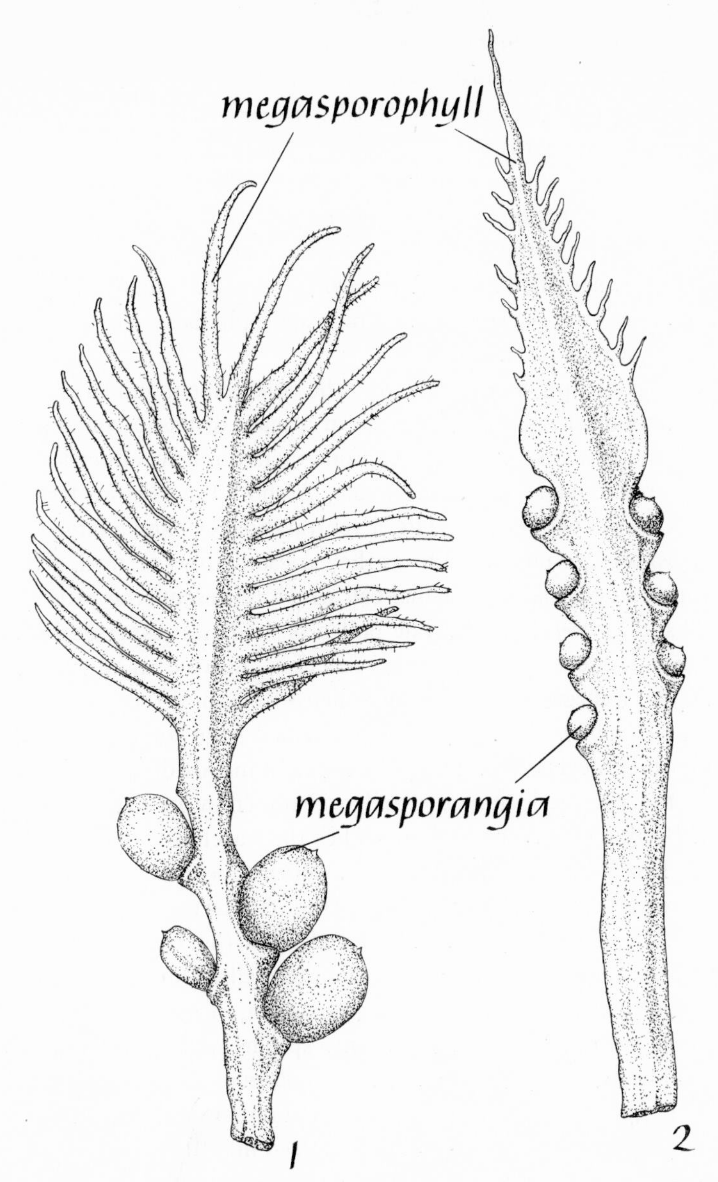

Figure 320 *Megasporophylls with megasporangia of*
1 Cycas revoluta *and*
2 C. circinalis.

from tropical and subtropical zones, are dioecious, the sporangia-bearing leaves (micro- and megasporophylls) being produced on separate plants. In the genus *Cycas*, the megasporophylls are pinnate, almost leaf-like structures with several large conspicuous megasporangia borne along their margins (fig. 320). Each megaspore is enclosed in a cup-like upgrowth, which may be compared with the integument of an ovule. This opens to the exterior by way of a micropyle. In other genera, such as *Zamia* and *Dioon*, the megasporophylls are highly reduced structures, not at all leaf-like, aggregated into a compact cone (fig. 321). The *microsporophylls* in all genera occur in cones, the so-called *staminate strobili*, which are somewhat smaller than the female cones. The lower surfaces of the microsporophylls are covered with crowded microsporangia (see fig. 322).

The female gametophyte, derived from the enlargement and subsequent division of a single functional megaspore, consists of a mass of tissue contained within the nucellus and integuments of the ovule. Four or five much reduced archegonia are formed at the micropylar end of the ovule. A short time before fertilization each archegonium consists of two neck cells, a ventral canal cell and a large egg (fig. 323).

The microspores, or pollen grains as they are sometimes termed, give rise by two divisions from a single male prothallial cell which represents the male gemetophyte, to a *tube cell* and a *generative cell*. The pollen is shed and dispersed by wind at this 3-celled stage in its development, and on reaching an ovule on an *ovulate cone*, or in the case of *Cycas* a megasporophyll, the pollen will land, if the ovule is mature, in a mucilaginous *pollination drop*. This drop is formed from some of the upper cells of the nucellus which degenerate. The pollen is held in this drop until it is eventually drawn down the micropyle into the pollen chamber by its drying and subsequent contraction. By this means the pollen reaches the nucellus at the base of the pollen chamber, and here it germinates and forms a pollen tube, which grows down through the nucellus towards the archegonium. During its passage the generative cell, now in the pollen tube, divides into *stalk* and *body* cells (fig. 322). The body cell some two months later divides into two sperm mother cells. During this time the pollen tube has caused the degeneration, by enzyme action, of much of the nucellar tissue. The contents of each mother cell mature into sperms which, with the breakdown of the mother cell walls, are liberated into the cytoplasm of the pollen tube. The sperms are relatively large ovoid bodies bearing a large number of cilia arranged in the form of a spiral band. Eventually the sperms are released into the archegonial chamber and swim the short remaining distance to fertilize the egg within the base of the archegonium (fig. 323).

Figure 322 1 *View of undersurface of microsporophyll from male cone of a* Dioon *sp.*
2 *A group of microsporangia (pollen sacs) of a* Dioon *sp.*
3 *A pollen grain of* Dioon *sp.*
4 *Germination of a pollen grain of* Dioon *sp.*
5 *Pollen tubes with male gametes of* Dioon *sp.* (*All after Chamberlain.*)

Figure 321 *Female cone of the cycad* Dioon spinulosum.

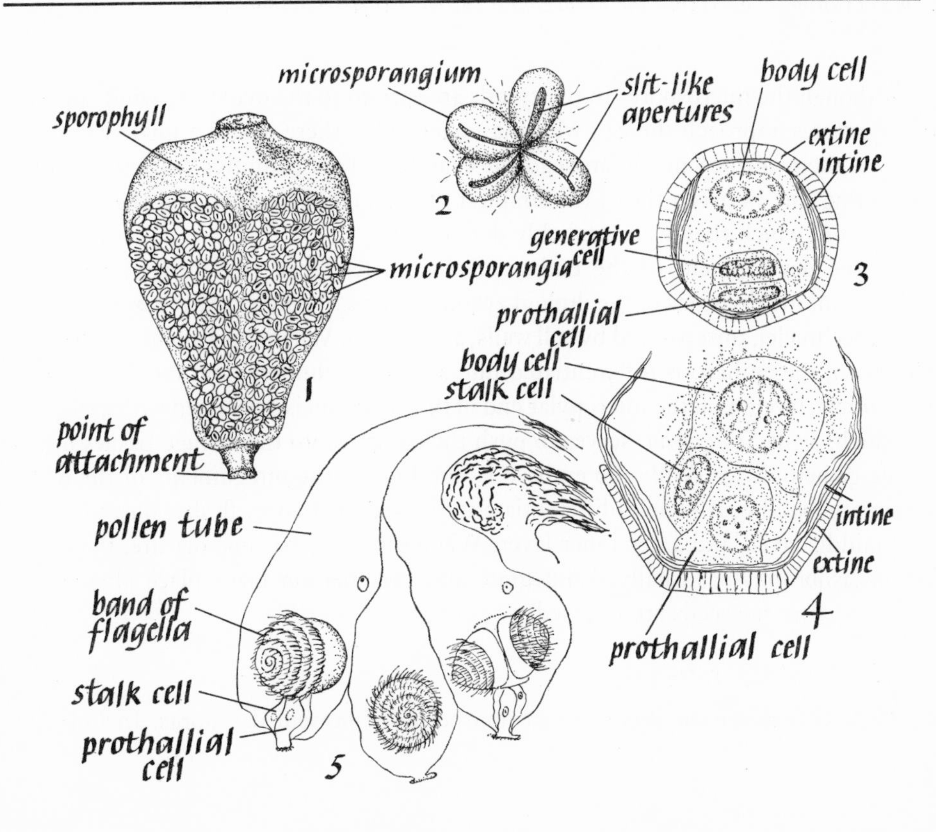

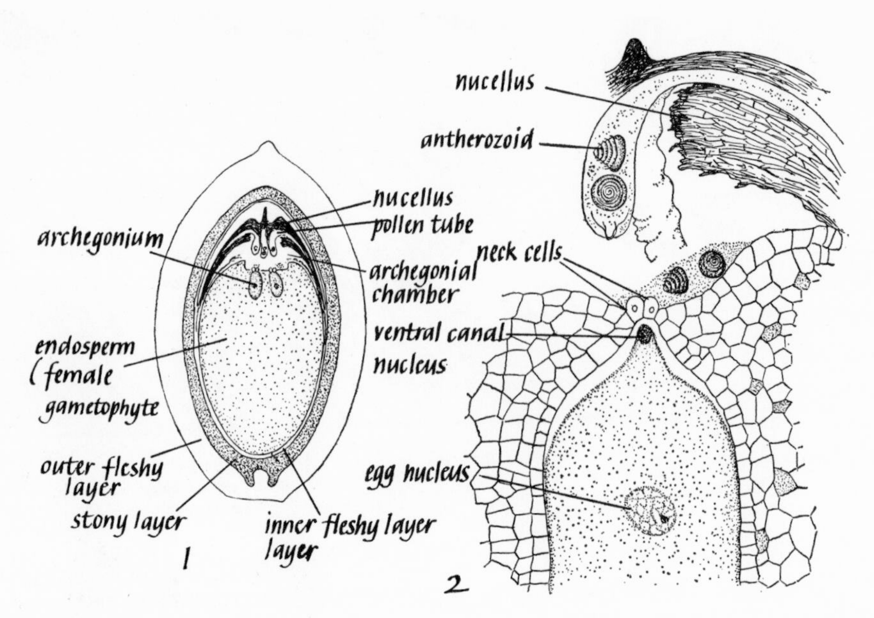

Figure 323 1 *L.s. ovule of* Dioon *showing pollen tubes within the archegonial chamber.* 2 *Detail of part of the L.s. of an ovule of* Dioon *showing the liberation of the male gametes* (*antherozoids*) *into the archegonial chamber* (*after Chamberlain*).

Although the microspores in the cycads are carried to the ovules by wind, and the male gametes approach the egg within a pollen tube, there is still a final swimming stage in their journey in the archegonial chamber. This primitive feature affords a connecting link between these, the simplest of the Gymnosperms, and the fern-like plants from which they were probably derived.

In the development of the embryo from the fertilized egg there arises, by a series of mitotic divisions of the diploid zygote nucleus, the *free nuclear* stage in which up to 1000 nuclei, unseparated by cell walls, are formed. When the walls are eventually laid down, the embryo is differentiated into a radicle, plumule, and two cotyledons. The radicle develops at the micropylar end of the ovule and is associated with a suspensor which, as in *Selaginella*, serves to push the embryo into the storage tissues of the female gametophyte. While the embryo is developing, the integuments of the ovule become the seed coat. These differentiate into a red or orange, fleshy, outer layer, a hard middle layer, and a dry inner layer. When the seeds become mature, the cones (or megasporophylls) usually disintegrate and germination takes place almost immediately after the seeds are released.

Sub-class Coniferophytae

The Conifers are the dominant gymnosperms of present day floras. Included in this sub-class are the pines, spruces, firs, cedars, cypresses, and yews; closely related forms were, however, common during Carboniferous and Perminan eras, as the fossil record shows. Most of the living representatives of the Conifers or softwoods (see p. 126) dominate forests in a wide belt encircling the world in the northern part of the North Temperate Region, between the treeless zone of the Arctic and the broad-leaved, deciduous forests of more southerly latitudes. Conifers also form extensive belts or altitudinal zones in mountainous regions in the tropics far to the south of the so-called conifer belt. In contrast to the cycads, the conifers, whose foliage leaves are simple and commonly scale-like or needle-shaped in form, may attain a very great age and grow to heights of over 300 feet.

The Scots Pine, *Pinus sylvestris*, affords a common example of a conifer, though it must be remembered that the construction and arrangement of its vegetative parts may not be taken as typical for all members of the group. The characteristically needle-shaped leaves of these often massive trees are borne in pairs on very short *branches of limited growth*, termed *dwarf shoots*, which arise in the axils of *scale leaves* surrounding them. These shoots are sometimes termed *bifoliar spurs* since each bears only two leaves. They are shed only at the end of two or three seasons after their formation; thus *Pinus* is an evergreen. The main branches of the tree, *branches of unlimited growth*, bear only spirally arranged scale leaves. These normal branches possess a terminal bud with a whorl of lateral buds immediately below it. Increase in the length of any branch results from the renewed annual activity of the terminal bud, while the adjacent lateral buds give rise to a whorl of new branches, also of unlimited growth (fig. 324).

The characteristic feature of conifers, as the name implies, is the organization of their sporophylls into cones or strobili. Cones are of two kinds, microsporangiate or *staminate cones* and megasporangiate or *ovulate cones*. Male and female cones are usually produced on the same plant. In *Pinus*, staminate cones arise in large numbers in the axils of scale leaves near the base of new shoots (fig. 327). Each cone is a small structure consisting of a central axis bearing a number of overlapping scales, the microsporophylls. Under each scale at the base are two microsporangia or pollen sacs. The microspore mother cells arising from the central tissue of each sporangium gives rise by meiosis to a tetrad of microspores (fig. 325).

Each microspore before it is shed consists of a single cell with a prominent nucleus and two air filled bladders or wings which assist in the spore's dispersal (fig. 326). Before dispersal, which occurs with the dehiscence of the pollen sac, the microspore nucleus divides once to produce the first cell of the male prothallus. This cell becomes pressed and almost flattened against the microspore wall. The remaining nucleus divides again to produce the second cell of the male prothallus and the much more conspicuous antheridial cell. The two prothallial cells, which together may be regarded as homologous with the male gametophyte of more primitive plants, very soon disintegrate. Just before the pollen is liberated, the antheridial cell divides unequally to give a small *generative cell* and a *tube cell*. These two cells can be seen in the mature pollen

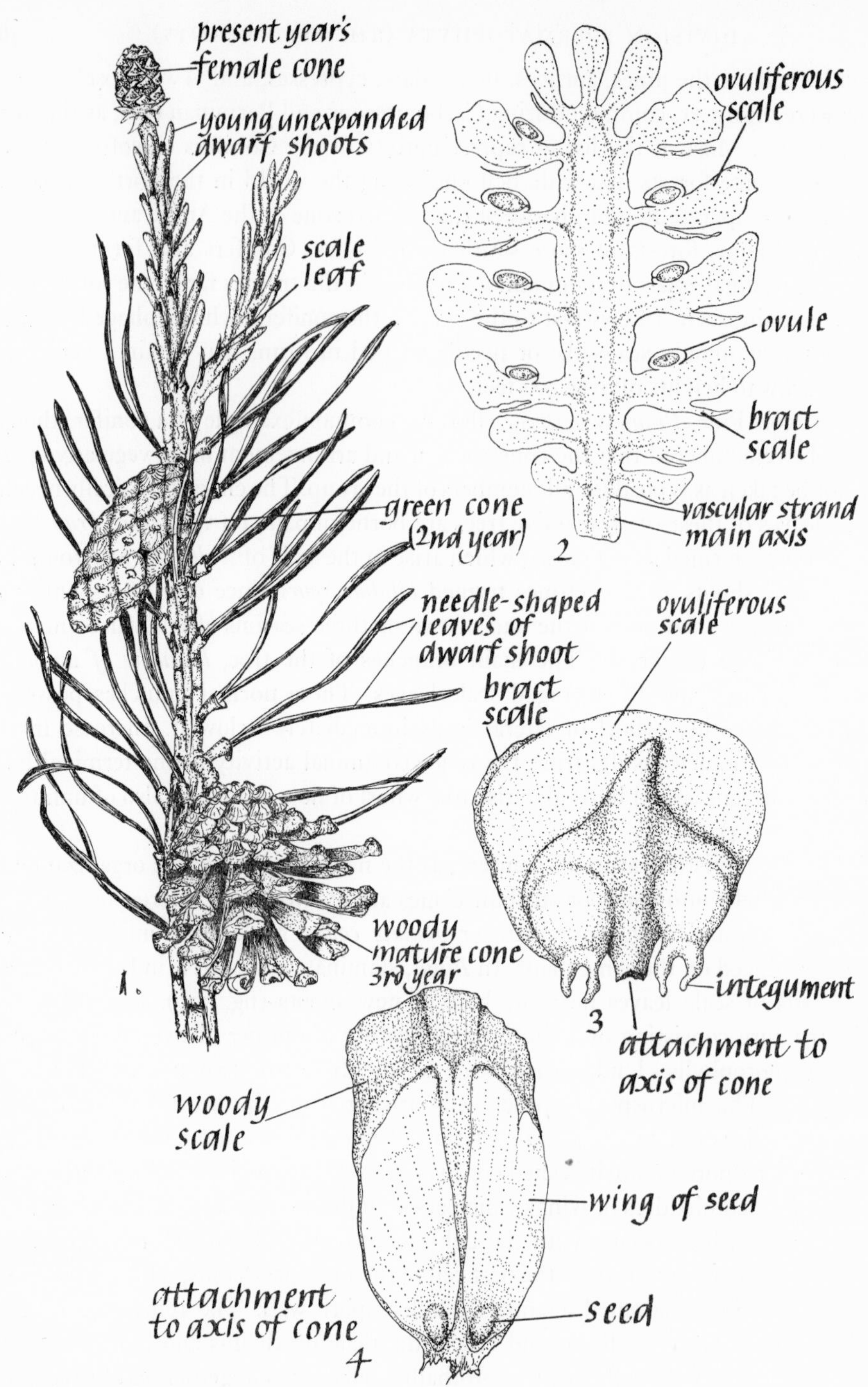

Figure 324 Pinus sylvestris

1 *Shoot with ovulate cones of different ages.*
2 *L.s. of ovulate cone.*
3 *Scale from young ovulate cone.*
4 *Woody scale with winged seeds.*

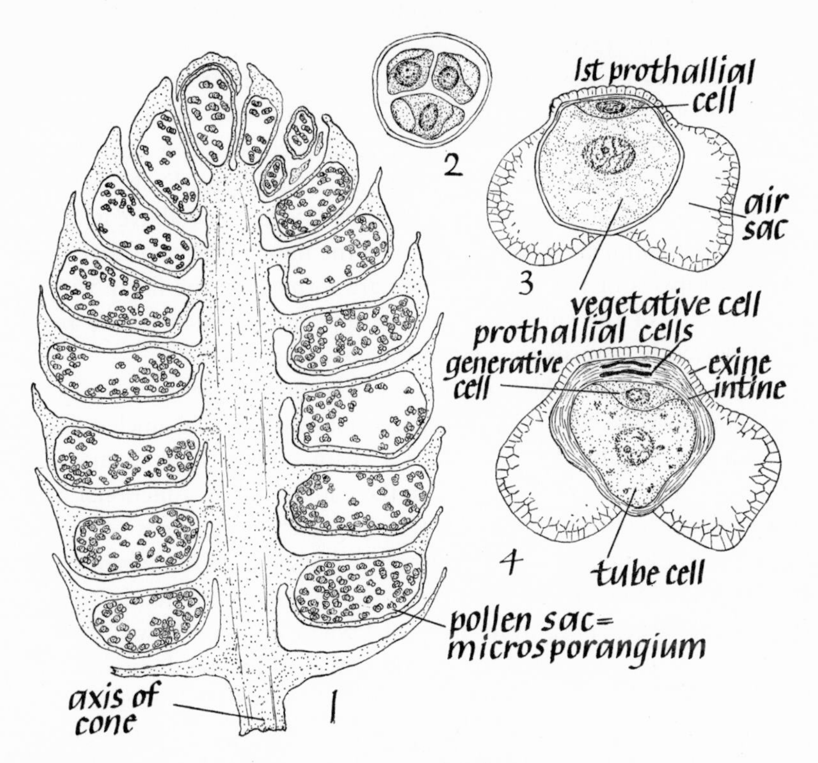

Figure 325 *Male cone and pollen development in* Pinus

1 *L.s. of male cone of* Pinus sylvestris.

2 *Tetrad of pollen grains of* P. laricio.

3-4 *Stages in the formation of prothallial, generative and tube cells in* P. laricio.
(2-4 *after Chamberlain.*)

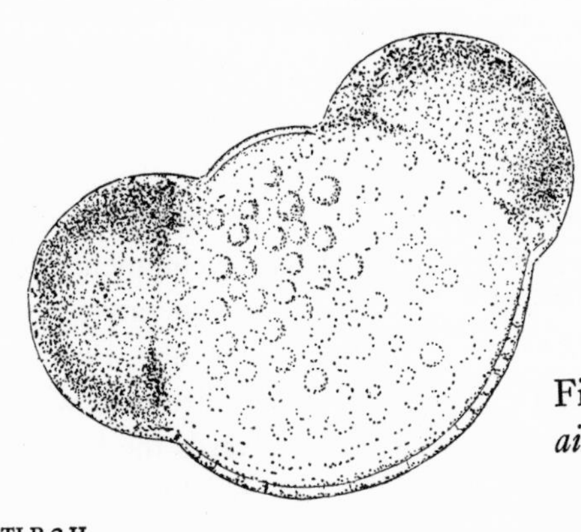

Figure 326 *Pollen grain of* Pinus *showing air bladders.*

grain quite clearly, after treatment with concentrated hydrochloric acid and staining with acetic orcein (fig. 325).

The female cones are less numerous than the males and are produced towards the ends of new shoots, in positions corresponding to those of buds on branches of unlimited growth. These ovulate cones of *Pinus* also consist of a central axis and a double set of closely overlapping scales, the megasporophylls. Each megasporophyll consists of a small *lower bract scale* and a larger *ovuliferous scale* above it. Two ovules, each a megasporangium, are borne exposed on the upper surface of each ovuliferous scale. The micropyles of the ovules, which are formed by the fairly widely flared, cup-shaped mouth of the single integument surrounding each ovule, are directed obliquely downwards towards the axis of the cone (fig. 324).

The megasporangium, which in the ovule is termed the nucellus, contains a large single uninucleate cell, the megaspore mother cell. The nucleus of this cell eventually divides meiotically to produce a chain of four haploid megaspores, of which only the inner one persists to act as the embryo sac or functional megaspore. The embryo sac, which represents the female gametophyte, rests for a while in a central position in the nucellus and then there follows a series of divisions, producing about 2000 nuclei. After some time these nuclei become separated by walls and the whole becomes a large, solid, ovate mass of tissue extending down to the basal or *chalazal* end of the ovule, while the nucellus comes to form a dome over the upper micropylar end. Archegonia, usually between two and five in number, develop at the micropylar end of the female gametophyte. Each consists of a very short neck, a ventral canal cell and a large egg.

The ovule does not reach this stage in its development until the second summer of its life, though its pollination will have occurred the previous summer. When pollination occurs the young female cone stands erect at the end of its branch. When the pollen grains are mature they are shed in vast quantities as clouds of yellow dust, and penetrating between the scales of the cone they reach the ovule at the base of the megasporophylls. Here the pollen is drawn into the micropyle of the ovule by the drying up of a resinous material exuded from within. This brings the pollen into contact with the tissues of the nucellus and after some time the grains put out a pollen tube, penetrating the nucellus. Early in its growth the tube nucleus of the pollen grain migrates into the tip of the pollen tube. The ovule, however, is still not ready to be fertilized and the pollen tube remains in the tissues of the nucellus during the remainder of that summer and over the following winter and spring.

It is usually not until the end of June in the year after pollination that the ovule with its archegonia is fully mature. During the final stages of its development the pollen grain in the nucellus also completes its development. The generative cell divides to form a stalk cell and body cell which passes into the pollen tube. Finally the body cell divides to produce two non-motile male gametes. The pollen tube with these gametes then continues to grow through the nucellar dome towards the female gametophyte with its archegonia. Eventually the tip of a pollen tube reaches the neck

Figure 327 *Ripe male cones of* Pinus sylvestris. *There is one three-year-old ovulate cone on the right of the picture.*

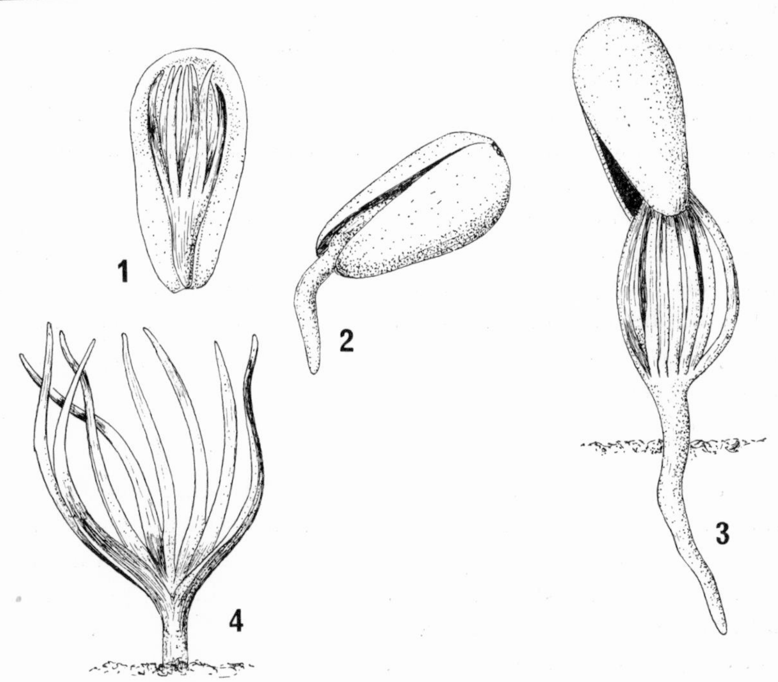

Figure 328 1 *Seed of* Pinus *opened to show embryo embedded in endosperm.* 2-4 *Stages in the germination of the seed.*

of one of the archegonia, forces itself between the neck cells and then ruptures, discharging the two male gametes into the cytoplasm of the egg. Fertilization is accomplished by the fusion of one of the sperm nuclei with the egg nucleus. This fusion takes place slowly, so that the fertilized egg shows distinct groups of maternal and paternal chromosomes for some time. In all there is about eleven months between pollination and fertilization.

The development of the embryo of the new sporophyte generation begins soon after fertilization by the division of the zygote nucleus. The two nuclei which result then divide to form four nuclei, which migrate to the base of the egg cell where they divide once more. Wall formation accompanies these divisions, and by still further divisions gives rise to a 16-celled *proembryo* of four tiers of cells. The lowest of these four celled tiers eventually gives rise to the embryo itself while the tier adjacent to it forms the suspensor. This elongates, as in *Cycas*, and pushes the growing embryo into the tissues of the old gametophyte, which is rich in stored food.

The fully developed embryo of *Pinus* consists of a whorl of up to fifty cotyledons. These surround the shoot apex or plumule. There is a short hypocotyl and a primary root or radicle facing the micropyle. The embryo is embedded in endosperm derived from the tissues of the female gametophyte which itself becomes surrounded by a seed coat. This consists of a hard outer layer derived from the stony layer of the integument, while the inner fleshy layer of the integument degenerates so that when the seed is ripe it is reduced to a thin papery membrane.

During the second winter of the ovulate cone's life, it changes colour from a deep green to brown. By the third spring it has become quite dry, and the original sporophylls become scaly and separate widely from one another. In this condition the seeds, which each possess a wing-like outgrowth developed from the integument, are shaken out of the cone and so dispersed (fig. 324).

Following a period of dormancy the seeds germinate. The radicle emerges first; then the hypocotyl elongates, and carries the cotyledons, which are for a time still embedded in the endosperm, up above the soil. Gradually, however, the cotyledons separate and the plumule between them elongates to produce a shoot bearing single, needle-like primary foliage leaves. Thus a new sporophyte generation becomes established (fig. 328).

CLASS ANGIOSPERMAE

Because the angiosperms have their ovules enclosed within a hollow ovary, they are considered to be more advanced than the naked-seeded gymnosperms. The angiosperms are the dominant group of the vascular plants of present day floras and exist in a wide range of habitats from desert to aquatic conditions, while a few species even grow in the sea. As crop plants and sources of a wide variety of raw materials they are of the greatest economic importance to man.

Unfortunately the fossil record has provided few clues of real value about the origins or possible evolutionary developments of this most important and diverse group of plants. Even during the Cretaceous period, when the gymnosperms flourished, there is evidence that the angiosperms had reached an advanced stage of morphological development, and one of the great palaeobotanical puzzles is the sudden appearance of such a highly specialized group. It has been suggested that their history probably extends back into the Jurassic and Triassic periods, or even as far back as the late Palaeozoic era of some 200 million years ago. The reason for the lack of adequate fossils of these early angiosperms is that they probably developed initially in upland areas where conditions would be unsuitable for their preservation as fossils. Because of this gap in the fossil records the theories relating to the probable origins of the flowering plants are largely speculative. Of these speculations one of the most acceptable is that they were derived from seed-producing, fern-like plants, the *pteridosperms*, which flourished during the Palaeozoic era in the Lower Carboniferous.

Some idea of the great variety of form and structure of the vegetative and reproductive parts of the Angiosperms will have already been gained from earlier chapters. The angiosperm plant itself, as with all vascular plants, represents the diploid sporophyte generation, while the gametophyte structure attains a greater degree of reduction than in any of the less advanced groups of plants. This is, in fact, one of the definitive characteristics of the Class Angiospermae.

Even the concept of the flower, the most characteristic organ of all angiosperms, and its relationship to the spore-bearing organs in other groups of vascular plants, is a question about which botanists have expressed widely divergent views. Thus, some consider the flower as a shoot beset with sporophylls, that is to say, leaves bearing sporangia. Those who hold this view include as flowers the strobili of *Selaginella* and the cones of *Cycas* and *Pinus*. Others limit the term to a particular type of determinate sporogenous shoot with carpels as its most characteristic organs. Although carpels – whose evolutionary history, like that of stamens, petals and sepals, is unknown – resemble megasporophylls in function, they must be regarded as morphologically distinct, because the ovules or megasporangia are nearly always enclosed within the hollow basal ovary. Moreover, another distinctive feature is that each carpel terminates in a stigma, a specialized pollen-receiving structure. In this view the flower is a completely distinctive angiospermous structure occurring in no other class of the Plant Kingdom (Chapter 23).

Comparing the reproductive features of the gymnosperms and angiosperms, the microspores or pollen grains of the former are wind-dispersed and deposited directly on to the micropyle of the ovule, but in the angiosperms the pollen is deposited on a special receptive surface, the stigma, to which it is carried either by wind or by insects. Whereas in gymnosperms the male gametophyte consists of two prothallial cells, in the angiosperms there is no indication of any prothallus and the generative cell gives rise only to two non-flagellated male gametes.

The stages in the formation of the female gametophyte of angiosperms are similar to those of the gymnosperms. There is a meiotic division of the megaspore mother cell in the ovule, producing a row of four haploid megaspores. Only the lower or innermost of these develops further, and, by means of three successive divisions, produces the characteristic 8-nucleate embryo sac. This has a fairly uniform organization throughout the Class (see p. 284). When mature the embryo sac consists, in the majority of cases, of a single egg accompanied by two synergids (the egg apparatus), a group of three antipodal cells at the chalazal end and two polar nuclei in the central region. It is difficult to imagine how such a remarkable arrangement of cells could have been derived from any of the female gametophytes known to occur in gymnosperms. There is very little to support the suggestion that the egg apparatus is a reduced archegonium.

Another distinctive feature of the sexual reproduction of angiosperms is that both the male gametes enter the embryo sac in the pollen tube and both are involved in the process of fertilization. One of these gametes unites with the egg to form the zygote from which the diploid embryo of the seed develops. The other fuses with the two polar nuclei to form the triploid endosperm nucleus. Thus the endospermic food reserve tissue of the angiosperms is quite different in origin from that of gymnosperms, where it is the haploid, female gametophyte itself. However, the early stages of its development, without wall formation, are reminiscent of the early stages in the establishment of the prothallial tissues in the ovule of gymnosperms.

Pollination and fertilization in the angiosperms lead to the development of another highly characteristic structure, the fruit, which contains one or more seeds (see Chapter 24). Each seed contains an embryo sporophyte, which is not dependent, as are the lower vascular plants, on the gametophyte until it establishes itself. The nutrition of the angiosperm embryo is entirely dependent on the parent sporophyte of the previous generation as explained on page 1 of this book.

GLOSSARY

Numbers after definitions refer to the main entries in the book

abscission – the organized shedding of a part of a plant by means of an abscission layer. 142

abscission zone – a layer of parenchymatous cells which develops across the base of a petiole or of a branch, or is embedded in bark, through which the leaf or branch, or a scale of bark, separates off. 142

accessory floral parts – organs such as petals and sepals not directly involved with actual reproductive processes. 259

achene – a dry, indehiscent, one-seeded fruit, formed from a single carpel, and with the seed distinct from the fruit wall. 300

acid – a substance which dissolves in water with the formation of hydrogen ions. 150

acquired character – a character altered by the environment during the development of an organism, thus not usually inherited. 324

acropetal succession – the development of lateral members in such order that the youngest is nearest the tip of the axis. 257

actinomorphic – star-shaped; therefore radially symmetrical, and divisible into two similar parts by more than one plane passing through the centre. Also known as radially symmetrical. 261

active absorption – the absorption of water by roots, resulting from osmotic phenomena and depending on the expenditure of energy derived from metabolism. 161

adaptation to environment – any morphological or physiological characteristic which may be supposed to help in adjusting the organism to the conditions under which it lives. 324

adenosine diphosphate (ADP) – an organic metaphosphate intimately concerned with the transfer of energy in respiration. When the phosphate chain of this compound is lengthened by another phosphate unit it acquires energy and becomes ATP. 224

adenosine triphosphate (ATP) – (see ADP above). One of the phosphates of ATP is transferable to other substances by enzyme action, and takes with it a considerable amount of energy. This transfer seems to be the principal mechanism by which cells make energy available for all vital activities within the plant, e.g. all syntheses, osmotic work, etc. 224

adsorption – the taking up of one substance at the surface of another. 152, 163

adventitious root – a root which develops from some part of a plant other than a pre-existing root. 16

aecidial cup – see aecidium. 409

aecidiospore – a spore of a rust fungus formed in an aecidium. 409

aecidium – a spore-producing structure characteristic of many rust fungi. It consists of a cup-shaped peridium of sterile hyphae, containing closely-packed chains of aecidiospores. 408

aerobic respiration – a form of respiration in which elementary oxygen is used for the oxidation of organic compounds with the formation of water and carbon dioxide, and the liberation of energy. 222

aggregate cup fruit – a fruit derived from perigynous flowers. 298

aggregate free fruit – a fruit derived from the superior ovaries of hypogynous flowers. 298

aggregate fruit – the fruit formed by a flower with several free carpels. 297

akinete – a specialized resting spore in algae, derived from an entire vegetative cell. 362

albuminous – pertaining to seeds containing no free endosperm. 3

alcohol dehydrogenase – an enzyme which catalyses oxidation by the removal of hydrogen. 226

aldehyde – a group of organic compounds containing the CO- radical attached to both a hydrogen atom and a hydrocarbon radical. 190

aleurone grains – reserve protein material occurring in granules in the aleurone layer, a special layer of cells just below the surface of the grains of various cereals, and in the seeds of other plants. 199

algae – a large and diverse assemblage of simple photosynthetic plants including seaweeds, pond scums and phytoplankton. Simplest forms unicellular; larger seaweeds complex multicellular plants with internal differentiation of tissues. All possess unicellular organs of reproduction. 351

alkaloids – natural organic bases found in plants; characterized by their specific physiological action. 312

allelic pair – genes situated at comparable positions in the two members of a pair of homologous chromosomes. 309

allelomorph – in Mendelian inheritance, one of a pair of contrasted characters, inherited alternatively with its partner, and assumed to depend on genes situated in homologous chromosomes. 305

allopolyploid – a polyploid possessing unlike sets of chromosomes, one complement coming from one species, the other from another. 313

alternation of generations – the alternation of a sexually reproducing haploid gametophyte generation with an asexual, spore producing, diploid sporophyte generation. The two generations often differ fundamentally in their morphology. 243

amino acids – a group of fatty acids in which a hydrogen atom of the hydrocarbon radical is exchanged for an amino (NH_2) group. Fundamental constituents of living matter because their molecules combine in the formation of proteins. 197

anabolism – the chemical syntheses proceeding in living organisms with the formation of complex substances from simpler ones, together with the storage of chemical energy. 28

anaerobic respiration – a form of respiration in which the organism obtains its energy by reactions in which elementary oxygen is not directly involved, and carbon dioxide, together with such products as ethyl alcohol, is formed. 225

anaphase – the stage in mitotic or meiotic nuclear division when the chromosomes or half-chromosomes move away from the equatorial plate towards the poles of the spindle. 35, 252

anastomosis – communication by cross-connexions to form a network. 396

anatropous – said of an ovule in which the body is curved so that the micropyle lies close to the insertion of the funicle. 283

androecium – the whole of the stamens in one flower. 257

angle of divergence – the angle between successive leaves as arrayed on the axis of a shoot (see phyllotaxis). 84

anion – in an electrolyte the ion which carries the negative charge and which migrates towards the anode under the influence of an applied potential difference. 150

anisogamy – the fusion of gametes differing chiefly in size. 363

annual – a plant which, in the same season that it develops from a seed, flowers, fruits and dies. 2, 21, 55

annual ring – a ring representing the annual increment of secondary wood in the roots and stems of woody perennial plants of temperate climates. 134

annular thickening – the internal rings of thickening on walls of protoxylem vessels which occur at intervals along their length adding strength but allowing longitudinal extension. 111

annular vessel – a vessel of the protoxylem, bearing rings of thickening material on its walls. 100

annulus – a zone of cells beneath the operculum of the sporangium of a moss, which break down and assist in the liberation of the operculum. 411, 433, 444

antagonism – the mutual interaction between two salts and their respective ions. 180

anther – the fertile part of a stamen, usually containing four sporangia, or pollen sacs, and producing pollen. 271

antheridia (plural of antheridium) – the gametangia which produce the male gametes in lower plants. 366, 388, 423

antheridial chamber – a chamber produced by the upward growth of gametophyte tissue around the developing antheridium. 423

antheridial cup – cups borne at the tips of leafy shoots of mosses, in which antheridia are produced. 432
antheridiophores – a special branch in liverworts, bearing one or more antheridia. 427
antherozoid – a motile male gamete, spermatozoid, or sperm. 366, 425
anthocyanin pigments – the water-soluble colouring matters of many plants and flowers, of glucoside structure. 181
anticlinally – divisions occurring perpendicular to the surface of a growing point. 104
antipodal cell – the three nuclei at the funicular end of an embryo sac which usually become enclosed by cell walls. 284
apetalous – devoid of petals. 261
apical cell – a cell at the end of a filament, or of a multicellular organ, capable of repeated division, and yielding a progeny of cells from which the tissues of the organ are ultimately derived. 380
apical meristem – a group of meristematic cells at the tip of a stem or root; from it, all the tissues of the mature axis are ultimately formed. 32
aplanospore – a non-motile spore. 362
apocarpous – consisting of two or more carpels, all distinct from one another. 278, 279, 298
apogamy – in ferns, when a diploid gametophyte cell gives rise directly to a sporophyte. 374
apophysis – the swollen distal end of the seta beneath a moss sporangium. 433
apothecia – plural of apothecium – an open cup-shaped fructification, or a club-shaped derivative from it, producing ascospores. 419
appressorium – a flattened outgrowth which attaches a parasite to its host. 408
archegoniophores – a specialized branch of the thallus of liverworts bearing archegonia. 427
archegonium – female sex organ of bryophytes, pteridophytes, and some gymnosperms; a sessile or stalked flask-shaped structure containing one egg and opening by a neck. 420
aril – an outgrowth on a seed, formed from the stalk or from near the micropyle; it may be spongy or fleshy, or may be a tuft of hairs. 295
artificial system – a classification based on one or a few arbitrarily chosen characters, and giving no attention to the natural relationships of the organism. 339
asci (plural of ascus) – enlarged cells of Ascomycetes, in which four or more (usually eight) spores are formed. 402
ascocarp – the fructification of an Ascomycete, containing asci and ascospores. 399
ascogonium – the female branch in the Ascomycetes, or a derivative from it. 399, 406
ascogonous hyphae – hyphae from which one or more asci are formed. 400
ascospore – a spore formed within the ascus. 396
ascus – see asci. 386, 396
asexual reproduction – any form of reproduction not depending on a sexual process, or on a modified sexual process. 242
aspergillosis – a contagious infection of the respiratory organs of birds due to moulds of the genus Aspergillus. 398
autecology – the study of the ecology of any individual species. 229
autoecious – a term applied to parasitic fungi which complete the whole of their development on one species of the host plant. 409
autonomic movement – movement resulting from internal stimuli, e.g. circumnutation. 81
autopolyploid – a polyploid having similar sets of chromosomes in its total chromosome complement. 312
autospore – a daughter cell formed within an algal cell and having all the characters of the parent in miniature before it is set free. 359
autotetraploid – a tetraploid with four similar sets of chromosomes in its nuclei. 312
autotrophic – able to build up food materials from simple substances. 343, 385
auxanometer – an instrument used to measure the rate of elongation of a plant member. 374
auxin – a general name for a class of hormone-like substances formed in actively-growing parts of plants, and having the power of affecting the subsequent growth and development of the plant. 44, 374

auxospore – a resting spore formed by diatoms after a sexual fusion. 374
axil – the solid angle between a stem and the upper surface of a leaf base growing from it. 20
axile (placentation) – the condition where the ovules are attached to tissue lying in the axis of the ovary. 278
axillary branch – a branch situated in an axil. 57
axillary bud – a bud situated in an axil. 20, 122
bacilli (plural of bacillus) – rod-shaped members of the Bacteria. 346
back-crossing – the crossing of a hybrid with one of its parents. 306
bacteriochlorophyll – chlorophyll pigment in bacteria. 345
balanced (solution) – a solution of two or more salts in such proportions that the toxic effects of the individual salts are mutually eliminated. 180
bark – all outer tissues easily removed when woody stems are peeled; in most cases tissues outside the cambium. 140
basal cell – the cell lying towards the micropylar end of the embryo sac. 293
base – a substance which dissolves in water with the formation of hydroxyl ions. 150
basidia (plural of basidium) – a row of cells, or more often a single round- to club-shaped cell, which bears the basidiospores, in the Basidiomycetes. 386, 406, 411
basidiospore – the characteristic spore produced, two or four on each basidium. 408
benthos – the sedentary plant life living on the bottom of lakes, ponds, and the sea. 352
berry – a many-seeded succulent fruit with an entirely fleshy wall. 302
bicollateral – said of a vascular bundle with two strands of phloem, one internal to and one external to the single strand of xylem. 109
biennial – a plant which arises from seed one year, lives to the next season, and then flowers, sets seed and dies. 58
bifoliar spurs – shoots bearing only two leaves. 463
bilabiate – with two lips. 263
bilocular – consisting of two loculi or chambers. 278
bimodal – having two peaks. 308, 450
binary division – division of the nucleus into two daughter nuclei, followed by similar division of the cell-body. 346
biological privilege of survival – the struggle for existence under conditions in which organisms produce more offspring than can survive and again reproduce their kind, and the competition arising from that struggle. 329
biotic factor – an ecological factor relating to living organisms. 229
bivalent – one of the pairs of homologous chromosomes present during meiosis. 249
bleeding – the exudation of sap from wounds. 161
blending – a Darwinian concept of heredity. 330
bloom – a covering of grains, short rods, or crusts of waxy material occurring on the surface of some leaves and fruits. 90
body cell – a cell in a pollen grain of Gymnospermae, from which the male nuclei are set free. 460
bole – the trunk of a tree. 75
bordered pit – a thin area in the wall between two vessels or tracheids, surrounded by overhanging rims of wall thickening. 126
botryoidal – shaped like a bunch of grapes. 346
bract – the leaf which subtends an inflorescence or a flower. 265
bracteole – a leaf, generally very small, borne on the stalk of a flower. 257
branch gap – an interruption in the vascular cylinder at the point of origin of a branch or flower. 114
branch trace – the primary vascular supply to a lateral branch. 114
branches of limited growth – the very short branches on which the needleshaped leaves of the pine are borne. 463
branches of unlimited growth – the main branches of the pine bearing spirally arranged scale leaves. 463
bud – the undeveloped or embryonic stage of a branch. 19
budding – a means of artificial propagation, in which a bud taken from one plant is inserted under the bark of another, subsequently developing into a shoot. 144
buffer action – the action of certain solutions in opposing a change of hydrogen ion concentration. 151
bulb – a large underground bud consisting of swollen leaf bases containing much

reserve food material, arranged on a short conical stem. 68

bundle sheath – a sheath of one or more layers of parenchymatous or of sclerenchymatous cells, surrounding a vascular bundle. 121

callose – a carbohydrate, insoluble in cuprammonia, but soluble in the cold in 1% solutions of caustic alkalies. 104

callus – a tissue composed of parenchymatous cells produced by a callus cambium at a wound surface. 144

calyptra – membranous covering over the young capsule of a moss or liverwort, derived from part of the archegonium wall. 38, 93, 425

calyx – the outer whorl of the flower, consisting of sepals. 257, 261

cambium – a cylinder, strip or layer of meristematic cells, which divide mostly in one plane and give rise to daughter cells from which permanent tissue is ultimately formed. 126

campylotropous – pertaining to an ovule, one side of which is curved in such a way that the chalaza and micropyle do not lie in a straight line. 283

canker – a name applied to various diseases of trees, caused by fungi. 323

cap cell – the cell which surmounts the antheridium of a fern and is thrown off when the antheridium liberates the sperms. 364, 425

capillaries – (in soil); spaces of minute or hair-like diameter forming a network which aids the rapid movement of water through the soil, especially towards the surface and the root systems of plants. 162

capillary translocation – the movement of material in solution within a soil by virtue of the network of capillaries separating its particles. 168

capitulum – a racemose inflorescence in which the sessile flowers are crowded on the concave, flat, or convex surface of the enlarged apex of the receptacle, the whole group being surrounded and covered in bud by an envelope of bracts forming an involucre. 268

capsule – the portion of the sporogonium of Bryophyta which contains the spores. 425
– a fruit formed from a syncarpous gynaeceum, not fleshy when ripe and splitting at maturity, releasing the seeds. 300

capsule – a coating of mucilaginous material outside a bacterial cell. 345

carinal canal – present in the stem of Equisetum spp; a canal opposite a ridge on the surface of the stem. 447

carpel – the ovule-bearing structure which, either singly or in association or combination with two or more other carpels, forms the gynaeceum of the flower. 257, 275

carpellate – bearing carpels. 259

carpogonia (plural of carpogonium) – female sex organs in the Division Rhodophyta. 354

caruncle – an outgrowth from the neighbourhood of the micropyle of a seed. 11, 296

caryopsis – the fruit of a plant in which the pericarp and testa are adherent. 300

Casparian strip – the strip of material, impermeable to water, present in the radial walls of endodermal cells when these are in the primary condition. 95

catabolic – pertaining to the sum-total of the disruptive metabolic processes in an organism, organ or cell, leading to liberation of energy. 28

catalase – an enzyme present in animal and vegetable tissues, characterized by readiness to decompose hydrogen peroxide. 200

cation – the ion in an electrolyte which carries the positive charge and which migrates towards the cathode under the influence of a potential difference. 149

cation exchange – exchange of cations between clay particles and the soil solution. 182

catkin – a spike of unisexual reduced flowers. 259

cauline leaves – leaves growing from the stem and not from the base of the plant (cf. radical leaves). 57

cell – one of the specialized units, consisting of nucleus and cytoplasm, which compose the bodies of plants and animals. 25

cell differentiation – the organization of mature tissues from generalized rudiments. 92

cell plate – a delicate membrane formed across the equator of the achromatic spindle as cell division proceeds; it provides the foundation of the wall between the daughter cells which result from the division. 35

cell sheath – the outer, tough gelatinous or mucilaginous layer of an algal cell wall. 353

cell turgidity – the condition of rigidity when the cells of a plant member are distended and press against one another, owing to their turgor pressure. 40

centric diatom – a diatom in which the valves are built on a radial plan. 372, 373

centrifugal – developing from the centre towards the outside. 265

centripetal – developing from the outside towards the centre. 265

centromere – the mechanical centre of a chromosome; the only part in actual contact with the spindle at its equator. 33

chalaza – the basal portion of the nucellus of an ovule. 283

chalazogamy – the entry of the pollen tube through the chalaza of the ovule. 288

chemical energy – the energy liberated in a chemical reaction. 205

chemosynthetic – pertaining to the formation of organic material by some bacteria by means of energy derived from chemical changes. 344

chemotaxis – movement of the whole organism in a definite direction in relation to a chemical stimulus. 54

chiasma – the point where there is an exchange of parts between paired chromosomes during nuclear division. 249

chiasmata – plural of chiasma. 250

chlamydospore – a thick-walled fungal spore, capable of a resting period, and often formed inside a hypha. 395

chlorenchyma – tissue containing chloroplasts. 447

chlorophyll pigments – the two green and two yellow pigments, present in the chloroplasts of all plants which are able to synthesize carbohydrates from carbon dioxide and water, enabling the plants to utilize energy derived from light in the synthesis of carbohydrates. 28, 211

chloroplast – a plastid containing chlorophyll, with or without other pigments, contained singly or in considerable numbers in the cytoplasm of a plant cell. 28, 213

chlorosis – an unhealthy condition due to the deficiency of chlorophyll; shown by yellowing of the plant. 181

chromatid – one of the halves of a chromosome which appears as a result of its longitudinal splitting during the prophase of mitosis or meiosis. 33

chromatin – the material which forms the bulk of a chromosome and has a strong affinity for basic dyes such as aceto-carmine or acetic orcein. 33

chromatophores – a plastid containing one or more pigments, not necessarily chlorophyll. 345, 354, 375

chromatoplasm – the peripheral region of the protoplast in Cyanophyta, containing the photosynthetic pigments of the cell. 353

chromomeres – the bead-like granules, probably regions of super-coiling, seen at intervals along the length of chromosomes during leptotene and zygotene of meiosis. There is a specific attraction between homologous chromomeres during zygotene. 244

chromonema – one of the threads which make up the nuclear reticulum; and during prophase of mitosis contract and thicken to become chromosomes. 33

chromosomal mutation – alterations to chromosomes or parts of chromosomes which give rise to profound phenotypic changes including deletions, translocations, and polyploidy. 311

chromosome – one of the deeply-staining rod-like bodies, constant in number, size, and shape for any given species, which becomes condensed and thus visible, during meiosis or mitotis, and in which the genes are located. 28, 33

chromosome map – a diagram which purports to show the position of the genes in a chromosome. 310

cingulum – the side of the cell wall of a diatom frustule, at right angles to the epitheca. 372

circumnutation – the rotation of the tip of a growing stem so that it traces a helical curve in space. 43

clamp connection – a short backwardly directed hypha, present across the septa of hyphae of some Basidiomycetes; developed as the nuclei divide and making possible the movement of the daughter nuclei into the two segments formed from the terminal segment of the hypha. 409

clay – a fine textured, sedimentary or residual deposit. 165

clay micelles – a particle of clay of colloidal size, especially a colloidal ion. 182
cleistogamous – pertaining to the production of small flowers, often simplified and inconspicuous, which do not open, and in which self-pollination occurs. 287
cleistothecium – a closed ascocarp, opening by rupture. 399
climatic factor – a condition such as average rainfall, temperature, and so on, which plays a controlling part in determining the features of a plant community. 229
closing layer – a sheet of closely-packed cells lying across a lenticel, preventing the diffusion of gases and vapours through the lenticel. 142
cocci (plural of coccus) – minute spherical bacteria, 345
coenzyme – a substance accompanying and essential to, the activity of an enzyme. 202
colchicine – an alkaloid of unknown constitution, obtained from the root of the autumn crocus; living nuclei dosed with colchicine may subsequently divide abnormally with an increase in the number of chromosomes and the establishment of a condition of polyploidy. 312
coleoptile – the first leaf to appear above ground in a seedling of a grass; it forms a sheath around the younger leaves within it, and contains little or no chlorophyll. 14, 40
coleorhiza – a layer of protective cells on the tip of the radicle of the embryos of some flowering plants. 14
collateral (bundle) – a vascular bundle with a strand of xylem and a strand of phloem lying externally to it and on the same radius. 109
collenchyma – a mechanical tissue characteristic of petioles and of young stems. It usually lies close to the periphery, and consists of elongated cells with their walls strengthened by longitudinal strips of cellulose thickening material, so that the cell walls are not of uniform thickness. 107
colloid – a substance composed of minute particles, dispersed through a medium. 152
colloidal solution – a liquid colloid, a sol. 152
columella – a dome-shaped wall in the middle of the sporangium of some moulds. 393
– a central column of sterile tissue in the sporangium of a moss or a liverwort. 433
companion cell – a nucleated cell associated with a segment of a sieve tube, and apparently playing some part in assisting the sieve tube to conduct food material. 104
compensation point – the light intensity, at which, at any given temperature, respiration and photosynthesis just balance in a green plant, so that there is neither liberation nor absorption of carbon dioxide and of oxygen. 212
competition – the struggle between organisms for the necessities of life. 234
complementary tissue – a loose assemblage of thin-walled, unsuberized cells, fitting loosely together, lying in the cavity of a lenticel, and allowing gases and vapours to diffuse through them. 142
complete flower – a flower which has both calyx and corolla. 259
compound leaf – a leaf the lamina of which consists of a number of quite distinct leaflets, being divided down to the midrib; the leaflets may fall independently of one another as the leaf dies. 88
compound palmate leaf – a compound leaf with lobes radiating from a common point. 88
compound pinnate leaf – a compound leaf, having parts arranged along two sides of an axis. 88
compound umbel – a racemose inflorescence consisting of a number of secondary axes radiating obliquely upwards from the end of a main branch and bearing in their turn a number of flower stalks similarly arranged. 268
conceptacle – a flask-shaped cavity in the thallus, opening to the outside by a small pore, and containing reproductive structures. 383
cone – a specialized branch bearing closely-grouped sporophylls – a strobilus. 446
conidia – asexually-formed spores, cut off externally at the tip of specialized hypha and produced by many species of fungi. 398
conidiophore – a simple or branched hypha bearing one or more conidia. 391, 396

conjugation – the temporary or permanent union of two cells or individuals preparatory to the development of new individuals, more particularly the union of isogametes. 370
conjugation tube – a tubular outgrowth by means of which the contents of a male gametangium are conveyed into the female gametangium. 370
connective tissue – sterile tissue in an anther, lying between the lobes, and usually a prolongation of the filament. 271
contractile vacuoles – a cavity filled with fluid which periodically collapses and expels its contents into the surrounding medium. 356
cork cambium – the layer of meristematic cells lying a little inside the surface of a root or stem forming cork on its outer surface and phelloderm internally. 138
cork formation – a layer of dead cells on the outside of a stem or root, having suberized walls, and relatively impermeable to air or water. 138
corm – a rounded swollen underground stem, resembling a bulb in general appearance, but solid, and not composed of overlapping, fleshy leaf bases. 66
corolla – the general name for the whole of the petals of a flower. 257
corpus – the central tissue of irregularly arranged cells lying beneath the tunica in the shoot apex. 106
cortex – a cylinder of chiefly parenchymatous cells lying between the epidermis and the starch sheath in a young stem, and between the piliferous layer and the endodermis in a young root. 93, 94, 107
cortical – pertaining to the cortex. 106
cortical cells – the cells of the cortex. 94
corymb – a racemose inflorescence in which the flower stalks become shorter and shorter as they arise closer to the top of the inflorescence axes. As a result the flowers lie in a flat-topped cluster. 268
cotyledon – one of the leaves of the embryo of a flowering plant. 3
crenate – having a margin bearing rounded teeth all more or less of the same size. 88
crossing over – mutual exchanges between homologous pairs of chromosomes during meiosis (see chiasmata). 249
cross-pollination – the conveyance of pollen from the anther of one flower to the stigma of another, either on the same or on a different plant of the same species. 285
culture – an experimental preparation containing a micro-organism growing on or in a medium. 179
cupule – a small cup-shaped outgrowth from the thallus of a liverwort, containing gemmae. 422
cutin – a mixture of fatty substances which is deposited on or in the outer layer of the cell walls as cuticularization proceeds. 106
cyclic – having the parts arranged in whorls, not in spirals. 84
cyme – an inflorescence in which the main axis ends in a flower, and in which subsequent flowers are produced at the ends of the lateral axes or of successive branches from these. 265
cymose inflorescence – see above. 265
cytokinesis – the division of a cell by the laying down of a new cell wall as distinct from nuclear division. 33
cytoplasm – all the protoplasm of a cell, apart from that of the nucleus. 27
daughter chromosomes – the two sets of chromosomes resulting from the mitosis of a single cell. 35
day-neutral plants – flowering under a wide range of day lengths, provided that other environmental conditions leading to their ripeness to flower are fulfilled. 255
decarboxylation – the loss of one or more carbon atoms. 226
deciduous – the shedding of leaves, usually after a lengthy season of growth and functioning, generally before cold or drought sets in. 176
decussate – with leaves in pairs, each pair being at right angles to the pairs above and below. 86
degrade – to convert into simpler substances. 196
dehiscent – the spontaneous opening at maturity of a fruit, anther, sporangium, or other reproductive body. 275, 300
dehydrogenase – an enzyme which catalyses oxidation by the removal of hydrogen. 202
deletion – the loss of a portion of a chromosome. 311
denaturation – irreversible changes in the fundamental chemical structure of living matter. 5
dentate – having a toothed margin. 88

deoxyribose nucleic acid (DNA) – a compound of high molecular weight occurring in the chromosomes, containing pentose sugar, phosphoric acid, and N-containing base. The chemical basis of heredity. 315
determinate – said of an inflorescence which ends in a flower. 265
development – the succession of stages in the life of a plant, as distinct from the simple growth of the plant. 19
diakinesis – the stage of meiotic prophase immediately preceeding the break-down of the nuclear membrane and the passing on of the bivalents to the spindle. 251
diarch – having two protoxylem strands. 97
dichasial branching – a shoot or inflorescence in which each branch bears two lateral branches, both of about the same strength of development. 73, 265
dichogamy – the condition in which, in a given flower, the stamens and stigmas are not mature at the same time. 287
dichotomous branching – the production of two branches of the same size by the apical cell or apical growing point dividing into two equal parts, each then growing into a branch. 380
dicotyledon – a plant of which the embryo has two cotyledons. 13
diffuse porous – the condition of xylem when the vessels are scattered uniformly throughout, or when there is little difference between the vessels formed at different times of the growing season. 137
diffusion – the movement of molecules resulting in their equal distribution throughout a medium. 154
dihybrid – the product of a cross between parents differing in two heritable characters. 307
dikaryon – a cell with two independent nuclei which divide at the same time. 409
dioecious – having the male and female organs on separate plants, of the same species, each plant being unisexual. 259
diplococcus – a coccus in which the individuals tend to form pairs. 346
diploid – having the somatic number of the chromosomes characteristic of the species. 242, 363
diplophase – the period in the life cycle of any organism when the nuclei are diploid. 398
diplotene – the stage of meiotic prophase, in which homologous chromosomes are visibly double, and in which a crossing over takes place. 249
disaccharide – a sugar consisting of two molecules of monosaccharide. 192
disjunction – the separation during meiosis of the two members of each pair of homologous chromosomes. 309
dispersal – the establishment of individuals in a new area; the process of reaching such a new area. 295
dissociation – the reversible or temporary breaking-down of a molecule into simpler molecules or atoms. 150
diurnal rhythm – the changes in the rate of a process in the course of a day. 172
dominant – of a pair of allelomorphic characters, the one which will be manifested if both are present. 305
dormancy – a condition of inactivity caused by some structural or physiological condition. 4
dormant bud – a bud which remains inactive for an indefinite period. 73
double flower – a flower with more than the normal number of petals. 261
drupe – a succulent fruit formed from a superior ovary, usually one-seeded, with the pericarp clearly differentiated into epicarp, mesocarp, and endocarp. 302
drupelet – a small drupe. 302
druse – a crystal aggregate occurring in some cells. 30
dry fruit – a fruit in which the pericarp does not become fleshy at maturity. 298
duplication – the union of a fragment of a chromosome with a whole chromosome of the same sort. 311
dwarf male – a male organism which is greatly reduced in size, and usually in complexity of internal structure also, in comparison with the female of the same species. 366
dwarf shoot – a short branch borne in the axil of a scale leaf and bearing the true foliage leaves of the plant. 463
ecological isolation – resulting from different races of a population occupying different habitats. 327
ecology – the study of organisms in relation to their environment. 229
ectotrophic – feeding on the surface of other plants. 416
edaphic factor – the influence of soils on plants. 229

egg-apparatus – the egg and the two synergidae in the embryo sac of an angiosperm. 284
egg cell – the ovum as distinct from any other cells associated with it. 284
elater – elongated cell with spiral thickenings on the wall, found mixed with the spores of some liverworts. 427
electrolyte – a substance which on dissolution in a suitable solvent conducts electrolytically. 149
embryo – a young plant in a rudimentary state of development, usually contained in a seed or surrounded by a protective tissue. 2
embryo sac – a cavity in the ovule of an angiosperm, formed by the enlargement of the megaspore, and usually containing eight nuclei, of which the most important is the egg nucleus. 284
empirical formula – a formula expressing the simplest numerical relationships between the atoms of the elements in a compound. 192
emulsion – a colloidal suspension of one liquid in another. 152
endemic species – species confined to a particular region such as an island. 328
endocarp – the inner layer of a pericarp. 298
endodermis – a sheath of cells, one layer thick, at the boundary between the cortex and the stele. 95
endogenous – formed inside another organ of the plant. 57, 104
endoplasmic reticulum – fine network of membranous canals lined with ribosomes which extend from the nuclear membrane into the cytoplasm of cells. Seen only in electronmicrographs. 31
endosperm – a multicellular tissue formed inside a developing seed, serving in the nutrition of the embryo. 2
endospore – a spore formed inside a mother cell. 345
endotrophic – occurring almost entirely inside the body of an associated plant, and feeding on it. 416
entomophilous – pollinated by insects. 285
enucleate – having the nucleus of the cell removed. 103
enzyme – a catalyst produced by living cells, most of which activate only one kind of substrate and requiring definite optimum conditions for their operation. Largely proteinaceous. Unstable, being easily destroyed or inactivated. 7, 200
ephemeral – a plant which completes its whole life history in a very short time, often in a few weeks. 2
epicotyl – the part of the axis of a seedling between the cotyledon and the first leaf or whorl of leaves. 9
epidermis – a sheath of closely united cells forming a layer over the surface of the roots, leaves, flowers, fruits, and young stems of a plant. 93, 94, 106, 115
epigeal – germinating with the cotyledons appearing above the surface of the ground. 13
epigynous – having the calyx, corolla, stamens inserted on the top of the inferior ovary. 281
epinasty – the occurrence of stronger growth on the upper than on the under side of a plant member. 77
epipetalous – arising from the upper surface of a petal. 271
epiphyte – a plant which grows attached to the stems or leaves of another plant, but is not a parasite. 354, 438
epitheca – the older and therefore larger of the two valves forming the wall of a cell of a diatom. 372
erect habit – set at right angles to the ground or the organ from which it grows. 55
ergastic substance – a non-protoplasmic cell inclusion, playing a part in respiration and other metabolic activity of the cell. 30
ergot – disease of cereals and grasses caused by species of the fungus *Claviceps*. 404
erosion – the lowering of the land surface by weathering, corrosion, or transportation under the influence of gravity, wind, and running water. 234
etiolated – the condition of a green plant which has not received sufficient light; the stems are weak, with abnormally long internodes, the leaves are small, yellowish or whitish, and the vascular strands are deficient in xylem. 41
evergreen – a plant that does not lose its leaves seasonally and is green throughout the year. 69, 176
evolution – the gradual development over many generations of more complex organisms from simpler ones. 324
exalbuminous – seeds lacking endosperm. 3

exocarp – the outer layer of a pericarp. 298
exodermis – a more or less cuticularized region formed from the outer cells of the cortex of a root, and constituting a temporary protective sheath. 95
exstipulate – without stipules. 90
extine – the outer wall-layers of a pollen grain. 287
eye-spot – a small mass of light-sensitive pigment found in some lower plants. 356
fascicular cambium – the flat strand of cambium between xylem and phloem in a vascular bundle. 124
fats – an important group of naturally occurring substances consisting of the glycerides of higher fatty acids. 195
fatty acids – a term for the whole group of saturated and unsaturated monobasic aliphatic carboxylic acids. 196
fertilization – the union of two sexually differentiated gametes to form a zygote. 290
fibrous layer – a layer of cells having their walls thickened irregularly by thin bands of material, occurring in the wall of an anther. 275
fibrous root system – the complex of adventitious roots. 57, 413
field layer – the herbaceous layer in the strata of vegetational cover. 237
filament – the stalk of a stamen. 271
– a chain of cells set end to end, especially in algae. 360
filling tissue – see complementary tissue. 142
flagellum – a threadlike extension of the cytoplasm of a cell or of a motile spore. 345
fleshy fruit – thick and soft, but not necessarily juicy. 298
florets – an individual flower in a crowded inflorescence. 268
flower – a specialized reproductive shoot typical of angiosperms. 256
flower bud – a bud enclosing one or more young flowers, but no foliage leaves. 123
fluorescence – the absorption of radiation of a particular wavelength by a substance and its re-emission as light of greater wavelength. 217
foliose – flattened and leaf-like. 420
follicles – a fruit formed from a single carpel and containing several seeds. 300
foot – a specialized part of the young sporophyte in Bryophyta and Pteridophyta attached to the gametophyte and serving as an absorbing organ, obtaining and conveying nourishment to the young plant. 425
foot cell – a small thick-walled segment of the hypha from which a conidiophore of a mould arises. 398
free central placentation – the grouping of the ovules on the surface of a placenta which stands up from the base of the ovary and is not united with the walls of the chamber, either at the side or at the top. 279
free nuclear division – nuclear division unaccompanied by the formation of cell walls. 462
frond – the leaf of a fern. 380
fructification – any spore-bearing structure, whether formed after fertilization or by purely vegetative development. 409
fruit – a fertilized and developed ovary. 295
frustule – the cell of a diatom consisting of two silicified valves fitting one into the other like a box and its lid, with its living contents. 372
fundamental tissue – the general mass of parenchymatous tissue outside and between the vascular strands in a young stem or root. 94
fungi – a group of colourless simple plants which live as saprophytes and parasites. 385
funicle – the small stalk which unites the ovule to the placenta. 4
funiculus – see funicle. 283
fusiform – elongated and tapering towards each end, like a spindle. 99, 125
gametangium – the organ in which the gametes are formed. 363, 376, 388, 392
gametes – reproductive cells which will unite in pairs to produce zygotes. 242, 357
gametophyte – the haploid generation which is derived from a spore and which bears the gametangia and gametes. It alternates with the diploid sporophyte. 243
gamopetalous – having a corolla consisting of a number of petals united by their edges. 261
gamosepalous – having the sepals united by their edges. 261
gel – the apparently solid, often jelly-like, material formed from a colloidal solution on standing. 153

gemmae – special vegetative or asexual reproductive bodies of bryophytes, often formed in groups. 422

gene mutation – a heritable variation caused by spontaneous changes at single points in the chromosomes. 311

generative cell – a cell in a pollen grain of gymnosperms which divides to give a stalk cell and a body cell. 275, 460, 463

genes – hereditary units carried in chromosomes. The determinants of inherited characters. 308

genetics – the study of variation and heredity. 304

genotype – a group of individuals all of which possess the same genetic constitution. 305

genus – a taxonomic group consisting of a number of similar species. Similar genera are grouped together into families. 340

geographical race – a collection of individuals within a species which differ constantly in some slight respects from the normal characters of the species, but not sufficiently to cause them to be classified as a separate species, and which are peculiar to a particular area. 327

geotropism – the reaction of a plant member to gravity, shown by a curvature caused by one side growing faster than the other, tending to bring the axis of the member into line with the direction of gravity. 49

germ cell – see gametes. 305

germination – the onset of the growth and development of a spore or seed leading to the production of a new plant. 304

germ line – the cells or tissues which eventually produce gametes. 311

germ tube – the tubular outgrowth put out by a germinating spore, from which the thallus develops by subsequent branching or on which a germ sporangium is formed. 387

gill – one of the vertical plates of tissue that bear the hymenium in an agaric. 411

glycolosis – the enzymatic decomposition of glucose into pyruvic acid. 225

grafting – the insertion of a part of one plant into a part of another so that organic union, followed by growth, ensues. 144

grana (plural of granum) – minute globules of pigment in the colourless stroma of a chloroplast. 29, 214

grand period of growth – the period in the life of a plant, or any of its parts, during which growth begins slowly, gradually rises to a maximum, gradually falls off and comes to an end; when plotted graphically, this growth produces a sigmoid curve. 21

ground tissue – see fundamental tissue. 94

growth – a change in the body of an organism, and in the cells composing it, accompanied by cell division, by the utilization of material, and, nearly always, by increase in the size and weight of the organism, or of the part under consideration. 19

growth form – the characteristic form of a plant, genetically predetermined, and depending largely on the extent of branching and internodal growth, e.g. tree, shrub, climber. 55

guard cell – one of the two specialized epidermal cells which border on the pore of a stoma and together cause it to close or to open. 107, 116

guttation – the exudation of drops of fluid from an uninjured part of a plant, commonly from the ends of the main veins of leaves, usually under conditions of high humidity. 175

gynaeceum – the carpel or carpels in a flower. 257

habit – the growth form of a plant. 55

habitat – the normal locality or place of abode of an organism. 229

hair – a superficial outgrowth consisting of one or more cells. 90, 118

haploid – having half the number of chromosomes of the somatic cells. Typical of nuclear constitution of gametes and gametophytes. 242

haplophase – the period in the life-cycle of any organism when the nuclei are haploid. 398

haptonastic movement – a nastic movement stimulated by pressure or touch. 53

haptotropic movement – one-sided growth leading to curvature; being the response of an elongated plant organ which has been stimulated by touch or slight pressure. 82

hardwood – dense close-grained wood from deciduous trees. 126, 130

haustoria (plural of haustorium) – lateral hyphae produced by the mycelium of a parasitic fungus, which obtains nutriment by penetrating the host cells. 402

head of flower – a dense inflorescence of small, crowded, sessile flowers, surrounded by an involucre. 268

heartwood – the dense and often dark-coloured wood which lies in the inner part of a trunk or branch, making up the bulk of such a member. 134, 136

helicoid – spirally coiled. 265

heredity – the study of the factors which cause the persistence or disappearance of characters in successive generations. 204

heterocyst – an enlarged thick-walled cell occurring in the filament of members of the Cyanophyta. 353

heteroecious – said of a parasitic fungus which forms one or more kinds of spores upon one host, and one or more distinct kinds of spores upon a second host which is not of the same species as the first. 408

heterospory – the formation of more than one kind of spore. 450

heterothallic – plants in which the male gametangia are produced on one filament or plant and the female on another. 395

heterotrophic – unable to make food from simple beginnings and therefore dependent for food on dead or living organisms of another species, and ultimately on the green plant. 343, 385

heterozygous – possessing both the dominant and the recessive characters of an allelomorphic pair. 305

hexaploid – nuclei containing six basic sets of chromosomes. 312

hilum – the scar left on the testa when the seed separates from its stalk. 4, 296

hinge cells – thin-walled cells on the inner epidermis of certain xerophytic leaves which bring about folding. 176

holdfast – any organ, other than a root, which attaches a plant (especially algae) to a substratum. 362

homosporous – having spores all of the same kind. 450

homothallic – plants on which the male and female gametangia are produced on the same filament or plant. 395

homozygous – the condition of having inherited a given genetical factor from both parents, and therefore of producing gametes of only one kind as regards that factor. 305

horizontal classification – a classification which considers organisms without reference to their past history. 339

hormone – an internal secretion formed in actively growing parts of the plant; they diffuse within the plant to other regions of the plant body, and regulate and influence development. 44

humidity – the quantity of water vapour present per unit volume in the air. 231

humus – organic matter present in the soil, and so far decomposed that it has lost all signs of its original structure. 166

hybrid – plants resulting from a cross between genetically-unlike parents. 305

hybrid swarm – offspring arising from the mating of different kinds of plants. 327

hydathode – a water pore, usually at the end of a vein of a leaf, from which liquid water is exuded. 175

hydrogen ion concentration – a measure of the acidity of a solution. 150

hydrolysis – the decomposition of a chemical compound, brought about in living cells by enzymes, and accompanied by the addition of water. 7, 148

hygroscopic – absorbing water readily and showing a change of form as a result. 167

hymenium – a layer of asci and paraphyses, more or less parallel with one another, in the fructification of an ascomycete. 411

hypertonic – having a higher osmotic pressure than a standard solution. 159

hypha – one of the simple or branched filaments of the thallus of a fungus. 385

hypocotyl – the part of the axis of a seedling between the insertion of the cotyledons and the radicle. 13

hypogeal – remaining beneath the surface of the ground. 11

hypogynous – said of the flower in which the calyx, corolla, and androecium, or one or more of these, arise from the receptacle below the gynaeceum. 279

hyponasty – the more vigorous growth of the flattened under-side of an organ, usually causing some change in the position of that organ. 77

hypotheca – the younger and smaller of the two valves in the cell wall of a diatom. 372

hypotonic – having a lower osmotic pressure than a standard. 159

imbibition – the absorption of water by colloidal substances, especially gels. 162

imperfect flowers – lacking either stamens or pistils. 259

incipient plasmolysis – the stage in plasmolysis when the cell wall is fully contracted, but when the protoplast has not yet shrunk away from the wall at any point. 159
incomplete flowers – said of flowers lacking one or more of the following: calyx, corolla, pistil, or stamen. 259
indehiscent – not opening naturally when ripe. 300
indeterminate inflorescence – inflorescence in which there is no flower at the end of the axis. 265
indusia (plural of indusium) – protective structures associated with the sorus in a fern. 441
inferior – said of the gynaeceum when it is enclosed by the receptacle, so that the calyx, corolla, and stamens are developed above it. 281
inflorescence – the part of the shoot which bears flowers. 58, 263, 265
initials – cells which remain meristematic, divide repeatedly, and give rise to many daughter cells, from which, after further divisions, the permanent tissues of the plant are differentiated. 106
integument – one or more cellular layers covering the ovule, leaving only a small pore, the micropyle. 458
intercalary growth – growth as a result of the activity of a meristem lying between other bodies in a row. 24
intercellular hyphae – hyphae situated between cells. 387
intercellular space – space between cells. 94
interfascicular cambium – a cambium developing between the vascular bundles. 124
internode – the length of a stem between two successive nodes. 20
interphase – the metabolic stage of the nuclear cycle when the nucleus is not undergoing mitosis. 33, 252
intine – the inner layer of the wall of a pollen grain. 287
intracellular hyphae – hyphae situated within the cell. 387
invasion – the movement of plants from one area to another, and their establishment in the latter. 237
inversion – the reversal in position of a portion of a chromosome. 311
invertase – an enzyme which hydrolyses cane sugar. 192
involucral bract – one of the leafy members forming an involucre. 268
involucre – a tissue of the thallus which protects the archegonia. 425
irritability – the ability to receive and respond to external stimuli. 48
isodiametric – of the same length vertically and horizontally. 125
isogamete – one of a pair of uniting gametes of similar size and form. 362
isotonic – having the same osmotic pressure. 159
kelps – a general name for large brown seaweeds. 377
lamina – the flattened blade of a leaf. 57, 87, 378
lateral branches – branches which arise from the side of the parent axis. 106
lateral buds – buds which arise from the side of the parent axis. 71
lateral conjugation – the conjugation of adjacent cells in the same filament. 370
lateral meristem – a meristem located to the side of a parent member. 32, 124
lateral root – a root arising from the side of the parent axis. 57
lateral shoot – a shoot arising from the side of the parent axis. 20
laterites – aeolian clay formed under tropical climatic conditions by the weathering of igneous rocks, usually of basic composition. Consists chiefly of hydroxides of iron and aluminium, grading through increase of the latter into bauxite. 232
leaching – the removal, by percolating water, of mineral salts from the soil. 183
leaf base – the base of the leaf stalk where it joins the stem. 78, 79, 115
leaf blade – see lamina. 78
leaf gap – an interruption of the vascular tissues of the stem, beneath the insertion of the leaf. 114
leaf margin – the edge of the leaf. 88
leaf mosaic – the arrangement of the leaves on a shoot or a plant in such a way that as much leaf surface as possible is exposed to light and as little as possible is shaded by other leaves. 87
leaf primordium – the cells on the shoot apex which eventually give rise to a new leaf. 106
leaf scar – the scar left on a stem where a leaf has fallen off; it is commonly covered by a thin sheet of cork. 70

leaf stalk – see petiole. 78, 82
leaf trace – the vascular tissue between the stele and the base of the leaf. 114
legume – a fruit formed from a single carpel, splitting along the dorsal and ventral sutures, and usually containing a row of seeds, borne on the inner side of the ventral suture. 298, 300
leguminous plants – plants bearing legumes. 185
lenticel – a tiny pore in the periderm, which is packed with loose corky cells and allows gaseous diffusion to occur between the interior of the plant and the atmosphere. 70, 141
leptotene – the first stage of meiotic prophase, in which the single chromonema with their chromomeres become apparent. 244
lichens – a large group of composite plants, consisting of an alga and a fungus in intimate association, and divided into genera and species as if they were independent plants. 417
lignin – a complicated mixture of substances formed by certain cells of plants and deposited in thickened cell walls, particularly in woody tissue. 97
ligule – a small outgrowth, commonly membranous, from the upper surface of a leaf or leaf-like member, and arising close to the base of the leaf, or at the junction of the lamina and petiole. 89
limiting factor – the slowest-acting factor of a group of factors simultaneously affecting a physiological process in a plant. 213
linear – having parallel edges, and at least four to five times as long as broad. 89
linkage group – a group of hereditary characteristics which remain associated with one another through a number of generations. 309
lipase – a fat-digesting enzyme. 196, 201
liquid – a state of matter in which the shape of the given mass depends on the containing vessel, but the volume is independent thereof. A liquid is a practically incompressible fluid. 149
loam – a muddy soil, of clay, sand, and animal and vegetable matter. 164, 165
locule – one compartment in an anther or an ovary. 271, 278
long-day plant – a plant which needs alternating periods of comparatively prolonged illumination and correspondingly reduced periods of darkness for the proper development of flowers and fruit. 255
lumen – the space enclosed by the cell walls; used especially when the contents of the cell have disappeared. 133
lysigenous cavity – the space formed by the breakdown and dissolution of cells. 112
major coils – large coils in the chromosomes of some plants which, during the meiotic metaphase, produce the final shortening and thickening of the chromosomes. 252
major nutrient elements – the group including calcium, magnesium, potassium, phosphorus, sulphur and nitrogen. 179
maritime soils – soils by the sea which may occur as shifting sand dunes or as salt marshes. 234
mating type – nuclei in cells of the mycelium which are capable of fusing. 409
mature soils – soils which are fully developed, for example, podsols and brown earths. 234
mechanical tissue – tissues, usually made up of thick-walled cells e.g. sclerenchyma, which give support to the plant body. 97
medulla – a cylinder of cells, chiefly parenchymatous, lying centrally in an axis and surrounded by vascular tissue (pith). 109
medullary rays – a sheet of cells, usually mostly parenchymatous, lying radially in a stem or root, appearing in cross section as a narrow radial streak, in radial longitudinal section as a plate of cells. 109, 133
megasporangium – a sporangium which contains megaspores. 383, 455
megaspore – a spore which gives rise to a female gametophyte or its equivalent. 284, 455
megasporophyll – a leaf-like member which bears or subtends one or more megasporangia. 458
meiosis – special nuclear divisions, the first reductional, the second equational, by which the chromosomes are reduced from the diploid to the haploid number so that four haploid spores are produced. 242
Mendelism – the laws relating to the behaviour of contrasting hereditary factors as studied by breeding experiments. 304
meristele – a vascular strand, enclosed in a sheath of endodermis; present in stems of some pteridophytes. 441

meristem – in higher plants, a group of undifferentiated cells, each of which is capable of division, giving rise to at least one daughter cell, able to divide again, and so on. From such divisions permanent tissues are derived. Meristems may occur at the tips of roots and stems, between vascular bundles (cambium), or in the cortex (phellogen or cork cambium). 32

meristoderm – the outer meristematic layer of thallus of brown seaweeds. 380

mesocarp – the middle layer of a pericarp. 298

mesophyll – the parenchymatous tissue between the upper and lower epidermises of a leaf, chiefly concerned with photosynthesis. 115, 120

mesophytes – plants occurring in places where the water supply is neither scanty nor excessive. 176

metabolic nucleus – a nucleus when it is not dividing, and when the chromatin is in the form of a network. 35

metabolism – the sum-total of the chemical and physical processes constantly taking place in living cells. 28

metachromatic – showing other than the basic colour constituent after staining. 345

metaphase – the stage in mitosis in which the chromosomes aggregate on the equator of the mitotic spindle prior to division. 33, 251

metaxylem – primary xylem in which the vessels have either reticulate thickening or pitted walls. 99

micelle – a particle of colloidal size, especially a colloidal ion. 194

micron – a unit of length equal to one thousandth of a millimetre. 25

micropyle – a tiny opening in the integument at the apex of an ovule, through which the pollen tube usually enters. 281
– the corresponding opening in the testa of a seed. 4

microsome – a granular or bladder-like inclusion in the cytoplasm, of very small size. (see ribosome). 31

microsporangium – a sporangium which produces microspores. 383, 455

microspore – a spore which gives rise to a male gametophyte or its equivalent. 383, 455

microsporophyll – a leaf-like organ, more or less modified, bearing or subtending one or more microsporangia. 460

microtome – an instrument for cutting thin sections of specimens. 25

middle lamella – a thin layer of primary wall forming the middle layer of the wall between two sister cells. 36

midrib – the main vein of a leaf. 87

minor elements – trace elements of importance in plant nutrition such as iron, manganese, copper, etc. 179

mitochondria – protoplasmic inclusions of all living cells which take the form of spherical or rod-like bodies and are intimately concerned with respiration, containing many important respiratory enzymes. 29, 224

mitosis – the series of changes through which the nucleus passes during ordinary cell division, and by which each of the daughter cells is provided with a set of chromosomes identical to that possessed by the parent cell. This is usually followed by cytokinesis, during which the cell itself is divided into two by a new cell wall. 32, 33

mode – the value of greatest frequency. 308

molecule – the smallest particle of a substance that is capable of independent existence while still retaining its chemical properties. 149

monochasial – pertaining to a cymose inflorescence in which each successive branch bears one branch in its turn. 265

monocotyledon – a plant of which the embryo has one cotyledon. 13

monoecious – having separate staminate and pistillate flowers on the same individual plant. 259

monokaryon – a fungal cell (Basidiomycete) containing only one nucleus. 490

monopodial – pertaining to a branch system in which each or any branch continues to increase in length by apical extension and bears similar lateral branches in acropetal succession. 62, 70

moulds – a popular name for any of numerous small fungi appearing on bread, jam, cheese, etc., as a fluffy or woolly growth. 392

mountain soils – soils subject to the action of erosion from wind. 234

multiple fruit – a fruit formed from the flowers of an inflorescence, and not from one flower. 297

mutation – the inception of a heritable variation. 311

mycelium – the thallus of a fungus when it consists of hyphae. 385
mycologist – one who studies fungi. 385
mycorrhizae – a symbiotic association between a fungus and a higher plant most often consisting of an intimate relation between the roots of the higher plant and the mycelium of the fungus. 413
mycosis – a fungal disease of an animal. 385
naked flower – a flower lacking a perianth. 259
nastic movement – a curvature of a plant member, brought about by its response to a diffuse stimulus. 52
natural selection – a theory of the mechanism of evolution which postulates the survival of the best-adapted forms, with the inheritance of these distinctive characteristics wherein their fitness lies, and which arise as small uncontrolled variations. 325
natural system – a classification based on the presumed relationships of plants in descent. 339
neck canal cell – one of the cells on the central canal in the neck of an archegonium. 425
nectary – a glandular organ or surface from which nectar is secreted. 285
needle – a long, narrow, stiffly constructed leaf from which water does not readily escape; characteristic of pine trees and related plants. 78
neo-Darwinism – pertaining to the modern version of the natural selection theory of Darwin. 333
nitrogen cycle – the sum-total of the transformations undergone by nitrogen and nitrogenous compounds in nature in relation to living organisms. 186
nitrogen fixation – the conversion of atmospheric nitrogen into a combined form. The formation by soil bacteria and blue-green algae of nitrogenous compounds from elementary nitrogen. 185
node – the place where a leaf is attached to a stem. 19
non-endospermic – see albuminous. 3
non-essential floral parts – sepals and petals. 259
nucellus – a mass of thin-walled cells occupying the middle of an ovule, protected by the integument or integuments, and containing the embryo sac. 281
nuclear membrane – the delicate bounding membrane of the nucleus. 28
nucleic acids – the non-protein constituents of nucleoproteins. They are complex organic acids of high molecular weight consisting of alternate units of phosphate and a pentose sugar which has a purine and pyrimidine base attached to it. See RNA and DNA. They probably play an important part in protein synthesis and in the transmission of hereditary characteristics. 315
nucleolar chromosome – the chromosome to which the nucleolus is attached. 35
nucleolar organizing region – the non-staining region of the nucleolar chromosome from which the nucleolus reorganizes itself. 36
nucleolus – a homogenous refractive spherical body, one or more of which occurs within each nucleus and containing RNA; associated with particular regions of certain chromosomes. 28
nucleotide – a coenzyme to compounds produced by partial hydrolysis of nucleic acids and also to the nucleic acids themselves, which may be considered as polynucleotides. 316
nucleus – the prominent spherical organ of each living cell, surrounded by a nuclear membrane which encloses the nucleolus, nuclear sap, and chromosomes. 28
nutrient solution – an artificially prepared solution containing some or all of the mineral substances used by a plant in its nutrition. 179
nyctonasties – sleep-movements. 52
octant – the division of an embryonic cell by walls at right-angles, giving eight cells. 293
oogamous – pertaining to the union of gametes of dissimilar size, usually of a relatively non-motile egg and a small active sperm. 366
oogonium – the single-celled female sexual organ in the algae and the fungi, which contains usually one egg. 366, 388
oosphere – the large unfertilized non-motile female gamete formed within an oogonium. 388
oospore – a thick-walled spore which normally only germinates after a period of inactivity, formed after the fertilization of the oosphere in lower plants. 366, 388

operculum – a cover or lid which opens to allow of the escape of spores from a sporangium or other container. 433

organelle – a cell organ. 204, 224

orthotropous – said of an ovule which is straight i.e., with the micropyle in a straight line with the funicle. 283

osmometer – an apparatus for the measurement of osmotic pressures. 156

osmosis – the diffusion of a solvent through a semi-permeable membrane into a more concentrated solution which tends to equalize the concentration on both sides of the membrane. 156

osmotic pressure – the pressure exerted by a dissolved substance in virtue of the motion of its molecules. 156

ostiole – the opening by means of which spores or gametes escape from a conceptacle or a perithecium. 383, 400

ovary – the basal enlarged part of a carpel or of a syncarpous gynaeceum, containing the ovules. 278

ovule – the nucellus containing the embryo sac and enclosed by one or two integuments, which after fertilization and subsequent development become the seed. 2, 278

ovuliferous scale – one of the scales in a fertile cone of Coniferae; it bears the ovules, and later the seeds, and the sum-total of all the ovuliferous scales present makes up the greater part of the mature cone. 466

ovum – a non-motile female gamete. 366

oxidases – a group of enzymes promoting oxidation. 202

pachytene – the third stage of meiotic prophase following zygotene pairing in which condensation of chromosomes commences. 249

palaeontology – that branch of geological science which is essentially the study of plant and animal life in past geological periods. 328

palisade tissue – one or more layers of palisade cells beneath the epidermis of a leaf. 120

palmate – having several lobes, segments or leaflets spreading from the same point, like the fingers from the palm. 88

palmelloid stage – a colonial stage in *Chlamydomonas* and related algae, produced by division taking place when the flagella are withdrawn and the organism is in a resting phase. 357

panicle – a branched raceme with each branch bearing a raceme of flowers. 268

papilla – a small conical projection. 94, 355, 370

papillionaceous – having some likeness to the form of a butterfly; said of flowers like those of a pea. 263

parallel venation – having the main veins running side by side for some distance in the leaf. 88

paraphysis – a sterile hair which may be simple or branched and may consist of one or more cells, occurring among reproductive structures in many lower plants. 378

parasite – an organism which lives in or on another organism and derives subsistence from it without rendering anything in return. 385

parasitism – a close internal or external partnership between two organisms, which is detrimental to one partner (the host) and beneficial to the other (the parasite); the latter obtains the nourishment at the expense of the host. 236

parenchyma – a tissue composed of usually isodiametric cells, having thin walls consisting of cellulose with intercellular spaces between cells. Often forming an unspecialized tissue among conducting and mechanical tissues. 94

parietal – attached to, or lying near to, and more or less parallel with the wall. 278, 354

parthenocarpy – the production of a fruit without a preliminary act of fertilization, and without any development of seeds within the fruit. 297

particulate inheritance – the inheritance, in one individual, of distinctive characteristics of both parents. 330

passage cell – a thin-walled non-suberized cell in an endodermis or an exodermis, through which solutions can diffuse in a transverse direction. 95

passive absorption – the entry of water into plants caused by the pull of the transpiration stream. 174

pathogenic – pertaining to a disease-producing micro-organism. 343

pedicel – the stalk which bears a single flower or later a single fruit. 257, 263

peduncle – the main stalk or stalks of an inflorescence. 263

pennate diatom – a diatom with an elongated cell, which is isobilateral, zygomorphic, or dorsiventral in structure. 372

pentose sugar – a group of monosaccharides containing five oxygen atoms in the molecule. 190

perennial – a plant which lives for three or more years and normally flowers and fruits at least in its second and subsequent years. 21, 59

perfect – a flower which has all organs in a functioning condition. 259

perianth – a general term for calyx and corolla together. 257

pericarp – the wall of a fruit, if derived from the wall of the ovary. 298

periclinal – pertaining to a cell wall which is parallel to the surface of an apical meristem or other part of the plant. 104

pericycle – a layer, one or more cells thick, of non-conducting cells at the periphery of a stele. 95

periderm – a protective layer which develops on those parts of plants which last for some time; it consists of cork, the cork cambium, and usually some phelloderm. 138

perigynous zone – the area of a flower in which the receptacle is developed into a flange or into a concave or deeply concave structure, on which the sepals, petals and stamens are borne; the receptacle remains distinct from the carpels. 281

periplasm – the plasma lying just within the oogonial wall in some Oomycetes; it contains degenerating nuclei and contributes to the formation of the wall of the oospore. 388

perisperm – a nutritive tissue present in some seeds, derived from the nucellus of the ovule. 292

peristome teeth – a fringe of elongated teeth along the mouth of the capsule of a moss; the teeth are formed from persistent remains of unevenly thickened cell walls. 433

perithecia – plural of perithecium – a globose or flask-shaped structure with a sterile wall enclosing asci and paraphyses, the characteristic fruit body of certain Ascomycetes. 419

permanent wilting point – the point at which a plant does not recover from wilting if placed in a saturated atmosphere. 167

petal – one of the leaf-like organs, often coloured, composing the corolla of a flower. 257

petiole – the stalk of a leaf. 13, 57, 82

phellem – the tissue formed externally to the phellogen; cork. 138

phelloderm – a layer or layers of thin-walled cells, with cellulose walls, often containing starch and sometimes chloroplasts, formed internally from the phellogen. 138

phellogen – the layer of meristematic cells lying a little inside the surface of a root or stem, forming cork on its outer surface and phelloderm internally; the cork cambium. 138

phenotype – one of a group of individuals all of which have a similar appearance regardless of their genetical constitution. 305

phialide – a short flask-shaped sterigma of certain Ascomycetes. 398, 399

phloem – the conducting tissue present in vascular plants, chiefly concerned with the transport of elaborate food materials about the plant. When fully developed the phloem consists of sieve tubes, companion cells and parenchyma, but companion cells may not be present. 102

phloem fibre – a sclerenchymatous element, or a strand of such elements, affording support to the delicate sieve tubes of the phloem. 104

photochemical – pertaining to the chemical effects of radiation, chiefly visible and ultra-violet, and of the direct production of radiation by chemical change. 210

photolysis – the breakdown of a substance as a result of the action of light. 208

photonasties – response to variation in the intensity of illumination, or to the stimulus of diffuse light. 52

photons – light quanta. 210

photoperiodism – the response of a plant to the relative lengths of day and night as these affect the amount of light received by the plant. 231

photosynthesis – the building up, in the green cells of a plant, of simple carbohydrates from carbon dioxide and water, with the liberation of elementary oxygen. The process only goes on when the plant is sufficiently supplied with light, the chlorophyll acting as an energy transformer, which enables the plant to use the light as a source of energy. 205

phototaxis – the locomotory movement of a motile plant or gamete in response to the stimulus of light. 53

phototropism – a growth movement of plants induced by the stimulus of light. 48

phragmoplast – the barrel-shaped structure, cytoplasmic in origin, which forms round the equator of a cell prior to the formation of the partition wall. 35

phycocyanin – the blue pigment present in the cells of Cyanophyta. 353

phycoerythrin – a red pigment of protein nature, soluble in water, present in the chromatophores of Rhodophyta. 351

phycology – the study of algae. 351

phyllotaxis – the arrangement of leaves on the axis of a shoot. 83

phylogeny – the history of the evolution of race. 339

phytoplankton – free-floating plant life of lakes, rivers, and the sea. 352

pileus – the widening cap-like portion of an agaric; by extension, the corresponding part of the fruit body of other fungi. 410

piliferous zone – the outermost cell layer of a young root, corresponding to the epidermis of a stem. It bears the root hairs. 94

pinnae – the leaflets of a compound fern leaf. 440

pinnate – said of a compound leaf when the leaflets are arranged in two ranks, one on each side of the rachis. 88

pinnules – one of the lobes or segments of a leaflet of a pinnate leaf which is itself more or less divided into parts in a pinnate manner. 440

pioneer colonizers – the first plant community to become prominent in a piece of ground which has been stripped of its vegetation and is being reoccupied by plants. 238

pistil – see gynaeceum. 259

pistillate – said of a flower which has a gynaeceum but in which the stamens are lacking or non-functional. 259

pit – a thin localized area in the wall of a cell or other element of plant structure. 101

pit cavity – the excavation in the wall when the thinning is apparent. 126

pit membrane – the thin sheet of unbroken wall between two opposite pit cavities. 126

pith – a cylinder of cells, chiefly parenchymatous, lying centrally in an axis and surrounded by vascular tissue; also called medulla. 102

pith ray – see vascular ray. 109

placenta – the portion of the carpel wall, often fleshy, to which the ovules are attached. 278

placentation – the arrangement of placentae in an ovary, and of the ovules in the placentae. 278

plant communities – any group of plants growing together under natural conditions, and forming a recognizable unit of vegetation. 237

plant pathogen – a plant-destroying organism. 348

plant succession – the succession of changes in constituents of the plant population of an area from its initial colonization until a vegetational climax is attained. 237

plasmalemma – a very thin membrane, forming the outer boundary of the cytoplasm where that is in contact with the cell wall. 27

plasmodesmata – extremely delicate strands of cytoplasm passing through a fine perforation in a cell wall, and, with many other plasmodesms, providing a connexion with the cytoplasm of contiguous cells. 28

plasmolysis – removal of water from a living cell by osmotic forces, with resultant shrinkage of the protoplast. 159

plumule – the first apical bud on the embryo in the seed; it is the rudimentary shoot. 8

plurilocular sporangium – said of a sporangium which is divided by septae into several compartments. 376

polar nuclei – two nuclei in the embryo sac which unite to give the polar fusion nucleus. 284

pollen grains – the microspores of Spermatophyta which, on germination, produce pollen tubes which carry the male gametes to the female ovule. 271

pollen mother-cell – a sporogenous cell in an anther which divides by meiosis to give four haploid microspores or pollen grains. 273

pollen sac – a cavity in an anther in which the pollen is formed. 271

pollen tube – a tubular outgrowth from the pollen grain, which grows to and into the embryo sac and conveys the male nuclei to the neighbourhood of the egg nucleus. 287

pollination – the transfer of pollen from an anther to a stigma; the process is a preliminary to fertilization. 285

polyarch – said of a stele having many protoxylem strands. 97

polypetalous – said of a corolla made up of distinct petals. 261

polyploid – a nucleus having more than twice the normal haploid number of chromosomes. 312

polysepalous – said of a calyx consisting of separate sepals. 261

pome – a term for a fleshy fruit containing a number of seeds inside a papery core formed from the inner walls of the united carpels. 302

porogamy – the entry of the pollen tube through the micropyle in early stages of fertilization. 288

position effect – the effect which a change in the position of a gene in a chromosome has, relative to other genes, on the characters it produces. 311

potential energy – energy possessed by a body in virtue of its position. 156

potometer – an instrument for measuring the rate at which a plant takes in water. 170

primary body – that part of the plant formed directly from cells cut off from the apical meristems. 92

primary endosperm nucleus – the diploid nucleus occupying the centre of a mature embryo sac which becomes triploid after fertilization and subsequently divides to form nuclei of the endosperm. 284

primary rays – the first formed medullary rays which extend from cortex to pith or medulla. 125, 133

primary tissue – tissue formed from the cells derived from the primary meristems. 92

pro-embryo – the group of cells, few in number, formed as the zygote begins to divide, and from one or some of which the embryo proper is organized. 293, 468

progametangium – a fungal hypha from which a gametangium is subsequently cut off by a transverse septum. 395

prophase – the preliminary stages of mitosis or meiosis leading up to the establishment of metaphase and the formation of the spindle. 33

prosthetic group – a non-proteinaceous substance which combines with proteins, especially enzymes. 202

prostrate – procumbent, or lying down. 420

protandry – the ripening of male germ-cells before female germ-cells, that is anthers maturing before carpels. 287

proteins – compound nitrogenous substances, composed of specific groupings of amino acids, which are essential constituents of living cells. Often combined with other substances such as nucleic acids. 197

proteolytic – said of enzymes which cause the breakdown of proteins into simpler substances. 198

prothallus – the haploid gametophyte generation of ferns and related plants which bear antheridia and archegonia. 438

protogyny – the ripening of female germ-cells before male germ-cells. 287

protonema – the early filamentous stages of some Bryophyta from which new adult plants develop from buds. 431

protoplast – the organized living part of a single cell as distinct from the cell wall. 27

protoxylem – the first xylem to be formed from the procambial strand; it has annular, spiral and loose scalariform vessels or tracheids, and these are usually of much smaller diameter than the corresponding elements of the metaxylem and secondary xylem. 99

proximal – pertaining or situated at the inner end, nearest to the point of attachment. 252

pseudoparenchyma – a mass of closely interwoven hyphae, appearing very like parenchyma, in prepared sections. 419

pseudoperianth – a cup-like envelope surrounding the archegonia in some Hepaticeae. 429

pteridosperm – an ancient group of plants known from fossils, but having no living representatives. They were fern-like in some respects, but produced seeds, often apparently on the edge of their leaves. 469

pulvinus – a swollen leaf base, often capable of changes of form, bringing about movement of the leaf. 79

pure culture – a culture containing a pure stock of one species of plant, especially of lower plants. 417

pure line – plants which are homozygous and therefore breed true for certain characters over successive generations and are obtained by intensive inbreeding. 308

pustule – a mass of fungal spores and the hyphae bearing them. 408

pycnidium – a flask-shaped fruiting body of certain fungi opening by an apical ostiole and producing spores internally. 408

pycnospore – a spore formed inside a pycnidium. 408

pyrenoid – a small mass of refractive protein occurring singly or in numbers in or on the chromatophores of some algae and Bryophyta and concerned in the formation of carbohydrates. 355

raceme – an indefinite inflorescence in which stalked flowers are borne in acropetal succession on an unbranched main stalk. 265

racemose inflorescence – an inflorescence which is a raceme. 265

rachis – the main axis of an inflorescence. 263, 440

radical leaves – appearing as if springing from the root at soil level. 57

radicle – the root of the embryo of a flowering plant. 9

ramenta – thin brownish scales, one cell-layer thick, occurring on the stems, petioles and leaves of ferns. 440

raphe – an elongated mass of tissue containing a vascular strand, and lying on the side of an anatropous ovule between the chalaza and the attachment to the placenta. Also, in diatoms, a cleft which runs from polar nodules to central nodule on valves. 297, 372

ray initials – cells of the cambium which take part in the formation of the medullary ray. 125

receptacle – the apex of a flower stalk which becomes enlarged and from which the various floral organs develop. Differently shaped in different flowers. 257

receptive spot – a clear area in the eggs of some fungi and algae through which the sperm enters. 366

recessive – (character) of a pair of allelomorphic characters, the one which will not be manifested if the corresponding dominant gene is present. 305

recombination – regrouping by independent assortment of chromosomes and their genes during gamete formation followed by their random union at fertilization. 310

reductional division – see meiosis. 242, 244

resins – the products from the secretion of sap from certain plants and trees, especially gymnosperms. 136

respiration – the interchange of oxygen and carbon dioxide associated with catabolic processes and accompanied by the release of energy in an aerobic organism; the corresponding processes in an anaerobic organism. 220

respiratory quotient – the ratio between the volume of carbon dioxide given off and that of oxygen taken in, during a given time. 222

respiratory substrate – the substance (e.g. carbohydrate, fat) broken down during respiration. 223

reticulate chloroplast – a chloroplast with a surface marked by a network of fine upstanding ridges. 364

reticulate thickening – thickening which forms a network. 111

reticulate venation – showing a network of veins. 87

reticulate vessels – vessels with net-like thickenings of their walls. 101

rhizoid – hair-like cells of lower plants, especially fungi and bryophytes and fern prothalli which function as organs of anchorage to the substratum and absorption. 421

rhizome – an underground stem containing stored food consisting of more than one year's growth, usually lying horizontally on the soil, having a superficial resemblance to a root, but bearing scale leaves and one or more buds. Organs of perennation and vegetative propagation. 64

rhizomorph – a densely-packed strand of fungal hyphae, looking like a root. 413

rhytidome – an external covering to a plant member made up of alternating sheets of cork and dead cortex or dead phloem. 140

ribonuclease – the enzyme which acts specifically on and digests ribosenucleic acid (RNA). 320

ribosenucleic acid (RNA) – the nucleic acid most abundant in the nucleolus and cytoplasm and thought to be concerned with the transfer of genetic information from nucleus to sites of protein synthesis. 317

ribosome – minute particles of nucleoprotein of submicroscopic size, containing enzyme systems and possible seat of protein synthesis in cytoplasm. 31, 317

ring porous – said of wood which contains more vessels or larger vessels in the spring wood than elsewhere, so that it is marked in cross section by rings, or portions of rings, of small holes. 136

root – the branching lower portion of the axis of a higher plant, usually growing down into soil and functioning in anchorage and absorption of water and nutrient salts. 92

root cap – a hollow cap of cells covering the growing tip of a root and protecting the meristematic cells from damage as the tip is pushed through the soil. 38, 93

root hair – a tubular outgrowth from a superficial cell of the piliferous layer of a young root, serving for the absorption of water and mineral salts from the soil. 94

root nodule – swellings resulting from infection by nitrogen-fixing bacteria of roots of leguminous plants. 186

root pressure – a pressure sometimes demonstrable in roots and shown by the exudation of fluid when the stem is cut just above ground level. As a result of this pressure, which results from active absorption, water passes from cortical cells of root into xylem vessels. 161

root-stock – see rhizome. 65

rosette – the habit in which leaves are arranged concentrically like petals of a flower. 47

runner – a prostrate shoot which roots at the end and there gives rise to a new plant. 62

salt – a compound which results from the replacement of one or more hydrogen atoms of an acid by metal atoms or electropositive radicals. 150

samara – a single-seeded, dry, indehiscent fruit (an achene), bearing a wing-like extension of the pericarp. 300

saprophyte – an organism which obtains its food from dead and decaying organic material. 343, 385

sapwood – the layer of recently-formed secondary wood forming a sheath over the whole of the surface of the xylem of a woody plant; it contains living cells, is able to conduct sap, and is usually light-coloured. 134, 136

satellite – a small part of a chromosome, attached to one end of the main body of the chromosome, by a fine thread-like connexion. 36

saturated solution – a solution which can exist in equilibrium with the excess of the dissolved substance. 149

scalariform – ladder-like. 101, 370

scalariform thickening – cell wall thickening which gives a ladder-like pattern. 111

scale bark – bark which becomes detached in irregular patches. 140

scale leaves – leaves, usually reduced in size, membranous, of tough texture, and ordinarily protective in function. 463

scion – a portion of a plant, usually a part of a young stem, which is inserted into a rooted stock in grafting. 144

sclerenchyma – a tissue composed of thick lignified walls and with little or no living contents. The cells are elongated with pointed ends which often interlock (fibres), or less often short and blunt-ended (sclereids). Sclerenchyma supports and protects the softer tissues of the plant. 97

sclerotium – a hard mass of fungal hyphae, usually black on the outside, crust-like to globular, and serving as a resting stage from which fructifications are formed later. 404

scorpioid (cyme) – a cymose inflorescence in which the branches develop alternately right and left, but do not all lie on one plane. 265

scutellum – a flattened portion of the embryo of a grass, probably the expanded cotyledon; it is applied to the endosperm and serves as an absorptive organ. 14

secondary body – that part of a plant produced as a result of secondary thickening. 92

secondary constriction – the constriction of a chromosome other than that caused by the centromere or primary constriction. 36

secondary growth – see secondary thickening. 92

secondary phloem – phloem formed by the activity of a cambium. 124, 137

secondary rays – medullary rays produced in secondary vascular tissues and thus not extending between cortex and pith. 133

secondary thickening – the increase in the diameter of a stem or root resulting from activity of the cambium, thereby providing an additional conducting and supporting structure and, in perennials, making up the greater part of the mature plant. 124

secondary tissue – tissue formed from the vascular cambium or other secondary meristem. 92

secondary xylem – xylem formed by the activity of a cambium. 124

section – a thin slice of plant material, sufficiently transparent to be capable of investigation with the compound microscope. 25

seed – a multicellular structure which is the product of a fertilized ovule, containing the embryo of a higher plant, with stored food, the whole protected by a seed coat or testa. The characteristic structure of the Spermatophyta. 2, 295

seed coat – see seed and testa. 295

seedling – the young plant which develops from a germinating seed. 19

segregate – the separation of hereditary factors or allelomorphs from one another during gamete formation, and hence into different offspring. 305

selection pressure – a measure of the effectiveness of natural selection in altering the genetic composition of a natural population. 332

selectivity – the power, sometimes said to be possessed by a plant, of taking in some substances and rejecting others. 158

self-pollination – the transfer of pollen from the anthers to the stigmas of the same flower, or to the stigmas of another flower on the same plant, or to those of a flower on another plant of the same clone. 285, 305

self-sterility – in a hermaphrodite plant, the condition in which self-fertilization is impossible or ineffective. 287

semi-permeable membrane – a membrane which permits the passage of water but is impermeable to certain dissolved substances. 158

sepal – one of the leaf-like members forming the calyx of a flower. 257

separation layer – the abscission layer. 142

septate fibre – a fibre of which the lumen is divided into several compartments by transverse septa. 133

septum – a wall or partition which divides a plant member into separate parts. 385

serrate – said of a toothed margin when the teeth are sharp, like those of a saw, and pointing outwards. 88

sessile leaves – having no stalk. 57

seta – the multicellular stalk which bears the capsule of mosses and liverworts. 425

shell bark – see rhytidome. 140

shoot – a leafy stem. 57

short day plant – a plant in which the onset of flowering is hastened by giving the plant alternating periods of relatively short illumination and relatively long darkness. 255

sieve plate – a perforated area in the lateral or end wall of a sieve tube. 103

sieve tube – a long tubular element enclosed by a thin wall of cellulose, and containing living contents but no nucleus, occurring in the phloem of vascular plants. Sieve tubes conduct elaborated food material about the plant, and communicate with each other by means of sieve areas or sieve plates. 103

sigmoid – curved like the letter S. 21

simple leaf – a leaf in which the lamina consists of one piece, which, if lobed, is not cut into separate parts reaching down to the midrib. 88

simple umbel – an umbel in which the flower stalks arise directly from the apex of the main stalk. 268

sinuate – a margin divided into wide irregular teeth or lobes, separated by shallow notches. 88

softwood – the wood of gymnosperms and consisting only of tracheids. 126

soil profile – the series of horizons which can be seen in vertical section through a soil from the surface down to the parent rock. 232

soil solution – the dilute aqueous solution of mineral salts present around the particles of soil and in the spaces between them, on which plants draw for supplies. 164

soil-water – see soil solution. 166

sol – a colloidal solution i.e. a suspension of solid particles of colloidal dimensions in a liquid. 152

solids – a state of matter in which the constituent molecules and ions possess no translational motion, but can only vibrate about fixed mean positions. 149

solitary – occurring singly. 263, 265

solute – a substance which is dissolved in another. 149

solution – an extremely intimate mixture of variable composition, of two or more substances, one of which is usually a liquid, which may be separated by simple physical processes. 149

somatic mutation – a mutation arising in a somatic cell and not in a reproductive structure. 311

soredia (plural of soredium) – one or more algal cells enclosed in hyphae, forming a tiny mass which separates from the lichen thallus and gives rise to a fresh thallus, if transported to a suitable place for growth. 419

sorus – in lichens, a powdery mass of soredia lying on the surface of the thallus; in ferns, fungi etc., a group of sporangia usually accompanied by some protective structures. 378, 438, 441

spathe – a large, usually coloured foliar organ, which subtends and more or less encloses a spadix. 257

species – a group of closely allied, mutually fertile individuals, showing constant differences from allied groups. The basic unit of classification. 326

specific name – the particular name given to a species thereby distinguishing it from other species of the same genus. 340

spermagonium – a flask-shaped structure in which spermatia are formed. 408

spermatia – non-motile male gametes in the red algae, which are carried by water to the trichogyne. 354

– spore-like structures formed by some lichens and some fungi, and which may have sexual functions. 408

spermatozoid – the flagellated, motile male gamete of many lower plants. 383

spike – an indefinite inflorescence with sessile flowers. 265

spindle – the framework of achromatic fibres which is formed between the poles during nuclear division at meiosis and mitosis. 33

spine – the end of a branch or leaf which has become rounded in section, hard and sharply pointed. 78

spiralization – the coiling and contraction of chromosomes during the mitotic or meiotic cycle. 250

spiral thickening – the spiral band of internal thickening on walls of xylem vessels or tracheids which, though providing support, permits longitudinal stretching. 111

spiral vessel – a vessel in which the secondary wall is laid down in the form of spirally-arranged thickenings. 100

spongy parenchyma – a loosely constructed layer of irregularly-shaped cells, separated by large intercellular spaces, above the lower epidermis of a dorsiventral leaf, and contains many chloroplasts. 120

sporangiophore – a hypha or filament on which a sporangium is borne. 388

sporangiospore – a spore, usually a non-motile spore, formed within a sporangium. 393

sporangium – a walled structure in which spores are formed. 363, 383

spore – an asexual reproductive body characteristic of plants. It mostly consists of one cell or sometimes of a few cells, never contains an embryo, and when set free may, if conditions are favourable, give rise to a new plant. 353

spore mother cell – a cell which divides by meiosis to form four haploid spores. 273

sporogenous cell – a spore mother cell. 273

sporogonium – the spore-bearing plant in Bryophyta. 425

sporophores – the spore-bearing structure or fructification in the fleshy fungi. 396, 409

sporophyll – a leaf, more or less modified, which bears one or more sporangia, or subtends a sporangium. 437

sporophyte – the spore-bearing, asexual generation, normally diploid. 243

spring wood – wood formed early in growing season, usually containing larger vessels than wood formed later in the season. 134

spur – a tubular prolongation of the base of a petiole of a gamopetalous corolla. 261

spurious fruit – a group of fruits having the appearance of a single fruit. 302

stamen – one of the organs of the flower which produces pollen. It usually consists of a slender filament surmounted by an anther in which the pollen develops. 257

staminate – said of a flower containing stamens but not carpels. 259

staminate cone – a gymnosperm cone bearing microspores or pollen. 463

staminode – an imperfectly developed or vestigial stamen. 270

starch sheath – a one-layered cylinder of cells lying on the inner boundary of the cortex of a young stem, with prominent starch grains in the cells. 108

stele – the central vascular cylinder of a stem or root containing the vascular tissue often with a central pith and an external sheath, the pericycle and endodermis. 452

stellate – radiating from the centre like a star. 354

sterigma – a short and somewhat swollen hypha, on which fungal spores, or chains of spores, are borne. 408, 411

stigma – the distal end of the style, more or less enlarged, on which pollen alights and germinates. 14, 278

stipe – the stalk of the fruit body of a fungus when it consists of a large number of more or less interwoven hyphae, or of larger brown seaweeds, especially *Laminarias*. 378

stipule – one of the two appendages, usually leaf-like, often present at the base of the petiole of a leaf. 79

stock – the rooted stem into which the scion is inserted when grafted. 144

stolon – a prostrate, horizontally growing stem, rooting at nodes and producing new plants from its buds e.g. strawberry.
– a long hypha produced by some fungi, which lies on the substratum, forming tufts of rhizoids and of sporangiophores at intervals. 396

stoma – a minute perforation in the epidermis of a leaf or young stem, together with two guard cells, one on either side of the pore, and sometimes accessory cells: concerned with regulation of gaseous exchange. 107, 115, 116

stomata – plural of stoma. 107

stomium – a part of the wall of a fern sporangium, composed of thin-walled cells; splitting begins here when the sporangium dehisces. 275, 444

strain – a form of a species with distinct morphological and/or physiological characters. 308

stratification – the grouping of the vegetation of a wood into two or more well-defined layers differing in height, as trees, shrubs, and ground vegetation. 232

strobilus – a group of sporophylls with their sporangia, more or less tightly packed around a central axis, forming a well-defined group; a cone. 446, 449

stroma – a dense mass of interwoven hyphae, fleshy to horny in texture, cushion-like, columnar, club-shaped or branched, in which many fungi develop their fructifications. 400, 404

style – the portion of the carpel between the ovary and the stigma; it is often elongated and thread-like. 278

suberin – a complex mixture of fatty substances present in the cell walls of cork tissue, rendering them waterproof and resistant to decay. 95

subhymenium – a layer of hyphae immediately beneath a hymenium. 411

sub-species – a category of individuals within a species distinguished by certain common characteristics from typical members of the species. 327

sub-stomatal chamber – a large intercellular space beneath a stoma. 117

substrate – the substances used by a plant in respiration. 201, 204

succulent fruit – juicy, soft and thick. 298

sucker – a shoot originating below ground, which later becomes aerial. 61

suction pressure – the avidity with which the cell takes in water; it is equivalent to the difference between the osmotic pressure of the cell sap, which tends to bring water into the cell, and the pressure exerted by the elastic cell wall, which tends to force water out of the cell. 157

summer wood – wood, usually with smaller vessels than springwood, formed in the latter part of the growing season. 134

superior – inserted on the receptacle above the other parts of the flower. 279

suspensor – a small tier of cells which forces the developing embryo of a higher plant down into nutritive tissue. 293
– a hypha which forms the stalk of the gametangium of Zygomycetes (*Mucor*). 395

symbiosis – an internal, mutually beneficial partnership between two organisms, usually of a physiological nature. 417

sympodial – said of a branch system in which the main axis ceases to elongate after a time, and one or more lateral branches grow on; these cease to grow and give laterals which repeat the process. 61, 71

synapsis – the pairing of homologous chromosomes at zygotene of meiosis. 244
syncarpous – said of a gynaeceum consisting of two or more united carpels. 278, 279
syncarpous fruit – a fruit derived from a flower with united carpels. 298
synecology – the study of plant communities. 229
synergidae – two naked cells which lie in the embryo sac at the end towards the micropyle and possibly play some part in guiding the tip of the pollen tube towards the egg nucleus. 284
syngamy – fusion of gametes. 242, 290
tactic movement – the locomotory movement of cells (bacteria and algae) or gametes in response to an external stimulus. According to the nature of the stimulus this movement may be chemotactic, phototactic, etc. 53
tapetum – a layer of cells surrounding a mass of spore mother-cells, which finally breaks down and contributes material which is used in the nutrition of the developing spores. 273
tap root – a strongly developed main root which grows vertically downwards and normally bears lateral roots much smaller than itself. 19, 55
taxonomy – the science of classification as applied to living organisms. 339
tegumen – the inner layer of a testa. 11
teleutospore – a thick-walled spore consisting of two or more cells, formed by rust fungi towards the end of the season; capable of remaining quiescent for some time and then germinating to give one or more small promycelia, on which the basidiospores are developed. 408
telophase – the period of reorganization of nuclei which follows the separation of the daughter chromosomes at the anaphase in mitosis and meiosis. 35
tendril – a slender, simple or branched, elongated organ used in climbing; at first soft and flexible, then becoming hard and stiff. It may be a modified stem, leaf, leaflet, or inflorescence. 79
terminal bud – a bud at the tip of an axis. 58
terminalization – the movement of chiasmata to the distal ends of chromosome bivalents during diakinesis to metaphase of meiosis. 250
testa – the seed coat, several layers of cells in thickness, derived from the integuments of the ovule. 4, 295
tetrad - a group of four spores remaining together until they are nearly or quite mature. 346
tetraploid – possessing twice the normal or diploid number of chromosomes. 312
tetrarch – a primary xylem star in dicotyledonous roots having four arms. 97
thallus – the unicellular or multicellular body of simple plants which is not differentiated into root or shoot. 354, 362
theca – the capsule of a moss. 425
thermonasties – nastic movements in a plant in relation to temperature variations. 52
thigmonastic movement – see thigmonasties. 53
thigmonasties – nastic movements in response to touch. 53
thigmotropic – growth response to the stimulus of touch or contact. 82
tissue – an aggregate of similar cells forming a definite and continuous fabric, and usually having a comparable function. 92
tolerance – the ability of a plant to endure certain environmental conditions. 229
tonoplast – the cytoplasmic membrane surrounding a vacuole in the protoplast. 27
topography – the delineation of the natural and artificial features of an area. 231
torus – the thickened centre of the pit-membrane in a bordered pit. 126
trabeculae – rod-like structures, or rod-like cells, running across a cavity. 433, 452
trace elements – nutrient elements which must be provided though only in minute amounts for the normal healthy growth of a plant. Lack of these may cause serious deficiency diseases. 179
tracheary elements – conducting elements of the xylem. 99, 122
trama – the somewhat loosely packed hyphae which occupy the middle of the gill of an agaric. 411
transition zone – the portion of the axis of a young plant in which the change from root structure to shoot structure occurs. 113
translocation – the movement of soluble elaborated food materials in solution inside the body of higher plants by way of phloem. 99, 149, 227
– the transfer of a portion of a chromosome either to another part of the same chromosome or to a different chromosome. 311

transpiration – the loss of water vapour from a plant, mainly through the stomata. 149
triarch – having three arms of protoxylem in the stele of a primary dicotyledon root. 97
trichogyne – a thread-like extension of the female organ in some fungi, and in green and red algae, which functions in receiving the male organs. 406
trilocular ovary – an ovary with three chambers. 278
triploid – having three times the haploid number of chromosomes for the species. 312
tropism – a response by a growth curvature to an external stimulus, the direction of curvature being directly related to the direction of the stimulus. 48
tuber – swollen end of an underground stem, or less often a root, consisting mainly of parenchymatous cells containing much stored food material. 63
tunica – peripheral layers of apical meristem enclosing corpus. 106
turgid – said of a cell which is distended and tense, well supplied with water. 157
turgor – the balance between the osmotic pressure of the cell sap and the elasticity of the cell wall. 28
turgor pressure – the hydrostatic pressure set up within the cell by the water present acting against the elasticity of the wall. 157
tylose – a bladder-like growth of parenchymatous cells through a pit into the lumen of a neighbouring vessel or tracheid; the vessel or tracheid becomes blocked by tyloses and ceases to function as a conducting element; often abundant in heartwood. 136
umbel – an inflorescence consisting of numerous small flowers in flat-topped groups, borne on stalks all arising from about the same point on the main stem; in most umbels, this sort of branching is repeated, the stalks which bear the groups of flowers themselves arising at about the same point on a main axis. 268
unilocular – having one chamber or compartment. 278
unilocular sporangia – sporangia consisting of a single compartment. 376
uredospore – an orange or brownish spore formed by rust fungi when growth is vigorous and serving as a means of rapid propagation; it gives rise to a mycelium which may produce more uredospores, or, later in the year, uredospores and teleutospores. 408
vacuolation – the formation of vacuoles. 39
vacuole – a small space or cavity in cytoplasm, generally containing fluid. A single vacuole is present in most plant cells and the contained fluid is cell sap. 27
vallecular canal – the internal canal in stems of horsetails lying between the ridges in the stem. 447
variation – the difference between offspring of a single mating; the differences between the individuals of a race, sub-species, or species. May be due to environmental differences during development or inborn genetic differences. 304
variety – the taxon below the sub-species. 326
vascular – pertaining to vessels which convey fluids. 106
vascular bundle – a strand of conducting tissue, consisting of xylem and phloem, sometimes separated by cambium. 109
vascular cambium – the cambium arising in vascular bundles and giving rise to secondary xylem and phloem. 124
vascular cryptogam – a non-flowering plant which has vascular tissue, such as ferns and horsetails as distinct from liverworts and mosses. 437
vascular cylinder – see stele. 93, 95, 108
vascular strand – a strand of conducting tissue. 70
vascular tissue – xylem and phloem which forms a continuous conducting system throughout stems, roots, leaves, and other organs of higher plants. 94
vegetational climax – plant community in equilibrium with existing environmental conditions. 238
vein – one of the smaller strands of conducting tissue (i.e. vascular bundle) in a leaf. 121
velum – an evanescent membrane over the gills of an agaric. 411
venation – the arrangement of the veins; by extension, the veins themselves considered as a whole. 87
venter – the dilated basal flask-shaped part of an archegonium, containing one egg. 425
ventral canal cell – the basal cell in the neck of an archegonium. 425

vernalization – the cold treatment of seeds before they are sown, which affects their flowering. 256

vesicle – a thin-walled globular swelling, usually at the end of a hypha or arising from a cell. 387

vessel element – one of the cells which with many others above and below it forms a vessel. 100

vitamins – organic substances required, in relatively small amounts, for the proper functioning of plants and animals. Possibly prosthetic groups of some enzymes. 204

water blooms – large masses of floating algae which sometimes develop very suddenly in bodies of water. 353

weathering – the breakdown of rocks due to the action of rain, frost, and sun. 232

whorled – having a group of several members arising from the same level on a stem and forming a circular group around it. 85

wild population – a natural, heterozygous population. 308

wilting – the loss of rigidity in leaves and young stems following on marked loss of water from plant cells. 167, 176

wind pollination – the conveyance of pollen from anthers to stigmas by means of the wind. 285

wood fibre – a thick-walled, elongated, dead element found in wood. 126

wood parenchyma – undifferentiated living cells occurring in xylem. 126

woody perennials – plants which persist from year to year and whose bulk is added to annually by secondary growth resulting from cambial activity. 69

wound parasite – a parasite which gains entry to the body of the plant by means of a wound. 348

wound tissue – a pad of parenchymatous cells formed by the cambium after wounding; it may give rise to groups of meristematic cells from which roots and buds form. 144

xanthophyll – photosynthetic yellow pigment occurring in chloroplasts and plastids and associated with chlorophyll. 216

xerophytes – plants able to inhabit places where the water supply is scanty, or where there is physiological drought. 176

xylem – wood: usually consisting of vessels, fibres, and/or tracheids, all with lignified walls, together with some parenchyma, with more or less lignified walls. 97

zoochlorella – unicellular green algae occurring in bodies of certain animals, especially coelenterates and ciliates. 359

zoosporangium – a sporangium in which zoospores are formed. 364

zoospore – an asexual reproductive cell which can swim by means of flagella. 357

zygomorphic – divisible into half by one longitudinal plane only. 263

zygospore – a thick-walled resting spore formed after the union of isogametes or of isogametangia. 370, 395

zygote – the product of the union of two gametes. 243, 357

zygotene – the second stage of meiotic prophase in which the homologous chromosome threads pair chromomere by chromomere. 244

Suggestions for

FURTHER READING

Part I

THE GROWTH AND DEVELOPMENT OF FLOWERING PLANTS

G. E. Fogg: *The Growth of Plants*. Penguin Books. 1963

A. C. Leopold: *Auxins and Plant Growth*. University of California Press. 1960

E. W. Sinnott: *Plant Morphogenesis*. McGraw-Hill Book Company. 1960

L. J. Audus: *Plant Growth Substances*. Leonard Hill. 1959

R. Van Der Veen and G. Meijer: *Light and Plant Growth*. Philip's Technical Library. 1959

G. B. Wilson and J. H. Morrison: *Cytology*. Reinhold Publishing Corporation. 1961

Part II

CELL DIFFERENTIATION AND THE INTERNAL STRUCTURE OF PLANTS

K. Esau: *Plant Anatomy*. John Wiley & Sons. 1953

K. Esau: *Anatomy of Seed Plants*. John Wiley & Sons. 1960

F. W. Jane: *The Structure of Wood*. A. & C. Black. 1956

A. J. Eames and L. H. MacDaniels: *An Introduction to Plant Anatomy* (2nd edition). McGraw-Hill Book Company. 1947

S. Carlquist: *Comparative Plant Anatomy*. Holt, Rinehart & Winston. 1961

Part III

PLANT NUTRITION

A. S. Crafts, H. B. Currier, C. R. Stocking: *Water in the Physiology of Plants*. Chronica Botanica Company. 1949

E. J. Russell: *The World of the Soil*. Collins. 1957

P. J. Kramer: *Plant and Soil Water Relationships*. McGraw-Hill Book Company. 1949

H. H. Dixon: *Transpiration and the Ascent of Sap in Plants*. Macmillan & Company. 1914

Part IV

PLANT NUTRITION: METABOLISM

K. Harrison: *A Guide Book to Biochemistry*. Cambridge University Press. 1959
W. D. McElroy: *Cellular Physiology and Biochemistry*. Prentice-Hall. 1961
J. A. V. Butler: *Inside the Living Cell*. Allen & Unwin. 1959
J. Bonner and A. W. Galston: *Principles of Plant Physiology*. Freeman & Company. 1951
W. O. James: *Introduction to Plant Physiology*. Oxford University Press. 1963
A. S. Crafts: *Translocation in Plants*. Holt, Rinehart & Winston. 1961
K. Esau: *Plants, Viruses and Insects*. Harvard University Press. 1961
M. Ashby: *Introduction to Plant Ecology*. Macmillan & Company. 1961
W. Leach: *Plant Ecology* (4th edition). Methuen. 1956
W. B. Turrill: *British Plant Life*. Collins. 1948

Part V

REPRODUCTION, HEREDITY AND EVOLUTION

M. J. D. White: *The Chromosomes* (5th edition). Methuen. 1961
J. McLeish and B. Snoad: *Looking at Chromosomes*. Macmillan & Company. 1958
F. B. Salisbury: *The Flowering Process*. Pergamon Press. 1963
P. Maheshwari: *An Introduction to the Embryology of Angiosperms*. McGraw-Hill Book Company. 1950
D. M. Bonner: *Heredity*. Prentice-Hall. 1961
A. M. Srb and R. D. Owen: *General Genetics*. Freeman & Company. 1957
W. Weidel: *Virus*. University of Michigan Press. 1960
S. E. Luria: *General Virology*. John Wiley & Sons. 1953
F. C. Bawden: *Plant Diseases* (2nd edition). Nelson. 1950
S. A. Barnett (editor): *A Century of Darwin*. Mercury Books (London). 1962
P. M. Sheppard: *Natural Selection and Heredity*. Hutchinson. 1961
G. W. P. Dawson: *An Introduction to the Cytogenetics of Polyploids*. Blackwell (Oxford). 1962
C. D. Darlington: *Chromosome Botany and the Origins of Cultivated Plants*. Allen & Unwin. 1963

Part VI

THE PLANT KINGDOM – A SURVEY

A. J. Oparin: *The Origins of Life on the Earth* (3rd edition). Oliver & Boyd. 1957
G. H. M. Lawrence: *Taxonomy of Vascular Plants*. Macmillan Company (New York). 1951

J. Heslop-Harrison: *New Concepts in Flowering Plant Taxonomy*. Heinemann. 1953

W. Umbreit: *Modern Microbiology*. Freeman & Company. 1962

L. E. Hawker, A. H. Linton, B. F. Folkes and M. J. Carlile: *An Introduction to the Biology of Micro-Organisms*. Edward Arnold. 1960

L. H. Tiffany: *Algae: the Grass of Many Waters*. Chas. C. Thomas, Springfield, Illinois. 1958

G. M. Smith: *Cryptogamic Botany*, Vols. I and II (2nd edition). McGraw-Hill Book Company. 1955

G. M. Smith (editor): *Manual of Phycology*. Chronica Botanica. 1951

E. C. Large: *The Advance of the Fungi*. Jonathan Cape. 1940

C. J. Alexopoulos: *Introductory Mycology*. John Wiley & Sons. 1952

C. T. Ingold: *The Biology of Fungi*. Hutchinson. 1960

A. S. Foster and E. M. Gifford: *Comparative Morphology of Vascular Plants*. Freeman & Company. 1959

K. R. Sporne: *The Morphology of Pteridophytes*. Hutchinson. 1962

C. J. Chamberlain: *Gymnosperms*. University of Chicago Press. 1935

INDEX

INDEX

Main references appear in bold type. References to figures are set in italics at the end of each entry

abscission, 49, **142-143**
  zone, 142
absorption, 183, 416
  active, 161, 168, 169 *132*
  differential of light, 217 *154*
  of light, 208, 209-210, 217
  passive, 174
Acacia, 6
accessory floral parts, 259
Acer spp., 70, 86 *67*
acetaldehyde, 226
acetic acid, 151
acetylene, 336
achene, 300 *207*
acid, 150
  carboxyl group, 197
  fatty, 196, 201, 203
  nucleic, 181, **314-318**, 319
  organic, 150, 151, 184, 225
  strong, 150
  weak, 150
acquired characters, inheritance of, 324
acropetal succession, 257
actinomorphic flower, 261
action spectrum of photosynthesis, 217 *154b*
adaptation to environment, 324
adenine, 315
adenosine diphosphate (ADP), 224
adenosine triphosphate (ATP), 209, 224
adhesion, 174
Adoxa moschatellina, 65
adsorption, 152, 163
adventitious roots, 16, 61, 63, 66, 68 *31, 40*
aecidial cup, 409 *269*
aecidiospore, 409 *269*
aecidium, 408 *269*
aeration of cultures, 180
aeration of soil, 165, 166, 223
aerobic respiration, 220
Aesculus hippocastranum, 88 *50, 51, 70*
after-ripening, 4, 5
agar gel, 153, 163, 347
Agaricus bisporus, 409-413 *270-273*
  A. campestris, 409-413 *270-273*
Agave americana, 254
aggregate
  cup fruits, 298
  free fruits, 298
  fruit, 297
Agrobacterium tumefaciens, 347 *224-225*
akinetes, 362
alanine, 197
Albugo candida, 388-392 *256-259*
albuminous seeds, 3
alcohol, 200, 203, 225
  dehydrogenase, 226
aldehyde group, 190, 191, 192, 216
alder, 259 *170*
aleurone grains, 199
algae, 28, 32, 183, 207, 212, 337-341, **351-384**,
    419, 437
  benthic, 352
  blue-green, 343, **352-354**, 419 *229*
  brown, 163, 351, **374-384**
  epiphytic, 354
  golden yellow, 351, **372-374**
  green, 351, **355-371**, 419
  marine, 184, 351, 354, **374-384**
  planktonic, 207, 352, 353, 372
  red, 351, 354 *230*
alkaline solution, 150
alkaloid, 312
allelic pair, 309
allelomorph, 305, 310
Allium spp., 268
  A. cepa, 18 *9*
allopolyploid, 313, 332
alternate leaves, 84 *71*
alternation of generations, 243, 362, 374, 376,
    378, 398, 420, 437
Althaea rosea, 61
aluminium, 179
Amanita, 417
Amaryllidaceae, 268
amino-acids, 185, 197, 198, 201, 203, 314
ammonium salt, 182, 185
Ammophila arenaria, 176 *141*
amylase, 203
Anabaena, 353 *229*
anabolism, 28

anaerobic respiration, 220, 225 *157*
Anagalis arvensis, 263 *176*
anaphase
  meiotic, 252
  mitotic, 35
anastomoses, 396
anatomy, 25
  primary body, 92-123 *72-102*
    leaf, 115-123 *94-102*
    root, 92-105 *72-85*
    stem, 106-114 *86-93*
  secondary body, 124-145 *103-125*
    roots, 126 *107, 108*
    stem, 124-126 *103-106*
anatropous ovule, 283, 296 *196*
androecium, 257, 270-275 *182-188*
Anemone nemorosa, 64 *45*
Angiospermae, 341, 458, 468-470
  anatomy, 92-145 *72-126*
  evolutionary origins, 468-469
  reproduction, 254-302 *163-210*
angiosperms, 468
angle of divergence, 84, 85
animals, 236
anion, 150, 182, 184
  divalent, 180
  monovalent, 180
  in the soil, 182, 183
anisogamy, 363 *232*
annual ring, 134 *116-118*
annuals, 2, 21, 55-58, 124, 238
annulus, 411, 433
  of fern, 444
antagonism, 180
anther, 271-275 *183-188*
antheridia, 366, 378, 388, 399, 402, 404, 423, 432, 438
antheridial
  chamber, 423, 429 *286*
  cups, 432
antheridiophore, 427 *289*
antherozoid, 366, 383, 425, 438, 455
Anthocerotae, 421
anthocyanin pigment, 181
anticlinal division, 104, 122
antipodal cells, 284 *195*
apetalous flower, 261 *171*
aphid, 228, 322 *158*
apical
  bud (see bud, terminal)
  cell, 380, 384, 422, 432, 434, 438
  dominance, 74
  meristem, 32, 58, 76, 93, 106, 115, 123, 181
aplanospore, 362 *234*
apocarpous, 278, 297 *189*
apocarpous (*cont.*)
  fruits, 298
  ovary, 279
apogamy, 374
apophysis, 433 *298*
apothecia, 419 *280*
apple, 302 *210*
appressorium, 408
Aquilegia vulgaris, 61
archegonial chamber, 460 *323*
archegoniophore, 427 *289*
archegonium, 420, 425, 429, 432, 438 *287*
archesporial cell, 273
aril, 295 *205*
Aristotle, 339
arithmetic mean, 308
Armillaria mellea, 413 *275*
Arum maculatum, 265
ascocarp, 399
ascogonium, 399, 402, 404, 406
ascogonous hyphae, 400, 402, 404
ascomycetes, 386, 396-406, 419
ascospores, 396, 400, 402, 404, 406
ascus, 386, 396, 400, 402, 404, 406
asexual reproduction, 242
asexual spore (see zoospore, aplanospore, autospore, conidiospore)
ash (tree), 88, 100, 133, 137, 259 *70, 116*
  of combustion, 179
Aspergillus, 398
Asperula odorata, 85 *66*
Asphodelus, 295
assimilation of carbon (see photosynthesis)
aster, 255
atmosphere, saturation deficit of, 172, 231
ATP (adenosine triphosphate), 209
autecology, 229
autoecious, 409
autonomic movement, 81
autopolyploids, 312
autospores, 359
autotrophic nutrition, 343, 385
autumn crocus, 312
auxanometer, 40, 41 *23*
auxins, 44-46, 48, 49, 50, 74, 143, 297
auxospore, 374 *247*
Avena sativa, 268
avens, 281
axil, 20, 57, 58, 61, 64, 70, 76 *35*
axile placentation, 278
axillary
  branch, 64, 71
  bud, 20, 61, 64, 68, 71, 74, 106, 122 *53*
axis, floral, 257, 261, 263, 265, 268
azotobacter, 185

Bacillariophyceae, 372-374 *243-247*
bacillary bacteria, 345
bacillus, 346
back crossing, 306
Bacteria, 54, 164, 166, 185, 187, 225, 319, 337, 343-350 *221-228*
  aerobic, 347
  anaerobic, 347
  bacillary, 345
  botryoidal, 346
  cell, 344 *221*
  chemosynthetic, 344
  coccal, 345
  diplococci, 346
  nitrifying, 344
  nitrogen fixing, 185
  pathogenic, 343
  reproduction and growth, 346 *223*
  sexual conjugation, 348
  soil, 185-186 *142*, *143*
  spirillar, 345
  sulphur, 344
  tetrads, 346
bacterial metabolism, 344
  plant diseases, 348 *224-228*
bacteriochlorophyll, 345
barberry, 408
bark, 70, 140, 227 *122-124*
  scale, 140 *122*
  shell, 140 *122*
barley, 3, 7
barriers, 327, 329
basal cell, 293
bases, 150
Basidiomycetes, 386, **406-417**
basidiospores, 408, 413
basidium, 386, 406, 408, 411
Beagle, H.M.S., 325
beech, 4, 70, 71, 81, 84, 133, 141, 142 *55*, *59*, *124*
beet, 58, 160, 180 *37*
Bellis perennis, 52
benthos, 352
Berberis, 408
berry, 302
Berthelletia excelsa, 199
Berthelot, 185
Beta vulgaris, 58 *37*
Beyerinck, 319
bicarbonate, 184, 207
bicarpellate fruit, 300
biennial plants, **58-59**
bifoliar spur, 463
bilabiate corolla, 263
bilberry, 238
bi-locular ovary, 278
bimodal distribution, 308, 450
binary
  division, 346
  fission, 373 *223*
bindweed, 261 *174*
biocatalyst, 200
biochemical genetics, 406
biotic factors, 234-236
birch, 133, 142 *123*
bivalent chromosomes, 249
blackberry, 281, 302 *210*
black bind weed *34*
blackleg, 348 *226*
Blackman F. F., 213
bladder campion, 300 *208*
blade, leaf, 57, 78
bleeding, 161
bloom, of leaf, 90
bloom, water, 353
blue-green algae, 343 *229*
body
  cell, 460
  primary, 92, **106-114**
  secondary, 92, **124-145** *103-125*
bog, 237
bog whortleberry, 238
Boletus, 417
Boraginaceae, 265
bordered pit, 126, 130, 133 *110*, *111*
boron, 179
bracken, 438
bract, 265
bracteoles, 257
branch
  creeping, 62 *40*
  gap, 114 *93*
  lateral, 57, 106
  of limited growth, 463
  traces, 113-114
  of unlimited growth, 463
branching
  dichasial, 73 *52*
  dichotomous, 380, 384, 398, 421, 422
Brassica campestris, 58
  B. oleracea, 76, 313 *54*
Brazil nut, 199
broadbean, 74, 185, 203
  chromosomes, 36 *19*, *21*
  germination, 6, **8-11** *3*
  root growth and development, 19, 22, 38, 56 *36*, *42*
  seed structure, 3, 5, 8 *2*
  shoot development, **19-20**, 41, 74 *10*, *13*, *24*
bromelin, 203

broom, 6
brown algae, 351, 374-384 *248-252*
brown earths, 233
Brussels-sprout, 76, 77 *54*
Bryonia dioica, 81 *62*
Bryophyllum, 57
Bryophyta, 341, **420-434**, 437
Buchner, 200
bud
  axillary, 20, 61, 64, 68, 71, 74, 122 *53*
  dormant, 21, 73, 74
  flower, 20, 58, 62, 123
  lateral, 68, 70, 73 *53*
  leaf, 19, 20, 58, 61, 64, 70, **76-90**
  scales, 77 *55, 56*
  summer, 76 *54*
  terminal, 19, 58, 61, 70, 71, 73, 74, 76, 265
  winter, 47, 68, 70, 76, 77 *50, 51, 55, 56*
budding, 144, 397
buffer action, 151
bulb, 68, 77, 89
bundle
  bicollateral, 109 *90*
  collateral, 109, 112 *88, 89, 92*
  petiolar, 121
  sheaths, 121 *101, 102*
  vascular, 109-112 *88-92*
button stage (of *Agaricus*), 411

cabbage, 313, 388
Calamites, 444
calcium, 179, 181, 182
  pectate, 181
Callistephus chinensis, 255
callose, 104 *83, 84*
Calluna vulgaris, 417
callus, 144 *31, 126*
Caltha palustris, 261 *171*
calyptra, 38, 93, 104, 425 *72, 85*
calyx, 257, 261 *173*
  gamosepalous, 261
  polysepalous, 261
cambium
  callus, 144 *126*
  cork, 138 *120*
  fascicular, 124 *104, 106*
  interfascicular, 124 *104, 106*
  vascular, 124-126 *103-107*
Cambrian, 337 *220*
campylotropous ovule, 283 *196*
candytuft, 268
canker, 322
cap cell, 364, 425
capillary, 162, 167
  translocation, 168
capitulum, 268 *180*
Capsella bursa-pastoris, **55-58** *35*
capsule, 300, 425, 433, 444 *208*
  bacterial, 345 *221*
carbides, 336
carbohydrase, 203
carbohydrate, 3, 8, 181, **190-195**, 205, 209, 212, 220, 227 *145, 146*
carbon, 179, 205, **206-207**, 336
  ring, 192
carbonate, 182, 207
carbon dioxide, 8, 29, 149, 200, 203, 205, 206, 208, 209, 211-213, 217-219, 220-226 *149, 156a, 156b*
  -acceptor, 209
  cycle, 206, 207 *149*
carbonic acid, 149, 219
Carboniferous era, 444, 450, 463
carboxylase, 226
Careya arborea, 296
carinal canal, 447 *309*
carotin, 216 *153*
carpel, 257, 278, 281, 297, 300, 302, 469 *189, 190*
carpellate flower, 259 *170*
carpogonia, 354
carrot, 58 *37*
caruncle, 11, 12, 296 *4*
Caryophyllaceae, 265, 278
caryopsis, 300
Casparian strip, 95, 108, 452 *75*
castor oil, 6, **11-13**, 195, 199, 203, 296 *4, 5*
catabolism, 28, 30
catalase, 200, 201, 203
cation, 149, 150, 182, 184, 232
  divalent, 184
  exchange, 182
  monovalent, 184
catkin, 259 *170*
cauliflower, 256
cauline leaves, 57 *35*
celandine, 79 *57*
cell, 25, 27-32, 157, 321 *15a, 16*
  antipodal, 284 *195*
  apical, 380, 384, 422, 432, 434, 438
  archesporial, 273
  artificial, 156
  bacterial, 344 *221*
  basal, 293
  body, 460
  buffer action in, 151
  cap, 364, 425
  companion, 104, 111, 137 *83, 84*
  complementary, 142 *125*
  differentiation, 92, 93, 105, 106, 318 *72*

cell (*cont.*)
  division, 32-36, 47, 48, 93, 181, 242, 364, 368 *16*
  egg, 284 *195*
  elongation, 39, 45, 47, 48, 93 *72*
  enlargement, 39, 40, 124
  enucleate, 103
  filling, 142 *125*
  foot, 398
  generative, 275, 460, 463 *187*
  germ, 305
  growth, 39
  guard, 107, 116, 219 *94-97*
  hinge, 176 *141*
  initials, 106
  isodiametric, 125
  lumen, 133
  neck canal, 425, 438
  passage, 95
  permeability, 180
  plate, 35 *20*
  pro-cambial, 126
  sap, 27, 157, 159, 174
  sheath, 353
  stalk, 383, 460
  subsidiary, 116 *96, 97*
  tapetal, 284
  terminal, 293
  tube, 275, 460, 463 *187*
  turgidity, 28, 40, 52, 148, 157, 159, 176, 219, 387
  vegetative, 275 *187*
  ventral canal, 425, 438 *287*
  wall, 27, 33, 35, 36, 39, 194, 195 *20, 146*
    bacterial, 344
    primary, 35, 100, 143 *19, 20*
    secondary, 100-101 *80-82*
cellulose, 36, 95, 140, 163, 194
central nodule, 373 *245*
centric diatoms, 372 *245, 246*
centrifugal opening of flowers, 265
centripetal opening of flowers, 265
centromere, 33, 36, 250, 252
centuary plant, 254
cereal, 3, 6, 13
chalaza, 283, 288 *195, 196*
chalazogamy, 288
Charophyceae, 355
Cheiranthus cheiri, 265
chemical energy, 156, 181, 205, 208
chemical potential gradient, 156
chemosynthetic bacteria, 344
chemotaxis, 54, 425, 440
cherry, 142, 281
chiasma, 249, 252 *169*
chiasmata, proximal, 252, 310
chitin, 385
Chlamydomonas, 32, 54, 252, **355-357** *231, 232*
chlamydospore, 395
Chlorella, 32, 212, 217, **359**, 417 *234*
  C. pyrenoidosa, 359 *234*
  C. vulgaris, 359 *234*
chlorenchyma, 447 *309*
chloride, 149, 183
chlorine, 179, 182
chlorococcales, 359
Chlorophyceae, **355-371**
chlorophyll, 28, 180, 181, 190, 205, 208, 211, 213, **214-217** *153*
  a, 216 *153*
  b, 216 *153*
  of bacteria, 343
Chlorophyta, **355-371**, 419
chloroplast, 28, 31, 204, 210, **213-219** *150-155*
  reticulate, 364 *237*
  spiral, 368 *241*
  structure, 213-214 *151, 152*
chlorosis, *181*
Christmas rose, 261 *172*
chromatid, 33, 244, 253
chromatin, 33
chromatography, 217
chromatophore, 354, 374, 375 *248*
  discoid, 354, 380
  parietal, 354
  stellate, 354
chromatoplasm, 353
chromomeres, 244 *166*
chromonema, 33 *166*
chromosomes, 28, 33, 36, 204, **242-253**, 309-313, 345 *16, 21, 163-168*
  deletions, 311
  diploid complement, 312
  disjunction, 309
  DNA, 316
  duplications, 311
  hexaploid complement, 312
  inversions, 311
  map, 310
  Mendelism, 308
  mutations, 311-313
  pairing, **244-249**, 312
  pentaploid complement, 312
  polyploid complement, 312
  ring-like configuration, 251 *168*
  translocation, 311, 331
  triploid complement, 312
Chroococcus, 353 *229*

Chrysophyceae, 372
Chrysophyta, 372-374
chytrids, 385
cingulum, 372
circumnutation, 43, 81 *25*
Cirsium spp., 118
citric acid, 151, 225
  cycle, 225
clamp connections, 409 *270*
Clapham, Tutin, and Warburg, 340
Class, 340
  Angiospermae, 468-470
  Anthocerotae, 421
  Ascomycetes, 396-406
  Bacillariophyceae, 372-374
  Basidiomycetes, 406-417
  Chlorophyceae, 355-371
  Chrysophyceae, 372
  Cyclosporae, 380-384
  Gymnospermae, 458-468
  Hepaticeae, 421-431
  Heterogeneratae, 377-380
  Isogeneratae, 375-377
  Musci, 431-434
  Phycomycetes, 386-396
classification, 339, 341-342
  artificial system, 339
  binomial system, 340
  horizontal, 339
  natural system, 339
  nineteenth century, 341
  phylogenetic, 339
  present day, 342
  sexual system, 339, 341
  vertical, 339
Claviceps purpurea, 402-404 *267*
clay, 164, 166, 167, 182
cleistogamy, 287
cleistothecium, 399 *263*
Clematis, 300
climate, 134
climatic factors, 229, **230-232**, 330
climbers, 55 *34*
closing layer, 142
Closteridium, 185
clover, 185
club-mosses, 437, 450 *312*
coagulation, 153
coccal bacteria, 345
cocci, 345
coelenterates, 207
coenzyme, 202, 204
cohesion, 174
coils, major of chromosomes, 252
colchicine, 312
Colchicum spp., 66 *48*
  C. autumnale, 312
coleoptile, 14, 16, 40, 44, 48 *26, 28*
coleorhiza, 14 *6*
collenchyma, 107, 302 *87*
colloid, **151-152**, 163, 165, 166, 182, 199, 201, 336
  size range, 152
colloidal
  solution, 152
  system, 152
colonies, daughter, 359
colonization, 238, 332
colonizers, pioneer, 238, 353, 419
coltsfoot, 61, 254
columbine, 61
columella, 393, 433 *260, 299*
companion cell, 104, 111, 137 *83, 84*
compensation point, 212
competition, 234
complete flower, 259
Compositae, 194, 263, 268
concentration gradient, 156, 183
conceptacle, 383 *252*
cone, 446, 452 *321*
  ovulate, 460, 463, 466 *324*
  staminate, 463 *325, 327*
conidia, 398, 399, 402, 405 *263, 264, 266-268*
conidiophore, 391, 396, 398, 399, 402, 405 *263*
conidiosporangia, 391
conidiospore, 391 *257, 258*
conifer, 70, 462
Coniferophytae, 462
conjugation
  lateral, 370 *242*
  scalariform, 370
  in *Spirogyra*, 370, 395 *242*
  tube, 370 *242*
connecting band, 372
connective, 271
contractile vacuoles, 356
Convolvulus arvensis, 261 *174*
copper, 179, 202
Coprinus, 409
coral, 207
cork, 25, 64, 70, **138-141** *119-121*
  cambium, 138 *120*
  oak, 142
corm, 66 *48*
corolla, 257, 261
  bilabiate, 263
  gamopetalous, 261 *174*
  papillonaceous, 263
  polypetalous, 261 *172*
  tube, 261

corpus, 106, 122
Correns, 305
cortex, 93, 106, 161, 174, 185 *131*
of root, 94-95
of stem, 107-108
Cortonarius, 417
Corylus avellana, 259
corymb, 268 *178*
cotton, 195, 256
cotyledon, 3, 7, 8, 9, 11, 12, 14, 18, 194
creeping buttercup, 61 *40*
Crepis spp., 36 *21*
C. pulchra, 242 *21*
Crick, 316 *213*
crocus, 66 *48*
crossing over, 249, 310 *167*
cross-pollination, 285, 287, 305 *198*
crown gall, 347 *227*
Cruciferae, 265, 388
Cryptogamae, 341
Cryptogamia, 341
crystal aggregate, 30 *17*
crystalloids, 199
cuckoo-pint, 265
cucumber, 7
Cucumis melo, 7
C. sativus, 7
Cucurbitaceae, 109 *90*
culture, 179, 212, 360, 417
replicate, 212
cupules, gemmae, 422 *282*
curvature, growth, 44, **48-52** *26*, *28-30*
cutin, 106, 115, 176
cyanide, 183
Cyanophyta, **352-354**, 419 *229*
Cycadophytae, 458
Cycas, 460
cyclical change, 238 *162*
cyclic structure, 192
Cyclosporae, 375, **380-384**
Cymbidium walton setonii *175*
cyme, 265 *177*
dichasial 265
helicoid, 265 *177*
monochasial, 265
scorpioid, 265 *177*
cymose inflorescence, 265 *177*
Cystopus candida, 388
cytase, 203
Cytisus scorparius, 6
cytogenetics, 309, 313
cytokinesis, 33, 35, 253, 290 *20*
cytoplasm, 27, 28, 30, 31, 32, 39, 163, 197, 204, 373
cytoplasmic membranes, 27, 158
cytosine, 315

daffodil, 68, 257
dahlia, 194
daisy, 52, 61
damping off fungi, 386
dandelion, 52, 61 *39*
dark reaction, 209
Darwin, Charles, 44, 48, **324-333**, 339
Daucus carota, 58 *37*
daughter chromosome, 35
day length, 231
day-neutral plants, 255
De Bary, Anton, 417
decarboxylation, 226
deciduous, 70, 76, 176
deficiency, mineral, 180-182
degradation, 196
dehiscence, 275, 300
dehydrogenase, 202, 203
Delesseria, 354 *230*
deletions, chromosomal, 311
Delphinium ajacis, 61
denaturation of proteins, 5, 40, 201
denitrification, 187
deoxyribose, 315
deoxyribose nucleic acid (DNA), **315-318**, 345, 352 *212*, *213*
De Saussure, 179, 205
descent with modification, 329
determinate inflorescence, 265
development, **19-24**, 47, 48, 190
of anther, 273-275
of buds, 73-75, 76-78 *55-56*
of flowers, 20, **256-257** *169*
of leaves, 77-78
of ovules, 281
of pollen, 274, 288 *200*
of roots, 19
of shoots, 19
developmental history, 237
De Vries, 305, 331
diakinesis, 251 *163*, *164*
diaminopimelic acid, 344
diastase, 203
diatoms, 372-374 *243-247*
centric, 372
pennate, 372
dichasial branching, 73 *52*
cyme, 265
dichlorophenoxyacetic acid (2.4-D), 50
dichogamy, 287
dichotomous branching, 380, 384, 398, 421, 422
dicotyledon, 13, 50, 88, 108, 133

differentiation, 92, 93, 105, 106, 318 *72*
diffuse porous wood, 137 *117*
diffusion, 7, **154-156**, 161, 172, 183, 219 *127*
  and chemical potential gradient, 156
  gradient, 163
  and osmosis, 156
  shell, 173 *136*
Digitalis purpurea, 58, 279 *192*
dihybrid, 307
dikaryon, 409
dinoflagellates, 352
dioecious plant, 259, 287, 427
Dioon, 460 *321-323*
diplococci (bacteria), 346
diploid chromosome complement, 242, 244
diplophase, 398
diplotene, 249, 310 *163*, *164*
disaccharide, 192, 209
discoid, chromatophores, 354
disease, 181, 385, 396, 398
dispersal of seeds, 295
dissociation, 150, 151, 155
distribution of species, 325
diurnal rhythm, 172
division of cells, **32-36**, 47, 48, 93, 181, 242, 364, 368 *16*
  anticlinal, 104, 122
  periclinal, 104, 122, 123, 125, 257, 293 *105*
division of labour (*Volvox*), 359
Divisions of the plant kingdom, 340-342
  Bacteria, 343-350
  Bryophyta, 420-434
  Chlorophyta, 355-371
  Chrysophyta, 372-374
  Cyanophyta, 352-354
  Eumycophyta, 385-419
  Phaeophyta, 374-384
  Pteridophyta, 437-457
  Rhodophyta, 354
  Spermatophyta, 458-470
Dixon, 174
DNA (deoxyribose nucleic acid), 315-318, **345**, 352 *312*, *313*
docken, 58
domestication, 324, 329
dominance, imperfect, 306
dominant factors, 305
dormancy, 4, 5, 47
double flowers, 261
downy mildews, 386
Dracena, 85
dragon tree, 85
Drosera spp. 287
Drosophila melanogaster, 309
drought, 3, 219
  resistance, 68, **176-178**
drum auxanometer, 40
drupe, 302 *210*
druplet, 302 *210*
druse, 30 *17*
dry fruit, 298
Dryopteris felix-mas, 438-444 *300-305*
dry weights, air, 6, 8, 19, 21
duplications of chromosomes, 311
dwarf male of *Oedogonium*, 366
dwarf shoot of *Pinus*, 463
dynamic equilibrium of molecules, 150

ear of oat, 298
ecological niche, 327
ecology, **229-239**, 256
Ectocarpus, 375-377 *248*
  E. siliculosus, 375 *248*
ectotrophic mycorrhizae, 413
edaphic factors, 229, **232-234** *159*
egg-apparatus, 284 *195*
egg cell, 284 *195*
Eichler classification, 341
elater, 427, 449
elder *49*
electrolysis *149*
electrolyte, 149, 150, 151
electron microscope, 30, 195, 320
elements
  major nutrient, 179, 182
  minor nutrient, 179, 182
  trace, 179, 202
elm, 137
Elodea canadensis, 54
embryo, **2-8**, 14, 18, 36, 148, 290, 462 *204*
  development, 292-294 *204*
  sac, 284, 290, 466, 470 *195-197*
empirical formula, 192
emulsifier, 152
emulsion, 152
emulsoid sol, 152
encystment, 391
endemic species, 328
endocarp, 298
  sclerified, 300
endodermis, 95, 104, 452 *75*, *76*, *77*, *79*
endogenous origin of roots, 57, 104 *85*
endoplasmic reticulum, 31 *18*
endosperm, 2, 3, 7, 8, 9, 11, 14, 18, 194, 290 *18*
  development of, 290
endospermic seeds, 3, 292
endospores, 345

endotrophic mycorrhizae, 417
energy, 8, 45, 156, 183, 196, 200, 205, 210, 220, 224 *128*
  chemical, 156, 181, 205, 208
  fixation, 224
  light, 205, 208
  radiant, 210
  release, 220, 224
  solar, 209
  transformation, 224
Enquiry into Plants (Theophrastus), 339
Enteromorpha, 355
entomophilous flowers, 285
environment, 4, 55, 172, 212, **229-239**, 325, 330, 337
  and heredity, 307-309
environmental adaptation, 324
enzymatic digestion, 195, 220, 320
enzymes, 7, 153, 180, 192, 196, **200-204**, 208, 220, 224, 226, 288, 314, 316, 318, 320
  and fermentation, 200, 203, 226
  and food reserves, 7, 195, 196
  and heredity, 204, 314, 318
  hydrolytic, 7, 192, 196, 198, 201, 203, 220, 224, 320
  oxidizing, 202, 203, 222, 224
  proteolytic, 198, 202, 203
  reducing, 203, 226
  respiratory, 204, 224, 226
  and synthesis, 198, 200, 201, 204, 208, 316
  and vitamins, 204
ephemerals, 2
epicotyl, 9
epidermis, 27, 93, 94, 106, 107, 138, 142, 159, 178 *15b*, *74*, *87*, *120*, *121*
  leaf, 115-119 *94-100*
  root, 94 *74*
  shoot, 106, 115
epigeal germination, 13
epigynous, 281, 298
epigyny, 281
epinasty, 77
epipetalous stamen, 271 *183*
epiphytes, 354, 438
epiphytic algae, 354
epitheca, 372
equational division, 244
equilibrium pressure, 156
Equisetum, 444-450 *306-311*
  E. arvense, 446
  E. limosum, 446
  E. telmatia, 444, 446
ergastic substances, 30 *17*
ergot, 404
Erica tetralix, 176 *140*
Erodium cicutarium, 270
erosion, 234
Erwinia atroseptica, 347 *226*
Erysiphe, 400-402 *265*, *266*
esterase, 203
ester linkage, 196
ethyl alcohol, 203, 226
etiolation, 41 *24*
Eucaryota, 341, 342, 352
Eudorina, 359 *233*
euglenoids, 352
Euglenophyta, 352
Eumycophyta, 385-419
Euphorbia pulcherrima, 265
Eurotium (*Aspergillus*), 398-400 *263*
evaporation, 168, 170, 172, 174, 176
evergreens, 69, 176
evolution, 2, 32, 243, **324-332**, 336-338, 339, 420, 437, 458
  survival, 324
  theory, **324-330**, 332
evolutionary trends, 2
exalbuminous seeds, 3
exocarp, 298, 300
exodermis, 95 *74*
extine, 287
eye of potato, 64 *44*
eye-spot, 356, 376 *231*

Fagus sylvatica, 81 *55*, *59*
Family, 340
fascicular cambium, 124 *104*, *106*
fat, 3, 6, 8, **195-196**, 201, 203
fatty acid, 196, 201, 203
female prothallus, 455, 456, 458, 462, 466, 469
fermentation, 200-203, 220, 226, 396
fern, 437, **438-444**
fertilization, 242-243
  in algae, 357, 362, 363, 366, 374, 378, 384 *247*, *250*, *232*, *236*, *239*
  in angiosperms, 290, 297 *201-202*
  in bryophytes, 425, 429, 432
  in fungi, 388, **391-392**, 398, 399, 402, 404, 406, 409, 425, 429, 432 *255*, *259*, *262*, *263*, *268*
  in gymnosperms, 460, 468 *323*
  in pteridophytes, 440, 450, 455 *300*
fibres, 133, 195
  septate, 133
fibrous layer, 237, 275
field poppy, 261 *173*
filament, 271
filaments in algae, 360, 364, 368
Filicopsida, 437, 438

filling cells, 142 *125*
filterable viruses, 319
flaccidity, 176
flagella, 356, 360, 378
  bacterial, 345
flax, 195
fleshy fruit, 298, 300 *210*
floret, 268 *180*
floridean starch, 354
flower, **256-294**, 297, 469
  actinomorphic, 261
  apetalous, 261 *171*
  bud, 58, 123, 257 *169*
  carpellate, 259 *170*
  complete, 259
  double, 261
  imperfect, 259 *170*
  incomplete, 259
  naked, 259
  perfect, 259
  pistillate, 259 *170*
  sessile, 265, 268 *178*, *180*
  solitary, 263 *176*
  stalk, 257
  staminate, 259 *170*
  zygomorphic, 263 *175*
flowering, 47, 58, 73, 227, 231
fluorescence, 217
foliose lichens, 419
follicle, 300
food
  reserves, 7, 11, 21, 58, 63, 68, 136, 183, 190, 195, 197, 199, 200, 209, 290
  storage, 94, 99, 133, 181, 195, 227 *77*
fool's parsley, 268
foot, 425, 433, 455
  cells, 398
forget-me-not, 265 *177*
formaldehyde, 208
fossils, 328, 337
foxglove, 58, 279 *192*
Fragaria vesca, 61, 281 *41*, *193*
Fraxinus excelsior, 88 *70*
free central placentation, 279
free nuclear stage, 290
Fritillaria spp., 275
frond, 380
frost, 3, 256
fructification, 409, 410
fructose, 191, 192, 194, 209
  diphosphate, 225
fruit, 14, **297-303**, 458, 470 *206-210*
  aggregate, 297
  apocarpous, 298
  bicarpellate, 300

fruit (*cont.*)
  dehiscent, 300
  dry, 298
  fleshy, 298, 300 *210*
  indehiscent, 300
  multiple, 297
  spurious, 302 *210*
  succulent, 298
  syncarpous, 298
frustule, 372
fruticose lichens, 419
fucoxanthin, 351, 374
Fucus, 380-384 *250-252*
  F. serratus, 383 *252*
  F. spiralis, 383 *252*
  F. vesiculosus, 380, 383 *250*
Funaria, 431-434
fundamental tissue, 94
fungi, 2, 41, 46, 164, 166, 185, 200, 225, 341, **385-419**
Fungi imperfecti, 386
funicle, 4, 296
funiculus, 283, *195-196*
fusiform
  initials, 125
  tracheids, 99-100
fusion-cell, 395

galactose, 191
Galanthus nivalis, 68, 257, 261 *48*
Galium, 263
gametangia, 363, 376, 388, 392
gamete, 242, 284, 285, 288, 304, 311, 357, 362, 366, 376, 383
  formation in pollen, 288-290 *200*
gametophyte, 243, 363, 378, 383, 420, 433, 437, 450, 455, 458, 466, 469
  female, 455, 456, 458, 462, 466, 469
  male, 455, 456, 460, 463, 469
gamopetalous corolla, 261 *174*
gamosepalous calyx, 261
garden geranium, 118
garden pea, 3, 79, 185, 298, **304-307** *1*, *58*
gas, 149
gaseous exchange, 212, **222-223**
gel, 153, 163
  carbohydrate, 163
gemmae, 422, 432 *284*, *285*
  cups, 422 *284*
Genera Plantarum (Linnaeus), 339
generative cell, 275, 460, 463 *187*
generic name, 340
genes, 305, 309
  linked, 309-310

genes (*cont.*)
mutations, 311
position effects, 311
recombination, 310, 331
replication, 310
genetic exchange, 327
isolation, 327
genetics, 204, **304-311**, 314, 320, 347, 405, 406
and evolution, 330-331
genotype, 305, 306
Genus, 340
geographical races, 327
geological periods, 337 *220*
geotropism, 49 *29, 30*
Geranium pratense, 270
germ cells, 305
line, 311
tube, 387, 388, 395, 408
germinal substance, 304
germination
of seeds
angiosperm, **2-18**, 19, 20, 36, 40, 148, 222, 225, 236 *3, 5, 7, 8, 9*
broad bean, 8-11 *3*
castor oil, 11-13 *5*
conditions necessary for, 4-8
gymnosperm, 462, 468 *328*
of spores
algal, 366, 370, 374 *239, 242*
bryophyte, 427, 431, 434
fungal, 388, 391, 393, 395, 400, 408, 409 *252-258*
pteridophyte, 44 *304*
germling, 380
Geum, 281
Gibberella fujikuroi, 46
gibberellin, 46-48 *27*
gills, 411
girdle, diatom, 372
girdling experiments, 227
glucose, 190, 191, 192, 194, 197, 203, 208, 209
residue, 194
glycerol, 196, 201, 203
glycine, 197
glycogen, 386
glycolosis, 225
golden-yellow algae, 351, **372-374**
Gonium, 359 *233*
gooseberry, 302
gorse, 176, 270
Gossypium spp., 195, 256
grafting, 144
Gramineae, 263, 268, 300
gram-negative, 345
-positive, 345
grana, 29, 214 *151, 152*
grand period of growth, 21
granules, bacterial, 345
grape, seedless, 297
grass, 79, 85, 89, 175, 195, *71*
green algae, 351, **355-371**, 419
ground
layer, 237
tissue, 94, 109
groundsel, 78 *57*
growth, **19-43**, 44-52, 148, 176, 179, 181, 190, 196, 198, 314, 336
of branch systems, 70-75 *50-53*
of buds, 77-78 *55-56*
of cells, 32, 39
curvatures, 44, **48-52**, 82 *26, 28-30*
in dark, 41 *24*
and external stimuli, 48-53 *28-31*
factors affecting, 40-41
forms, 55-75 *34-53*
grand period of, 21 *11*
increments, 22
intercalary, 24 *13*
lateral, 124
of leaves, 77-78 *55, 56*
measurement of, 39-40 *23*
phases of, 39, 92
primary of roots, 92, 93
primary of stems, 92, 106
rate, 21
secondary of roots, 126
secondary of stems, 124, 134, 138
substances, **44-53**, 74, 232, 255
guanine, 315
guard cell, 107, 116, 219 *94-97*
gum, 143
guttation, 175 *139*
Gymnospermae, 341, **458-468**
gymnosperms, 458
gynaecium, 257, **276-284** *189-197*

habitat, 229
habit, erect, 55
haemoglobin, 216
hairs, 118, 176, 231 *98, 99, 140, 141*
glandular, 118 *99*
multicellular, 118 *99*
simple, 118 *98, 99*
stinging, 118 *98*
haploid chromosome complement, 242, 244, 253
haplophase, 398
haptonasties, 53 *33*
haptotropism, 82

hard pan, 233
hardwood, 126, **130-133** *116-117*
Hartig, 227
  net, 413 *277*
haustoria, 402, 408
hazel, 259
heartwood, **134-136** *118*
heath, cross leaved, 176 *140*
heather, 237, 417
Hedera helix, 88
Helianthus tuberosus, 63
helicoid cyme, 265 *177*
Helleborus spp., 261, 278, 279, 298 *172, 189, 190*
hemicellulose, 36, 195, 203, 292
Hepaticeae, 421-431
Heracleum sphondylium, 287 *198*
herbaceous plants, 55-69
heredity, 28, 36, 204, **304-318**, 324, 330
Heterobasidiomycetes, 406
heterocysts, 353
heteroecious, 408
Heterogeneratae, 374, **377-380**
heterospory, 450, 456, 458
heterothallism, 363, 395, 396, 406
heterotrophic nutrition, 343, 385
heterozygosity, 305-307, 331
hexaploid chromosome complement, 312
hilum, 4, 8, 296
hinge cells, 176 *141*
Hippuris, 76 *86*
hogweed, 287 *198*
holdfast, 362, 364, 378, 380
holly, 70
hollyhock, 61
Homobasidiomycetes, 409
homospory, 450
homothallism, 395
homozygosity, 305-307
honey agaric, 413
Hooke, Robert, 25
horizons, soil, 232 *159*
hormone, **44-53**, 74, 232, 255
  inhibitors, 48
horse chestnut, 73, 76, 88 *50, 51, 70*
horsetail, 437, 444
humidity, 172, **230-231**
humus, 166, 187, 232, 233, 413
hyaline fluid, 27
hybrid, 305, 307, 313, 327
  swarms, 327
hydathode, 175 *138, 139*
Hydra viridis, 359
hydrocarbons, 336
hydrochloric acid, 6, 149, 150, 151

hydrogen, 149, 179, 182, 197, 220, 336
  acceptor, 208
  bonds, 316
  ion concentration (pH), **150-151**, 153
  peroxide, 201, 203
hydrolase, 201, 203
hydrolysis, 7, 148, 192, 196, 198, 201, 203, 224
hydrolytic cleavage, 192
hydrostatic pressure, 156
hydroxyl group, 190, 191, 192, 196
  ions, 150, 184, 336
hygroscopic, 427, 231, 434
hymenium, 411
hypertonic solution, 159
hyphae, 385, 387, 388, 393, 413
  intercellular, 387, 408, 413
  intracellular, 387
hypocotyl, 13, 16, 59 *37*
hypogeal germination, 11, 13
hypogyny, 279, 281
hyponasty, 77
hypotheca, 372
hypotonic solution, 159

IAA (indoleacetic acid), 44, 50
Iberis amara, 268
Ilex, 70
imbibition, 19, 162
imperfect
  dominance, 306
  flower, 259 *170*
impermeability, 4, 6
incomplete flower, 259 *170*
indehiscence, 300
independent assortment, 307, 309
indeterminate inflorescence, 268
indian lotus, 4
indoleacetic acid (IAA), 44, 50
indusium, 441, 444 *302*
infection, 322, 348, 386, 388, 392, 402, 404, 408, 409
inferior gynaecium, 281
inferior ovary, 281 *194*
inflorescence, 58, 73, 123, **263-269** *176-180*
  capitulum, 268 *180*
  determinate, 265
  head, 268 *180*
  indeterminate, 265, 268
  racemose, 265 *178*
Ingen-Housz, 205
inheritance (see heredity)
  of acquired characters, 324
  multiple factor, 307
inherited factors, 307

initials, 106
  fusiform, 125
  ray, 125
insect, 228, 236, 285, 322
  pollination, 285
integument, 281-295, 458, 460 *195*
intercalary growth, 24 *13*
intercellular space, 27, 94, 120, 141, 172, 219
    73, *100*, *155*
interface, 152
interfascicular
  cambium, 124 *104*, *106*
  regions, 109
internode, 20, 22, 41, 57, 61, 77 *13*
interphase, 33, 252
intine, 287
inulin, 194
invasion, 237
inversions, chromosomal, 311
invertase, 192, 203
involucral bract, 268 *181*
involucre, 425
iodine, 9, 210
ion, 149, 150, 180, 182, 183
  absorption, 183-184
  accumulation, 183, 184
  divalent, 180, 184
  monovalent, 180, 183, 184
ionization, 150
Iris, 65 *46*
  I. versicolor, 290
iron, 179, 181, 182, 202
irritability, 48-54
Isoetes, 450
isogametes, 362
isogamy, 363
Isogeneratae, 374, **375-377**
isolation
  ecological, 327
  genetic, 327
  geographical, 327
  population, 327
isotonic solution, 159
Ivanovski, 319
ivy, 88

Jerusalem artichoke, 63, 194
Johanssen, 305

kelp, 377
  giant, 378
ketone group, 191
kidney bean, 43
kinetins, 46-48
Knop, 179
Krebs, Sir Hans, 225
  cycle, 225

Labiatae, 85, 263, 285
Laburnam anagyroides, 88
Lactarius deliciosus, 413
Lamark, 324,
Lamarkism, 332
lamellae, 214 *151*, *152*
lamina, 57, 78, **87-90**, 121, 378 *68*, *69*, *70*, *71*
Laminaria, 163, **377-380** *249*
  L. digitata, 378
laminarin, 351, 374
Lamium purpureum, 85 *65*
land utilization, 231
larkspur, 61
lateral
  bud, 68, 70, 73 *53*
  conjugation, 370
  growth, 32, 124-142 *103-108*
  meristems, 32, 124-126, 138-141 *103-107*,
    120, *121*
  root, 13, 19, **55-57**, 59, 70, 104, 186 *36*, *85*
  formation, 104-105 *85*
laterite, 232
Lathyrus odoratus, 271 *182*
laurel, 70
Laurus nobilis, 70
Lavandula vera, 118
lavender, 118
leaching, 183
leaf, **76-90**, 170, 175, 178, **180-182**, 210, 213,
    216-218, 228, 441 *54-71*, *141*, *150*, *155*
  alternate, 84 *71*
  anatomy, **115-123**, 176-178 *94-102*, *140*,
    141
  axil, 57, 58, 61, 64, 70, 76
  base, 77, 78, **79-81**, 115 *56*, *57*, *58*, *59*
  blade, 57, 78
  bloom, 90
  bud, 20, 58
  compound, 88 *70*
  compound palmate, 88 *70*
  compound pinnate, 88 *70*
  deciduous, 70, 76, 176
  dicotyledonous, 120 *94*, *100*
  epidermis, 115-119 *94-100*
  exstipulate, 90
  fall, 70, 142
  form, 88-90 *69-71*
  gap, 114, 441 *93*
  hair, 90, 176 *140*, *141*
  linear, 89
  mid-rib, 87, 121 *68*, *100*
  monocotyledonous, 120, 121 *95*, *97*, *101*

leaf (*cont.*)
mozaic, 87 *64, 67*
petiole, 82-83, 87, 121 *63*
primordia, 106, 122 *86*
radical, 57
scale, 61, 63, 64, 66
scar, 70, 71 *50, 51*
sessile, 57, 78, 89 *57*
shade, 232
shape, 88 *69, 232*
sheath, 79, 89 *48, 71*
simple, 88 *70*
skeleton, 87
stalk, 57, 78, **82-83** *63*
stipulate, 90
sun, 232
surface, 90
trace, **113-114**, 440 *93*
variegated, 211
legume, 298, 300 *207*
Leguminosae, 6, 185, 263, 285
leguminous plants, 185
lenticel, 70, **141-142**, 223 *49, 125*
closing layer, 142
leptotene, 244 *163, 164*
leucosin, 372
lever auxanometer, 40
lichen, 417-419
life cycle, 20
light, 5, 41, 48, 52, 79, 83, 172, **209-210**, 211, 212, 230-232, 255
absorption, 217 *154*
energy, 205, 208
and germination, 8
hard seeds, 8
intensity, 212, 213, 231
and photosynthesis, 205, **208-211**
reaction, 208, 209
saturation, 212
sensitive seeds, 8
tactic movements and, 53-54
lignin, 97, 99, 100
ligule, 89, 268 *71*
Ligustrum vulgare, 88
lilac, 73, 77
Liliaceae, 278
Lilium spp., 274, 284
lily, 274, 278, 284
lime (tree) *117, 119*
limiting factors, 176, 212
linkage, 309
ester, 196
groups, 309
incomplete, 310
relations, 310
Linnaeus, Carl, 339-341
Linnean Society, 325
Linum usitatissimum, 195
lipase, 196, 201, 203
lip cell, 275
lipids, 195
liverworts, 421
loam, 164, 165
locule, 271, 278
long day plants, 255
lower bract scale, 466
lumen, 133
lupin, 61, 185
Lupinus albus *18*
L. nootkatensis, 61
Luria, 321
Lycopodium selago, 450 *312*
Lycopsida, 437, 450
Lysenko, 256
lysigenous cavity, 112 *92*

mace of nutmeg, 296 *205*
Macrocystis, 377
macrozoospores, 360
magnesium, 179, 181, 182, 202, 216
maize, 3, **13-16**, 44, 112, 170, 256, 309 *6, 7, 8, 92*
major coils, 252
male (or shield) fern, 438-444 *300-305*
male prothallus, 455, 456, 460, 463, 469
malic acid, 151, 440
maltase, 203
Malthus on population, 329
Malus, 263, 281 *194*
manganese, 179, 202
mannitol, 351, 374, 386
mannose, 191, 192
manometer, 161
maple, 70, 86, 161 *67*
Marchantia polymorpha, 421-431 *282-285, 289-292*
marram grass, 176 *141*
marsh marigold, 261 *171*
mass flow, 174, 228
and translocation, 228
mating types, 409
matrix, chromosomal, 33
meadow buttercup, 65, 279, 340
meadow cranesbill, 270
mechanical tissue, 97
medulla, 109, 380 *88*
medullary
ray, 109, 125, 126, 133 *104, 106, 108, 112-114, 158*
zone, 419

megasporangium, 383, 455, 458, 460, 463, 466
megaspore, 284, 455, 458, 460 *195*
  mother cell, 284, 466, 469 *197*
megasporophyll, 458, 460, 466 *320*
meiosis, **242-253**, 274, 284, 309, 370, 406 *163-168*
  I, 253
  II, 253
meiotic
  anaphase, 252
  metaphase, 251 *163, 364, 168*
  mitosis, 253
  prophase, 244-251 *163, 164*
melon, 7
membrane
  cytoplasmic, 27, 158
  protoplasmic, 27, 158
  semipermeable, 157, 158, 161, 180, 181, 183, 201
Mendel, Gregor, 304-310
Mendelian inheritance, 304-310
Mendelism, **304-310**, 330
Mentha viridis, 63 *43*
Merismopedia, 353 *229*
meristele, 441
meristem, **32**, 70, 104, 124, 257, 378
  apical, 32, 58, 76, 92, 93, 106, 115, 123, 124, 181 *72*
  lateral, 32, 124-126, 138-141 *103, 104, 120, 121*
  terminal (see meristem apical)
meristematic region, 32, 36
meristoderm, 380
Mesembryanthemum, 203
mesocarp, 298, 300 *210*
  fleshy, 300, 302 *210*
mesophyll, 115, **120-121**, 172, 213, 219 *100, 101, 150, 155*
mesophyte, 176, 178
metabolic nucleus, 35
metabolism, 28, 180, 181, 190-199, 200, 204, 220, 321
  carbohydrates, 190-195, 205, **207-208**
  and enzymes, 200, 208, 220
  fats and oils, 195-196
  and growth, 40-41
  and photosynthesis, 205, **207-208**
  proteins, 197-199
  and respiration, 220
metachromatic granule, 345
metaphase
  meiotic, 251 *163, 164, 168*
  mitotic, 33, 252, 312
metaphosphates organic, 181, 224
metaxylem, 99, 102, 111, 112 *77-79, 92*
methane, 336
methyl group, 197, 216
micelles, 194
  clay, 182
microclimate, 230
Microcystis, 353
microfibrillar units, 194 *146*
microfibrils, 194 *146*
Micrographia, The, 25 *14*
micron, 25
micropyle, 4, 5, 6, 8, 9, 281, 288, 460 *196, 201*
microsome, 31
microsporangium, 383, 455, 460, 463 *316, 322, 325*
microspore, 383, 455, 460, 463 *316, 325, 326*
microsporophyll, 460, 463 *316, 325*
microtome, 25
microzoospore, 360
middle lamella, 36, 100, 143 *80*
midrib, 87, 121 *68, 100*
Miescher, 315
Millon's reagent, 9
Mimosa pudica, 53
mineral debris, 234 *160*
  deficiencies, 180-182
  elements, 148
  matter, 164, 179
  nutrition, 179-187
mint, 63, 118 *43*
mitochondria, 29, 31, 204, 224
mitosis, **32-35**, 186, 252 *16, 19*
  anaphase of, 35
  prophase of, 33
Mnium, 432
mode, 308
molecule, 149
molecules, random movement of, 154
molybdenum, 179
monochasial cymes, 265 *177*
monocotyledon, 13, 18, 50, 89, 109, 211
monoecious plant, 259
monokaryon, 409
monopodial growth, 61, 68, 70, 73, 265 *50*
monosaccharide, 192, 209
moor pan, 233
Morgan, T. H., 309-310
moschatel, 65
mosses, 234, 421, 431
moss peat, 234
moulds, 392
mountain crowberry, 238
movements,
  of algae, 53, 356, 373
  of climbing stems, 43
  of cytoplasm, 30, 373

movements (*cont.*)
of leaves, 77, 83, 87
tactic, 53, 425, 440
of tendrils, 82
Mucor, 392-396 *260*, *261*
mud crowfoot, 340
mullein, 58, 79
multiple factor inheritance, 307
multiple fruit, 297
Musci, 421, **431-434**
mushroom, 409
mutant species, 331
mutation, 204, **310-313**, 327, 331
chromosomal, 311
dominant, 311
gene, 311
recessive, 311
somatic, 311
mycelium, 385, 388, 393, 397, 398, 402, 408, 409, 413
mycology, 385
mycorrhizae, 413-417
mycosis, 385, 392
Myosotis palustris, 265 *177*
myxomatosis, 236

Naegeli, 343
naked flowers, 259
Narcissus, 68, 89, 257
nastic movement, 52-53 *32*, *33*
nasties, 52, 77
nasturtium, 83, 261 *63*, *173*
natural selection, 325, **329-330**, 332, 337
Navicula oblonga *247*
neck canal cell, 425, 438
nectar, 285
nectaries, 285
needle, 69, 78, 178, 463
Nelumbium speciosum, 4
neo-Darwinism, 332
Neptunia oleracea, 53 *33*
Nereocystis, 377
nettle, 29, 61, 85, 118 *65*, *98*
Neurospora crassa, 405
N. sitophila, 405
neutral solution, 150
Nicotiana, 46
Nitella, 183
nitrate, 183, 185, 186, 203
nitrite, 203
Nitrobacter, 185
nitrogen, 149, 179, 180, **184-188**, 197, 206
cycle, 186 *144*
fixation, 185, 343, 353, 417
in soil, 166
nitrogenous food reserves, 197, **199**
Nitrosomonas, 185
node, 19, 57, 61, 63
nomenclature, 339-340
binomial system, 340
non-electrolyte, 149, 151, 183
non-endospermic seed, 3, 292
non-essential floral part, 259
normal distribution, 308
nucellus, 281, 458, 460, 466 *195*
nuclear
apparatus, 345
membrane, 28, 33, 35
nucleic acid, 181, **314-318**, 319
nuclein, 315
nucleolar
chromosome, 35, 36
organizing region, 36
nucleolus, 28, 33, 251 *15*
nucleoplasm, 352
nucleotide, 316
nucleus, 28, 32, 197, 204, 242, 304, 315
dikaryotic, 409
diploid, 242, 243
endosperm, 290 *202*
haploid, 242, 243
metabolic, 35
somatic, 311
Nuphar lutea, 88, 340
nutmeg, mace of, 296
nutrient solution, 179
nutrition, 148, 164, 166, **179-187**
autotrophic, 343, 385
heterotrophic, 343, 385
nyctonasties, 52 *32*
Nymphaea alba, 296

oak, 4, 70, 71, 137
oats, 3, 7, 268
Oedogonium, 364-368 *237-239*
Oenothera lamarkiana, 331
oil, 3, 6, 11, 30, 118, **195-196** *17*
onion, 18, 27, 159 *9*, *15b*
oogamy, 366, 383
oogonium, 366, 378, 388, 391, 406 *239*
oosphere, 388
oospore, 366, 388, 392
operculum, 433
Ophrydium, 359
orchid, 417
Order, 65
organelle, 204, 224
organic
acid, 150, 184, 225
matter, 29, 41, 164, 166, 336, 343

organic metaphosphate, 181, 224
origin of life, 336
Origin of Species, 324-333
orthotropous ovule, 283, 296 *196*
Oscillatoria, 353 *229*
osmometer, 156, 157
osmosis, 156-161
osmotic pressure, **156-159**, 174, 219
ostiole, 383, 400, 404, 408 *252*, *266*
ovary, 2, **279-281**, 297, 458 *189-191*
apocarpous, 279
inferior, 281 *194*
superior, 279
syncarpous, 279
ovulate cone, 460, 463, 466 *324*
ovule, 2, 123, 278, **281-284**, 458, 460, 466 *198*, *191*, *195-197*
ovuliferous scale, 466 *324*
ovum, 366, 378, 383 *239*, *250*
Oxalis acetosella, 52, 53, 287 *32*
oxidase, 202, 203
oxidation, 202, 220
oxidative phosphorylation, 209
oxide, 179
cuprous, 191
oxidizing enzyme, 203
oxygen, 4, 5, 7, 8, 40, 54, 149, 179, 205, 206, 208, 212, 220, 223
bridge, 192, 194
tactic movements in response to, 54

pachytene, 249 *163*, *164*, *166*
pairing of chromosome, 244
palaeontology, 328
pallisade tissue, 120, 213, 219 *100*, *150*, *155*
palmelloid-stage, 357
palms, 124
panicle, 268
papain, 203
Papaveraceae, 279
Papaver rhoeas, 261 *173*
papaya, 203
paper chromatography, 217
papillae, 94, 364, 370
in *Chlamydomonas*, 263
Paramecium, 359
paraphysis, 378, 404, 432 *249*, *294*
parasite, 354, 385, 386, 392, 400, 402, 417
parasitism, 236
parenchyma, 94, 99, 104, 107, 109, 120, 143, 195, 380 *73*, *87*, *88*
phloem, 111, 137
spongy, 120 *100*
xylem, 126, 131, 133
parietal chromatophores, 354
placentation, 278
parsley, 268
parthenocarpy, 297
Parthenocissus tricuspida, 81 *61*
passage cells, 95
passive absorption, 174
pathogenic bacteria, 343
peat, 234, 417
pectin, 36
Pectobacterium carotoferum, 347 *226*
pedicel, 257, 265
peduncle, 263
Pelargonium, 118, 161
Pellia, 421 *281*, *286-288*
Penicillium, 398-400 *264*
pennate diatoms, 372
pepsin, 202
peptide bonds, 197
chains, 198
perennial plants, 21, **59-75**, 238, 254
herbaceous, 61
woody, 124
perfect flower, 259
perianth, 257, **261-263**
pericarp, 298, 300
periclinal division, 104, 122, 123, 125, 257, 293 *105*
pericycle, 95, 104, 26, 185 *76*, *77*, *107*
periderm, 138, 140, 144
perigynous zone, 281
perigyny, 281
periplasm, 388
perisperm, 292
peristome teeth, 433 *299*
perithecium, 400, 402, 404, 405, 406, 419
permanent wilting point, 167
permeability, 4, 180
petal, 261 *172*, *174*
petiole, 13, 57, 78, **82-83**, 121 *63*
Pettigera canina, 419
pH (H-ion concentration), **150-151**, 153
Phaeophyta, 374-384
Phanerogamae, 341
Phaseolus multiflorus, 43 *25*
P. vulgaris, 43
phellem, 138 *120*, *121*
Phelloderm, 138 *120*
phellogen, 140, 141, 142 *120*, *125*
phenolic substance, 203
phenotype, 305, 311
phialides, 398, 399 *263*, *264*
Philosophia Botanica (Linnaeus), 339
phloem, **102-104**, 109, 111, 126, 227 *83*, *84*, *92*, *158*

fibres, 137 *119*
function of, 227-228
parenchyma, 111, 137
secondary, 124, **137-138** *103-107, 119*
Phoma, 417
phosphate, 182, 183, 315
acceptor, 224
3-phospho-glyceric acid, 209
phospholipid, 181, 195
phosphoric acid, 151
phosphorous, 166, 179, 181, 183
phosphorylation, 225
photochemical change, 210
photolysis, 208
photon, 210
photonasties, 52
photoperiodism, 231, 255
photosynthesis, 8, 29, 41, 176, 181, 190, 192, **205-219**, 337
action spectrum, 217 *154b*
'dark reaction', 209
energy and, 205-206, 208-210, 217
gaseous exchange and, 176, **217-219**
light and, 205, **208-211**, 213, 217
'light reaction', 208-209
limiting factors in, 212-213
measurement of, 211-212
products of, 209, **210-211**
and respiration, 205-206
and starch formation, 210-211
and transpiration, 176
photosynthetic
phosphorylation, 209
pigments, 213, **214-217**, 337 *153*
phototaxis, 53
phototropism, 48, 81, 83, 87 *28, 63, 67*
phragmoplast, 35 *20*
phycocyanin, 353, 354
phycoerythrin, 351, 353, 354
phycology, 351
Phycomycetes, 386-396
phyllotaxis, 83-87 *64-67*
alternate, 84, 85 *65-67*
cyclic, 84, 85 *65-67*
divergence, 84, 85
quotient, 84
spiral, 84 *64, 65*
verticillate, 85 *66*
whorled, 84, 85 *65-67*
phylogeny, 339
Phytophthora infestans, 386
phytoplankton, 207, 352, 353, 372
Picea spp., 70 *53*
pigments
anthocyanin, 181
pigments (*cont.*)
carotinoid, 216, 217
photosynthetic, 213, **214-217**, 337 *153*
pileus, 410 *271*
piliferous zone, 94 *72*
pine, 69 (cf. Scots Pine)
pineapple, 203
pink family (Caryophyllaceae), 265 *177*
pinnae, 440
Pinnularia, 372, 373 *245*
pinnules, 440
Pinus spp., 69
P. sylvestris, 178, 417, 463 *109, 113, 141a*
pioneer colonisers, 353
pistil, 259 (cf. carpels)
pistillate flower, 259 *170*
Pisum sativum, 3, 79, **304-307**, 309 *1, 58*
pit, 100, 101, 130, 133
bordered, 126, 130, 133 *110, 111*
cavity, 126 *110*
membrane, 126 *110*
pith, 102, 109 *79, 88*
ray, 109
placenta, 278
placentation, 278
axile, 278
free central, 279
parietal, 278
plant
communities, 236-237
kingdom, 2, **341-342**
pathogens, 347
succession, 237-238 *162*
Plantago lanceolata, 61 *38*
plantain, 61 *38*
plasmodesmata, 28 *18*
plasmolemma, 27
plasmolysis, 159, 180 *130*
incipient, 159
Pleurococcus, 419
plum, 281
Plumaria, 354
plumule, 8, 14, 18, 70
plurilocular sporangia, 376 ***248***
podsol, 232 *159*
poinsettia, 265
polar
nodule, 373 *245*
nuclei, 284
pole of nucleus, 33, 252 *19*
pollen
germination, 287 *189*
grains, 275, 460, 464
mother-cell, 273-275
sac, **271-275**, 463 *183, 185, 186*

pollen (*cont.*)
sac wall, 275 *186*, *188*
tetrad, 275
tube, 287, 290, 460
pollination, **284-288**, 417, 466 *198-200*
drop, 460
Polygonum convolvulus *34*
polynucleotide chain, 316
polypeptide, 198, 203
polypetalous corolla, 261 *172*
polyploidy, **312-313**, 331
and evolution, 332
polysaccharide, **192-195**, 209
polysepalous calyx, 261
Polytricum, 432
pome, 302 *210*
pond scum, 351, 352, 368
poplar, 70, 76
poppy, 175 *139*
population, 327, **329-330**
Populus spp., 70
pore, 4
diffuse porous, 137 *117*
ring porous, 136 *116*
in timber, 136-137 *116-117*
porogamy, 288
Porphyra, 354
porphyrin ring, 216
position effects of genes, 311
potassium, 179, 181, 182, 183, 184,
potato, 64, 322, 347, 386 *44*, *218*, *226*, *227*
Potentilla anserina, 61 *42*
potometer, 170 *135*
powdery mildew, 400
Precambrian, 337 *220*
pressure
hydrostatic, 156-157
osmotic, **156-159**, 174, 219
root, 161 *132*
suction, **157-159**, 161, 173, 174 *131*
turgor, **157-159**, 288
Priestly, Joseph, 205
primary
body, 92, **106-114**
endosperm nucleus, 284 *195*, *201*
ray, 125, 133, 137 *104*, *106*, *108*, *119*
root, 8, 25
tissues, 92
primordia, 106, 122, 257 *86*, *169*
primrose, 65, 261, *47*, *174*
Primulaceae, 278
Primula floribunda, 332 *219*
P. kewensis , 332 *219*
P. verticillata, 332 *219*
P. vulgaris, 65, 261 *47*, *174*

privet, 77, 88
Procaryota, 341, 342, 352
pro-embryo, 293, 468
progametangia, 395
propagation, vegetative, 62-69
prophase
meiotic, 244-251 *163*, *164*
mitotic, 33 *19*
prosthetic group, 202, 204
prostrate habit, 420
protandry, 287 *198*
protease, 203
protein, 3, 7, 8, 9, 31, 151, 181, 187, **197-199**, 201, 203, 314, 319 *147*
proteolytic enzyme, 198, 202
prothallus, 438, 444, 450, 455, 456 *300*, *311*
protogyny, 287 *198*
protonema, 434, 444
protoplasmic membrane, 27, 158
protoplast, 27
protoxylem, 99, 101, 111, 112, 126 *78*, *79*, *89*, *90*, *92*, *108*
protozoa, 359
pruning, 144
Prunus avium, 42, 281
pseudoparenchyma, 419
pseudoperianth, 429
Pteridium aquilinum, 438
Pteridophyta, 341, **437-457**
pteridosperms, 469
Ptilota, 354 *230*
Puccinia graminis, 406-409 *269*
pulvinus, 79
pure line, 308
purine, 315
pustule, 408
pycnospore, 408
pyrenoid, 355, 359, 362, 364
pyridine nucleotide (TPN), 209
pyrimidine, 315
pyrrole nuclei, 216
Pyrrophyta, 342
pyruvate, labelled, 225
pyruvic acid, 225
Pythium debaryanum, 386-388 *253-255*

quadrant stage, 293
quanta, 210, 217
Quercus suber, 142
quillwort 450

raceme, 265 *178*
rachis, 263
of fern, 440

radical leaf, 57 *35*
radicle, 9, 18, 22, 92 *12*
radio-isotope, 208, 225
radish, 58, 313 *37*
rain, 183, 185, 232
rainfall, 230, 231
ramenta, 440
Ranunculaceae, 278, 279, 300
Ranunculus acris, 279, 298, 340
  R. bulbosus, 65
  R. ficaria, 79 *57*
  R. lutarius, 340
  R. repens, 61 *40*
Raphano-brassica hybrid, 313
Raphanus sativus, 58, 313 *37*
raphe
  of diatom frustule, 372
  of seed, 297
raspberry, 281, 302
ray
  initial, 125
  medullary, 109, 125, 126, **133** *104*, *106*, *108*, *112-114*
  primary, 133, 137 *104*, *106*, *108*, *119*
  secondary, 133 *113*, *114*
receptacle, 257, 281 *193*
receptive spot of oogonium, 366
recessive genes, 305, 306, 311, 331
recombination, 310, 331
red algae, 342, 351, 354 *230*
red bread mould, 405
red dead nettle *65*
reducing enzyme, 203
  sugar, 191
reductase, 203
reduction division, 242, 244
relational coiling, 249
relic coils, 252
rennin, 202
replication, 310, 314, 337
reproduction, **242-253**, 254-256
  anisogamous, 358, 363 *232*
  asexual (see vegetative reproduction)
  conjugation, 370
  isogamous, 363 *236*
  oogamous, 366
  physiology of, 254-256
  sexual, 242, 254
    in algae, 354, 357, 362, 363, **364-366**, 370, 374, 376, 378, 383 *232*, *235*, *236*, *239*, *242*, *247*, *248*, *249*, *250*
    in angiosperms, 254-303 *169-210*
    in bacteria, 348
    in bryophyta, 423-425, 427-429, 432 *286*, *287*, *289*, *291*, *294*, *295*
reproduction, sexual (*cont.*)
    in fungi, 388, 391, 395, 398, 399, **402**, 404, 406, 408, 409 *255*, *260*, *262*, *263*, *268*, *270*
    in gymnosperms, 460-462, 463-468 *320-325*
    in pteridophytes, **438-440**, 450, 455 *300*, *311*, *317*, *318*
    vegetative, **62-69**, 242, 254, 311, 312, 321, 380, 422
reproductive
  capacity, 234
  development, 20
resin, 136, 140
respiration, 5, 8, 40, 106, 162, 181, 183, 192, 205, 206, 209, 212, **220-226**, 228
  aerobic, 220, 248 *156a*, *156b*
  anaerobic, 220, 225, 348 *157*
  biochemistry of, 225-226
  factors influencing, 223
  and mitochondria, 224
  and photosynthesis, 205-206
  significance of, 220
respiratory
  energy, 224, 226
  inhibitor, 183
  quotient (RQ), 222-223
  substrate, 192, 212, 222-223
reticulate
  chloroplast, 364
  thickening, 101, 111
  venation, 87 *68*
Rhacomitrium lanuginosum, 238 *162*
Rheum officinale, 65
Rhizobium, 185
rhizoid, 362, 380, 421, 431
rhizome, 64, 194, 438, 440
rhizomorph, 413
Rhizopus, 392-396 *261*
  R. nigricans, 392, 395, 396 *261*
Rhododendron, 85, 288 *64*
Rhodophyta, 354 *230*
rhubarb, 65
rhytidome, 140
Ribes uva-crispa, 302
ribonuclease, 320
ribose, 316
ribosenucleic acid (RNA), 317, 320
ribosome, 31, 317
rice, 354
  fields, 354
  grass, 332
Ricinus communis, 11-13 *4*, *5*
ring porous wood, 136 *116*
ripeness to flower, 254

RNA (ribosenucleic acid), 317, 320
Robinia, 6
  R. pseudacacia, 81 *59*
root, 8, 49, 161, 164, 181, 182, 194, 203, 223
  adventitious, 16, 50, 57, 61, 63, 66, 68 *31*, *40*
  anatomy, **92-105**, 126 *72*, *76*, *77*, *78*, *79*, *85*
  apex, 93 *72*
  cap, 38, 93, 104 *72*, *85*
  diarch, 97
  dicotyledonous, 97 *77*, *78*
  endogenous origin, 57, 104
  fibrous, 57, 66
  hair, 94, 161, 169, 174, 185 *72*, *131*
  lateral, 13, 19, **55-57**, 59, 70, 104, 186 *36*, *85*
  monocotyledonous, 97 *79*
  nodules, 186
  polyarch, 97 *79*
  pressure, 161 *132*
  primary, 8, 25
  secondary, 56
  stock, 65 *47*
  system, 19, 58, 168, 176, 183, 236
  system, fibrous, 413
  tap, 19, 55, 61, 70 *39*
  tetrarch, 97, 126 *77*
  tip, 22, 36, 38, 168, 413 *22*
  triarch, 97 *78*
Rosa spp., 281 *193*
Rosaceae, 278, 281
rose, 281, 298
  hip, 298 *207*
rosette, plant, 47, 57, 58, 61, 123, 256 *38*
Rubus spp., 281, 302 *210*
  R. idaeus, 302
Rumex obtusifolius, 58
runner, 61 *41*, *42*
Russula, 417
rust nectar *408*
rusts, 406
rye, 168, 402 *267*

Saccharomyces, 200-225, 396-398 *262*
  S. cerevisiae, 397
Sachs, Julius, 22, 179
salmon testes, 315
salt marsh, 184
salts, formation of, 150
samaras, 300 *209*
Sambucus niger *49*, *120*, *121*
sand, 164, 167, 182
  dune, 176
saponin, 152
saprophyte, 343, 385, 392, 413
sapwood, 134-136 *118*
Sargasso sea, 352
Sargassum, 352
satellite, 36
saturation of solution, 149
  deficit, 172, 231
Scabious spp., 268
scalariform conjugation, 370
scale leaf, 19, 61-64, 66, 77, 463
scar, 4, 70, 71, 73, 77
scarlet pimpernel, 263 *176*
scarlet runner bean, 43 *25*
Schizomycetes 343
scion, 144
sclereid, 97
sclerenchyma, 97, 112, 231 *92*
  fibre, 99, 104 *88*, *89*
sclerotium, 404 *267*
scorpioid cyme, 265 *177*
Scots pine, 417, 463 *325-327*
Scrophulariaceae, 285
scutellum, 14
sea lettuce, 362
seaweed, 2, 351, 354, 374
  brown, 163, 351, 374, 384
  green, 351, 355, 362
  red, 351, 354 *230*
Secale cereale, 168
secondary body, 92, **124-145** *103-125*
  constriction, 36 *21*
  growth, 92, 124 *103-107*
  ray, 133 *113*, *114*
  thickening, 124-143 *103-125*
  tissue, 92
seed, **2-18**, 162, 181, 195, 199, 290, **295-303**, 458, 462, 470
  coat, 4, 8, 295
  dispersal, 4, 295
  germination (see germination of seeds)
  habit, 458
seedling, 2, 5, 8, 11, 19, 59 *37*
segration, 305
  law of, 305
Selaginella, 450-456 *313-319*
  S. biformis, 453
  S. krausiana, 452
  S. martensii, 453
  S. spinosa, 450
selection
  experiment, 308
  pressure, 332
self-pollination, 285, 287, 305
  -replicating cycle, 314
  -sterility, 287

Senecio vulgaris, 78 *57*
sepal, 257, **261** *173*
separation layer, 142
septae, 385, 393, 396, 410
septate fibres, 133
sessile leaves, 57, 78 *35, 57*
seta, 425
sexual
  classification, 339, 341
  conjugation, 347
  reproduction, 242, 254, 331, 338
shade leaf, 232
shepherd's purse, **55-58**, 283, 287 *35*
shoot, 8, 19, 55, 57
  lateral, 20
short day plants, 355-356
shrub, 69
  layer, 237
sieve
  element, 103, 122
  plate, 103 *83, 84*
  plate, compound, 103
  tube, 103, 111, 137, 181, 227, 228 *83, 84, 158*
sigmoid curve, 21 *11*
Silene inflata, 300
silicon, 179
silt, 164
silverweed, 61 *42*
sleep movement, 52, 79 *32*
slime, 104 *83*
  layer, 345
smuts, 406
snowdrop, 257
sodium, 179, 184
  acetate, 151
  hydroxide, 150
soft rot, 396
softwood, **126-130**, 463 *109-111, 113*
soil, 7, 161, **164-169**, 179, 182, 185, 187, **232-234** *131-134, 159*
  acidity, 182
  aeration, 164, 223
  bacteria, 185-186 *142, 143*
  capillary force, 167, 168
  fertility, 354
  field capacity, 166
  formation, 238
  horizon, 232 *159*
  immature, 234, 419
  maritime, 234 *161*
  mature, 234
  mountain, 234
  organic matter, 234, 392
  particle, **164-166**, 167 *132, 133*
soil (*cont.*)
  profile, 232 *159*
  respiration, 206, 207 *149*
  solution, 164, 166, 182, 183
  stratification, 232
  texture, 166
  type, 232
  water, 161, **166-169**, 175 *131, 133, 134*
    capillary, 167
    gravitational, 167
    hygroscopic, 167
sol, 152
Solanum lycopersicum, 161
  S. tuberosum, 64 *44*
solar radiation, 209-210
solitary
  flower, 263 *176*
  terminal flower, 265
solubility, 149
solute, 149, 154
  chemical potential of, 156
  net movement of, 154
solution, 149
  balanced, 180
  colloidal, 152
  hypertonic, 159
  hypotonic, 159
  isotonic, 159
  mass flow of, 228
  nutrient, 179
  saturated, 149
  unbalanced, 180
solvent, 154
somatic nucleus, 311
soredium, 419
sorus, 378, 438, 441
space exploration, 360
Spartina alterniflora, 332
  S. maritima, 332
  S. townsendii, 332
spathe, 257, 265
species, **326-327**, 331, 340
  formation, 313
specification of amino-acids, 314
specific name, 340
spectrum, 208, 210
spermagonium, 408
spermatia, 354, 408
Spermatophyta, 437, 458-470
spermatozoid, 383
sperm mother cell, 423, 440, 460
Sphagnum spp., 237
Sphenophyllum, 444
Sphenopsida, 437, 444
spiderwort, 274

spike, 265 *178*
Spinacea oleracea, 6
spinach, 6, 29, 213
spindle, 33, 312
spine, 78
spiralization, 250 *168*
spirillar bacteria, 345
Spirogyra, 28, **368-371** *240-242*
spongy parenchyma, 120
sporangium, 363, 383, 387, 393, 441, 444 *254*
  plurilocular, 376 *248*
  unilocular, 376, 378 *248*
sporangial drop, 393
sporangiophore, 388, 393 *308*
sporangiospore, 393
spore, 243, 353, 388, 393
  asexual (see zoospore, aplanospore, autospore, conidiospore)
  mother cell, 425, 429, 444
sporogonium, 425
sporophore, 396, 409, 410 *271, 274*
sporophyll, 437, 449, 455, 463
sporophyte, 243, 363, 378, 420, 433, 437, 469
spruce, 70 *53*
spur, 261 *173*
spurious fruit, 302 *210*
squash, cytological, 36 *21*
stalk cell, 383, 460
stamen, 257, **270-275**, 287 *182-186*
  epipetalous, 271 *183*
staminal hair, 27, 30 *15b*
staminate
  flower, 259 *170*
  strobili, 460, 463
staminode, 270
starch, 3, 9, 30, 153, 161, 192, 203, 209, 213 *17, 145*
  floridean, 354
  formation, 210-211
  sheath, 108
stele, 452
stellate chromatophores, 354
stem, 49
  anatomy, 106-114 *86-93*
  dicotyledonous, 108-109, 111 *88-90*
  monocotyledonous, 111, 112 *91, 92*
  rust, 406
Stentor, 359
sterigma, 408 *269, 273*
sterigmata, 411 *272*
stigma, 14, 278, 469
  of algae, 356
stimuli, 48-54
stipe, 163, 378, 410 *271*
stipule, 79-81 *58, 59, 60*
stock, 144
  root, 65-66 *47*
stolon, 64, 396 *44*
stoma, 116, 400 *96, 97*
stomata, 107, 115, 141, 170, 172, 176, 217, 223, 231, 433 *94-99, 155*
stomatal movements, 217-219
stomatal pore, 118, 172 *97*
stomium, 275, 444
stone of fruit, 300
stonewort, 183
storksbill, 270
strain, genetic, 308
stratification in soils, 232
strawberry, 61, 256, 281, 302 *41, 193, 210*
strobilus, 446, 449, 452, 463
  staminate, 460, 463 *325, 327*
stroma, 404
structural formulae, 191
struggle for existence, 325, 330
style, 278, 287
stylet of aphid, 228 *158*
suberin, 95, 140, 143
subhymenium, 411 *272*
sub-microscopic structure, **30-32**, 195 *18*
subsidiary cell, 116 *96, 97*
sub-species, 326-327
sub-stomatal chamber, 118, 172 *97*
substrate, 192, 201, 204
succession, plant, 238 *162*
succulent fruit, 298
sucker, 63 *43*
sucrose, 156, 192, 203, 209, 228
suction pressure, **157-159**, 161, 173, 174 *131*
sugar, 3, 161, 183, 196, 200, 219, 228
  beet, 192
  cane, 192
  hexose, 190, 203, 208, 220, 225
  monosaccharide, 191
  pentose, 190, 209, 315
  reducing, 191
sulphate, 183
sulphur, 179
summer bud, 76
Sumner, J. B., 201
sundew, 287
sunflower, 6, 124, 195
sun leaf, 232
superior apocarpous ovary, 279
  syncarpous ovary, 279
survival
  and evolution, 324
  of fittest, 325, 329-330
suspension, 151
suspensoid, 152

suspensor, 293, 395, 455 *204*
sweet pea, 271
sweet violet, 287
sweet woodruff, 85 *66*
sycamore, 70, 85
symbiosis, 186, 417
symbiotic nitrogen fixation, 186
sympodial growth, 61, 65, 68, 71, 265 *50*
synapsis, 244 *166*
syncarpous, 278, 297 *191*
  fruits, 298
  ovary, 279
synecology, 229
synergidae, 284 *195*
syngamy, 242, 290
synthesis, 28, 31, 39, 40, 45, 196, 198, 200, 204, 224, 321

tactic movements, **53-54**, 425, 440
tannin, 136, 140
tapetal cell, 284
tapetum, 273, 275 *188*
tap root, 19, 55, 58, 61, 70 *39*
Taraxacum kok-saghys, 290
  T. officinale, 52, 62 *39*
taxonomy, 339
tegumen, 11
teleutospore, 408 *269*
telophase
  meiotic, 252
  mitotic, 35
temperature, 5, 7, 40, 52, 172, 176, 201, 212, 223, 230, 256, 376
  and diffusion, 154, 176
  as an ecological factor, 230
  and enzymes, 201
  and germination, 7
  and growth, 40
  limiting photosynthesis, 213
  and permeability, 176
  and transpiration, 172, 176
tendril, 79, **81-82** *58, 59, 60, 61, 62*
tensions in sap, 173-174
terminal bud, 58, 70, 73, 74, 76
  cell, 293
terminalization of chiasmata, 250
testa, 4, 8, 11, 18, 295
Thallophyta, 341, 385
thallus, 263, 354, 380, 419, 421
theca, 425
Theophrastus, 339
thermonasties, 52
thickening
  annular, 100, 111, 112 *81, 92*
  reticulate, 101, 111, 130 *82*
thickening (*cont.*)
  scalariform, 101, 111, 132 *81*
  secondary, **124-143** *103-125*
  spiral, 101, 111, 112 *81*
thistle, 118
thygmonasties, 53 *33*
thygmotropism, 82
thymine, 315
tissue, 92, 106, 160
  complementary, 142 *125*
  fundamental, 94
  ground, 94, 109
  mechanical, 97
  primary, 92
  secondary, 92
  vascular, 94, 108
  wound, 144 *126*
toadstool, 409
tobacco, 46
tobacco mosaic disease, 319
tobacco mosaic virus, 320 *214, 216*
tolerance, ecological, 229
tolerance of species, 229
tomato, 161, 302, 312
tonoplast, 27
topography, 231
torus, 126 *110*
TPN (pyridine nucleotide), 209
TPNH, 209
trabeculae, 433, 452
trace
  elements, 179, 202
  leaf, **113-114** *93*
tracheary elements, 99, 122 *80-82*
tracheid, 100, 121, 126, 130, 173, 441 *101, 102, 109, 111, 113*
Tracheophyta, 342, 438
Tradescantia spp., 27, 30
  T. virginiana, 274 *15b*
trama, 411 *272*
transition zone, 113
translocation, 45, 99, 149, 198, 220, **227-228** *158*
  chromosomal, 311, 331
transpiration, 149, **170-178**
  -cohesion-tension theory, 174
  control of, 176
  diurnal rhythm, 172
  and passive absorption, 174
  rates, 170-172 *135*
  significance of, 174-176
  and temperature, 172, 176
tree, 62, 69, 126
tribe, 340
Trichodesmium erythraeum, 353

trichogyne, 406
trilocular ovary, 278 *191*
triploid chromosome complement, 312
Tropaeoleum majus, 83 *63*
tropical rain forest, 230
tropism, 48-52, 82, 83, 87
trypsin, 202
tube cell, 275, 460, 463 *187*
tuber, 64, 181, 194 *44*
  soft rot, 348 *228*
Tulbaghia, 36
tulip, 52, 68, 275, 322 *48*, *217*
tundra, 230
tunica, 106, 122
turgor, 28, 40, 52, 148, 157, 159, 176, 219, 387 *130*
  enlargement, 148
  pressure, 157-159, 228
turnip, 58
  yellow mosaic virus, 320
Tussilago farfara, 61, 254
Tutankamen, 4
tylose, 136, 143
tyrosinase, 202
tyrosine, 202

Ulex europaeus, 176, 270
Ulothrix, 360-362 *325*
Ulva, 362-364 *236*
  U. lactuca, 362-364 *236*
umbel, 268 *179*
  compound, 268
  simple, 268
Umbelliferae, 263, 268, 279
unilocular
  ovary, 278
  sporangia, 376 *248*
united
  cup fruits, 298
  free fruits, 298
urea, 201
urease, 201
uredospore, 408 *269*
Urtica dioica, 29, 118 *98*
Usnea barbata, 419 *279*

Vaccinium myrtillus, 238
  V. uliginosum, 238
vacuolation, 39, 93, 100, 106
vacuole, 27, 39, 157, 160, 180, 199
  contractile, 356
vallecular canal, 447 *309*
Valonia, 184
valve, diatom, 372
Van Leuwenhoek, 343
variation, 304, 307-308, 325, 331
varieties, 326
vascular
  cambium, 124-126 *103-107*
  cryptogams, 437
  cylinder, 93, 95-104, 114 *93*
  strands, 70
  system, 115, 121, 124, 438
  tissue, 106, 108-112
vascular bundles, 109, 125, 143 *88*, *104*
  bicollateral, 109, 121 *90*
  collateral, 109, 112, 121 *88*, *89*
  petiolar, 121
Vaucheria, 372
vegetational
  climax, 238 *162*
  cover, 237
vegetative
  cell, 275 *187*
  development, 20
  propagation, 62-69
  reproduction, 242, 311, 312, 321, 380, 422
vein, 87, 115, 121, 173, 175, 181 *100-102*
  lateral, 87, 121
  main, 87, 121 *100*
velum, 411 *271*
venation, 87-88
  palmate, 88
  parallel, 88
  pinnate, 88
  reticulate, 87
venter, 425, 440
ventral
  canal cell, 425, 438 *287*
  suture line, 300
Verbascum thapsus, 58, 79
vernalization, 256
vesicle of fungi, 387, 392, 398 *254*, *259*
vessel, 130-133, 134, 174, 227 *116*, *117*
  annular, 100, 111, 112 *81*, *92*
  elements, 100 *80-82*
  reticulate, 101, 102, 111 *82*
  scalariform, 101, 102, 111 *81*
  spiral, 100, 102, 111 *81*
Vicia faba, 8-11, 36 *2*, *3*, *21*
Viola, 279, 288
  V. odorata, 287
Virginia creeper, 81 *61*
virus, 236, 319-321 *215*, *218*
virus diseases of plants, 321, 322 *218*
vitamins, 204
volutin, 345
Volvox, 359
Von Baeyer, 208

Von Tschermak, 305

wall
  lignified, 100
  primary, 100 *80*
  secondary, 100 *80*
Wallace, Alfred Russell, 325
wallflower, 265
water, 8, 40, **148-153**, 164-169, 206, 208, 220
  absorption, 6, 7, **154-163**, 164, 170, 173, 174, 176
  blooms, 353
  capillary translocation of, 168
  germination, 5
  hygroscopic, 167
  lily, 296 *68*, *205*
  loss, 118
  properties of, 149-153
  in soil, 179
  vapour, 164, 167, 170, 172
Watson, 316 *213*
wax, 6, 195
weathering, 164, 232
weed killer, selective, 50
weight
  dry, 6, 162, 179
  fresh, 179
Went, Fritz, 44
wheat, 3, 7, 256, 406, 408
  winter, 256
white
  bryony, 81 *62*
  rusts, 386
  water lily, 296 *205*
wild population, 308
willow, 4, 296
wilting, 167, 176
  point, 167
wind, 230-231
  pollination, 285
winged seeds, 295, 286, 300 *209*
Winogradsky, 185
winter bud, 47, 68, 70, 76, 77 *50*, *51*, *55*, *56*
witches' broom, 322
wood, 126-138
  anemone, 64 *45*
  fibres, 126, 133
  hard, 126, **130-133** *116*, *117*
  heart, 134-136 *118*
  parenchyma, 126, 133 *112*
  sap, **134-136** *118*
  soft, **126-130**, 463
  sorrel, 52, 287 *32*
  spring, 134, 136 *117*
  summer, 134, 136 *117*
woodlands, 231, 237, 413
woody perennials, **69-75**, 124, 126, 176
woolly fringe moss, 238 *162*
wound, 136, 161
  parasite, 347 *228*
  tissue, 144, 227 *126*
wracks, 380

Xanthophyceae, 372
xanthophyll, 216
Xanthoria parietina, 419 *280*
xerophyte, 176-178 *140-142*
X-ray, 198, 210, 311, 319
xylem, **97-102**, 109, 126, 134, 161, 174, 175
  function of, 174, 227
  parenchyma, 112 *92*
  secondary, 124 *103-107*

yeast, 44, 200, 203, **396-398**
yellow water lily, 88, 340
yew, 463

Zamia, 460
Zea mais, **13-16**, 112 *6*, *7*, *8*, *73*, *74*, *76*, *79*, *92*
zinc, 179, 202
zoochlorella, 359
zoosporangium, 364
zoospore, 357, 360, 362, **363**, 364, 370, 376, 378, 387, 391 *231*, *237*, *254*, *258*, *259*
zygomorphic flower, 263 *175*
zygospore, 370, 395 *242*, *260*
zygote, 243, 290, 357, 362, 363, 366, 380, 384, 440, 455
zygotene, **244-249**, 312 *163*, *164*, *166*
zymase, 203